THE SKIN SENSES

John Paul Nafe

THE SKIN SENSES

Proceedings of the First International Symposium
on the Skin Senses
Held at The Florida State University
in Tallahassee, Florida

Compiled and Edited by

DAN R. KENSHALO, Ph.D.

Department of Psychology
The Florida State University
Tallahassee, Florida

CHARLES C THOMAS · PUBLISHER
Springfield · Illinois · U.S.A.

93672

Published and Distributed Throughout the World by
CHARLES C THOMAS • PUBLISHER
BANNERSTONE HOUSE
301-327 East Lawrence Avenue, Springfield, Illinois, U.S.A.
NATCHEZ PLANTATION HOUSE
735 North Atlantic Boulevard, Fort Lauderdale, Florida, U.S.A.

© *1968, by* CHARLES C THOMAS • PUBLISHER
Library of Congress Catalog Card Number: 67-21770

With THOMAS BOOKS *careful attention is given to all details of manufacturing and design. It is the Publisher's desire to present books that are satisfactory as to their physical qualities and artistic possibilities and appropriate for their particular use.* THOMAS BOOKS *will be true to those laws of quality that assure a good name and good will.*

Printed in the United States of America
N-1

The efforts of some of us who have contributed to this volume are humbly dedicated to John Paul Nafe. He has had a profound influence upon our thinking and especially upon our approach to the mysteries of life.

PARTICIPANTS AND GUESTS

*Lloyd M. Beidler, Ph.D.
Division of Physiology
The Florida State University
Tallahassee, Florida

Fred B. Benjamin, M.D., Ph.D.
Office of Space Medicine
NASA Headquarters
Washington, D.C.

K. L. Casey, Ph.D.
Department of Physiology
University of Michigan
Ann Arbor, Michigan

Nikolajs Cauna, M.D., D.Sc.
Department of Anatomy and
  Cell Biology
University of Pittsburgh School
  of Medicine
Pittsburgh, Pennsylvania

Leslie L. Clark
International Research Information
  Service
American Foundation for the
  Blind, Inc.
New York, New York

*Hallowell Davis, M.D.
Central Institute for the Deaf
St. Louis, Missouri

E. G. Eijkman, D.Sc.
Laboratory for Medical Physics
Roman Catholic University
Nijmegen, Netherlands

M. J. T. FitzGerald, M.D., Ph.D.
Department of Anatomy
St. Louis University School of Medicine
St. Louis, Missouri

A. Pharo Gagge, Ph.D.
John B. Pierce Foundation
  Laboratories
New Haven, Connecticut

Frank A. Geldard, Ph.D.
Department of Psychology
Princeton University
Princeton, New Jersey

Robert H. Gibson, Ph.D.
Department of Psychology
University of Pittsburgh
Pittsburgh, Pennsylvania

J. A. B. Gray, D.Sc.
Department of Physiology
University College London
London, England

John F. Hahn, Ph.D.
Psychological Laboratory
University of Virginia
Charlottesville, Virginia

James D. Hardy, Ph.D
John B. Pierce Foundation
  Laboratories
New Haven, Connecticut

Fred Harris
School of Medicine
University of Washington
Seattle, Washington

Glenn R. Hawkes, Ph.D.
Basic Sciences Research Branch
U. S. Army Medical Research and
  Development Command
Washington, D.C.

Herbert Hensel, M.D.
Physiological Institute
University of Marburg
Marburg/Lahn, West Germany

Ainsley Iggo, Ph.D., D.Sc.
Department of Veterinary Physiology
Royal (Dick) School of Veterinary
  Studies
Edinburgh, Scotland

Dan R. Kenshalo, Ph.D.
  Department of Psychology
  The Florida State University
  Tallahassee, Florida

Frederick W. L. Kerr, M.D.
  Section of Neurologic Surgery
  Mayo Clinic
  Rochester, Minnesota

Robert K. S. Lim, Ph.D., D.Sc.
  Medical Sciences Research Laboratory
  Miles Laboratory
  Elkhart, Indiana

Sidney L. Marvin, Colonel, USA
  Behavioral Science Research Branch
  U. S. Army Research and Development
    Command
  Washington, D.C.

Ronald Melzack, Ph.D.
  Department of Psychology
  McGill University
  Montreal, Quebec, Canada

John Paul Nafe, Ph.D.
  Department of Psychology
  The Florida State University
  Tallahassee, Florida

Samuel G. Nord, Ph.D.
  Bio-Electric Laboratory
  Department of Psychology
  Lehigh University
  Bethlehem, Pennsylvania

*Carl Pfaffmann, Ph.D.
  Rockefeller University
  New York, New York

*Walter A. Rosenblith
  Center for Communication Sciences
  Research Laboratory of Electronics
  Massachusetts Institute of Technology
  Cambridge, Massachusetts

Sol Roy Rosenthal, M.D., Ph.D.
  Institution for Tuberculosis Research
  Tice Laboratory
  University of Illinois
  Urbana, Illinois

Burton S. Rosner, Ph.D.
  Department of Psychiatry
  University of Pennsylvania
    Medical School
  Philadelphia, Pennsylvania

Harvey E. Savely, Ph.D.
  Air Force Office of Scientific Research
  Washington, D.C.

Carl E. Sherrick, Ph.D.
  Department of Psychology
  Princeton University
  Princeton, New Jersey

Kenneth Smith, M.D.
  Section of Surgery
  St. Louis University
  St. Louis, Missouri

Joseph C. Stevens, Ph.D.
  Laboratory of Psychophysics
  Harvard University
  Cambridge, Massachusetts

J. A. J. Stolwijk, Ph.D.
  John B. Pierce Foundation
    Laboratories
  New Haven, Connecticut

Arnold L. Towe, Ph.D.
  Department of Physiology
    and Biophysics
  School of Medicine
  University of Washington
  Seattle, Washington

William R. Uttal, Ph.D.
  Department of Psychiatry
  Mental Health Research Institute
  The University of Michigan
  Ann Arbor, Michigan

A. J. H. Vendrik, D.Sc.
  Laboratory for Medical Physics
  Roman Catholic University
  Nijmegen, Netherlands

Ronald T. Verrillo, Ph.D.
  Laboratory of Sensory Communication
  Syracuse University
  Syracuse, New York

Kenneth Wagoner, Ph.D.
Department of Psychology
DePauw University
Greencastle, Indiana

Patrick D. Wall, D.M.
Department of Biology and Center for
Communications Sciences
Massachusetts Institute of Technology
Cambridge, Massachusetts

Sidney Weinstein, Ph.D.
Neuropsychological Laboratory
Albert Einstein College of Medicine
Yeshivah University
New York, New York

Gerhard Werner, M.D.
Department of Pharmacology
School of Medicine
University of Pittsburgh
Pittsburgh, Pennsylvania

R. K. Winkelmann, M.D., Ph.D.
Section of Dermatology
Mayo Clinic
Rochester, Minnesota

David L. Winter, M.D.
Department of Neurophysiology
Walter Reed Army Medical Center
Washington, D.C.

Yngve Zotterman, M.D., D.Sc.
Wenner-Gren Center
Stockholm Va., Sweden

---

*Chairman

PREFACE

THE PARAMOUNT AIM OF THE *Proceedings of the International Symposium on the Skin Senses* is to present the reader with current information and discussion of the morphology, physiology, and psychology of the systems which are responsible for the sensations of touch, pain, warmth, and cold. The contributions of the various authors can be divided into five broad categories. These are histology of the skin, physiological and psychological investigations of mechanical, thermal, and painful stimuli, and central processes associated with cutaneous stimulation.

These proceedings were held at The Florida State University in Tallahassee, Florida, March, 1966.

No attempt was made to cover a specific topic in cutaneous sensitivity comprehensively. Rather, a more profitable approach seemed to be to display as much breadth as possible of the methods used to investigate the skin senses. Although never explicitly stated as one of the conference aims, specificity versus nonspecificity of nerve terminals became the underlying theme and much discussion centered about it. However, the interdisciplinary nature of the program fostered attempts by the participants to identify correlations between structure, function, and sensation.

At the end of four days of concentrated thought, several of the participants were not yet exhausted and wished to include additional remarks which were an outgrowth of the symposium. These are included in the Epilogue.

Unfortunately, Doctors W. R. Uttal, and A. L. Towe were unable to attend the symposium, but the papers which they would have presented have been included.

DAN R. KENSHALO

ACKNOWLEDGMENTS

A$_N$ EXPRESSION OF APPRECIATION is due many who contributed to the success of the symposium. First and foremost among these are the participants themselves who produced as fine a collection of papers as has been bound between two covers. Special thanks are due to Dr. Glenn Hawkes and the Office of the Surgeon General, Department of Army (Grant No. DA-MD-49-193-65-G171), without whose help it would not have been possible to assemble this group of scientists in one place at one time. Thanks are due President John E. Champion, Dr. Karl Dittmer, Vice President for Academic Affairs, and Dr. E. Laurence Chalmers, Dean of the College of Arts and Sciences of The Florida State University for assistance in making facilities available for the symposium. A large part of the labor in preparing the entire manuscript for printing was done by Judy McCoy, Carolyn Weymark, Mary Sperry, and Anne Armstrong for which appreciation is expressed. A special appreciation is due my "needle," Kay Fite, who planted the idea for the symposium. Last, but by far my greatest appreciation is due my wife, Gene, who assumed the details of correspondence in arranging the symposium and the details of hospitality which contributed extensively to the comfort and pleasure of the participants and guests.

We are grateful to the publishers of the following books and journals who have cooperated by permitting us to reproduce figures and other material: The Acoustical Society of America, *Journal of the Acoustical Society of America;* The American Association for the Advancement of Science, *Science;* American Foundation for the Blind, Inc., *Proceedings of the International Congress on Technology and Blindness,* Leslie L. Clark (Ed.); American Medical Association, *Archives of Dermatology (Chicago);* American Physiological Society, *Journal of Applied Physiology, Journal of Neurophysiology;* American Psychological Association, *Journal of Experimental Psychology;* Blackwell Scientific Publications, Ltd., *Anatomies of Pain,* K. D. Keele; California Institute of Technology, *Proceedings of the Symposium on Information Processing in Sight Sensory Systems,* P. W. Nye (Ed.); Cambridge University Press, *Journal of Anatomy, Journal of Physiology;* Karl M. Dallenbach, *American Journal of Psychology;* Karolinska Institute, *Acta Physiologica Scandinavica;* Pergamon Press, *Olfaction and Taste, Vol. 2,* Y. Zotterman (Ed.); Psychonomic Press, *Perception and Psychophysics, Psychonomic Science;* Journal Press, *Journal of General Psychology;* W. B. Saunders Company, *Anatomy of the Nervous System*

(10th ed), S. W. Ranson and S. L. Clark; *Neurophysiology* (2nd ed), T. C. Ruch, H. D. Patton, J. W. Woodbury, and A. L. Towe; *Physiology and Biophysics* (19th ed), T. C. Ruch and H. D. Patton; Springer-Verlag, *Temperatur und Leben, Pflügers Archiv fur die Gesamte Physiologie des Menschen und der Tiere;* Wistar Institute of Anatomy and Biology, *The Anatomical Record, The Journal of Comparative Neurology.*

D. R. K.

CONTENTS

Contents
xvii

THE SKIN SENSES

WELCOMING ADDRESS

Karl Dittmer

Vice President for Academic Affairs, Florida State University
Tallahassee, Florida

Dr. Beidler, Dr. Kenshalo and members of the International Symposium on Skin Senses: We just finished the inauguration of a president, and one of the speakers toward the end of the ceremony yesterday afternoon, Dr. Paul McCracken, from the University of Michigan, said the mind can take only as much as the seat can stand. I hope you will find these chairs comfortable and our campus relaxing.

In 1960, I attended a National Science Symposium in Washington at which Dr. Lloyd V. Berkner spoke about the need of graduate work in the sciences. He pointed out that there is a need for additional graduate centers. He went on to develop the theme that there is no possibility of converting an existing undergraduate institution into the much needed oriented type university. He felt that the only hope for such developments can be expected in the large metropolitan areas, such as New York City, where of course the Rockefeller University was in the midst of developing with a few years' start. Other possible areas mentioned were Portland, Oregon and Dallas, Texas. He emphasized that only by starting new universities can new graduate centers of quality be developed. Examples are the Universities of California at Riverside and Irvine and Brandeis University which were all developed since World War II. In general, Dr. Berkner was right, but he did not know what was happening in the sticks of Florida, here in Tallahassee.

When graduate programs were started in 1949, Florida State University had been a women's undergraduate college with 2500 students. The first Ph.D. was awarded in chemistry, February of 1952. A faculty was collected at that time, many of whom are still here today, to wit, Dr. Beidler, Dr. Kenshalo and a large number in all of the areas of the sciences as well as the other fields. In 1962, ten years later, and since then, more than one hundred doctoral degrees have been awarded each year at the Florida State University. Somebody asked me the other day, "Are most of these in the School of Education?" and I was a little bit afraid to look. I have looked since and a relatively small number of this total is in the School of Education. The largest number come from the Department of Psychology each year. Today there are about a hundred postdoctoral fellows on campus and about 2500 graduate students are enrolled. It is the largest graduate school in the

State of Florida. We are pleased to acknowledge this academic development since World War II.

Recently the American Council on Education made a study of the quality of graduate programs. Florida State University's chemistry department was ranked among the thirty best in the nation, placing in the "Strong" category. Six other departments were judged among the "Adequate plus," including physiology, psychology, physics, botany, zoology, and biochemistry.

I believe this clearly shows that Florida State University has made a good start toward quality graduate programs.

At this particular time, we are moving into a new phase which we accept with enthusiasm. We are abandoning the academic trimester calendar and adopting the quarter system. This provides the opportunity to review our curriculum in depth and to try new ideas, which only a school that is not yet very set in its ways can undertake with pleasure rather than with resistance. It will be a tough job; but there is really nothing that is good that doesn't take a lot of work; each of you knows that better than I do.

Therefore, with this little picture of the Florida State University, particularly slanted toward graduate work for your particular consumption this morning, I welcome you to the campus. We hope your stay will be enjoyable and that you can make use of the facilities which we have to offer. Like every major campus we have holes in the ground and a lot of noise as new buildings take shape. Fortunately this beautiful University Union building is fairly well insulated and we hope you will have a good time. Thank you very much.

Chapter 1

NEURAL CORRELATES OF SENSATION*

JOHN PAUL NAFE

THE VERY EXCELLENT REVIEW of the work on cutaneous sensory mechanisms by Dr. Melzack and Dr. Wall (1962) makes another review, at this time, superfluous. Two of the problems I will comment upon are, first, the nature of stimulation and adaptation and, second, the "pattern theory" of nerve action. Both of these problems arise from the gratuitous assumption of different kinds of peripheral, afferent nerve fibers.

Sensory adaptation often is referred to, or even defined, as due to "some sort of fatigue in nerves," and often nerve fibers are distinguished as "long adapting" or "short adapting" implying a difference in nerve fibers on this basis. On the contrary, it is well established that fatigue in nerve, in the sense of failure from overwork, simply does not occur. The correct answer became apparent when Adrian, Cattell, and Hoagland (1931) found that movement of a hair resulted in nerve response and that, with cessation of movement, the nerve responses immediately ceased. They suggested movement as the adequate stimulus.

Following the publication of their results, Dr. K. S. Wagoner and I (Nafe and Wagoner, 1941a) monitored the responses of tissue to a weight placed upon the skin, something never before done, to our knowledge, and we found that pressure sensation continued until the movement of tissue in response to the weight practically ceased. To show that this is not a fatigue phenomenon we allowed complete adaptation and then increased the weight of the stimulus. If the first failure were due to fatigue, there should be no aroused sensation — but there was. Definite proof of this relationship between movement and stimulation was obtained by removing the weight (Fig. 1-1). We found that if the movement of tissue back to its normal position is sufficiently rapid, it again results in sensation without the presence of any stimulus other than the movement of tissue.

Dr. D. R. Kenshalo and I (Nafe and Kenshalo, 1958) recorded nerve discharges in the dorsal cutaneous nerve of frog and the femoral nerve of rat under conditions similar to those used by Nafe and Wagoner with similar results (Figs. 1-2, 1-3, and 1-4.). So adaptation proves to be a failure of stimulation rather than a failure of nerve. Dr. Wall (1959; 1960) reported the cessation of nerve response in the presence of a "constant stimulus and with continued deformation of the tissues," and concluded that

*This research was supported by USPHS Grant # NG02992 and NSF Grant GB 2473.

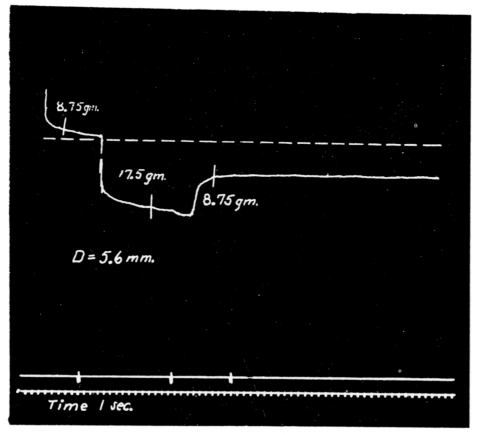

Figure 1-1. Weight released upon the skin. Hash mark indicates adaptation. Weight upon skin then doubled and then weight reduced by half (Fig. 10, Nafe, J. P., & Wagoner, K. S., *J. Gen. Psychol.*, 1941, **25**, 295).

adaptation is a function of stimulation rather than a function of nerve. Doctors Eijkman (1959) and Eijkman and Vendrik (1960) substantiated our findings but proposed some form of central adaptation. Dr. Loewenstein (1956) showed that adaptation has a mechanical basis and that the touch receptors of toad and frog skin are changed from "fast" to "slow adapting receptors," simply by stretching the tissues. Dr. Gray (1959) also has suggested a mechanical basis for adaptation and many others have objected to explanations in terms of nerve or other fatigue.

We must conclude that it is the tissues that adapt to the presence of a stimulus object such as a weight or other pressure and that the true stimulus to nerve discharge is movement or, more accurately, is rapid depolarization usually resulting from movement. It may, of course, also result from electric shock and from injury.

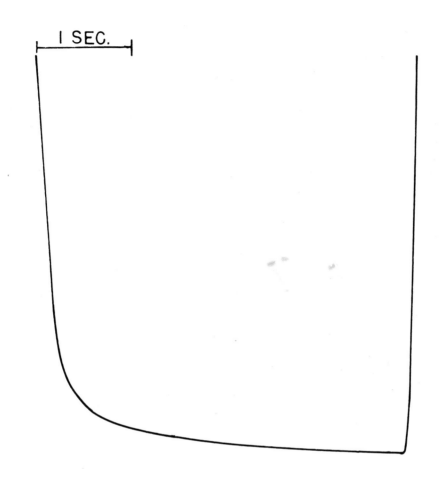

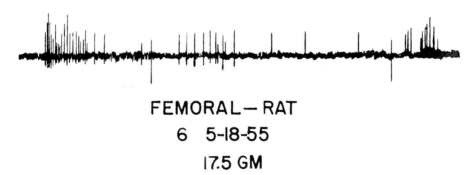

FEMORAL— RAT

6   5-18-55

17.5 GM

Figure 1-2. Weight released upon the skin and, after adaptation, the weight removed. Movement of tissue back to normal shows nerve response.

To help clarify this difficulty, perhaps wholly semantic, it should be understood that stimulation is a *process* and not an *object*. The objects that are used to stimulate are for the purpose of effecting such a process and to refer to them as "the stimulus" is only to use a shortcut as we do in referring to "warmth fibers" and "cold fibers." Such movement of the nerve fiber upon itself is the only stimulus demonstrated to be adequate for pressure sensations. Adequate stimulation of muscle, joint, skin and visceral sensitivity have all been definitely associated with such movement.

The second problem, that of "patterning" versus "specificity," needs clarification as to just what is meant by "pattern theory" of nerve excitation

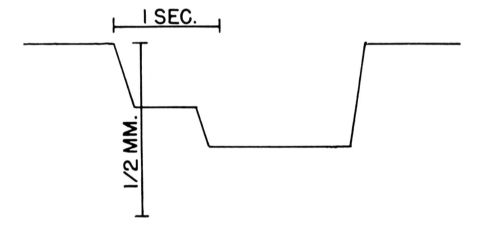

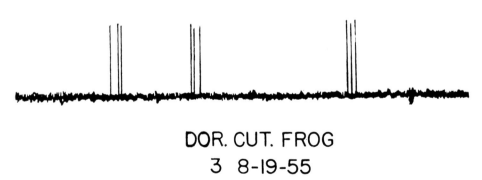

DOR. CUT. FROG
3 8-19-55

Figure 1-3. Forced depression of skin in two steps. Release of tissue shows movement as the sole stimulus (Fig. 6, Nafe, J. P., & Kenshalo, D. R., *Amer. J. Psychol.,* 1958, **17,** 199).

as opposed to a theory of nerves specific in their responses to different aspects or qualities of stimulation — Johannes Müller's "specific nerve energies." Thomes Young (1802) is the first person on record to posit single fiber specificity, which he did, or inferred, in the presentation of his theory of visual color. Bell (1811; 1869) wrote of single fiber specificity. It is not certain that Müller thought in terms of specific single fibers but Helmholtz (1852) did, both in his acceptance of Young's color theory and his own auditory theory. Max von Frey (Boring, 1932) applied it to skin sensitivity in his work from 1894 to 1897. In spite of much work done since that time, evidence for differences in nerve fibers has always been lacking. Sperry (1952) says flatly that there are no known differences in nerve fiber which could possibly be related to different qualities of sensation. An objection has been raised to the somewhat cavalier treatment accorded von Frey by the proponents of "pattern theory" and perhaps justly, but such an attitude on our part is not real. Everyone who studies the work of von Frey and his contemporaries must have great respect for them and for their work, much of which was done with very limited facilities. It is the very general acceptance of their conclusions that is objectionable. To avoid semantic difficulties a definite statement may be made: the theory of specificity definitely implies different kinds of nerve fibers. We reject such a hypothesis on the grounds that it is both undemonstrated and unnecessary.

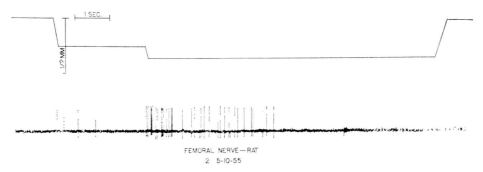

Figure 1-4. Forced depression of skin showing neural responses (Fig. 8, Nafe, J. P., & Kenshalo, D. R., *Amer. J. Psychol.,* 1958, **71**, 199).

What then are the facts that incline some of us to displace such a theory (Nafe, 1934)? Specificity of some kind we must have because we do sense qualitative differences. It appears that the volley of aroused nerve impulses is patterned in such a manner as to reflect, with a very high degree of integrity, all of the discernible differences in stimulation. Specificity lies in the nonnervous tissues which contain the peripheral nerve terminals. For example, some reports of Skogland (1956), of Mountcastle and Powell (1959), and Poggio and Mountcastle (1960) offer excellent examples. Let it be understood that I am not making any statement concerning the beliefs of any of these researchers as to specificity, but a correct theory must be able to subsume all the facts that bear upon it, regardless of who describes them. In the studies of nerve activity associated with movement of joints, they report discharges in one group of nerve fibers when movement of the joint is in one direction and a failure of these fibers to respond with the other movement. A second group of nerve fibers responds to the second movement but not to the first. From these findings it appears that nerve responses depend upon a specific relationship between the nerve endings and the tissues in which they terminate, and not at all in specific differences between the nerve fibers themselves.

Consider a more general example: an electric signboard, such as is used in advertising. It consists of a number of electric lamps arranged in rows vertically and horizontally, and the picture seen is a result of the patterns of lights exhibited from place to place and from moment to moment. Somewhere is a revolving cylinder with contact points, or its equivalent, and a cable of wires connecting cylinder and signboard. The pattern of contact points on the revolving cylinder, which in this case is "the stimulus," is a correlate or an analogue of the picture seen; and again, the brief electrical currents or impulses set up within the individual wires of the cable also constitute an analogue of the picture. The picture seen on television is a still better example but a bit more complicated. In auditory experience a music box serves as a similar example.

In a similar manner, an object comes into contact with the skin, the tissues are moved, with them the nerve fibers within the stimulated area are moved, and a volley of nerve impulses is set up over many fibers resulting in a feeling of pressure that has something of intensity, shape, and temporal course. The essential point is that not only is a volley of nerve discharges set up — we have all known that for a long time — but within this volley there is order, an order determined in every detail by the conditions of stimulation, much as the eye does in viewing a picture, and as the ear does in hearing a tonal complex. In the discharge of a single nerve fiber there is only one variable, frequency of discharges, which is correlated with the intensity of stimulation. The duration of such a discharge may be limited by adaptation or by other changes in the conditions of stimulation. All other aspects of the discharge are determined by the location and connections of the nerve fiber, its diameter and degree of myelinization — all of which are constant. Within a volley of nerve impulses there are other variables. The frequency of discharge in each nerve fiber varies with the intensity of stimulation at a given point, in a given moment. The whole number of fibers activated, i.e., the area, is a variable and may vary from moment to moment. The relative density of discharging fibers within the activated area is still another variable. Here we have all the essential conditions of the electric sign and just as many patterns are possible as different pictures are possible on the signboard.

There is another much neglected variable in the nerve discharge. The principles involved in the visual perception of movement also apply to the skin, indicating some interaction between the individual nerve fibers involved in such a volley of discharges. Adrian (1930) showed that although activity in one nerve fiber is not known to excite activity in another fiber, yet it may influence it. The volley of nerve impulses is much more complicated than the lights of the signboard, because, from the moment of its arousal, it is subject to inhibiting and reinforcing influences, and to aroused efferent impulses (feedback) which may alter the conditions of stimulation. In the example of the signboard any one of the lights may appear in many combinations with other lights, and this also is true of the units in a volley of nerve impulses.

So far the idea of patterned nerve discharges aroused by movement of skin tissue is relatively simple, but we may go further. Deprivation of food, according to Cannon and Washburn (1912), Carlson (1916), and others, results in activity of certain plain muscle elements of the digestive tract which are correlated with feelings of hunger. In other biological needs or urges, other bodily changes, many of them obvious, are correlated with certain neural and sensory consequences. Thus, in thirst, nausea, the urge to urinate, to defecate, to copulate, there are bodily changes which are similar from time to time and which arouse similar patterns of nerve discharge and similar feelings, and so become named hunger, thirst, etc.

It is within this context that we investigated sensations of warmth and cold (Nafe and Wagoner, 1937). This context includes the excision experiments in which small areas of the skin, especially sensitive to warmth or to cold, are located and the area excised and examined for end-organ or terminal structure. Some 12 to 15 such experiments have been reported and in no case has any such structure been found except that Goldscheider (1886), in the first of these experiments, reported that the one characteristic of such areas is a cluster of blood vessels. The context also includes the well-known facts that one may feel cold in fear or may even have a chill during a fever, and that one feels warm in anger or in passion. These events are not analogies. The sensations are very real; they indicate that if warmth and cold can be felt without any change in temperature, then they cannot be dependent upon any end-organ or other structure which is specific to temperature change but must be due to some action that may be induced by temperature change or reflexly by some bodily change.

The problem, as we saw it, was to find whether or not this particular system of bodily movements, i.e., vascular action, could be related to thermal sensitivity. As is well known, the vascular system, among its many other duties, is involved in temperature control in constant-temperature animals. As a part of these functions the peripheral arterioles of the skin constrict when cooled, driving the blood deeper within the tissues and so conserving heat (pale skin). These same blood vessels dilate in warmth above normal skin temperature, up to some 45°C (stimulus temperature) which allows the blood to run nearer to the surface and so lose bodily heat (flushed skin). When the surrounding temperature rises above body temperature (37°C) these vessels again constrict, thus keeping the excessive heat further from the blood stream. These changes correspond very closely with feelings of cold, warmth, and heat, and they also correspond with the facts that Dr. Zotterman (1959) and others have found for the ranges of temperature that excite "cold fibers" and "warmth fibers." The fact that temperature change, arterial response, neural response, and sensory response vary together sets up a presumption that each is an analogue of the others. Dr. Wagoner, Dr. Kenshalo, and I have presented evidence of such a relationship.

Of late Dr. Minut-Sorokhtina (1966) reports an investigation of the location of the peripheral endings of the warm and cold nerve fibers described by Iggo (1960) and others. She states that she separated the afferent nerve fibers terminating in the peripheral blood vessels from those of the skin proper and that those of the blood vessels responded to thermal stimulation after those of the skin had been removed. She concludes that the changes of temperature associated with thermal sensitivity effect transient vascular action, due not to reflex vascular action but as a direct reaction to temperature change. If her findings and conclusions are sustained, "patterning" will cease to be known as a theory and accepted as a demonstrated fact.

To summarize: pattern theory involves a view, as a working hypothesis, that all nerve fibers are essentially alike, they transmit no messages but conduct only impulses. The one adequate stimulus besides electrical shock and injury is movement, which may be induced mechanically or by changes in temperature. Whether or not a nerve fiber will respond to a given aspect of stimulation depends upon the relation of the nerve fiber to the tissues in which it terminates, and it is the tissues which adapt to stimulation. Qualitative differences in common sensation are correlated with the pattern of bodily activity that stimulates, and the temporal and spatial relationships of the nerve impulses aroused within a resulting volley of nerve impulses.

In conclusion I wish to note that we have here been speaking of the pressure sense, with its correlates, as if it were an independent entity, which we know that it is not. It is part of a much larger system, but to understand that system it is necessary to know what is delivered to it and under what conditions such deliveries are made.

REFERENCES

Adrian, E. D. The effects of injury on mammalian nerve fibers. *Proc. Roy. Soc. [Biol.]*, 1930, **106**, 596.

Adrian, E. D., Cattell, M., & Hoaglund, H. Sensory discharges in single cutaneous nerve fibers. *J. Physiol. (London)*, 1931, **72**, 377.

Bell, C. Idea of a new anatomy of the brain. Distributed monograph, 1811.

Bell, C. Idea of a new anatomy of the brain. *J. Anat. Physiol.*, 1869, **3**, 154.

Boring, E. G. Max von Frey. *Amer. J. Psychol.*, 1932, **44**, 584.

Cannon, W. B., & Washburn, A. L. An explanation of hunger. *Amer. J. Physiol.*, 1912, **29**, 441.

Carlson, A. J. *The Control of Hunger in Health and Disease.* Chicago: Chicago Univer. Press, 1916.

Eijkman, E. G. J. Adaptation of the senses of temperature and touch. Doctoral thesis, Univer. of Nijmegen, 1959.

Eijkman, E., & Vendrik, A. J. H. Dynamics of the vibration sense at low frequency. *J. Acoust. Soc. Amer.*, 1960, **32**, 1134.

Goldscheider, A. Histologische Untersuchungen über die Endigungen der Hautsinnesnerven beim Menschen. *Arch. Anat. Physiol., Physiol. Section,* 1886, 191.

Gray, J. A. B. Initiation of impulses at receptors. In J. Field (Ed.), *Handbook of Physiology. Section 1: Neurophysiology.* Washington, D. C.: Amer. Physiol. Soc., 1959. pp. 431-458.

Helmholtz, H. L. F. Ueber die Theorie der Zusammengesetzen Farben. *Ann. Phys. Chem.*, 1852, **163**,, 45.

Iggo, A. Cutaneous mechanoreceptors with afferent C fibers. *J. Physiol. (London)*, 1960, **152**, 337.

Loewenstein, W. R. Excitation and changes in adaptation by stretch of mechanoreceptors. *J. Physiol. (London)*, 1956, **133**, 588.

Melzack, R., & Wall, P. D. On the nature of cutaneous sensory mechanisms. *Brain,* 1962, **85**, 331.

Minut-Sorokhtina, O. P. Some debatable problems of thermal reception. *Fed. Proc. [Transl. Suppl.]*, 1966, **25**, T5.

Mountcastle, V. B., & Powell, T. P. S. Central nervous mechanisms subserving position sense and kinesthesis. *Bull. Hopkins Hosp.*, 1959, **105**, 173.

Nafe, J. P. The pressure, pain, and temperature senses. In C. A. Murchison (Ed.), *Handbook of General Experimental Psychology.* Worcester: Clark Univ. Press, 1934. Pp. 1037-1087.

Nafe, J. P., & Kenshalo, D. R. Stimulation and neural response. *Amer. J. Psychol.*, 1958, **71**, 199.

Nafe, J. P., & Wagoner, K. S. The insensitivity of the cornea to heat and pain derived from high temperatures. *Amer. J. Psychol.*, 1937, 49, 631.

Nafe, J. P., & Wagoner, K. S. The nature of pressure adaptation. *J. Gen. Psychol.*, 1941, **25**, 323. (a)

Nafe, J. P., & Wagoner, K. S. The nature of sensory adaptation. *J. Gen. Psychol.*, 1941, **25**, 295. (b)

Poggio, G. F., & Mountcastle, V. B. A study of the functional contributions of the lemniscal and spinothalamic systems of somatic sensibility. Central nervous mechanism in pain. *Bull. Hopkins Hosp.*, 1960, **106**, 266.

Skogland, S. Anatomical and physiological studies of knee joint innervation in the cat. *Acta Physiol. Scand.,* 1956, **36, 7**. (Suppl. 124.)

Sperry, R. W. Neurology and the mind-brain problem. *Amer. Sci.,* 1952, **40**, 291.

Wall, P. D. Repetitive discharge of neurons. *J. Neurophysiol.,* 1959, **22**, 305.

Wall, P. D. Cord cells responding to touch, damage, and temperature of the skin. *J. Neurophysiol.,* 1960, **23**, 197.

Young, T. On the theory of light and colours. *Philos. Trans.,* 1802, **92**, 20.

Zotterman, Y. Thermal sensations. In J. Field (Ed.), *Handbook of Physiology. Section 1: Neurophysiology*. Washington, D. C.: Amer. Physiol. Soc., 1959. Pp. 431-458.

Chapter 2

LIGHT AND ELECTRON MICROSCOPAL STRUCTURE OF SENSORY END-ORGANS IN HUMAN SKIN*

Nikolajs Cauna

Nerve terminals have been studied for over a century, yet the basic structure of the sensory end organs is still a much debated question. The employment of the electron microscope and histochemical techniques in recent years has produced a remarkable amount of new information which is helping to clarify some controversial issues. The functional significance of these findings, however, awaits careful evaluation in most cases.

The cutaneous receptor organs occur in a variety of forms, and the nerve fibers that supply these organs range from thick myelinated axons to very fine nonmyelinated fibers.

PRETERMINAL SEGMENT OF THE SENSORY NERVE FIBER

Prior to reaching the end-organs, nerve fibers undergo changes, characterized by ramification of the stem axons and by rearrangement of their sheaths. The Pacinian corpuscle seems to be the only receptor in the human tissues supplied by a whole, undivided myelinated axon (Cauna and Mannan, 1958). In a corpuscle of an infant, the axon loses its myelin sheath at the point where it enters the receptor organ. In postnatal life, the Pacinian corpuscle increases in size by apposition of new lamellae around its periphery and around the terminal part of its myelinated axon. As a result, in adult individuals the myelinated axon becomes progressively incorporated within the proximal portion of the receptor organ (Cauna, 1965).

Unlike the Pacinian corpuscles, the superficial receptors of the human skin have a shared nerve supply. The sensory stem axons ramify to a considerable extent, and their branches proceed to a number of end-organs sometimes dispersed over a large skin area (Cauna, 1959; Weddell, 1941).

The manner of ramification of the thick myelinated stem axons and the course of their branches have been traced by neurohistological methods and optical microscopy in great detail (Cauna and Mannan, 1961; Miller, Ralston and Kashara, 1958; Weddell, Pallie, and Palmer, 1954). Ramification of the fine myelinated and nonmyelinated sensory fibers has not been fully demonstrated by optical methods and requires the aid of the electron microscope.

*This study was supported by United States Public Health Service grant No. NB 04147.

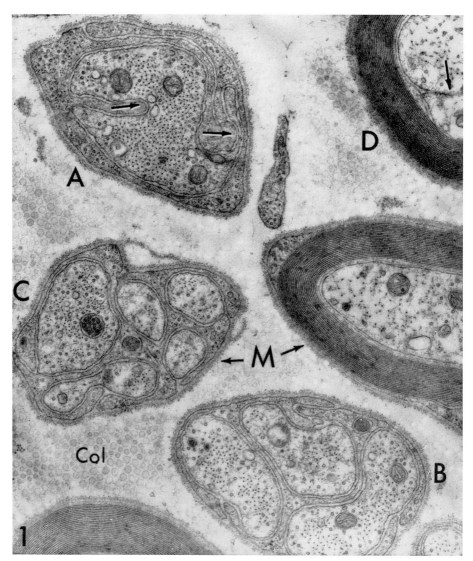

Figure 2-1. Part of a small nerve fascicle cut transversely from the skin of the rat's auricle. *A*—axon that has lost its myelin lamellae and is undergoing division (*arrows*). *B*—three branches derived from a myelinated axon contained within a common Schwann sheath. *C*—a set of five nonmyelinated fibers contained within a common Schwann sheath. The origin of these fibers was not established; they may constitute a set of postganglionic autonomic fibers, nonmyelinated sensory fibers derived from the dorsal root of the spinal nerve, or branches of an originally myelinated axon as in *B*. *D*—myelinated axon dividing prior to loss of its myelin sheath (*arrow*). *M*—basement membrane. *Col*—collagen fibers cut transversely (X 32,000).

Small nerve fasciles of the corial plexus usually contain a mixed fiber population and are suitab!e for these studies. Electron micrographs show that such fasciles are surrounded by well-developed perineurial sheaths consisting of several concentric cell layers intimately linked together into a continuous tube (Pease and Pallie, 1959). The interstitial space within the fascicle contains collagen fibers of longitudinal orientation (*Col* in Fig. 2-1). Each single axon or a set of nonmyelinated fibers are separated from this space by a distinct basement membrane (*M* in Fig. 2-1) which surrounds the surface of each Schwann sheath. In some instances, it is possible to trace a fine myelinated axon for some distance within a fascicle and to observe the loss of its myelin lamellae, and its subsequent ramification. It can be seen that the branches derived from such an axon do not disperse but proceed in a compact bundle invested by a common Schwann sheat (*B* in Fig. 2-1). When the cleavage begins, the branches may remain in contact with one another for a short distance but soon they become spaced by cytoplasmic folds of the Schwann cell (Cauna, 1966). Frequently, the cleavage of the axon is concurrent with the process of infolding of the Schwann cell membrane (*A* in Fig. 2-1, *arrows*). After some divisions have taken place, the resulting set of branches has the same arrangement and appearance as the fine nonmyelinated sensory fibers that originate in the dorsal roots of the spinal nerves (Gasser, 1955). Furthermore, these sensory nonmyelinated fibers cannot be distinguished from postganglionic autonomic fibers on morphological basis.

In the superficial layer of the corium of the hairless skin, the autonomic fibers are absent, but even in these situations no distinction can be made between the sensory nonmyelinated fibers derived from fine myelinated axons and those that have travelled the who!e distance from the sensory ganglia. Indeed, the possibility has to be explored that nonmyelinated sensory fibers of the dorsal root may constitute branches of larger axons that have undergone divisions close to their origin from the ganglion cells. In such a case, the main difference between the two types of the sensory fibers would be in the length of their nonmyelinated segments.

Due to the limitations of electron microscopical techniques, changes in nerve fibers can only be traced for short distances. But it appears from observations based on a large number of different tissue blocks that nonmyelinated fibers divide regularly and that the fiber sets gradually split into smaller units. Single branches also leave such sets to continue their progress within their own Schwann cell coverings and to divide again.

When a unit of fibers is about to depart from a nerve fascicle, it enters a gap formed between layers of the perineurial sheath cells. On departure, it receives its own perineurial covering, one to two layers thick, which provides the fibers with a protective cellular tube until the endings are formed.

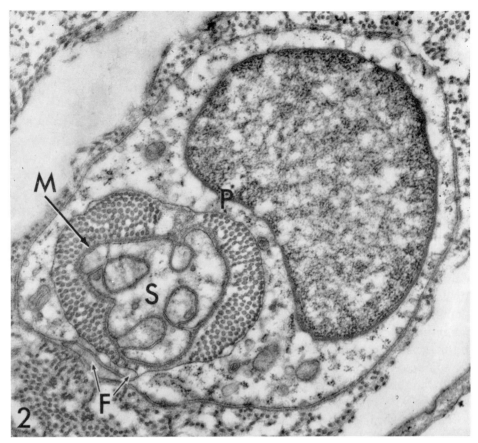

Figure 2-2. A set of four nonmyelinated nerve fibers at the base of a dermal papilla of the human digital skin. They are derived from a single myelinated stem axon and are contained within folds of a Schwann cell S. The cell and the surface areas of the nerve fibers that lack the Schwann cell covering are surrounded by a basement membrane M. The nerve unit is surrounded by collagen fibers of longitudinal orientation and enclosed in a cellular sheath that is continuous with the perineurial sheath of the parent nerve fascicle. P—perineurial cell. F—overlapping flaps of the perineurial cell. (X 32,000).

This is illustrated in Figure 2-2 which shows a set of four nonmyelinated sensory fibers at the base of the dermal papilla. The fibers are carried within a Schwann sheath (S) which is surrounded by a basement membrane (M). The latter forms a continuous coating over the free surface of the sheath as well as over the surfaces of the nerve fibers that lack the Schwann cell covering. Exterior to the fiber unit, the space contains collagen fibers of longitudinal orientation. The unit is separated from the surrounding tissues of the dermal papilla by a perineurial cell (P in Fig. 2-2) which is molded into a closed tube. The latter becomes open and is rapidly lost as the fibers begin to form the endings. The perineurial sheaths enclosing single nerve fibers have been recognized with the optical microscope, but it was believed that this sheath was continuous along the entire course of each fiber and therefore was termed *endoneurium*. Electron microscopical studies show that the *endoneurium* is absent while nerve fibers travel within a fascicle (Causey and Barton, 1959). Since the sheath in question is derived from the perineurium, the term *perineurial sheath* seems to be appropriate.

RECEPTOR ORGANS OF THE SKIN

Many attempts have been made in past and recent literature to establish a satisfactory classification of the receptor organs. While Krause (1881) and his contemporaries recognized almost a hundred types and variations of the end-organs, purely on morphological basis, Stöhr (1928) suggested that classification of these structures was an arbitrary process having no real significance. Many subsequent ventures in classification are modifications of either Krause's or Stöhr's views or combinations of both (Stilwell, 1957; Weddell *et al.*, 1954). Classification on a functional basis has always been the aim of morphologists and physiologists alike (von Frey, 1887), but attempts in this direction have met with difficulties (Bishop, 1960; Cauna and Alberti, 1961; Sinclair, 1955; Weddell, 1960).

Morphologically, the receptor organs can be divided into two primary groups: (a) free nerve endings, and (b) corpuscular receptors. The free nerve endings have a simple structure which blends with that of the surrounding tissues. Consequently, they are invisible in routine histological preparations and are only revealed by neurohistological or histochemical staining procedures. The corpuscular receptors possess specifically organized structure in which nonnervous tissue elements play a major part (Cauna, 1954; 1962). Because of this nonnervous structure, they can be recognized in routine histological preparations, and they remain conspicuous even after degeneration of nerves.

Free Nerve Endings

The transition of the nerve fibers into free endings is inconspicuous because of the simple morphology of the latter. It seems that the loss of the perineurial sheath may mark the beginning of the end-organ. Some free endings exhibit a positive butyrocholinesterase activity. In such cases their location may be determined histochemically (Cauna, 1960).

Contrary to older reports based on light microscope observations, the free endings never occur in the form of naked axoplasmic filaments. After the loss of the perineurial sheath, nerve fibers remain invested by the Schwann cells which become irregular, sometimes overlapping one another in layers around the nerve fibers. The basement membrane exterior to the ending is

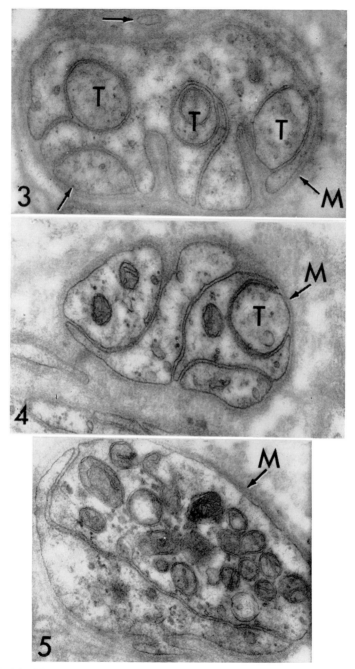

Figures 2-3, 2-4, 2-5. Free nerve endings in the tips of dermal papillae of the human digital skin. The perineurial sheaths have been lost, but the terminals retain their Schwann cell coverings and the basement membranes *M*. Figure 2-3—three terminal branches *T* contained within one Schwann cell body. Processes of other Schwann cells never lost. Variations in relationship between the nerve terminals and the associated Schwann cells are illustrated in Figures 2-3, 2-4, 2-5. Figure 2-3 shows three very fine terminal nerve fibers (T) contained within one Schwann cell body. Portions of other Schwann cells are also visible and are indicated by arrows. Figure 2-4 shows a single nerve terminal located in a groove of a cluster of Schwann cells. Figure 2-5 shows an end bulb located in a shallow groove of a Schwann cell, the remaining surface area of the nerve terminal being covered with the basement membrane (M). The axoplasm of this nerve terminal contains an accumulation of mitochondria which vary in size, density, and their internal structure.

Free endings have a widespread distribution in almost all tissues. In the human skin, they are located in the dermal papillae as well as in deeper layers of the corium. In some mucous membranes and some skin areas, e.g., the hairless skin of the nose of quadrupeds, free endings extend from the subepithelial connective tissues into the epithelia. When this happens, the Schwann cells are replaced by the epithelial cells as the endings reach the basal cell layer, and the basement membranes of the Schwann sheaths fuse with that of the epithelium (Munger, 1965; Whitear, 1960). The intraepithelial nerve fibers proceed towards the surface in grooves of the epithelial cells. There is evidence that intraepidermal nerve endings grow continuously with the epidermis. On approaching the stratum corneum they undergo atrophy and are gradually lost with the squamous cells (Cauna, 1959; Fitzgerald, 1961; Munger, 1965).

The nerve terminals of the free nerve endings may have the same morphological characteristics as the conducting fibers from which they are derived. Usually, however, the axoplasm of the terminals shows some accumulation of mitochondria, particularly in the enlarged segments of the beaded terminals and in the end bulbs (Fig. 2-5). In the distal segments of the nerve terminals, the mitochondria undergo certain changes, characterized by variation in size, density, and the arrangement of the cristae. The axoplasm of some nerve terminals may contain fine vesicles which may vary in size and thickness of their walls. Other terminals may contain fine granules of various sizes and density (Cauna, 1966). The cells of the free endings show a modest supply of mitochondria and a poorly developed endoplasmic reticulum. There is always some pinocytotic activity. The Schwann cells of some free endings give a positive butyrocholinesterase reaction. Both the terminal Schwann cells and the epithelial cells, in the

are indicated by unlabelled arrows. Figure 2-4—single nerve terminal in relation to a cluster of Schwann cells. Figure 2-5—end bulb; the nerve terminal is located in a shallow groove of a Schwann cell and is surrounded by a basement membrane M; it contains an accumulation of mitochondria which vary in size, density, and the internal structure (X 51,000).

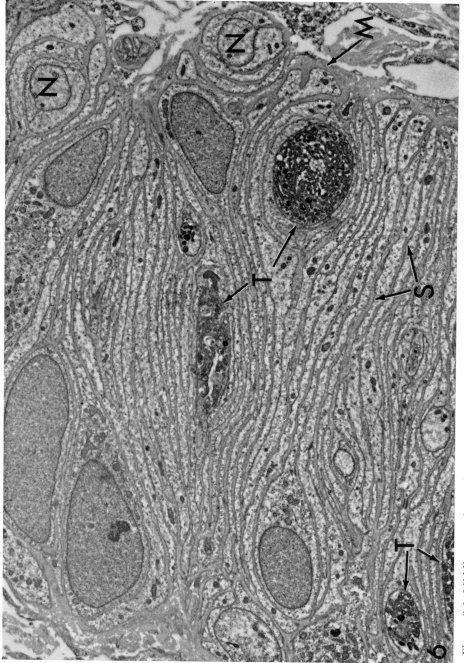

Figure 2-6. Middle part of a Meissner's touch corpuscle cut longitudinally. Human digital skin. On entering the corpuscle, nerve fibers N are surrounded by Schwann cells. Inside the corpuscle, the terminals T usually increase in diameter and their axoplasm becomes filled with mitochondria. The flattened laminar cells are in appositional relationship with the nerve terminals but are spaced from one another by an intercellular substance S. M—basement membrane of the corpuscle continuous with the intercellular substance and the basement membrane of Schwann cells.(X 6,100).

case of the intraepithelial endings, are in close appositional relationship with the nerve terminals. Areas of morphological specialization of the apposed membranes have not been described.

Corpuscular Receptors

In contrast to a free nerve ending, a corpuscular receptor possesses a well-defined structure of some complexity (Fig. 2-6). Moreover, the surrounding tissues, including the epithelium, are frequently modified in a definite manner (Fig. 2-8) and may constitute the principal part of the receptor organ (Fig. 2-9).

The human skin and some adjoining mucous membranes are rich in corpuscular receptors. The hairy areas contain Merkel's corpuscles in addition to the tactile hairs. The hairless areas also contain Merkel's corpuscles. The hairless skin of hands and feet contains Meissner's corpuscles which are associated with the papillary ridges (Cauna, 1954). Similar corpuscles but of simpler structure are found in other hairless areas and mucous membranes and are referred to as bulboid, lingual, genital corpuscles, mucocutaneous end-organs (Winkelman, 1960), etc. The deep tissues of the body contain lamellar corpuscles which range from simple forms in the vicinity of the joints, also known as Golgi or Golgi-Mazzoni corpuscles (Stilwell, 1957), to complex organs or pacinian corpuscles, the largest of which are concentrated in the subcutaneous tissues of hands and feet. Each pacinian corpuscle consists of a central core or inner bulb and a series of concentric cellular lamellae or the outer bulb. The central core contains the nerve terminal surrounded by its cellular covering probably derived from the Schwann sheath. It gives a strong positive butyrocholinesterase reaction. Although the lamellar corpuscles have attracted much interest and were first to be discovered, their fine structure has only been studied in the cat's mesentery (Pease and Quilliam, 1957). According to this study, the nerve terminal and the cells of the inner cord are in plain appositional relationship. The nerve terminal shows some accumulation of mitochondria.

The structure of Meissner's touch corpuscle has been described in some detail including its electron microscopical appearance (Cauna and Ross, 1960). This receptor consists of flattened laminar cells interleaved with nerve endings. The laminar cells are separated from one another by thin layers of intercellular substance (*S* in Fig. 2-6) which is continuous with the basement membrane investing the whole of the corpuscle (*M* in Fig. 2-6). Nerve fibers that supply the organ are branches of thick myelinated axons. On entering the corpuscle, they lose their Schwann sheaths and become invested by the laminar cells which appear to be of lemmoblastic origin.

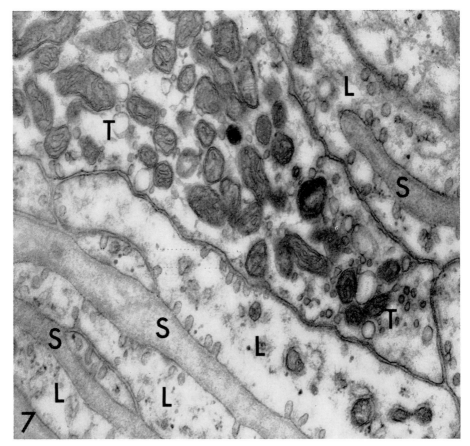

Figure 2-7. Field from a Meissner's corpuscle showing a nerve terminal *T*. Its axoplasm contains mitochondria, vacuoles, and fine vesicles. Laminar cells *L* are intimately related to the nerve terminal. Their cytoplasm contains pinocytotic vesicles. *S*—intercellular substance (X 51,000).

The intracorpuscular terminals are intimately related to the cell membranes of the laminar cells (*T* in Figs. 2-6 and 2-7, *cf.* with Figs. 2-3, 2-4, 2-5). Their axoplasm usually is packed with mitochondria which show the same variations that are observed in the free nerve endings. It may also contain vacuoles and vesicles of various sizes (Fig. 2-7). The fine morphology of the laminar cells is similar to that of the Schwann cells, except that their nuclei are of fine granular structure and their cell membranes exhibit a strong positive butyrocholinesterase activity.

In the tactile hair, the nerve terminals are attached to the epithelial sheath of the hair. The attachment zone extends over the middle one-third of the root which is subject to greatest displacement when the external shaft is bent, the deeper portion of the follicle being soft (Fig. 2-9). The axoplasm of the terminals contains an accumulation of fine vesicles and exhibits a positive acetylcholinesterase activity (Cauna, 1966).

The general organization of Merkel's touch corpuscles is reminiscent of that of the tactile hair. These corpuscles are situated on deep aspects of solid epidermal folds or pegs which project like the roots of the hairs into the loose areolar tissue of the corium. The corpuscles are sheltered from painful and thermal stimuli by their deep position but are stimulated mechanically by leverage when the surface of the epidermis is deformed. The receptor proper consists of a modified epidermal cell and a disc-shaped nerve terminal which is in appositional contact with the basal aspect of the cell. The surface of the terminal, which is not in apposition with Merkel's cell, is invested in the Schwann sheath. The terminal is packed with small mitochondria. A characteristic of the Merkel's cell is an accumulation of fine osmophilic granules in its basal part adjoining the nerve terminal. The nature of these granules has not yet been established. Merkel's corpuscles are devoid of cholinesterases.

DISCUSSION

The corpuscular receptors vary in their external form, and their appearance is also different from that of the free nerve endings. On the fine structural level, however, certain basic features are observed in common to all the cutaneous receptors that have been studied with the electron microscope so far.

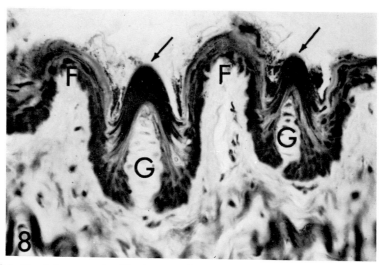

Figure 2-8. Genital corpuscles G, glans penis of the rat. The corpuscles have a nonnervous structure that can be recognized in routine histological preparations without staining of the nerves. The epidermis above each corpuscle forms projections (*arrows*) which possess keratinized caps. The folds of the epidermis between the corpuscles F are flattened during erection. Haematoxylin and eosin stain (X 360).

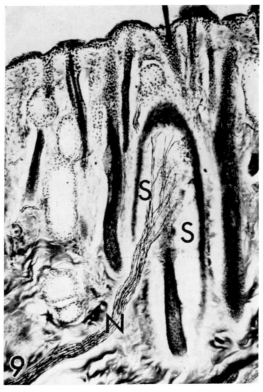

Figure 2-9. Sinus hair cut obliquely along the plane of distribution of its nerves *N*. Skin of the mole's nose. *S*—blood sinus surrounding the middle one third of the hair root which possesses the nerve endings. Silver preparation (X 85).

The free and the corpuscular receptor organs alike consist of neural and nonneural components. The latter may be of lemmoblastic or epithelial origin. The nerve terminals and the associated cells never form syncytial continuity, instead the axolemma of the terminal fiber and the plasma membrane of the supporting cells are in close appositional relationship. Morphologically specialized areas of the two apposed membranes, such as found in the neuromuscular junctions or the synaptic regions, are not observed. The nerve terminals are characterized by accumulation of mitochondria in their axoplasm which may signify a high rate of metabolic activity that is involved in propagation of impulses. The cells associated with the nerve terminals show a modest supply of mitochondria and a poorly developed, endoplasmic reticulum. They also contain pinocytotic vesicles, which are even observed in the epidermal cells if they enclose nerve terminals. A basement membrane always separates the end-organ from the surrounding intercellular matrix.

The differences in the cutaneous receptor organs are histochemical as well as fine morphological. Histochemically, they vary in respect to cholinesterase activity in the nerve terminals or the associated cells (Cauna, 1961; Hurley, 1958; Koelle, 1963; Montagna, 1960). The fine morphological variations mainly occur in the form of specialized axoplasmic components. Some nerve terminals contain microvesicles or granules which may vary in their size and electron density while other terminals are devoid of any particles of this kind. The variations in the fine structure of the associated cells so far have only been observed as osmophylic granules located in the cytoplasm of Merkel's cells.

Changes in size, density and the internal structure of the mitochondria that are observed in the distal segments of some nerve terminals may not be directly related to the specific functions of the receptor organs. These changes have been considered as signifying a process of involution of outworn organelles (Cauna and Ross, 1960).

Variations among the end-organs in respect to their histochemical characteristics and the fine vesicular and granular components are of particular interest in relation to their probable function. These variations occur in the free and corpuscular receptors alike, in apparently similar patterns. The superficial free endings of the skin which appear to be associated with pain and temperature sensation may contain the vesicular or granular component in the nerve terminals or may be devoid of either. They may or may not contain butyrocholinesterase in the associated cells. The superficial corpuscular receptors such as the tactile hair, Meissner's and Merkel's corpuscles, usually associated with tactile sensation, vary in a similar manner. The nerve terminals of the tactile hair contain fine vesicles and give a positive acetylcholinesterase reaction. The nerve terminals of Meissner's corpuscle are devoid of acetylcholinesterase, but the associated cells exhibit a strong positive butyrocholinesterase reaction. Merkel's corpuscles are devoid of cholinesterases but the cytoplasm of their cells contains fine osmophilic granules. While the functional role of the fine vesicular and granular components and cholinesterases remains subject to speculations, it seems unlikely that these features may reflect the capacity of the receptor organs for discrimination of sensory modalities.

The variations of the end-organs in their external form and the specialized organization of the tissue elements immediately related to these receptors have long attracted the attention of morphologists and physiologists and have caused speculations on their significance. The free nerve endings of the skin are well exposed to painful and thermal stimuli because of their superficial situation. Structurally, they blend with the texture of the surrounding tissues; therefore, the effect of mechanical stimulation is lessened. The corpuscular receptors are less exposed to painful stimuli and temperature changes under normal conditions because of their deep location. Their nonnervous components and the associated tissues that are interposed between the stimuli and the nerve terminals are so organized that mechanical stimulation applied to the surface of the skin is transmitted to the endings and increased in intensity by leverage. The factors considered above can only secure relative specificity for the receptor organs. The question arises, whether this may constitute an adequate morphological basis of sensation at the peripheral receptor level.

REFERENCES

Bishop, G. H. The relation of nerve fiber size to modality of sensation. In W. Montagna (Ed.), *Advances in Biology of Skin. Vol. 1.* New York: Pergamon, 1960. Pp. 88-98.

Cauna, N. Nature and functions of the papillary ridges of the digital skin. *Anat. Rec.,* 1954, **119**, 449.

Cauna, N. The mode of termination of the sensory nerves and its significance. *J. Comp. Neurol.,* 1959, **113**, 169.

Cauna, N. The distribution of cholinesterase in the cutaneous receptor organs, especially touch corpuscles of the human finger. *J. Histochem. Cytochem.,* 1960, **8**, 367.

Cauna, N. Cholinesterase activity in cutaneous receptors of man and of some quadrupeds. *Bibl. Anat.,* 1961, **2**, 128.

Cauna, N. Functional significance of the submicroscopical, histochemical, and microscopical organization of the cutaneous receptor organs. *Verh. Anat. Ges.,* 1962, **111**, 181.

Cauna, N. The effects of aging on the receptor organs of the human dermis. In W. Montagna (Ed.), *Advances in biology of Skin. Vol. VI.* New York: Pergamon, 1965. Pp. 63-96.

Cauna, N. The fine structure of the receptor organs and its probable functional significance. In O. E. Lowenstein (Ed.), *CIBA Foundation symposium: Touch, Heat and Pain.* London: Churchill, 1966. Pp. 117-136.

Cauna, N., & Alberti, P. Nerve supply and distribution of cholinesterase activity in the external nose of the mole. *Z. Zellforsch.,* 1961, **54**, 158.

Cauna, N., & Mannan, G. The structure of human digital Pacinian corpuscles (corpuscula lamellosa) and its functional significance. *J. Anat.,* 1958, **92**, 1.

Cauna, N., & Mannan, G. Organization and development of the preterminal nerve pattern in the palmar digital tissues of man. *J. Comp. Neurol.,* 1961, **117**, 309.

Cauna, N., & Ross, L. L. The fine structure of Meissner's touch corpuscles in human fingers. *J. Biophys. Biochem. Cytol.,* 1960, **3**, 467.

Causey, G., & Barton, A. A. The cellular content of the "endoneurium" of peripheral nerve. *Brain,* 1959, **82**, 594.

FitzGerald, M. J. T. Developmental changes in epidermal innervation. *J. Anat.,* 1961, **95**, 495.

Frey, M. von. Untersuchungen über die Sinnesfunktionen der menschlichen Haut. *Abhandl. math-phys. Cl. d. k. Sächs. Ges. d. Wiss.,* 1897, **23**, 169.

Gasser, H. S. Properties of dorsal root unmedullated fibers on the two sides of the ganglion. *J. Gen. Physiol.,* 1955, **38**, 709.

Hurley, H. J. Non-specific cholinesterase in specialized sensory nerve endings of human genital skin. *Brit. J. Derm.,* 1958, **70**, 284.

Koelle, G. B. Cytological distributions and physiological functions of cholinesterases. In O. Eichler & A. Farah (Eds.), *Handbuch der Exp. Pharmakologie. Ergänzungswerk. Vol. 15.* Berlin: Springer, 1963. P. 187.

Krause, W. Die Nervenendigung innerhalb der terminalen Körperchen. *Arch. Mikr. Anat.,* 1881, **19**, 53.

Miller, M. R., Ralston, H. J., III, & Kasahara, M. The pattern of cutaneous innervation of the human hand. *Amer. J. Anat.,* 1958, **102**, 183.

Montagna, W. Cholinesterases in the cutaneous nerves of man. In W. Montagna (Ed.), *Advances in Biology of Skin. Vol. 1.* New York: Pergamon, 1960. Pp. 74-87.

Munger, B. L. The intraepidermal innervation of the snout skin of the opossum. *J. Cell Biol.,* 1965, **26**, 79.

Pease, D. C., & Pallie, W. Electron microscopy of digital tactile corpuscles and small cutaneous nerves. *J. Ultrastruct. Res.,* 1959, **2**, 352.

Pease, D. C., & Quilliam, T. A. Electron microscopy of the Pacinian corpuscle. *J. Biophys. Biochem. Cytol.,* 1957, **3**, 331.

Sinclair, D. C. Cutaneous sensation and the doctrine of specific energy. *Brain,* 1955, **78**, 584.

Stilwell, D. C. The innervation of deep structures of the foot. *Amer. J. Anat.,* 1957, **101**, 59.

Stöhr, P., Jr. Das peripherische Nervenfaser. In W. H. W. von Möllendorff (Ed.), *Handbuch der Mikroskopischen Anatomie des Menshen. Vol. IV, 1.* Berlin: Springer, 1928. Pp. 143-201.

Weddell, G. The pattern of cutaneous innervation in relation to cutaneous sensibility. *J. Anat.,* 1941, **75**, 346.

Weddell, G. Studies related to mechanism of common sensibility. In W. Montagna (Ed.), *Advances in Biology of Skin. Vol. 1.* New York: Pergamon, 1960. Pp. 112-159.

Weddell, G., Pallie, W., & Palmer, E. The morphology of peripheral nerve terminations in the skin. *Quart. J. Micr. Sci.,* 1954, **95**, 483.

Whitear, M. An electron microscope study of the cornea in mice, with special reference to the innervation. *J. Anat.,* 1960, **94**, 387.

Winkelmann, R. K. Similarities in cutaneous nerve end-organs. In W. Montagna (Ed), *Advances in Biology of Skin. Vol. 1.* New York: Pergamon, 1960. Pp. 48-62.

DISCUSSION

DR. M. J. T. FITZGERALD: In this interesting comparison of the sensory nerve terminals, have you observed thickenings of cell membranes at the terminals which might suggest a synaptic relation?

DR. CAUNA: Although a lot of electron microscopical work has already been done in the field, the information is inadequate to make any generalized or specific conclusion. One may get the impression that the apposed membranes are thicker in one area than elsewhere along the course of the ending. When I first studied Meissner's corpuscles (Cauna and Ross, 1960), I though that there were condensations of the apposed membranes comparable to synaptic junctions, but further studies did not confirm these findings. The relationship between the neural and nonneural elements in the cutaneous receptor organs seems, as far as we can judge, to be very similar to the relationship between the Schwann cells and the conducting segments of the nerve fibers. I think the main difference between the synaptic regions and the peripheral endings is the large neural surface area that is exposed to stimulation, in the latter, as compared with the limited surface areas of considerable morphological specialization in the central synaptic areas.

Dr. R. K. Winkelmann: Dr. Cauna, you mentioned that when the individual axons occur within the epidermis, as they are rarely, that the Schwann cells are replaced by the epidermal cells. Have you seen, as Munger (1965) has mentioned, some epidermal mesaxon type of structure? Have you seen any complicated intracytoplasmic relationships between the intraepithelial axon in the epithelium?

Dr. Cauna: The general relationship between the epithelial cell and the nerve terminal is similar to that of the Schwann cells and an axon. A nerve terminal may be completely embedded within a fold of the epithelial cell, or it may be surrounded by several epithelial cells, but the nerve terminal is never running freely in the intercellular space in human material. Epithelial cell membranes surrounding the nerve fiber, in general, show no morphologic specialization, but it is interesting to note that the part of the cell membranes of the epidermal cell, which is related to the nerve terminal, may contain pinocytotic activity as compared to the rest of the cell. Merkel's cells are an exception.

Dr. Winkelmann: Several years ago you published a picture of a Merkel's cell, demonstrating secretory granules next to the nerve terminals. Do you find this commonly in epidermal nerve relationships?

Dr. Cauna: The Merkel's corpuscles are unique in this respect. In the cytoplasm of Merkel's cells there is an accumulation of fine osmophilic granules in areas adjacent to the nerve terminal (Cauna, 1962), but the nature of these granules has not yet been established. They may not be neuro-secretory granules. Attempts to demonstrate them, as such, have failed so far.

Dr. H. Davis: I am trying to make a mental connection between the structures that you showed us and the idea that Dr. Nafe stressed, which is motion. Is any work being done on tissues that are deliberately deformed in one direction or another before fixing, in order to give some insight into whether the protective cells around the nerve fibers tend to protect the fibers from motion, or whether, perhaps, to concentrate the deformation on what we must suppose are the sensitive areas? I think it will be an extremely interesting development if some dynamic aspect can be brought into the study of these structures.

Dr. Cauna: I think I can demonstrate the dynamic aspects of the corpuscular receptors. The free nerve endings blend with the surrounding tissues and, therefore, the mechanical deformations are softened, rather than being increased. But in the corpuscular receptors, the tissues which are involved in the formation of the corpuscles are arranged in such a way that there is a mechanical friction.

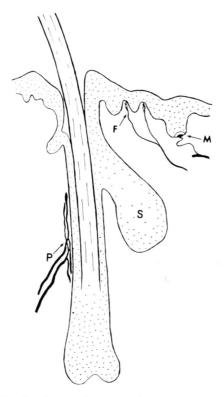

Figure 2-10. Diagram showing free and corpuscular receptors of the hairy human skin. The free endings *F* are imbedded in loose areolar tissue and are not coupled mechanically with the epidermis or its derivatives. Merkel's corpuscle *M* is attached to a solid epidermal peg which may act as a lever when the surface of the overlying skin is deformed, producing the highest amount of movement at the sensitive area of the receptor organ. This arrangement appears to be comparable to that of the tactile hair which contains a nerve plexus *P* around the middle one third of its epithelial root sheath. *S*—sebaceous gland.

Merkel's corpuscles are mounted on the bottom part of solid epidermal pegs or ridges which float in loose connective tissue (*M* in Figs. 2-10 and 2-11).

When the surface of the skin is deformed, the mechanical stimulus is transmitted to the deeply placed Merkel's corpuscles and increased in intensity by leverage. Indeed, the epidermal peg or ridge projecting into the corium can be compared with the root of the tactile hair in this respect (Fig. 2-10). Here is Eimer's organ from the mole's nose (Fig. 2-12).

It consists of a solid block of epidermis connected to adjacent organs by soft epidermis which permits each Eimer's organ to rock when its surface is mechanically stimulated. The bases of Eimer's organs are surrounded by large blood sinuses (*V, V* in Fig. 2-12) which facilitate mobility and can be

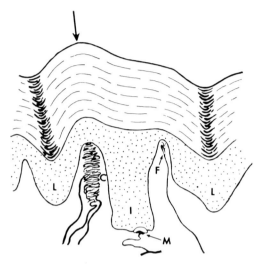

Figure 2-11. Diagram showing free and corpuscular receptors of the hairless digital skin of man. The free endings *F* are embedded in loose areolar tissue as in the hairy skin. Merkel's corpuscle *M* is attached to a solid epidermal ridge *I* which projects into the loose corial tissue underneath and acts as a magnifying lever for transmission of mechanical stimuli to the nerve terminals. The two limiting ridges *L, L* are devoid of Merkel's corpuscles and are firmly anchored to the corium. Meissner's corpuscle *C* is attached to the papillary ridge. Its most effective stimulation takes place through a surface elevation of the epidermis (*arrow*).

compared with the sinuses of the large tactile hairs. The nerve plexus at the base of an Eimer's organ is, therefore, well exposed to mechanical stimulation by leverage (*P* in Fig. 2-12).

DR. WINKELMANN: Dr. Cauna, do you have any direct evidence that the organ of Eimer is a tactile organ and not a heat organ like that of the pit viper?

DR. CAUNA: Well, the Eimer's organ is a very peculiar structure. When the myelin sheaths of the stem axons are lost, the resulting nerve plexus at the base of Eimer's organ (*P* in Fig. 2-12) receives a heavy Schwann cell covering. Segments of nerve fibers develop concentric layers of Schwann cells and appear like miniature Pacinian corpuscles, except that then central nerve fibers traverse these "corpuscles" and proceed as intraepidermal endings (Fig. 2-12). The question arises, whether Eimer's organ can be used as a multiple receptor. The intraepidermal terminals may perhaps be more sensitive to pain and temperature, while the plexus at the base of the organ may be more sensitive to mechanical stimulation. Of course, that is a controversial question but the anatomical structures really pose that question.

DR. L. M. BEIDLER: Dr. Cauna, as I understand it, the free nerve ending is always capped by an epithelial cell in the epidermis; this means, if you pour acid on your skin, it must go through this epidermal cell to get at the ending. It is possible that the epithelial cell could act as a transducer?

DR. CAUNA: Yes.

DR. WINKELMANN: Dr. Cauna, in your electron micrographic studies, how frequently have you seen intraepithelial nerve endings in the skin?

DR. CAUNA: I have never seen intraepidermal nerve endings in the normal human skin, but I have seen preparations by Dr. Weddell, where, under certain pathological conditions, the nerve fibers grow into the epidermis.

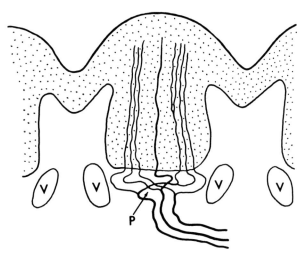

Figure 2-12. Diagram showing Eimer's organs from the external nose of the mole. The base of each organ is surrounded by circular blood sinuses *V* which facilitate movement and mechanical stimulation of the plexiform nerve endings *P*. Intraepidermal nerve endings derived from the plexus extend as far as the stratum corneum where they undergo atrophy.

These two fields are areas taken from the central portion of the vestibule of the nose of the rat and the cat (Figs. 2-13 and 2-14).

In the rat's vestibule of the nose, the epithelium is thin, only three to five cell-layers thick. The nerve fibers tend to form horizontal terminals underneath the basal cell layers, because the distance from the surface is short enough, apparently, for effective function. In the cat's vestibule of the nose, the epithelium is very thick, by comparison, and the nerve fibers penetrate into the epithelium to reach the stratum corneum. I think, in principle, the free corial and the intraepidermal endings are essentially similar. The physical conditions, such as the thickness of the epidermis, may determine why nerve fibers either enter the epidermis or remain in the corium.

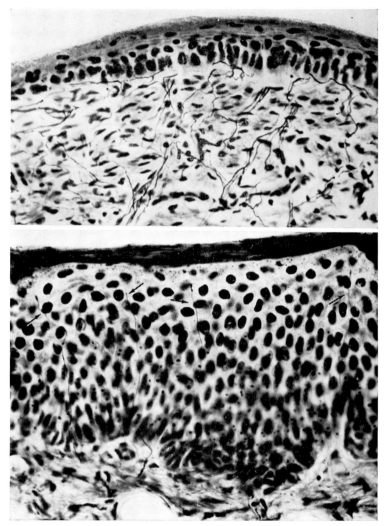

Figure 2-13. Skin from the vestibule of the rat's nose showing plexiform subepidermal nerve endings but no intraepidermal nerve fibers, probably because of the thinness of the epidermis (*cf.* with Fig. 2-14). Silver impregnation (X400) (Fig. 41, Cauna, N., *J. Comp. Neurol.*, 1959, **113**, 201).

Figure 2-14. Skin from the vestibule of the cat's nose showing intraepidermal nerve endings (*cf.* with Fig. 2-13). Silver impregnation (X400).

Dr. F. W. L. Kerr: Would you comment on the nonmyelinated fibers you see in the skin and what their relationship is to the myelinated fibers; that is to say, are the nonmyelinated fibers continuations of the myelinated fibers or are they continuations of the nonmyelinated fibers in the cutaneous nerves?

Dr. Cauna: This question is frequently asked. Occasionally we find myelinated axons which lose their myelin sheaths a very short distance prior to their termination and give origin to free nerve endings. Most nerve fibers, however, lose their myelin sheaths some considerable distance prior to their termination. Consequently, quite a number of nonmyelinated fibers that are found in the preterminal region are really branches of myelinated axons. There is another aspect about the nonmyelinated fibers which arrive from the dorsal root in sets contained within common Schwann sheaths. The possibility should be considered that these sets of nonmyelinated fibers may not be individual axons but rather branches of stem axons that have divided very close to the sensory nerve cell. This requires further studies.

Dr. Winkelmann: Is it not true that almost all of the subepidermal nerves are unmyelinated? In our preparations, there are nothing but unmyelinated nerve fibers in the preterminal region close to the surface.

Dr. Cauna: Yes, I agree with that, although there are fibers which enter the dermal papillae with their myelin sheaths retained. Even in Meissner's corpuscles, we may occasionally find the myelin sheath still present when the fibers enter the corpuscles.

Dr. Beidler: Dr. Cauna, I noticed that you said there are a large number of mitochondria in the free nerve endings. This means a lot of oxidative metabolism. Could this be related, in any way, to a moving about of the free nerve endings?

Dr. Cauna: The presence of the increased numbers of mitochondria is typical of most nerve terminals. It probably reflects the higher rate of metabolism that is involved in the nervous activity. There is one interesting feature, that is, that the mitochondria change their appearance as we approach the distal end of the terminal. They change in size and density and internal structure. This, in my estimation, may reflect a turnover of these organellae; they are being gradually lost and replaced. If we look at an intraepidermal nerve fiber, it does not end in the living epidermal cell, but it extends into the stratum corneum and then breaks into pieces and is being removed with squamous cells. The nerve terminals and the epidermal cells are intimately connected with one another and, therefore, the nerve grows continuously with the epidermis. A change in the mitochondria in the nerve terminals actually corresponds with the degree of degeneration of the worn-out end of the nerve fiber (Cauna, 1959; Cauna and Ross, 1960).

Dr. A. Iggo: I would like to turn to the question of the free nerve endings that Dr. Cauna has been describing because he has often used the expression "free nerve endings." He has said that they are not naked, but my impression is that they are not free nerve endings, either. I would like you to comment on this particular problem. Many of us think of free nerve endings as being free in some way to move in the tissues, but from your electron microscope pictures, it is fairly clear that they are far from being free to move.

DR. CAUNA: The terminology that we use is derived from the terminology that we find in the literature. I doubt that it would be advisable to propose new terminology until we know more. They are free in a sense that these nerve endings are not functionally dependent upon the surrounding tissues. The function of the corpuscular receptors is structurally dependent on the related tissues. Indeed, these tissues may constitute part of the receptor organ. These terms may not be the best, but they are well established, and I think they still can be used.

DR. IGGO: But I still feel there is some difficulty when you say that the nerve ending is not attached to the surrounding tissue. It seems, from the electron microscope, to be totally embedded in the surrounding tissues.

DR. CAUNA: The free nerve endings in the dermal papillae, for instance, are embedded in the surrounding tissues but they can be separated from these by maceration. On the other hand, the modified epidermis (in the case of Merkel's or genital corpuscles), the papillary ridge (in the case of Meissner's corpuscles) and the shaft of the hair are integral parts of the corpuscular receptors.

DR. WINKELMANN: I wonder if ultrastructural studies have not changed our attitudes about this a little. As we move toward the periphery, what we mean by "free" now is not what we meant by "free" in silver techniques years ago. We now mean that the Schwann cell investment is becoming lost. As you see in Dr. Cauna's preparations, and we have observed in ours, as a fiber is traced up to the epidermis, one comes to a point where the investment of the various neuronal sheaths is lost. Breaks begin to occur in the Schwann cell investment which results in an axon which is truly naked and in that sense is "free." But it is not free to move, necessarily, or free from the tissue, but free from the Schwann cell investment for gaps along its extent.

DR. IGGO: Dr. Cauna has shown us that the nonmyelinated terminal part of the nerve fiber could be totally encased in Schwann cells or other tissues. In that connection he was actually talking about caps of Schwann cells over the end. Does this mean there is quite a variety of different types of termination?

DR. CAUNA: Whatever the covering is, the Schwann cell, modified Schwann cell, or the epithelial cells, the nerve fiber apparently needs some supporting element for metabolism. Perhaps you can suggest other names for the two types of morphologically clearly recognizable end-organs. I think there is a clear distinction between what I choose to call free nerve endings and the corpuscular receptors.

Dr. Iggo: This is clearly very largely a question of terminology. Can we think of a suitable name describing these to get away from the confusion that is associated with the word *free*?

Dr. J. A. B. Gray: What is much more important than finding a name for this termination is that we should not make any prejudgments about the mechanical couplings. Mechanical coupling in a nonhomogenous system is pretty tricky, and I can see no reason whatever from the histological evidence that we have to say that there is a good coupling in some cases and not in others.

References

Cauna, N. The mode of termination of the sensory nerves and its significance. *J. Comp. Neurol.,* 1959, **113**, 169.

Cauna, N. Functional significance of the submicroscopical, histochemical, and microscopical organization of the cutaneous receptor organs. *Verh. Anat. Ges.,* 1962, **111**, 181.

Cauna, N., & Ross, L. L. The fine structure of Meissner's touch corpuscles in human fingers. *J. Biophys. Biochem. Cytol.,* 1960, **8**, 467.

Munger, B. L. The intraepidermal innervation of the snout skin of the opossum. *J. Cell. Biol.,* 1965, **26**, 79.

Chapter 3

NEW METHODS FOR THE STUDY OF
NERVE ENDINGS

R. K. WINKELMANN

T HE CLASSIC METHODS FOR THE study of nerve tissue have been the methylene-blue and silver-impregnation techniques in which great emphasis is placed on the difference that can be obtained between the stain of the axoplasm and surrounding tissue. This emphasis was necessary in order to establish what is nerve and what is not nerve. With new ultrastructural and histochemical investigation, it is possible to recognize many nonaxoplasmic structures as related to peripheral nerve tissue and sensory nerve endings. Since the amount, disposition, and structure of axoplasm have been so adequately described on many occasions (Weddell, Palmer, and Pallie, 1955; Winkelmann, 1960 b; 1960 c), the remaining area for new descriptive work is in the region of supportive structures for peripheral nerve endings. In this discussion, technical details will not be given but references that contain this technical information will be cited.

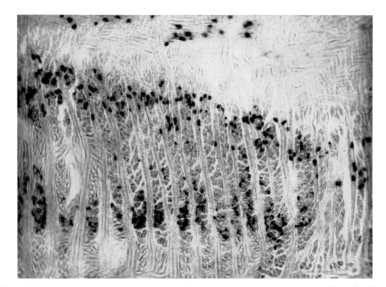

Figure 3-1. Motor end-plates of muscles of the bat tongue (nonspecific cholinesterase) (X 80).

A simple and reasonable place to begin this survey is at the motor endplate for, although it is not sensory in nature, it is a nerve ending composed of an axonal portion and a large, nonaxonal chemical part. As long as silver, gold, and methylene blue were used in our methods of study, our conception of the motor end-plate was limited. Cholinesterase and other hydrolytic esterase techniques, such as alpha-naphthol esterase or indoxyl esterase, demonstrate a plaque of enzyme activity upon which the axonal divisions impinge. Cholinesterase techniques make the counting and the study of the gross morphology of the motor end-plate very simple (Fig. 3-1). Quantitative study of the motor end-plate and study of its size, forms, and relationship to the muscle and nerve fibers may be accomplished by this technique. Specific species variations occur, and it is possible to demonstrate the motor end-plate in the kangaroo by means of alkaline phosphatase technique (Fig. 3-2). There are alkaline phosphatase techniques for fixed paraffin sections as well as a diazo-coupling method for frozen sections, and both techniques demonstrate motor end-plates in this type of marsupial (Winkelmann, 1965). Cholinesterase also is present, and motor end-plates contain "nonspecific" esterase (or alpha-naphthol esterase or indoxyl esterase). It is on the basis of such nonspecific esterase activity that the electron microscopic-histochemical techniques for motor end-plates have been described (Lehrer and Ornstein, 1959). These hydrolytic enzymes survive fixation and even embedding with methacrylate or an aliphatic epoxy resin (Epon®). Because of the permanent nature of the indigo product in the indoxyl esterase method, the simple frozen-section silver technique (Winkelmann) can be used after the histochemical method; this produces an axon stain together with enzyme localization. In Figure 3-3, one may observe silver-impregnated nerves running to motor end-plates that are stained a bright blue by the indoxyl esterase procedure. This

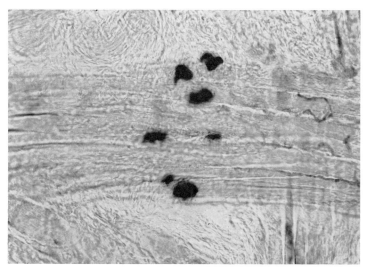

Figure 3-2. Motor end-plates of muscles of the kangaroo tongue (alkaline phosphatase diazo-coupling technique) (X 245).

wedding of histochemical and classic morphologic technology is the ideal way to study such structures. By the use of tritiated (Barnard and Ostrowski, 1964) or ^{32}P-labeled (Rogers, Ostrowski, and Barnard, 1965) diisopropyl fluorophosphate, it has been possible to study motor end-plates and even to approach some quantitation of the cholinesterase present.

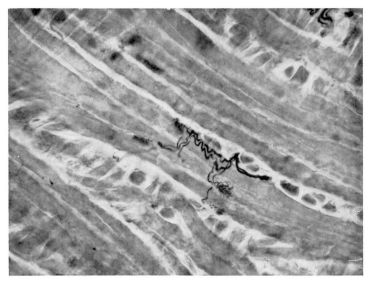

Figure 3-3. Bright blue motor end-plates in bat tongue demonstrated by indoxyl ester-ase with nerve supply demonstrated by Winkelmann silver method. (X 350).

It does not seem possible that the nerve network, as viewed by light microscopy (Fig. 3-4), could contain significant amounts of nonaxonal material demonstrable by histochemical techniques. One of the first histochemical approaches to this subject was the thionine tartrate stain of Feyrter, and it is still possible to use this metachromatic technique in order to demonstrate nerve networks in the skin. It is also possible by the use of Alcian blue or other acid mucopolysaccharide stains to demonstrate the content of acid mucopolysaccharide within the perineurium of most nerve bundles of the skin. Lipid stains will demonstrate the fatty myelin sheath as long as its dimensions are of a suitable size. The sensory nerve networks are only occasionally seen by cholinesterase techniques in the usual areas of the dermis, but intraepithelial nerve endings can be demonstrated with the specific cholinesterase. The surroundings of the nerve fiber probably have much to do with its demonstration by cholinesterase. A cholinesterase whole-mount technique has been developed for use with simple tissues where a fibrous matrix is the principal environmental tissue. Thus, nerves of the hands and spinal column can be demonstrated by the cholinesterase whole-mount method (Lipscomb and Winkelman, 1961). In addition, the innervation of the entire tendon or an entire fascial structure can be surveyed by this technique and the prime areas for the study of nerve endings can be selected by classic morphologic techniques (Figs. 3-5 and 3-6).

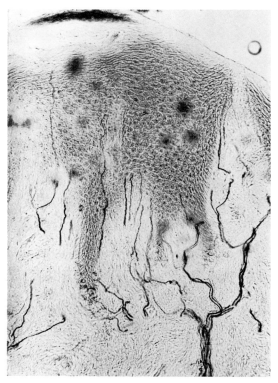

Figure 3-4. Nerve network near hard palate. Note intraepithelial nerve and tactile disks at base of rete Malpighi (Winklemann silver method) (X 180).

Thus far, areas studied include the lumbar ligaments of the spinal column and the annulus fibrosus of the intervertebral disk as well as the facet joint capsule and the dorsal and ventral tendon systems of the fingers. The study of the cornea by this technique has demonstrated nerve networks clearly down to its finest ramifications. The difference between ligaments and cornea and the common dermis is not apparent, but this same technique will not work for common dermal-nerve networks. It is possible, however, to use many histochemical techniques such as monoamine oxidase and beta-glucuronidase to demonstrate large nerve trunks in the dermis. This demonstration probably is related only to the larger nerve trunks with a myelin content and is a nonspecific stain rather than a specific enzymatic demonstration. The adenosine triphosphatase reaction seems more specific because it is found in small subepidermal nerve trunks; but the reaction is often so intense in blood vessels that it obscures nerve structures.

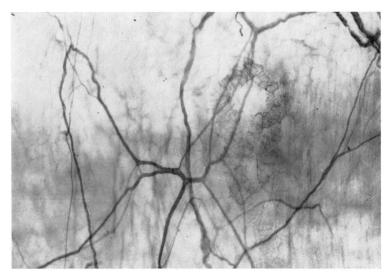

Figure 3-5. Nerve network in the long finger tendon at its insertion (specific cholinesterase whole-mount) (X 50).

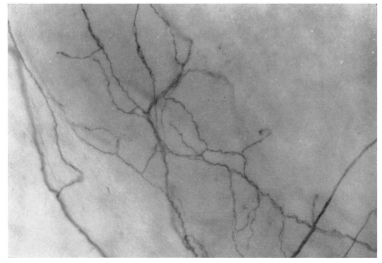

Figure 3-6. Perivascular nerve network in first finger tendon vincula. Note the free endings (specific cholinesterase whole-mount) (X 125).

HAIR FOLLICLE NERVE END-ORGANS

The nerve network about the hair follicle has a complex vertical and circular arrangement of nerve fibers (Fig. 3-7). This network is usually discussed as an axonal structure with terminations in the external root sheath. I believe that this is a nerve end-organ no less complex or important than any of the more classic described sensory nerve end-organs.

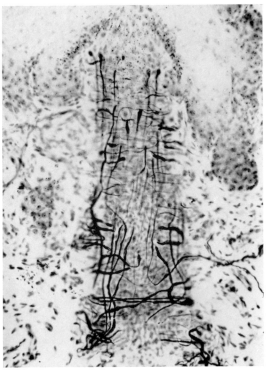

Figure 3-7. Perifollicular nerve plexus (Winkelmann silver method) (X 200) .

The histochemistry of the hair nerve end-organ is very impressive. The enzyme techniques outline a tissue mass below the junction of the sebaceous gland orifice with the hair follicle and encasing the hair follicle like a solid napkin ring of enzyme activity. The cholinesterases are found in this area in large amounts in all mammals studied (Fig. 3-8) . Human scalp has a rather capricious cholinesterase content in the hair follicle nerve end-organ, and, as shown by Montagna (1962) , cholinesterase activity is not related to the hair cycle. The relative amounts of specific and nonspecific cholinesterase vary greatly from one animal family to another. In some animals like the marsupial (kangaroo) , the hair nerve end-organ contains alkaline phosphatase also (Winkelmann, 1965) . This is striking and as characteristic as the cholinesterase content. The nerve fibers may be seen crossing through the areas of dense enzymatic activity and do not appear to contain this activity. Leucine aminopeptidase is found in the hair nerve end-organ in the skin of the Galago (Fig.3-9) . The characteristic structure and location of the hair nerve end-organ are the same whether the demonstration is by

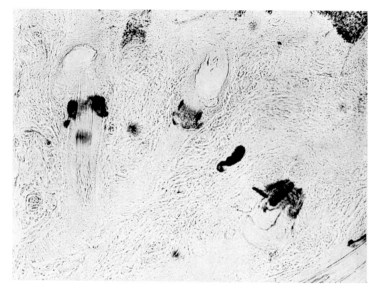

Figure 3-8. Cholinesterase in hair follicle nerve end-organ (specific cholinesterase) (X 110).

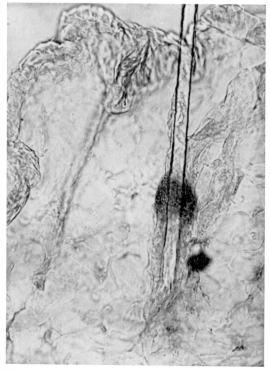

Figure 3-9. Hair follicle nerve end-organ in skin of the *Galago senegalensis* (leucine aminopeptidase) (X 350).

cholinesterase, leucine aminopeptidase, or alkaline phosphatase in the various animals that contain these specific hydrolytic enzymes.

SPECIALIZED NERVE END ORGANS

Demonstration of nerve end-organs of all types is possible by histochemical methods. The reactions of the end-organs of the glabrous skin of the primates are distinctive and are not confined to the area of the axon. Rather, they enclose a large circumscribed mass, usually oval shaped, through which may be seen passing as a faint clear line the axons that supply the corpuscle. The Meissner corpuscle-mucocutaneous end-organ may be demonstrated by nonspecific cholinesterase reactivity in all of the primates (compare Figs. 3-10 A, B, and C with Fig. 3-11). Alkaline phosphatase also is present in this end-organ in the gibbon. Steigleder and Schultis (1958) have reported that nonspecific esterase is present in the Meissner corpuscle in man, and Montagna and Yun (1962) have described nonspecific esterase in the Meissner corpuscles of Galago. A nonspecific esterase in the Meissner corpuscles in Galago is observed in Figure 3-12. The Meissner corpuscles of the opossum contain alkaline phosphatase but do not contain cholinesterase (Winkelmann, 1964). The kangaroo end-organs contain cholinesterase and, despite the alkaline phosphatase in motor endplate and hair follicle nerve end-organs, alkaline phosphatase is not found in the specialized end-organs of the kangaroo skin. Respiratory enzymes in the receptor of the Meissner corpuscle are easily represented by cytochrome oxidase demonstration of this enzyme in the skin of Galago (Fig. 3-13). This confirms the finding of Yasuda and associates (Yasuda, Aoki, and Montagna, 1961) and demonstrates the difference in respiratory activity in some specialized nerve end-organs as compared to the surrounding mesenchymal tissue. Mitchell (1965) reported a series of dehydrogenases in the Meissner corpuscle of the rhesus monkey, and I can confirm this finding from my own experience.

The mammalian end-organ common to the skin of all mammals was described by Krause (1860) and emphasized histochemically first in discussion of the skin of the cat (Winkelmann, 1960a). This end-organ is comparable to the inner bulb of the Vater-Pacini corpuscle and is an elongated sack of enzyme activity through which the axon passes (Figs. 3-14 A and B). The end-organ in the cat contains alkaline phosphatase as well as the nonspecific cholinesterase commonly observed in mammals (Fig. 3-15). The nerve end-organs of the badger and the coatimundi have been demonstrated to contain indoxyl esterase and, because of the nature of the indigo product, it is possible also to use the simple silver frozen-section technique after the histochemical procedure; thus the nerve is stained as it passes through the end-organ that is demonstrated by its indoxyl esterase content (Fig. 3-16).

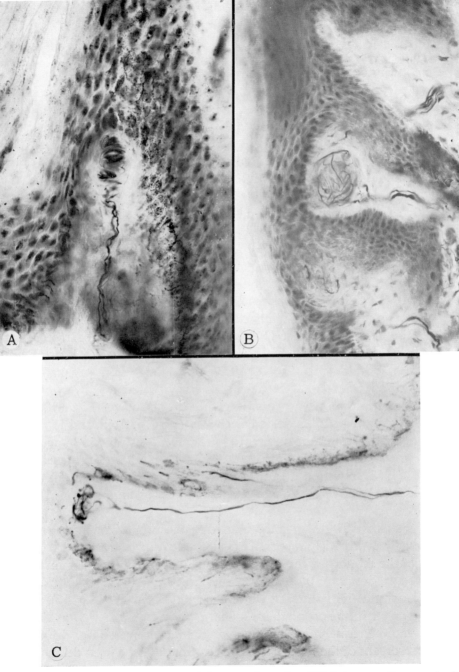

Figure 3-10. *A,* Meissner corpuscle of baboon fingertip (Winkelmann silver method) (X 500). *B,* Mucocutaneous end-organ of lip of *Cebus albifrons* (Winkelmann silver method) (X 500). *C,* Mucocutaneous end-organ of human prepuce (Winkelmann silver method) (X 500).

The Vater-Pacini corpuscle is found in all vertebrates and, although it has not been extensively studied in all animal forms, enough is known to indicate that it does have a number of special chemical qualities. The inner bulb is entirely analogous to the mammalian end-organ and, in most species, contains the same enzymes found in the other nerve end-organs. Nonspecific

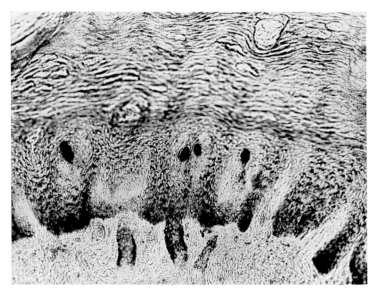

Figure 3-11. Meissner corpuscles in thumb of kangaroo (nonspecific cholinesterase) (X 120).

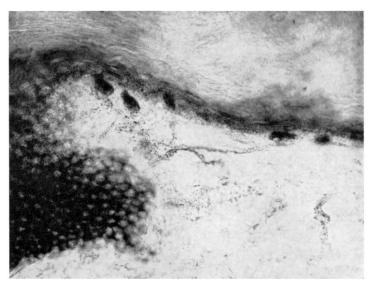

Figure 3-12. Meissner corpuscle in fingertip skin of the *Galago senegalensis* (naphthol ASEsterase) (X 325).

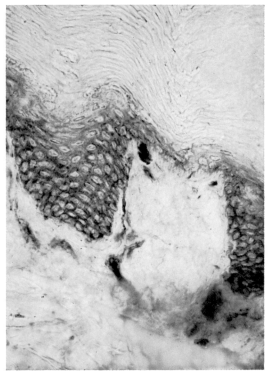

Figure 3-13. Meissner corpuscle in fingertip skin of the *Galago senegalensis* (cytochrome oxidase) (X 385).

cholinesterase should be expected as a characteristic of this end-organ filling the inner bulb. Alkaline phosphatase is found in the felines and in some marsupalia. Mitchell (1965) describes dehydrogenases in the inner bulb in the Vater-Pacini corpuscle of the rhesus monkey. Acid mucopolysaccharides have been described in the end-organ of the birds (Winkelmann and Myers, 1961), a very distinguishing characteristic from the end-organ of mammals. But in general structure, all Vater-Pacini corpuscles look alike and resemble the mammalian end-organ (Figs. 3-17 and 3-18).

THE AUTONOMIC NERVOUS SYSTEM

The autonomic nervous system may or may not have sensory functions, but separating it from dorsal root sensory pathways in the skin has been difficult. Autonomic nerve fibers are distinguished chemically from sensory nerve fibers because it is difficult to stain them selectively by silver methods that readily stain sensory nerves. They are also distinguished by their positive reaction for specific cholinesterase. The nerve network about the eccrine gland, the erector pili muscle, and about the larger muscular vessels of the deep dermis is characteristic of the innervation of the dermis. The innervation about the arteriovenous anastomoses in the skin may contain large amounts of cholinesterase, and such anastomoses may be recognized by this method (Fig. 3-19). Another new distinguishing method for demonstrating autonomic nerve fibers is by the catecholamine content. Using the freeze-drying apparatus, Falck and colleagues (Falck, Hillarp, Thieme, and Torp, 1962) have demonstrated that the catecholamines in autonomic nerve

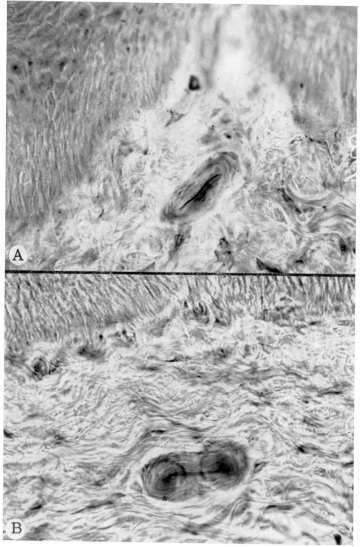

Figure 3-14. *A,* Oblique segment of mammalian nerve end-organ in kangaroo lip. (Winkelmann silver method). (X 550.) *B,* Mammalian end-organ as it sweeps through a 180° turn with the axon maintaining its central position (Winkelmann silver method) (X 575).

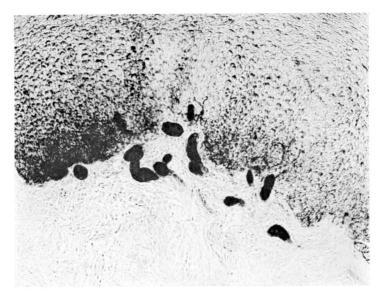

Figure 3-15. Many mammalian end-organs in lip of kangaroo (nonspecific cholinester-ase) (X 190).

Figure 3-16. Mammalian end-organ of North American badger demonstrated as a bright blue mass by indoxyl esterase technique followed by axon demonstration by Winkel-mann silver method (X 650).

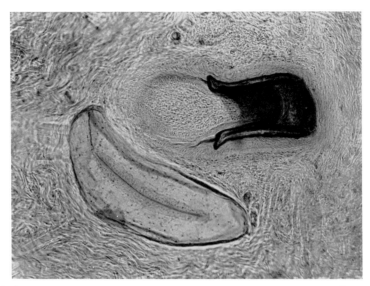

Figure 3-17. Vater-Pacini corpuscle in rooster cheek (Winkelmann silver method) (X 125).

tissue can be coupled with nascent, dry formaldehyde to form a fluorescent compound. Demonstration of these compounds with the fluorescent microscope gives a bright pattern of nerve tissue about the blood vessels, erector pili muscles, and sweat glands.

ELECTRON MICROSCOPIC STUDIES

Studies of sensory tissue with the electron microscope have been very fruitful thus far in indicating how small a portion of the total receptor is composed of axoplasm and is demonstrated by usual light microscopic technology. The receptor is composed of many lamellae of neural tissues, cells that may be Schwannian in nature, and endings that often have large numbers of mitochondria within them. These large amounts of nonaxonal tissue clearly indicate why histochemistry of these end-organs has proved so interesting and so useful. These are very vital and active centers of metabolism and are well organized nerve end-organs. Figure 3-20 demonstrates a Meissner corpuscle showing the many parallel lamellae characteristic of this end-organ. More sophisticated ultrastructural histochemistry will be an area of future interest and opportunity for significant study.

COMMENT

Histochemistry of the nonaxonal tissue of the peripheral nerve endings has provided new methods for the study of these nerve endings. New qualitative and quantitative evaluation of sensory nerve end-organs is now possible because of the discrete, definite, and reproducible nature of the techniques. The histochemical reactivity indicates how important the stromal tissue of sensory receptors may be and that, although its primary mission may be to facilitate impulse transduction and conduction, it may have other functions to perform. The relation of these loci of enzyme activity to other cutaneous functions is unexplored. Perhaps here is an area of "trophic" nerve effect upon the skin.

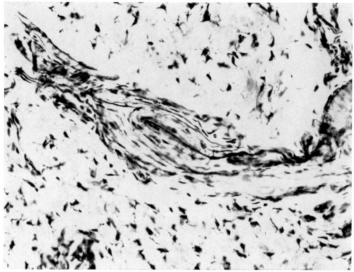

Figure 3-18. Mammalian end-organ in Echidna paw (Winkelmann silver method) (X 300).

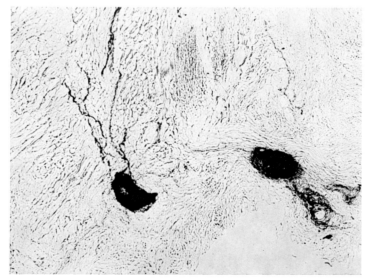

Figure 3-19. Arteriovenous anastomoses in skin of badger (specific cholinesterase) (X 110).

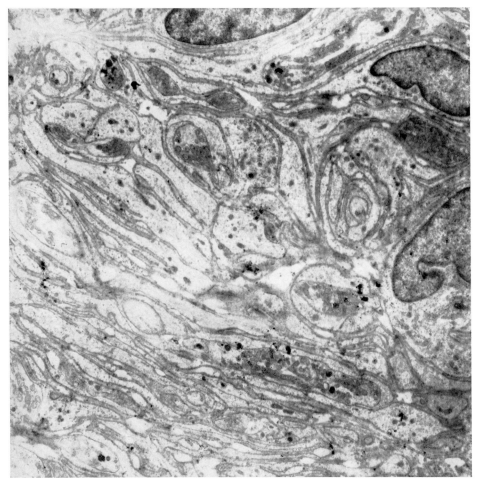

Figure 3-20. Ultrastructure of Meissner corpuscle of human fingertip reveals many parallel lamellae, stromal cells, and endings with many mitochondria. (X 78,300).

Inhibition of cholinesterase activity with diisopropyl fluorophosphate does not interfere with sensation (Hurley and Koelle, 1958). Cholinesterase is not present at all in the organized nerve end-organs of the opossum (Winkelmann, 1964), an animal that seems to have normal sensory function. Cholinesterase is present long after nerve sectioning has produced axonal degeneration in sciatic nerves (Winkelmann, 1962). These facts indicate that the enzymes are not necessary to normal sensation or to sensory receptor function. The enzymes do not spontaneously arise in the mesenchymal tissue of the skin, however. Our study of a patient with congenital analgesia in whom Meissner corpuscles never developed demonstrated that these enzymes were not present in the dermis where the sensory tissue had not developed (Bourland and Winkelmann, 1966a; Winkelmann, Lambert, and Hayles, 1962). The enzyme may be localized to the proper region of embryonic skin and visualized readily by histochemical techniques long before its related axon development can be readily recognized by conventional silver or methylene-blue studies. The histochemical properties accompany the development of a nerve end-organ and facilitate its ready recognition before very complex axonal structures are present. Also, the presence or absence of these enzymes does not seem to preclude the development and the subsequent function of the peripheral nerve tissue.

Most of the enzymes that seem to characterize peripheral nerve tissue are hydrolases. Because alkaline phosphatase and adenosine triphosphatase have been associated with blood vessels, originally it was believed that the appearance of such enzymes in nerve end-organs represented simply a reflection of the vascularity of the nerve. Also on occasion, cholinesterase is found in blood vessels, particularly traumatized ones. Study of these enzymes in many nerve end-organs in many parts of the skin in many types of mammals has indicated the specific localization of the enzyme to the supportive tissue of the nerve end-organ. A similar spectrum of enzymes is present in the Langerhans-cell-melanocyte system. Leucine aminopeptidase and ATPase characterize Langerhans cells of the guinea pig. Alkaline phosphatase is found in Langerhans cells of the Galago and the potto. Recently, cholinesterase was described in the melanocyte of the bat. It must be significant that all of these enzymes that have been described in nerve tissue occur in the Langerhans cell, a cell of embryologic neural origin. Other major neural tissues contain these enzymes (Fishman and Hayashi, 1962).

Grouping of mammals is possible by the histochemistry of their nerve end-organs and, because of the specific patterns of chemical reaction, certain types of skin can be recognized by histochemical examination (Winkelmann, 1963b). For example, the gibbon is the only primate with alkaline phosphatase in its specialized nerve end-organs, and the combination of alkaline phosphatase in the mammalian nerve end-organs and its absence in the blood vessels is typical of feline skin. Among the unique findings is the positive alkaline phosphatase in the Meissner corpuscle of the opossum associated with complete absence of cholinesterase activity. Such studies indicate the antiquity of the Meissner corpuscle found in the North American opossum, of which fossil remains have indicated no significant change for millions of years. The bush baby or Galago has masses of enzyme reactions in its end-organs, including peptidase, and I believe it would be an interesting species to study by electron microscope. These variations serve comparative anatomy in many ways including taxonomy, but they are also a pitfall for the investigator who studies the cat assuming that the skin, blood vessel, and nerve distribution of alkaline phosphatase is similar to man's.

These enzyme studies can be used to observe neuropathology of the skin. For years the dermal nevus has been considered to be a tumor that contains Meissner corpuscle forms, and the dermal nevus contains masses of cholinesterase-positive tissue. Similarly, the neurofibroma has been found to contain masses of cholinesterase-positive material. Because fibrous, histocytic, and smooth muscle tumors do not contain cholinesterase, it has been proposed that nerve tumors can be defined on the basis of cholinesterase content (Winkelmann, 1963a).

Quantitative assessment of the nerve-ending population in sensory receptor sites of the skin is now possible. The highly reproducible histochemical technique has made possible whole-mount preparations in which a standard biopsy size can be used and all of the nerve end-organs counted per unit area. By such a means, Bolton and co-workers (Bolton, Winkelmann, and Dyck, 1966) established normal Meissner corpuscle population for the little finger and little toe of men and women and followed this nerve end-organ population with age. The application of such techniques to the study of neuritis and sensory neuritis and sensory neuropathy has been initiated. Dickens and associates (Dickens, Winkelmann, and Mulder, 1963) have presented a series of cases that pointed out the usefulness of such study, and specific use of these techniques has been made by Dyck and associates (Dyck, Bolton, and Winkelmann, 1966) in a study of familial neuropathy.

Recognition of the hair nerve end-organ probably points the way to a new definition of a sensory receptor by means of its chemical properties and its organoid development of nonaxonal tissue as well as by its axonal morphology. All other recognized sensory nerve end-organs would demonstrate these features. The histochemical and electron microscopic studies of the past five years have pointed up the importance of the nonaxoplasmic tissue component of these structures and, rather than define them by simple axon-staining techniques, it seems wise to include the very complex organization implied by the form of the sensory receptors. Putting these criteria to a test, we immediately develop the idea that the arteriovenous anastomoses usually considered to be autonomic in nature possess a population of rich nerve fibers and that a massive structure is signified readily by the content of cholinesterase demonstrated in them. This presents an interesting hypothesis that these are sensory nerve end-organs whose principal functions have to do with the regulation of blood flow and that not all the sensory receptors of the skin are to be found near the surface or around the typical appendages of the epidermis. This discussion suggests some reexamination as to the features that are important to provide the structural attributes necessary for sensory reception and demonstrates some of the new exciting methods of neurohistology.

REFERENCES

Barnard, E. A., & Ostrowski, K. Autoradiographic methods in enzyme cytochemistry. II. Studies on some properties of acetylcholinesterase in its sites at the motor end-plate. *Exp. Cell Res.,* 1964, **36,** 28.

Bolton, F., Winkelmann, R. K., & Dyck, P. J. A quantitative study of Meissner's corpuscles in man. *Neurology (Minneap.),* 1966, **16,** 1.

Bourland, A., & Winkelmann, R. K. Nervenendorgane der Haut beim Dachs. *Acta Neuroveg. (Wein),* 1966, **29,** 140. (a).

Bourland, A., & Winkelmann, R. K. Study of cutaneous innervation in congenital anesthesia. *Arch. Neurol. (Chicago),* 1966, **14,** 223. (b).

Dickens, W. N., Winkelmann, R. K., & Mulder, D. W. Cholinesterase demonstration of dermal nerve endings in patients with impaired sensation. *Neurology (Minneap.),* 1963, **13,** 91.

Dyck, P. J., Bolton, C. F., & Winkelmann, R. K. Quantitation of Meissner's corpuscles in hereditary neurologic disorders: Charcot-Marie-Tooth disease, Roussy-Levy syndrome, Dejerine-Sottas disease, hereditary sensory neuropathy, spinocerebellar degenerations, and hereditary spastic paraplegia. *Neurology (Minneap.),* 1966, **16,** 10.

Falck, B., Hillarp, N. A., Thieme, G., & Torp, A. Fluorescence of catechol amines and related compounds condensed with formaldehyde. *J. Histochem. Cytochem.,* 1962, **10,** 348.

Fishman, J. S., & Hayashi, M. Enzymorphology of rat brains: β-glucuronidase, alkaline phosphatase esterase. *J. Histochem. Cytochem.,* 1962, **10,** 515.

Hurley, H. J., & Koelle, G. B. The effect of inhibition of non-specific cholinesterase on perception of tactile sensation in human volar skin. *J. Invest. Derm.,* 1958, **31,** 243.

Krause, W. *Die Terminalen Körperchen der einfach sensiblen Nerven.* Hanover: Hahn, 1860.

Lehrer, G. M., & Ornstein, L. A diazo coupling method for the electron microscopic localization of cholinesterase. *J. Biophys. Biochem. Cytol.,* 1959, **6,** 399.

Lipscomb, P. R., & Winkelmann, R. K. A whole-mount cholinesterase technic for study of innervation of the deep structures of the limbs. *J. Invest. Derm.,* 1961, **37,** 481.

Mitchell, J. C. Distribution of dehydrogenases in the skin of the rhesus monkey (*Macaca mulatta*). *J. Histochem. Cytochem.,* 1965, **13,** 668.

Montagna, W. *The Structure and Function of Skin.* (2nd ed.) New York: Academic, 1962.

Montagna, W., & Yun, J. S. The skin of the primates. VII. The skin of the great bushbaby (*Galago crassicaudatus*). *Amer. J. Phys. Anthrop.,* 1962, **20,** 149.

Rogers, A. W., Ostrowski, K., & Barnard, E. A. The measurement of acetylcholinesterase in motor endplates of the mouse. *J. Histochem. Cytochem.,* 1965, **13,** 703.

Steigleder, G. K., & Schultis, K. Zur Histochemie der Meissnerschen Tastkörperchen. *Acta Neuroveg.,* 1958, **18,** 335.

Weddell, G., Palmer, E., & Pallie, W. Nerve endings in mammalian skin. *Biol. Rev.,* 1955, **30,** 159.

Winkelmann, R. K. The end-organ of feline skin: A morphologic and histochemical study. *Amer. J. Anat.,* 1960, **107,** 281. (a)

Winkelmann, R. K. *Nerve Endings in Normal and Pathologic Skin.* Springfield, Ill.: Thomas, 1960. (b)

Winkelmann, R. K. Similarities in cutaneous nerve end-organs. In W. Montagna (Ed.), *Advances in Biology of Skin. Vol. 1.* New York: Pergamon, 1960. Pp. 48-62. (c)

Winkelmann, R. K. Effect of sciatic nerve section on enzymatic reactions of sensory end-organs. *J. Neuropath. Exp. Neurol.,* 1962, **21,** 655.

Winkelmann, R. K. Cholinesterases. *Ann. NY Acad. Sci.,* 1963, **100**, 924. (a)

Winkelmann, R. K. Nerve endings in the skin of primates. In John Buettner-Janusch (Ed.), *Evolutionary and Genetic Biology of Primates.* New York: Academic, 1963. Pp. 229-259. (b)

Winkelmann, R. K. Nerve endings of the North American opossum (*Didelphis virginiana*):A comparison with nerve endings of primates. *Amer. J. Phys. Anthrop.,* 1964, **22**, 253.

Winkelmann, R. K. Innervation of the skin: Notes on a comparison of primate and marsupial nerve endings. In A. G. Lyne & B. F. Short (Ed.), *Biology of the Skin and Hair Growth.* New York: Elsevier, 1965. Pp. 171-182.

Winkelmann, R. K., Lambert, E. H., & Hayles, A. B. Congenital absence of pain. *Arch. Derm. (Chicago),* 1962, **85**, 325.

Winkelmann, R. K., & Myers, T. T., III. The histochemistry and morphology of the cutaneous sensory end-organs of the chicken. *J. Comp. Neurol.,* 1961, **117**, 27.

Yasuda, K., Aoki, T., & Montagna, W. The skin of primates. IV. The skin of the lesser bushbaby (*Galago senegalensis*). *Amer. J. Phys. Anthrop.,* 1961, **9**, 23.

DISCUSSION

Dr. C. Pfaffmann: If the neural elements are gone, do the chemical properties still remain unchanged?

Dr. Winkelmann: Several years ago, we published a paper on the maintenance of this cholinesterase following nerve section (Winkelmann, 1960). We kept the cats for up to eighteen months thinking that by this time it certainly would have disappeared, but the phosphatase and the cholinesterase were still present. In some humans who have had evulsion of dorsal roots and in individuals who have had nerve section, where we have seen them two or three years later, we have found an absence of cholinesterase. We do not know how long it will last in primates. There may be a difference in primates or in different animals as to the length of time it may endure. This experiment needs to be done. From my personal point of view, I think that perhaps nerve regeneration is still possible as long as this marker or organizing influence is present, but the crucial experiment involved would take perhaps two to four years and has not been done.

Dr. N. Cauna: I note that you have studied pathological conditions of end-organs. Have you found any marked variations in enzymes or other agents which would make correlations of structure with function possible?

Dr. Winkelmann: No, unfortunately not; the differences that have been discussed in motor end-plate, for instance, with various types of myopathy or neuropathy do not appear to be much of a factor in congenital peripheral neuropathy, familial sensory neuropathy or acquired neuropathies that we have studied. We have only been able to identify the total loss of Meissner's corpuscle enzymes rather than some distortion of the enzymatic reactions.

Dr. H. Davis: This has been a very fascinating proposition, this chemical marking of the end-organs. You suggested one possible function of biological significance, and I hope you will speculate a little more. You implied that the peripheral marker shows something about how the proper neural connections were formed, or how the nerve got to the proper place, morphologically. I would like to ask whether the chemical may be marking some kind of peripheral tissue which has special structural characteristics that are essential for performance of the end-organ's duty. This kind of situation occurs in the ear, with the tectorial membrane and the organ of Corti. I think perhaps this is a direct analog. A third question, are there special chemicals involved in the excitation of the nerve? Do we have a chemical step here between the physical deformation and the excitation of the nerve?

For clarification, I think it may help us in our thinking if we begin referring to these nerve terminals, at the very end, not as axons but as dendrites. They are at the input end and I think it is pertinent in this context because the chemistry may be different for the original excitation or the mechanical sensitivity, if that is what it is, from that of the axon which is concerned with the transmission of the impulse.

DR. WINKELMANN: First, the enzyme is among the first of the manifestations in embryologic tissue. Before it is possible to see easily that an end-organ is there with silver or with other techniques, the enzyme is present. In a boy, who was born without Meissner's corpuscles and whom we have studied three or four times for various reasons, the Meissner's corpuscle enzyme, as well as the axon, is not present. If the corpuscle is going to develop, it is going to develop with the nerve. Whether the enzyme is a directing influence and occurs prior in time has not been established. The Meissner's corpuscle enzyme is not necessary for the transmission of impulses. Diisopropyl fluorophosphate iontophoresed into the skin will inhibit cholinesterase completely, but does not change the function of the corpuscle at all. We have no way to associate hydrolytic capacity with nerve function at the present time, that I know of. I do not even know of an adequate hypothesis to explain why hydrolases should affect nerve activity. I believe that they are just simply present, as Dr. Cauna has shown, in the associated tissues with the nerve endings. Finally, I am quite prepared to use the term "dendrite" for neural endings. It is just that looking at these under the electron microscope they are indistinguishable from axons and they are certainly unusual dendrites.

DR. M. J. T. FITZGERALD: Your remarks implied, I think, that the Meissner's corpuscle is the primate homologue of the mammalian end-organ in all other forms. Is it not true, also, that there is in primates a bulbous corpuscle comprising one or more axons, within a capsule, with the same distribution as the sausage-like mammalian corpuscle has in lower forms? In lower animals, the mammalian end-organ is also distributed in the deep tissues around blood vessels, in joint capsules around the adventitial tissue of the ducts of exocrine glands and Meissner's corpuscles are absent from these areas, whereas the bulbous corpuscle, or Golgi-Mazzoni ending, has a more closely linked distribution.

DR. WINKELMANN: The analogy that I would like to draw is between the Vater-Pacini corpuscle and the mammalian end-organ. I believe that, structurally, chemically, in every way, they are analogous. The only difference is their position in the skin and the use to which the body is put in placing them. The Vater-Pacini corpuscle is, after all, perhaps the oldest of these endings, extending all the way back into the reptilia and represents, perhaps, the first attempt to form some specialized end-organ. As the mammals came along, they did not need the type of tactile discrimination that humans have and so they put up with just this type of bulbous receptor in the haired skin and, as you point out, in deeper tissues as well as in superficial tissues. Primates do not make use of this type of end-organ, but in primates it never rises to the surface of the skin. As you point out, there are these encapsulated mucocutaneous end-organs, as I call them, or as other people call them, genital end-organs. The point is that the basic subepidermal receptors are different in primates and in the lower mammals. Deeper tissues are much more similar. The important thing is the subepidermal position of the receptor and its nature.

DR. R. H. GIBSON: Would you care to comment further on your idea that the humans, having good tactile discrimination, would require very small brain areas? I would think it would be rather the reverse.

DR. WINKELMANN: No, not necessarily, unless they develop something like the long nose of the anteater, or something of this nature. There are a number of animals that have developed a central rhinarium as well as a peripheral rhinarium, and it seems to me that this is a reasonable type of specialization to expect in primates as well as other animals. It just has not happened to man. But man does not require that kind of discriminatory specialization. He has a special discriminatory capacity rather than a discriminatory specialization, and I think that he does very well with a generalized type of fine sensory tactile discrimination.

DR. L. M. BEIDLER: Did I understand correctly that there is no known correlation between function and the amount of the enzymes?

DR. WINKELMANN: Yes, I think it is most important that everybody realizes that this is, at the present time, a wonderful tool and has no functional correlation at all. That is true for the cholinesterase, which you would think might have a more specific correlation, and it's true for all of these hydrolytic enzymes. Perhaps the closest correlation we could come to would be the cytochrome oxidase and succinic dehydrogenates that can be demonstrated in Galago. Here, I should think, electron microscopy could demonstrate incredible numbers of mitochondria for them to be able to bring out the end-organ by a technique of this type.

DR. BEILDER: And also, you indicated that for the same type of end-organ, but in different species, there are big differences in their chemical composition.

DR. WINKELMANN: Well, yes, they are fairly similar in the same family and genus. The feline family, for instance, has a common pattern. There are genus differences, however. This is a genetic quality. It is just like the markings, the bony phenomena, by which taxonomic differences can be established. These breed true and they can be followed through different species members of a genus.

DR. J. A. B. GRAY: Of the cholinesterases that you were finding, are any specific acetylcholinesterase, or are they mostly the others?

DR. WINKELMANN: Specific cholinesterase is found largely within nerve fibers, particularly autonomic nerve fibers and sensory nerve fibers. These end-organs contain largely nonspecific cholinesterase.

DR. A. IGGO: People have showed us the location of enzymes and, with counterstains, have been able to show the existence of the nerve fibers. We heard just a little before, from Dr. Cauna, how intimately wrapped up actual nerve endings are with the surrounding cells. I was wondering whether your particular technique is really able to distinguish, at the receptor terminal region, the location of the enzyme and the position of the axon ending. It seems you have a situation where you can demonstrate the axon as it approaches the nerve terminal, but you cannot demonstrate the actual terminal itself.

DR. WINKELMANN: I think that depends a great deal on how much discrimination one may want to try to interpret into the preparation. In a frozen section, 25 microns thick, a good deal of interpretation is required in order to decide whether one sees a true termination or not. What I demonstrated was that it is possible to show both the axon and the non-neural portion of the nerve terminal. I would not claim that any of these demonstrated the ultra-terminals within these corpuscles. In the motor end-plate, though, one can see the exoplasmic material, outlined by silver, fitting into the indentations of the motor end-plate, demonstrated by the indigo technique.

Reference

Winkelmann, R. K. The end-organ of feline skin: A morphologic and histochemical study. *Amer J. Anat.*, 1960, **107**, 281.

Chapter 4

THE INNERVATION OF THE EPIDERMIS*

M. J. T. FitzGerald

ALMOST A CENTURY HAS PASSED SINCE Langerhans (1868) claimed to have demonstrated nerve fibers in human epidermis by means of gold chloride impregnation. Since then, the question of epidermal innervation has formed part of a continual controversy concerning the morphology of peripheral nerve endings. The ingredients of the controversy have been the species, regional and technical variables in the material studied by different workers. The historical aspects of epidermal innervation have been covered by Weddell, Palmer, and Pallie (1955) and by Cauna (1959).

The aim of this paper is to examine the arrangement of epidermal nerve fibers in the normal animal, and their behavior under certain experimental and clinical conditions; and from this examination to derive a concept about the mechanism by which the innervation of the epidermis is controlled.

THE NORMAL EPIDERMIS

Man

Intraepidermal nerve fibers are present in human skin. A convincing photomicrograph of fibers in the spinous layer has been provided by Weddell and Palmer (1962) from a silver preparation of thigh skin. Arthur and Shelley (1959) have demonstrated a long intraepidermal fiber in a vertical section of forearm skin stained with methylene blue. In general, photographs made from whole mounts of skin stained with methylene blue are unsatisfactory because of the absence of cellular detail. Using the electron microscope, Dr. Malcolm McGavran (personal communication) observed a nerve fiber passing into the epidermis of the palm. The basement membrane of the final Schwann cell of this fiber became continuous with that of the epidermis. The axon escaped from the Schwann cell to end upon a Merkel cell in the basal layer of the epidermis. The Merkel cell displayed desmosomal contacts with neighboring keratocytes; it was without tonofilaments. The nerve ending is shown in Figure 4-1. The failure of many workers to identify nerves in human epidermis appears to be attributable to the rarity of such nerves (Jabonero and Perez Casas, 1960; Kadanoff, 1928; Woollard, 1936), rather than to technical shortcomings. It must be

*This work was aided in part by a grant from the American Cancer Society.

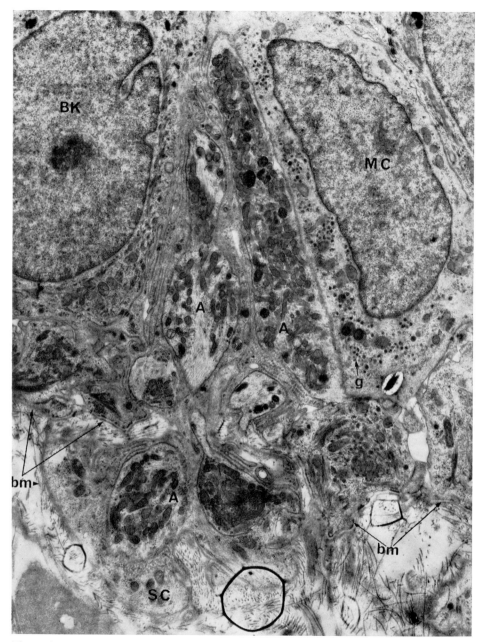

Figure 4-1. Electron micrograph from human hypothenar skin showing two unmyelinated axons *A* within the basal layer of the epidermis. The axons are enclosed in a Schwann cell *SC* within the dermis but leave it as they approach the epidermis. The basement membrane *bm* of epidermis and Schwann cell are continuous. The axon on the right abuts on a Merkel cell *MC* with its characteristic secretory granules *g. BK,* basal keratocyte (X 11,000). (Courtesy of Dr. Malcolm McGavran.)

recorded, however, that Arthur and Shelley's figures (in samples from 15 skin areas) yield a mean incidence of 410 per sq mm!

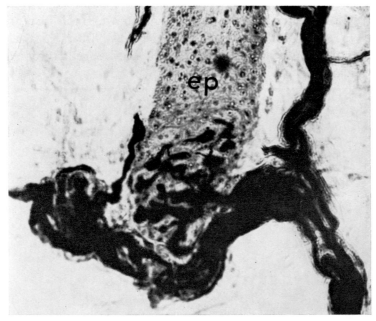

Figure 4-2. Nasal skin of an adult pig with an epidermal peg *ep* projecting into dermis. At the apex of the peg, numerous nervous expansions are applied to its surface. Frozen silver technique (FitzGerald, 1963a) (X 500).

Lower Mammals

The interfollicular epidermis of the hairy skin of most laboratory mammals is 20μ to 30μ thick and is penetrated by occasional nerve fibers derived from the subepidermal network. The rat and mouse are exceptions. Their epidermis is very thin (Fig. 4-5) and the nerve endings appear to be wholly subepidermal. The characteristic epidermal nerve ending of hairy skin is the "touch corpuscle" in which a group of axonal branches end upon Merkel cells in the basal layer. The detailed structure and function of this ending are a part of Dr. Iggo's communication. In pad skin and in the nipple, the epidermis is more deeply stratified and intraepithelial nerve fibers are more numerous.

The epidermis of the snout of many mammals (cat, dog, pig, opossum, ox, mole, etc.) is greatly thickened (150μ or more) and is pierced by long sensory nerves (Armstrong and Quilliam, 1961; Kadanoff, 1924; Szymonowicz, 1895). The individual fibers lose their Schwann sheaths as they enter the epithelium, the axolemma coming into direct contact with the plasma membrane of adjacent keratocytes. A minority of the fibers form terminal expansion upon Merkel cells in the basal layer (Fig. 4-2). The remainder course through the spinous layer (Fig. 4-3) where they are partially or wholly enveloped by successive cells (Cauna, 1959). Where the envelopment is complete, a mesaxon may serve to indicate the extracellular position of the fiber (Munger, 1965). Munger has described fibers in the opossum which, having become intimately related to Merkel cells, proceed further into the epidermis.

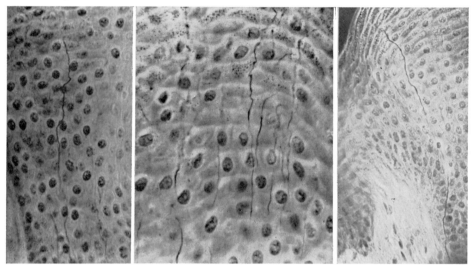

Figure 4-3. Three fields from nasal skin of six-weeks-old cat. The nerves pursue a re-markably straight course through the spinous layer. Double impregnation silver technique (FitzGerald, 1964) (Center field X 600, others X *c*. 500).

The finer axons end, usually without any terminal enlargements, at all levels within the deep spinous layer. The coarser axons reach the stratum granulosum and they tend to branch. They are often capped by axoplasmic vesicles or axonal segments which appear to be detached from the parent fibers. As they near the stratum corneum, the detached portions become pale-staining and irregular. The loss of terminal axonal segments increases sharply with advancing age (FitzGerald, 1961).

The innervation of the clitoris resembles that of the snout. In both regions the dermis contains a profusion of encapsulated nerve endings and in both the epithelium contains long sensory nerves (Fig. 4-4). The intra-epithelial nerves of the clitoris are less regular, however, they tend to be in scattered groups and their course is more meandering.

Relationship of Epidermal Innervation to Growth of the Skin

In the postnatal period the surface area of the skin increases enormously. Does the number of nerve endings increase proportionately, or are they

thinned out by cutaneous expansion? An accurate quantitative assessment
of epidermal nerve terminals seems beyond our reach, but in nasal skin it has
been possible to count the number of stem fibers that enter the epidermis
at selected intervals during the growth period. In the pig a twentyfold postnatal increase in the surface area of the skin of the nasal septum is accompanied by a fourteenfold increase in the number of epidermal stem fibers
(Fig. 4-6). In the same study it was possible to show a significant correlation
between the number of stem fibers, on the one hand, and the number of
subepidermal axonal bifurcations, on the other (Fig. 4-7). It was concluded
that the subepidermal nerve network provided a reservoir from which the
epidermis was supplied by an ever-increasing number of collaterals (Fig.
4-8).

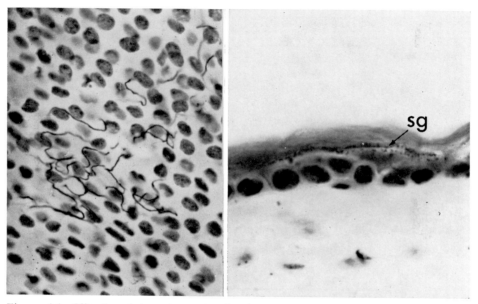

Figure 4-4. Clitoris, adult guinea pig showing tortuous intraepithelial nerve fibers.
Double impregnation (X 700).
Figure 4-5. Interfollicular epidermis of a normal adult mouse. Double impregnation
(X 1500).

Ramon y Cajal (1919) supposed that developing epithelia exert a
chemical attraction upon the regional nerve bundles, thus acquiring a
nerve supply. In terms of this hypothesis it seemed reasonable to suppose that
nasal epidermis, as it expanded, underwent relative denervation by reducing
the density of its nerve endings. This could be sufficient to attract collaterals
into the nerveless epithelium. As a corollary of this interpretation, partial
experimental denervation of the epidermis would be expected to provoke
extension of collaterals from the intraepidermal fibers at the margins of the

denervated area. Partial denervation of the epidermis has been carried out in the young pig (FitzGerald, 1963b). The snout of this animal is supplied entirely by the two infraorbital nerves which overlap across the midline for 1.5-2 mm. Surprisingly, unilateral infraorbital nerve section was without detectable effect upon the epidermal fibers of the contralateral nerve. Dermal and subcutaneous axons migrated slowly (about 2 mm per month) into the depleted contralateral Schwann sheaths, but no migration of either stem fibers or collaterals into the denervated epidermis occurred during the period of observation (six months). It is difficult to reconcile this finding with the supposed neurotropic activity of the epidermis.

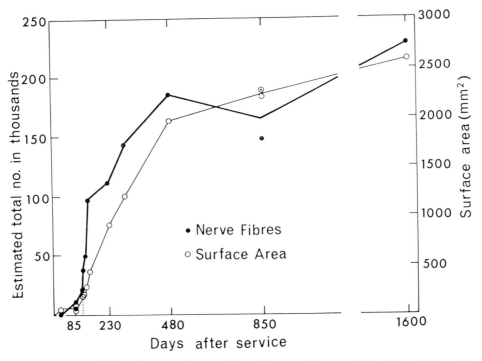

Figure 4-6. Correlation between the number of nerve fibers entering the pig's snout epidermis and the surface area of the epidermis. The data represent thirteen animals, ranging in age from one to 36 months after fertilization. The dotted line (at 120 days) indicates the average age at birth (Fig. 9, FitzGerald, M. J. T., *J. Anat.*, 1961, **95**, 495).

Innervation of Fetal Epidermis

An unexplained, transient population of intraepidermal nerves has been observed to follow the differentiation of the epidermis from the embryonic periderm. In man stratification of the epidermis begins in the third month of gestation, to be followed promptly by neural invasion (Levi, 1933; Szymonowicz, 1933). Before birth, the number of intraepidermal nerves is

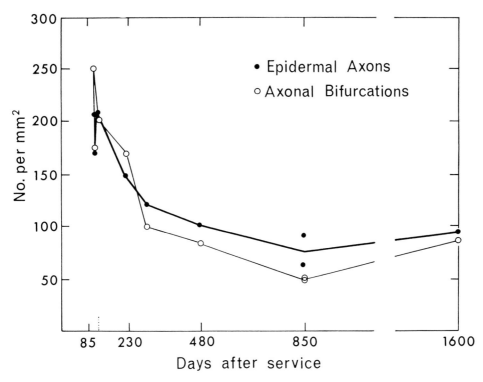

Figure 4-7. Correlation between the number of nerve fibers per mm² entering pig's snout epidermis and the number of axonal bifurcations within 250μ of the epidermal basement membrane in the same sections. Nine animals, ranging in age from 85 days to three years after fertilization (Fig. 11, FitzGerald, M. J. T., *J. Anat.*, 1961, **95**, 495).

greatly reduced (Jalowy, 1935; Pérez and Pérez, 1932; Wada, 1949). The same phenomenon has been studied recently in rodent skin (FitzGerald, 1966). In the rat and mouse differentiation of the epidermis commences two days before birth. During the following six days it is a deeply stratified, well-differentiated epithelium containing nerve fibers (Fig. 4-9). During the latter half of the first postnatal week it thins out to attain its adult depth (Fig. 4-5). As it does so, the nerve fibers withdraw to a subepidermal position. Any hypothesis concerning the organization of cutaneous nerves must take the phenomenon of "fetal innervation" into account.

THE EXPERIMENTAL BEHAVIOR OF CUTANEOUS NERVES

Specificity of Epidermal Innervation

Skin pieces transferred from one part of the body surface to another (i.e., autotransplants) retain their particular characters, showing no tendency to conform to the structure of the skin at the receptor site (Medawar, 1944).

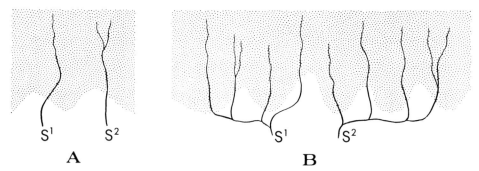

Figure 4-8. Scheme to show the mode of recruitment of nerve fibers by the expanding epidermis during the growth period. Shaded areas represent epidermis. *A,* young, *B,* older animal. S^1, S^2, subepidermal stem fibers.

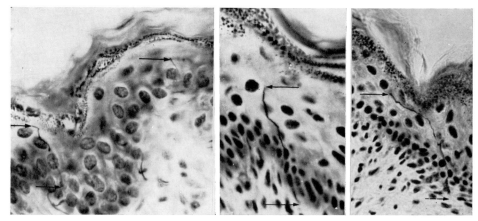

Figure 4-9. Abdominal skin of newborn mouse showing intraepidermal axons. In each field arrows indicate the point of origin and of termination of a nerve fiber. Double impregnation (A and B X 1000, C X 800).

Grafted skin is reinnervated by the local sensory and autonomic nerves. The process takes many months, and is often incomplete (Davis, 1934; Kernwein, 1948; Ponten, 1960). In the course of work in progress on the histology of autograft reinnervation (FitzGerald, Martin and Paletta, unpublished data) an effort was made to find whether the pattern of reinnervation of the epidermis is determined by the epithelium (i.e., is tissue-specific) or by the nerve source (i.e., nerve-specific). In five pigs, six to eight weeks old, a nasal split-skin autograft was implanted in the lumbar region. The nasal epidermis was easily identified two to eight months later as an island of deep glabrous epithelium (Fig. 4-10 A). The regional cutaneous nerves (dorsal rami of lumbar spinal nerves) traversed the graft bed. In three specimens, individual nerve fibers gained the blunt rete pegs and coursed

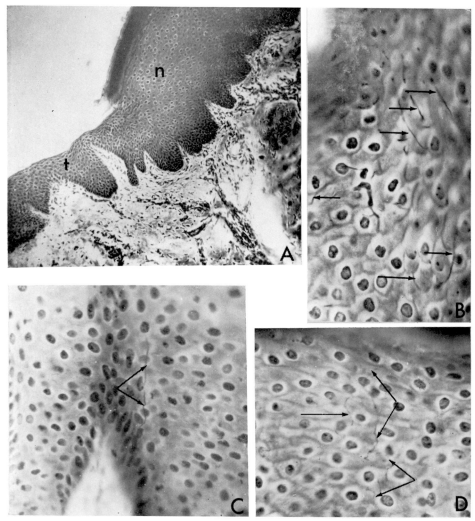

Figure 4-10. Split skin autograft of pig's nasal skin implanted in the lumbar region with six months' survival. *A,* junctional region between nasal epidermis *n* and trunk epidermis t. X 150. *B, C,* and *D* nerve fibers *(arrows)* in the nasal epidermis; double impregnation (X *c.* 600).

upwards through the donor epidermis (Figs. 4-10 B, C, and D). They terminated in the spinous and granular layers. Their size and disposition were typical of nasal skin. In the thin skin surrounding the grafts very fine axons gained the malpighian layer only occasionally. Under suitable conditions, therefore, the nasal epidermis is clearly able to determine its own pattern of innervation. In the absence of a specific neurotropic influence, how is this achieved?

Innervation of Hyperplastic Epidermis

Epidermal hyperplasia is the state of increased stratification that follows physical or chemical injury to the skin. It may also be a manifestation of local disease. The induction of hyperplasia does not require the infliction of a wound in the strict sense, i.e., the continuity of the epithelium need not be broken.

The following features characterize epidermal hyperplasia: (a) The onset is rapid, within 24 hours of infliction of injury. (b) The turnover time of the epidermis is shortened. The normal time shows species variation but is of the order of two to four weeks. Intensely hyperplastic epidermis has a turnover time of one week or less. (c) Subsidence following the removal of the stimulus is slow. The epithelium takes several weeks to return to its normal thickness. The dermis becomes thicker and shows an inflammatory response which varies in degree with the type of injury. The application of croton oil or turpentine, for example, elicits a brisk inflammatory reaction. Of the carcinogens, coal tar provokes the greatest degree of inflammation, methylcholanthrene the least.

Carcinogen Induced Hyperplasia

Julius (1929) and Ludford (1930) studied cutaneous innervation following repeated application of coal tar to the dorsal skin of mice. They observed a local proliferation of nerve fibers in the dermis, and attributed this to injury by the carcinogen. Epidermal innervation was not seen to be increased.

The reaction to painting the skin of cancer susceptible mice with methylcholanthrene has been well documented (Cramer and Stowell, 1942; Iverson and Bjerknes, 1963). The normal adult mouse epidermis comprises a continuous layer of basal cells and an interrupted sequence of spinous and granular cells, overlain by a few flakes of keratin (Fig. 4-5). Methyl-cholanthrene induces a deeply stratified epidermis with well-differentiated basal, spinous, granular and horny layers. The associated neurological picture has been recently studied by FitzGerald and Lavelle (1966). We observed that hyperplasia of epidermis and hair follicles in susceptible (BALB) mice is accompanied by pronounced changes in the pattern of sensory innervation of the skin. The following is a summary of the findings concerning epidermal innervation: (a) Normal adult interfollicular epidermis appears to be devoid of nerves. (b) From the fourth day after the commencement of painting the epidermis is invaded by collaterals from the subepidermal network (Figs. 4-11 A, B, C, and D). The new terminals are found at all levels within the epidermis, some even penetrating the stratum corneum. The shedding of terminal nerve fragments is common. In the

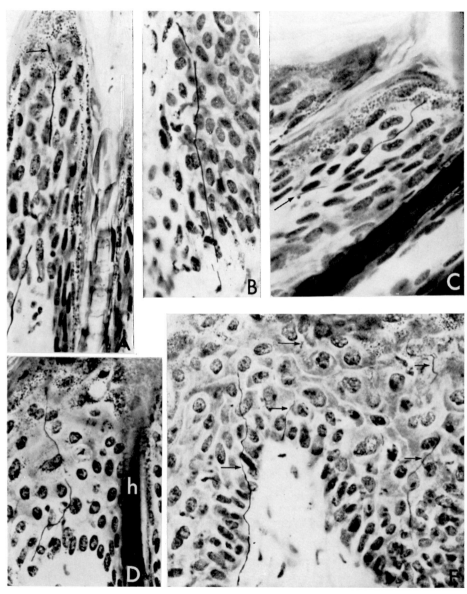

Figure 4-11. Mouse skin, painted twice weekly with a saturated solution of 20-methyl-cholanthrene in benzene. *A, B, C,* and *D,* five to eight weeks, *E,* 13 weeks after the commencement of twice weekly painting. In *A,* the epithelium forms a papilliform projection. The *arrow* indicates terminal fiber degeneration. Portion of a hair follicle is seen to the right of the field. In *C,* the arrow marks the point of entry of the fiber into the epidermis midway between hair follicles. *D* shows a hair canal *h. E* is a section from the base of a noninvasive tumor, 2mm in diameter. *Arrows* indicate nerve fibers. All sections doubly impregnated (X 800-1000) .

Haarscheiben, Merkel cells can no longer be identified (at least with the light microscope). The related nerve endings lose their disklike shape and grow freely into the overlying epidermis. (c) Although the number of nerves entering the epidermis varies greatly from one animal to another, it has been possible to show a significant positive correlation between this number and the thickness of the epidermis. (d) In the second three months of painting, hyperplasia gives way to neoplasia. The sensory nerves elongate to keep pace with epidermal growth (Fig. 4-11 E). (e) In nonsusceptible animals methylcholanthrene is without significant effect upon either the skin or its pattern of innervation.

A comparison of the effects of topical turpentine (a noncarcinogenic irritant) and sandpaper abrasion showed that the first elicited very little growth of epidermal nerve fibers in association with the hyperplasia and the second elicited none. However, it was impossible to assess the influence of the inflammatory and fibrotic responses to these agents on the nerve endings.

Human Hyperplastic Epidermis

In psoriasis, the epidermis increases up to three times its normal thickness. Weddell, Palmer, Cowan, and Ramaswamy (1965) found abundant evidence of growth, degeneration and renewal of cutaneous nerves in the affected regions. "Another remarkable feature was the regular presence of numerous intraepithelial nerves which could be followed from the dermis almost to the free surface of the skin" (Weddell, Palmer, Cowan, and Ramaswamy, 1965, p. 254).

In lichen simplex, the epidermis is again heavily stratified. Here too a turnover of cutaneous nerve endings is found. "Many more intraepidermal fibers (are) seen than ever occur in comparable hairy skin from healthy subject" (Cowan, 1964, p. 565).

Innervation of Wound Epithelium — Rodent Ear Tip

In adult rats and mice hair follicles are fewer at the ear tip than on the ear surface and the epidermis between the follicles is relatively thick. When these animals are more than a year old, the entire ear tip may be glabrous (Fig. 4-12). The epidermis here is penetrated by long nerve fibers. The resemblance to the thick, well-innervated nasal epidermis of these animals is very striking.

The possibility was entertained that the glabrous ear tip was a specific sense organ, homologous with the snout, designed to signal contact with the environment during fossorial activities. Other fossorial animals were therefore examined. The guinea pig shows a moderate thickening of the ear tip epidermis with occasional long intraepidermal nerves, but the rabbit, badger,* lemming,* chinchilla* and mole* yield no evidence of sensory specialization. The late appearance of the area in rodents — it is most obvious when the animals are positively elderly — suggests that recurrent minor injury could be responsible for its development. The structure of the underlying dermis is consistent with injury of the skin. It is densely fibrous and the cutaneous nerves appear distorted as they pass through (Fig. 4-12 A). It therefore became desirable to know whether wound epithelium is endowed with nerves under controlled conditions. This information was not available. Although the growth of nerves into wound beds has been studied in detail by Grushkin (1962) and his colleagues, their observations did not extend to the epithelium.

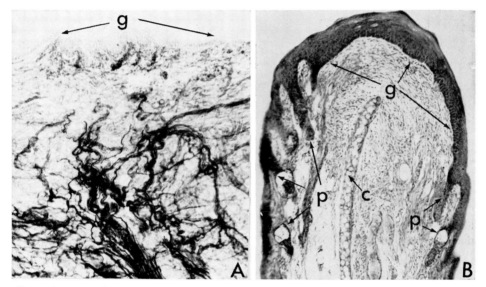

Figure 4-12. Ear tip of adult rat, showing glabrous epidermis *g*. *A*, section taken in plane of auricular cartilage. The subcutaneous axons have a distorted appearance. Frozen silver technique (X 200). *B*, vertical section showing pilosebaceous units *p*, and auricular cartilage *c*. Double impregnation (X 50).

In 24 mice, 21 to 25 days old, the outer three-fifths of the pinna was removed by a scissors cut. The wounds were unusual in that the edges did not face one another, as would be the case in wounds of a single surface. The regenerating epithelium from the dorsal and ventral ear surfaces was obliged to turn onto the cut surface in order to effect union. The result was a pronounced hypertrophy of the epithelium during the first two weeks of healing. (Figs. 4-13 and 4-14). The mice were sacrificed, 2 to 35 days after operation, in groups of four (each group comprising litter mates). At two

---

*Material by courtesy of Professor W. C. Osman Hill.

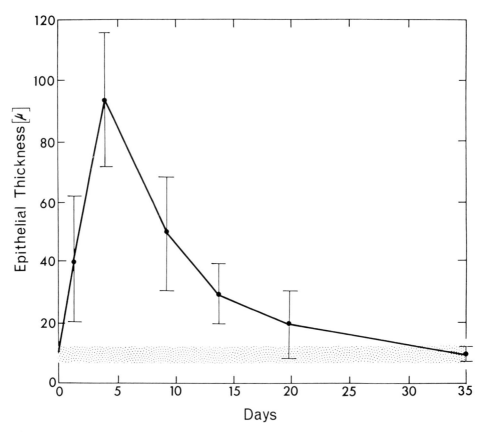

Figure 4-13. Thickness of wound epithelium of mouse ear two to 35 days after infliction of full thickness wound. Four animals are in each group. The shaded strip indicates
the normal thickness of the epidermis.

days, epithelialization of the wound was partial in two cases and complete in
the other two. In the second pair the epidermal basement membrane was
discernible, and the wound epithelium was penetrated by occasional nerve
fibers. On the fourth and ninth days the hypertrophic epithelium was richly
populated (Fig. 4-14). The fibers were of diverse size and length and they
branched freely in the spinous layer. The preparations bore an interesting
resemblance to those of Singer and Inoue (1964), who demonstrated abundant nerve fibers in the apical epithelial cap of the regenerating amphibian
limb. In addition, the murine terminals showed frequent evidence of degenerative fragmentation within the epithelium.

The later reduction of epithelial thickness was accompanied by a loss
of intraepithelial axons. At 35 days, the epidermis was within normal size
limits, and two of the specimens showed no intraepidermal axons. The
other two showed a few, short axons.

The results of ear tip wounds were compared to those of full thickness skin wounds, 3 to 5 mm in diameter, in the interscapular region (seven mice, sacrificed three to nine days after operation). Where the repair epithelium was less than 20μ in thickness, nerve infiltration was sparse.

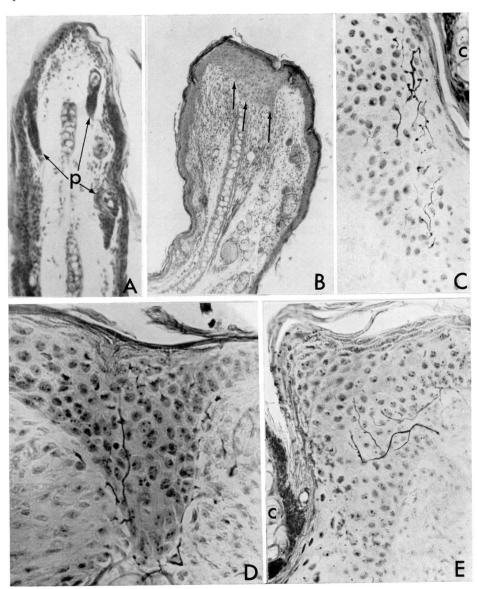

Figure 4-14. *A*, ear tip of normal four-week-old mouse: *p*, pilosebaceous units (X 50). *B*, ear of four-week-old mouse four days after infliction of full thickness wound. *Arrows* indicate base of wound epithelium (X 40). *C, D,* and *E* nerves in wound epithelium at four to nine days. In *C* and *E*, portion of the auricular cartilage *c* is being extruded from the wound. *C, D,* and *E*, double impregnation (X *c*. 800).

Where it exceeded 20μ, the density of infiltration was comparable to that of similar epithelium in the ear (Fig. 4-15).

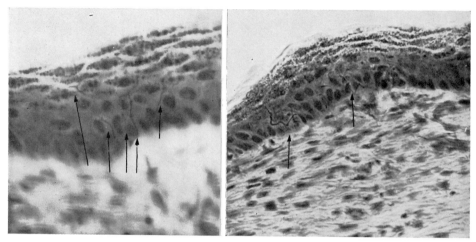

Figure 4-15. Two fields showing wound epithelium at six days, from interscapular region of mouse. *Arrows* indicate nerve fibers. Double impregnation (X 1000).

DISCUSSION

When we view this assemblage of situations and conditions, characterized by greater or smaller populations of intraepidermal nerves, the behavior of the nerves is seen to present some apparent incongruities. It is inevitable that we think teleologically. We ascribe the number of regional nerve endings to the regional sensory needs. The presence of deeply penetrating fibers within heavily stratified areas of epidermis we assign to a requirement that the terminals be near the surface of the skin in order to be effective sensors. But this attitude, sufficient perhaps to account for the innervation of the snout and of the clitoris, does not embrace all the phenomena we have examined. Why, for example, should the epidermis of the mammalian fetus be more richly innervated than that of the adult? And why does the epithelium of the finger or footpad contain fewer nerve fibers than that of a dorsal skin wound in which the epithelium is relatively thin? We cannot conclude that epithelia whose innervation is increased by artificial means acquire increased sensory acuity. In the case of psoriasis, we know from the observations of Weddell *et al.* (1965) that sensory acuity is not detectably improved.

We may consider the genesis of epidermal innervation with greater profit. In so doing, we may assume that the same basic mechanism operates throughout the epidermis of all mammals, and that it is so ordered as to permit the free passage of sensory terminals at one time or place and not at another.

A "Permissive" Concept of Epidermal Innervation

If we set aside neurotropic factors, we must conclude that the epidermis controls its innervation by some form of permissive effect. Some areas are poorly innervated because the epidermis has suppressed the normal tendency of nerve fibers to extend their territory, and others are richly supplied because the inhibitory influence of the epidermis is either poorly developed or has been removed.

Turning first to the transient intraepidermal innervation that follows the differentiation of the epidermis from the fetal periderm, could it be the very immaturity of the newly formed epithelium that permits the free entry of nerve fibers? If so, then the later reduction of the nerve supply would be the result of epithelial maturation. More specifically, this interpretation would imply that the epidermis, as it matures, exerts a repressive influence upon the growth of nerve terminals in the dermis. The information from healing wounds supports this view. Here too, an immature epithelium is presented to the underlying nerves. Invasion of the epithelium has already commenced when the epithelium is only two days old. The subsequent loss of fibers, as maturation proceeds, also mirrors the ontogenetic picture. The several kinds of hyperplastic skin present epithelia whose age is considerably reduced. The neurological result is consistent with a failure of the rapidly shed epidermis to exert an inhibitory effect upon the underlying nerves.

It is implicit in this concept that the putative negative feedback exerted by the normal epidermis is derived from its most mature cellular layer, that is, from the outer part of the stratum granulosum. In adult animals the epidermis of the nasal skin and of the clitoris is so thick that the stratum granulosum is far removed from the dermis. Consequently, it is reasonable to suppose that the damping effect of the granulosa cells may be buffered by the deep spinous layer so that the sensory nerves gain free entry. Alternatively, there may be a genetically determined reduction of feedback at these locations.

These considerations, although novel in the present context, are but an extension of Weiss and Kavanau's (1957) general theory of organ growth and homeostasis. These workers hold that each specific cell type manufactures not only the compounds or "templates," which are characteristic of the cell, but also freely diffusible "antitemplates" capable of blocking the production of these compounds. With a mounting population of the cell type the concentration of "antitemplates" in the intracellular spaces and within the cells is thought to increase. By inhibiting the reproductive activity of the homologous "templates," the "antitemplates" will depress the rate of cell reproduction and/or differentiation. Iversen and Bjerknes (1963), testing the theory in the instance of methylcholanthrene-painted mouse skin, found it to be valid on the additional assumption that the production of the feedback substance is proportional to the mean cellular age (Cowan, 1964). Methylcholanthrene is known to have a pronounced cytotoxic effect upon the superficial part of the epidermis. Iversen and Bjerknes consider the hyperplasia to be the result of loss of the normal inhibitory influence of the superficial cells upon the basal layer. The result is a deeply stratified epithelium whose cells have a reduced mean age.

The thickness of newborn rodent epidermis and of the early repair epithelium of a wound find an explanation in the same general terms. In both, the later reduction of epidermal thickness is attributable to cellular maturation. Psoriatic epidermis appears to belong to the same category although the reason for the failure of cellular maturation is obscure.

Speculation would be premature regarding the mode of action of mature granulosa cells upon the regional nerves or upon the intercellular spaces in which they lie.

Turnover of Epidermal Nerves

We have seen that a continuous turnover of nerve terminals is a feature of normal snout skin, and of hyperplastic and repair epithelia. If we attribute the degeneration of terminals to a loss of turgor following the diversion of axoplasm from old branches into new sprouts, then its increased incidence as the normal animal approaches the end of its postnatal growth span is expected. The perikarya of the dorsal root neurons must support an increase of more than tenfold in the number of their terminal branches. When the turnover of terminals in abnormal states is viewed in this light, fiber degeneration assumes the aspect of a purely secondary phenomenon, consequent on the growth of new processes from common stem fibers. This view implies that the *vis a fronte,* supplied by the altered state of the epidermis, is not matched by a *vis a tergo* derived from augmented axoplasmic synthesis in the perikarya. The nerve cells, as it were, appear to be uninformed as to what is going on in the periphery. Even the direct trauma to hosts of nerve endings, inflicted in the preparation of a donor site for the receipt of a graft, evidently fails to excite the parent cells. The rate of growth of nerve fibers into a graft is no faster than the rate of extension of uninjured fibers into partially denervated areas of skin.

SUMMARY

1. The innervation of the normal epidermis in man and lower mammals is briefly described.

2. During the growth period, the increase in surface area of the skin is

accompanied by the development of new epidermal fibers. These are collaterals from the subepidermal nerve network.

3. The results of partial experimental denervation of nasal epidermis (pig) do not support neurotropism as the mechanism by which the epidermis secures its nerve supply.

4. Regional variations in the pattern of epidermal innervation are determined by the character of the epithelium, not by the nerve source.

5. A "permissive" concept of epidermal innervation is put forward. The freedom with which the epidermis is penetrated by nerve fibers is considered to be regulated by a negative feedback mechanism by which the more mature, superficial epidermal cells tend to inhibit epidermal invasion by nerve fibers. A mechanism of this kind would account for (a) the large, transient population of intraepidermal nerves that follows differentiation of the skin in the fetus; (b) the increased epidermal innervation that accompanies hyperplasia induced by methylcholanthrene and by diseases such as psoriasis, and (c) the transient invasion of wound epithelium by nerve fibers. These three conditions are characterized by an immature epidermis. Where the normal epidermis is richly innervated, as in the snout and clitoris, the supposed feedback may be dampened by the deep spinous layer so that nerve fibers are permitted free entry or a reduced feedback in these areas may be genetically determined.

6. Turnover of epidermal nerves is seen where these are numerous and long. The degenerative element is considered to be due to autonomy of older nerve branches following the diversion of axoplasm into new sprouts.

REFERENCES

Armstrong, J., & Quilliam, T. A. Nerve endings in the mole's snout. *Nature (London)*, 1961, **191**, 1379.

Arthur, R. P., & Shelley, W. B. The innervation of human epidermis. *J. Invest. Derm.*, 1959, **32**, 397.

Cauna, N. The mode of termination of the sensory nerves and its significance. *J. Comp. Neurol.*, 1959, **113**, 169.

Cowan, M. A. Neurological changes in lichen simplex chronicus. *Arch. Derm. (Chicago)*, 1964, **89**, 562.

Cramer, W., & Stowell, R. E. The early changes of carcinogenesis by 20-methylcholanthrene in the skin of the mouse. II. Microscopic changes. *J. Nat. Cancer Inst.*, 1942, **2**, 379.

Davis, L. The return of sensation to transplanted skin. *Surg. Gynec. Obstet.*, 1934, **59**, 533.

FitzGerald, M. J. T. Developmental changes in epidermal innervation. *J. Anat.*, 1961, **95**, 495.

FitzGerald, M. J. T. A general-purpose silver technique for peripheral nerve fibers in frozen sections. *Stain Techn.*, 1963, **38**, 321. (a)

FitzGerald, M. J. T. Transmedian cutaneous innervation. *J. Anat.*, 1963, **97**, 313. (b)

FitzGerald, M. J. T. The double-impregnation silver technique for nerve fibers in paraffin sections. *Quart. J. Micr. Sci.,* 1964, **105,** 359.

FitzGerald, M. J. T. Perinatal changes in epidermal innervation in rat and mouse. *J. Comp. Neurol.,* 1966, **126,** 37.

FitzGerald, M. J. T., & Lavelle, S. M. The response of murine cutaneous nerves to skin painting with methylcholanthrene. *Anat. Rec.,* 1966, **154,** 617.

FitzGerald, M. J. T., Martin, F., & Paletta, F. X. The innervation of skin grafts. *Surg. Gynec. Obstet.,* in press.

Grushkin, G. I. Nervous structures in the granulation tissue of a skin wound. *Arkh. Pat.,* 1962, **24,** 53.

Iversen, O. H., & Bjerknes, R. Kinetics of epidermal reaction to carcinogens. *Acta Path. Microbiol. Scand.,* 1963. (Suppl. 165)

Jabonero, V., & Perez Casas, A. Über die feinere Innervation der Haut. *Acta Neuroveg. (Wien),* 1960, **22,** 352.

Jalowy, B. Über die De- und Reinnervation der Nervendigungen in den Fingerbeeren der Oberen Extremitäten der Affen (Macacus rhesus). *Z. Zellforsch,* 1935, **23,** 84.

Julius, H. W. Innervation and tumor growth. *Brit. J. Exp. Path.,* 1929, **10,** 185.

Kadanoff, D. Beiträge zur Kenntnis der Nervendigungen im Epithel der Säugetiere. *Z. Anat. Entwicklungsgesch.,* 1924, **73,** 431.

Kadanoff, D. Beiträge zur Kenntnis der Nervendigungen im Epithel der Säugetieren. *Z. Zellforsch.,* 1928, **7,** 555.

Kernwein, G. A. Recovery of sensation in split-thickness skin grafts. *Arch. Surg. (Chicago),* 1948, **56,** 459.

Langerhans, P. Über die Nerven der menschlichen Haut. *Virchow. Arch.,* 1868, 44, 325.

Levi, S. Osservasioni sullo svilupo delle terminazioni nervose intra-epiteliali, corpuscoli del Meissner e corpuscoli del Pacini. *Arch. Ital. Anat. Embriol.,* 1933, **32,** 149.

Ludford, R. J. Nerves and cancer. *Imp. Cancer Res. Fund Sci. Rep.,* 1930, **9,** 99.

Medawar, P. B. The behavior and fate of skin autografts and skin homografts in rabbits. *J. Anat.,* 1944, **78,** 176.

Munger, B. L. The intraepidermal innervation of the snout skin of the opossum. *J. Cell Biol.,* 1965, **26,** 79.

Pérez, R. M., & Pérez, A. P. R. L'évolution des terminaisons nerveuses de la peau humaine. *Trav. Lab. Rech. Biol. Univ. Madrid,* 1932, **27,** 187.

Ponten, B. Grafted skin. Observations on innervation and other qualities. *Acta Chir. Scand.,* 1960. (Suppl. 257)

Ramon y Cajal, S. Accion neurotropica de los epitelios. *Trav. Lab. Invest. Biol.,* 1919, **17,** 1.

Singer, M., & Inoue, S. The nerves and the epidermal apical cap in the regeneration of the forelimb of adult *Triturus. J. Exp. Zool.,* 1964, **155,** 105.

Szymonowicz, W. Beiträge zur Kenntnis der Nervendigungen in Hautgebieten. *Arch. Mikr. Anat.,* 1895, **45,** 624.

Szymonowicz, W. Über die Entwicklung der Nervendigungen in der Haut des Menschen. *Z. Zellforsch.,* 1933, **19,** 356.

Wada, Y. Sensory nerve endings in the adult palm. *Tohoku Med. J.,* 1949, **39,** 73.

Weddell, G., & Palmer, E. Die Nervenfasern und ihre Endigungen im menschlichen Integument. *Acta Neuroveg. (Wien),* 1962, **24,** 139.

Weddell, G., Palmer, E., Cowan, M. A., & Ramaswamy, S. Psoriatic skin. *Arch. Derm. (Chicago),* 1965, **91,** 252.

Weddell, G., Palmer, E., & Pallie, W. Nerve endings in mammalian skin. *Biol. Rev.,* 1955, **30**, 159.

Weiss, P., & Kavanau, J. F. A model of growth and growth control in mathematical terms. *J. Gen. Physiol.,* 1957, **41**, 1.

Woollard, H. H. Intra-epidermal nerve endings. *J. Anat.,* 1936, **71**, 54.

DISCUSSION

DR. R. K. WINKELMANN: You mentioned the work that Weddell (1965) did on psoriasis, and I would like to ask you to comment about his preparations. Have you seen his preparations? I wonder how you feel about this work? I would certainly confirm and agree that the psoriatic plaque does not have increased sensitivity, and it seems to me that it has not been established that there is an increased intraepithelial nerve supply.

DR. FITZGERALD: I have seen a number of Dr. Weddell's preparations and there is no doubt that the increased population of fibers is not merely within the dermis but also within the epidermis.

DR. H. HENSEL: Have you investigated the innervation of the tongue, and if you have done so, I have two questions. Did you find intraepithelial nerve fibers and did you find any encapsulated nerve endings in the tongue?

DR. FITZGERALD: I have tried to keep clear of the innervation of mucous membranes, in general, because I think that, to some extent, different principles of organization may apply. The tongue does contain intraepithelial nerves in rather small numbers and it contains encapsulated nerve endings in great profusion in the mucous membrane.

DR. S. R. ROSENTHAL: Would you conjecture as to what proportion of the intraepithelial axoplasms are probably destroyed in the fixation and preparation of all techniques that we have at this time?

DR. FITZGERALD: In general, preparations with methylene blue tend to yield a larger number of intraepithelial nerve fibers than do formalin-fixed preparations. In formalin-fixed preparations and, indeed, also in methylene blue, it is possible to observe fragmentation of nerve fibers within the epidermis and this does raise the question as to whether or not this is factitious. The number of visibly fragmented axons does increase with advancing age and, therefore, it is likely to be a physiological phenomenon rather than an artifact. Munger (1965) has also shown what appears to be degenerate fragments in the stratum granulosum of the opossum in which the deeper nerves appear normal.

DR. WINKELMANN: You mentioned Langerhans' cells in your beginning sentence, but you did not mention them again. We have been very impressed by the incredible richness of all epithelium with Langerhans' cells. They contain the same enzymes that we demonstrated in nerve end-organs, that is, cholinesterase in the bat, alkaline phosphate in certain of the lorisidae, nonspecific esterase, peptidase, and ATPase in guinea pig and man. I wonder to what extent they might represent some of these fragmented pieces of material that would take up silver. They do represent a cell population which is not normally seen by silver techniques but which, on occasion, particularly in hyperplasia or some change like carcinogenesis, might be altered in a way that would cause them to take up silver. It seems to me that this might be one of the explanations for the difference between the methylene-blue preparations and the silver preparations.

DR. FitzGerald: One has to bear in mind constantly the distinction between dendritic cells, of whatever kind, and nerve terminals within an epithelium. At times the cell processes can very closely mimic nerve processes, but it is almost always possible to trace these processes to a cell body. This also brings up the relationship between epidermal melanocytes and nerve endings, and it is generally considered that there is no relationship between them. The confusion may have arisen because of the use of different material. If one examines neonatal material, this is true of the rat and mouse, one can observe the melanoblasts festooned from nerve endings in the dermis with quite a definite relationship to the nerve endings, but it is reasonable to assume that these cells are in transit along the nerve bundles from the neural crest and have not yet reached the epidermis. When they do reach the epidermis, they lose all connections with the nerve fibers.

DR. G. WERNER: I am not sure I can follow your reasoning as to why increased peripheral sprouting should lead to increased sensory acuity. First of all, the peripheral branches that are newly formed derive from the same parent axons with its central connections and, secondly, I think that once an impulse was set up in one branch, it would tend to retrogradely invade other branches and, therefore, leave a certain period of refractoriness in other branches.

DR. FitzGerald: Yet, it is a case, is it not, that in the nasal skin, which we consider to be highly specialized for touch, the density of nerve fiber population is greater than anywhere else in the body surface.

DR. J. A. B. GRAY: There are two separate points here. There is the question of the discriminations that are possible, the amount of information which is being transmitted from the area, which will be limited by the total number of receptor units, regardless of how much they branch at the end. The question of sensitivity will depend on the physics of the actual receptor itself and of the supporting tissues. In any particular situation, one could change in one direction and the other could change in the other. One has to test discrimination and sensitivity separately. The mere branching of terminals would surely not affect the issue at all. One still has the same number of channels going to the nervous system.

References

Munger, B. L. The intraepidermal innervation of the snout skin of the opossum. *J. Cell Biol.,* 1965, **26,** 79.

Weddell, G., Palmer, E., Cowan, M. A., & Ramaswamy, S. Psoriatic skin. *Arch. Derm. (Chicago),* 1965, **91,** 252.

Chapter 5

ELECTROPHYSIOLOGICAL AND HISTOLOGICAL STUDIES OF CUTANEOUS MECHANORECEPTORS

AINSLEY IGGO

Mammalian cutaneous afferent units with myelinated fibres fall into two principal classes of mechanoreceptors, either rapidly adapting or slowly adapting. The two classes can be recognized in both hairy and glabrous skin (Iggo, 1963). In this paper I shall be dealing for the greater part with hairy skin.

RAPIDLY ADAPTING MECHANORECEPTORS

The first class adapt rapidly to displacement of hairs and can be excited, though less readily, by displacement of the skin around the hair follicles. The characteristic and classical response is a brief burst of impulses when the hair is moved. Careful rigid mounting of the skin and of the probe used to move the hair reveals that there is a response only during movement of the hair. The initial frequency of discharge is related to the rate of displacement so long as the latter is above the threshold value (Brown and Iggo, 1966a; 1966b). Three types of rapidly adapting hair follicle afferent units are distinguished by Brown and Iggo (1964), based on the following criteria: (a) the type of hair follicle innervated; (b) the size and kind of receptive field; (c) the displacement sensitivity of the receptor, and (d) the diameter of the afferent fibre. The most sensitive were those classed as Type D which innervate down hairs, and have small myelinated (Aδ) afferent fibres, conducting at less than 24 m/sec (Fig. 5-1). This class of unit was examined most carefully in cats and rabbits but was also recognized in the monkey and baboon.

It was a matter of some surprise to find, in the cat and rabbit, that so many of the A delta fibres supplied these sensitive receptors, although both Zotterman (1939) and Hunt and McIntyre (1960) reported results which can now be seen to support the new classification; whereas Wall (1960) found that as fibre diameter decreases within the single group (of myelinated fibres), the threshold for a pressure stimulus increases and the rate of adaptation to a maintained stimulus increases. As Wall pointed out, his methods failed to record any fibres in the dorsal roots with conduction velocities less than 25 m/sec, and the discrepancy may thus be capable of a simple explanation although even in the group above 25 m/sec in the present results there is no indication of the relation proposed by Wall. In fact, from a sample of about 400 hair follicle units, including 180 Type D units, the greatest sensitivity to hair movement, using a rigidly mounted probe, was found among the Type D units, whereas the large hairs, supplied by large myelinated axons (Type G and T units), were less sensitive to movement of the appropriate hair (Fig. 5-2). Type D units are normally silent when no intentional stimulus is applied to the receptive field, but because of their high sensitivity they are likely to carry a low frequency irregular discharge when a probe, such as a glass rod, is held by hand among the hairs. These latter units may correspond to the wide receptive field fibres of Maruhashi, Mizuguchi and Tasaki (1952).

This high sensitivity to hair movement possessed by the Aδ fibres has important consequences for the analysis of reflex mechanisms and somaesthetic pathways. On the one hand, the group III cutaneous fibres (i.e., 1μ to 6μ dia.) are commonly assigned a role as flexor reflex afferents (Holmquist and Lundberg, 1961) which is inappropriate if the group is regarded as homogeneous. If it is not, then electrical stimulation of the nerve trunk will evoke mixed central actions and great difficulty must then arise in assigning specific roles to any unidentified elements of the group. On the other hand, the small myelinated afferent fibres with receptors having an attributed insensitivity to mechanical stimulation are assigned a specific role in the mechanism of pain by Melzack and Wall (1965) for two reasons: first, because they are presumed to be carrying a continuous background discharge, which they do not, and second, because they are less likely to be excited by small hair movements, of which the converse is true (Fig. 5-1).

The sample of fine myelinated fibres examined in the summary mentioned above did not include, in the cat, any with conduction velocities less

Hair follicle units

Figure 5-1. Comparison of the response of two follicle afferent units to displacement of the appropriate hair at the same slope (rate of displacement). The Type D (down hair) unit responds with a stream of impulses, whereas the Type G (guard hair) unit fires twice. Both units were excited when the hairs were allowed to return to their original position. Rabbit ear preparation (Fig. 0, Brown, A. G., Iggo, A., & Miller, S., *Expt. Neurol.,* in press).

than 15 m/sec. Myelinated fibres conducted more slowly than this (4 to 9 m/sec) and termed post-δ, have been described by Koll, Haase, Schütz, and Muhlberg (1961) in compound action potential studies and attributed a role in nociceptive reflexes, whereas the Aδ fibres were claimed to be in-effective. Confirmation of at least part of Koll's experiments thus come from the single unit work on Type D units which are seen to comprise a large proportion of the Aδ group in the cat. A detailed single unit analysis of the so-called post-δ afferent units has not yet been made.

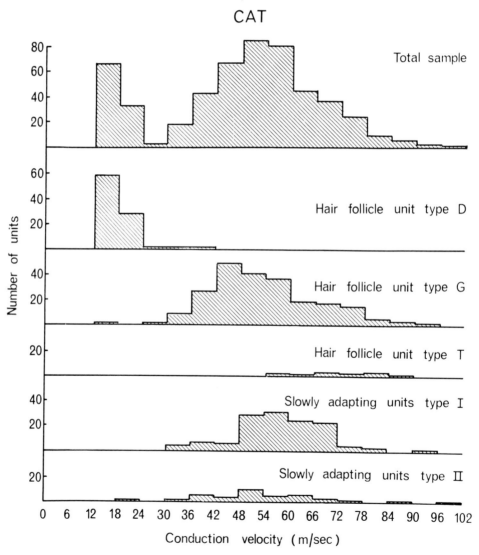

Figure 5-2. Histograms to show the relation between the conduction velocity of the axons and the afferent unit types in the saphenous nerve of (*a*) the cat and (*b*) the rabbit. In both animals almost without exception the most slowly conducting myelin-

The sensitive rapidly adapting units are all associated with hair follicles, and there may be good mechanical reasons for this. The receptor terminals are invariably at some depth in the skin, around the shaft of the hair and below the sebaceous glands if they are present. The precise relationship between the receptor terminals and the hair follicle has not yet been worked

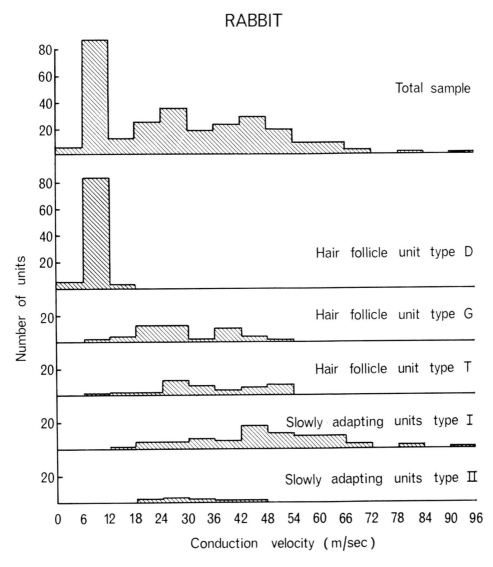

ated fibres (Aδ) innervate Type D follicle units. The remaining four classes of unit are all innervated by faster axons, and no clear-cut distribution of units according to conduction velocity is evident, except that in the rabbit the slowly adapting Type I units are supplied by the fastest axons and in the cat the Type T follicle units are not innervated by axons with conduction velocities of less than 54 m/sec.

out, so far as I know, but the movement of the free part of the hair has to be transmitted beneath the epidermis before it can act on the receptor terminals. Some hair units, particularly the large hairs of Straile's (1960) tylotrich follicle are readily excited by movement of the hair in its long axis in the follicle, when a regular stream of impulses can be set up during the movement. This apparent greater sensitivity may arise simply from the longer movement of the hair within the follicle. It could, however, arise because the receptors are arranged in a particular manner, either parallel or circular to the hair shaft. The parallel terminals, which also extend along a greater length of the follicle, may be particularly well placed to respond to either longitudinal or lateral displacement of the hair in the follicle. The Type T follicle units, particularly in the rabbit are invariably restricted to tylotrich follicles, and the Type G units to the guard hairs. One test of this hypothesis that the orientation of the nerve terminals affects their sensitivity to movement would be to examine the type of follicle innervation pattern and to relate this to directional sensitivity of the receptors. This has not yet been done in the cat or rabbit. T. FitzGerald (personal communication) has found in the mouse and rat that the down hairs have a very simple nerve supply consisting of one or two circular fibres, whereas the monotrichs have a "basket work" of circular and parallel nerve terminals, and the intermediate follicles (awl and auchenes) have a simpler basket work. The exact roles of the different elements are not established, but the circular and parallel terminals appear, in methylene-blue stained preparation, to arise from different axons, and so could comprise separate afferent units with a characteristic sensitivity to the direction of hair movement. It is at least clear that, among the myelinated afferent fibres innervating the hair follicles on the body surface of the cat and rabbit, at least three distinctive categories can be made.

There are regional differences in cutaneous innervation and the three types of unit are not present everywhere or in the same proportions. The afferent innervation of the ear of the rabbit differs from that just described for the body skin. These differences are important since far-ranging speculation has been based on both histological and physiological work done on the rabbit's ear. In a recent series of experiments Brown, Iggo and Miller (in press) could find only Type D and Type G follicle units in the dorsal skin of the rabbit's ear (Fig. 5-1). Hairs corresponding to both guard and down types could be recognized although the hairs on the ear are generally short and of fairly uniform length. There is greater variation in diameter and the finer hairs (corresponding to down hairs) emerge in groups from a common or from closely grouped follicles, whereas the larger hairs (corresponding to guard hairs) emerged singly. The relation between diameter of the afferent fibre and the kind of hair follicle innervated was the same as for the body skin of the rabbit. That is, the down hairs were supplied by Aδ fibres, and the guard hairs by larger myelinated fibres. Thus, these features were common to both kinds of skin. The numbers of hairs innervated by a single axon, although not carefully measured, were always larger for the Aδ fibres, even though the receptive fields were similar in area. No tylotrich follicle units (Type T) could be found electrophysiologically or by careful microscopical inspection of the skin, in contrast to the skin of the leg for which 23 per cent of the sample of 178 units in the rabbit were Type T. These results indicate the need for great caution in generalizing about the cutaneous innervation and sensation from the narrow base of the rabbit's ear, as is now acknowledged by Weddell (1966).

SLOWLY ADAPTING MECHANORECEPTORS

The second principal class of cutaneous myelinated afferent units give a slowly adapting or persistent discharge of impulses when the skin or special hairs are pressed on. This type of response comes from spot-like areas of the skin (Frankenhaeuser, 1949; Hunt and McIntyre, 1960; Iggo, 1963) or from tactile hairs (FitzGerald, 1940; Nilsson and Skoglund, 1965). The spot-like units will be considered first. Individual afferent fibres supply one to five spots, which in the skin of the thigh, leg, or foot are always closely grouped. When the sensitive spot is displaced there is a high frequency burst of impulses during the movement. The impulse interval of constant slopes is related to displacement, and becomes less (i.e., the frequency rises) as displacement continues, in contrast to the hair follicle units which are generally displacement insensitive and discharge at frequencies that show little amplitude dependence. The slowly adapting units also display, as do the hair follicle units, a rate of displacement sensitivity, with a critical minimal slope (Fig. 5-3). Two classes of afferent unit in the spot-like group in this category can be distinguished (Brown and Iggo, 1966a; 1966b). The first (Type I) very rarely carries a resting discharge of impulses at normal skin temperature (30 to 35°C) (Iggo, 1963). The adapted discharge of the Type I unit may initially have a regular impulse interval, as has so elegantly been established by Werner and Mountcastle (1965). This regular discharge, however, soon breaks up into an irregular discharge, and within 5 sec or longer a pattern emerges in which the impulse intervals are irregular and impulses may often be grouped. The mean frequency of discharge declines slowly during this period of irregular discharge and may eventually flatten out after 30 sec or 1 min. The discharge ceases abruptly when the displacement is removed and does not return unless the displacement is repeated. These Type I units form clusters of one to five spots per fibre and any spot is innervated by only one axon. The mechanical sensitivity is very highly restricted and normally the units are excited only by displacement

The Skin Senses

of the spot itself, not by movement of the surrounding skin. They are not excited, in the cat, by movement of hairs nor by stretching the skin. In the rabbit the sensitive spots are usually at or near the orifice of large hair follicles (tylotrich follicles) and in this species movement of the large hair may excite the receptor. Brown (in press), in carefully controlled experiments, recording simultaneously from two afferent fibers, one going to the hair (Type T) and the other to a spot (Type I) at the mouth of the same hair follicle, found that it was very difficult with mechanical stimulation to excite the follicle unit in isolation. Usually some measure of selective stimu-

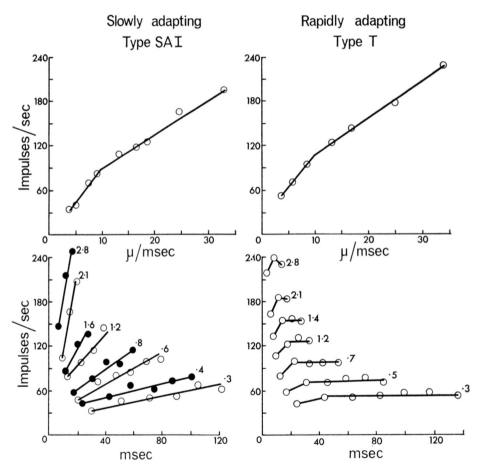

Figure 5-3. Comparison of the responses of a slowly adapting (Type SAI) and a rapidly adapting (Type T) cutaneous afferent unit to mechanical stimulus. The lower graphs show the frequency of discharge at various slopes (μ/msec) of mechanical displacement. The slowly adapting unit has a conspicuous displacement as well as rate of of displacement sensitivity whereas, the rapidly adapting unit shows a predominant rate of displacement sensitivity. The rate of displacement sensitivity, plotted as the mean frequency of discharge in the upper graphs, conceals this difference in displacement sensitivity.

lation could be obtained, especially when the stimulating probe was applied to the touch spot (Fig. 5-4). Hair movement usually excited both units but to unequal degrees. In the cat and monkey, by contrast, it was often difficult to excite the Type I units by hair movement. The Type I units are therefore a distinctive class physiologically, and shortly I will describe their highly distinctive morphological features. The afferent fibres were myelinated and ranged in diameter from 5μ to 16μ in the cat and 2μ to 16μ in the rabbit, with mean conduction velocities of 57 and 47 m/sec, respectively (Fig. 5-1).

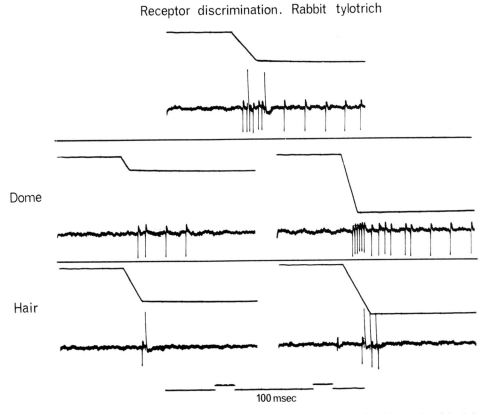

Figure 5-4. Selective mechanical stimulation of receptors associated with a tylotrich follicle in the rabbit. The afferent discharge was recorded simultaneously from a strand of the saphenous nerve. The upper record shows the response to movement of the whole follicle, with no attempt to excite either unit selectively. There are two afferent fibers, the spikes above the baseline are recorded from Type T (tylotrich) afferent unit axon and the downward deflection from the Type SAI unit axon. The next row of records (dome) show that the SAI unit can be selectively excited by directing the mechanical stimulator to the dome, at two levels of displacement. The lowest row (hair) shows the result of an attempt to excite the Type T unit only, by moving the hair. At all positions of the probe both the SAI and Type T unit were excited, but some degree of selective stimulation is evident since the T unit is firing at a relatively higher frequency.

The second class of slowly adapting unit (Type II), present in the hairy skin of cats, rabbits, monkeys and dogs, often carries a very regular low frequency (3 to 20/sec) discharge of impulses in the absence of any extrinsic stimulus (Fig. 5-5). This basal discharge can be accelerated by stretching the skin and by the close arterial injection of histamine or 5-HT (Fjällbrant and Iggo, 1961). This basal discharge, especially in the cat and rabbit, is an almost certain guide to the identity of the unit, with a few minor exceptions. These are the following: (a) the distortion of the skin by persistent stretching in forming the paraffin pool which in the rabbit may set up a low frequency irregular discharge from Type I units (Brown, in press), and (b) units with a cardiac rhythm. The latter are usually Type D follicle units in skin overlying an artery and excited by the pressure wave transmitted from the vessel. (c) In the monkey a background discharge may also arise from thermoreceptors with myelinated fibres (Iggo, 1964), but in these latter the discharge is usually in groups of three to six impulses. The discharge is unaffected by stretching the skin and is very sensitive to changes of temperature, so that confusion is unlikely to arise.

The Type II units have in most instances a single highly sensitive spot from which a high frequency discharge of impulses can be evoked. The Type II units are less sensitive to mechanical displacement than the Type I, and the impulse interval is very regular, without the fluctuations so characteristic of Type I (Fig. 5-5). They display an even more striking displacement sensitivity than the Type I units when tested with linearly rising displacements. One of the most distinctive features of these units is that they can be excited very easily by stretching the skin, and because of this they can easily be distinguished from Type I.

Another class of slowly adapting cutaneous mechanoreceptors was first described by FitzGerald (1940) who reported a directional sensitivity in afferent units excited by moving vibrissae around the mouth in the cat. In some current work on cutaneous thermoreceptors the afferent fibres in the infraorbital nerve of the dog have been examined. Many afferent fibres with a high mechanical sensitivity were found and some of these, when active, carried a very regular stream of impulses. The frequency of discharge was related to the position of hairs on the upper lip. Some units were excited by movement of single long vibrissae. The majority were excited by movement of shorter hairs that emerged singly from follicles interspersed between the long vibrissae and also covering the more rostral part of the upper jaw. Individual afferent fibres supplied only one hair (tactile hair) but it is not known whether each hair follicle was supplied by a number of afferent fibres. All the latter units were excited by a movement of the appropriate hair that decreased the angle at which it emerged from the skin. If a hair was held in such a new position an almost nonadapting discharge of impulses was elicited. The return of the hair to its normal position promptly stopped the discharge. These hair units, therefore, were silent unless the hair was moved, and in this respect are comparable to the rapidly adapting hair follicle afferent units; they are provisionally termed slowly adapting Type III. They were good detectors of movements of the highly mobile upper lips during breathing. The follicle units in the face of the dog may be comparable in some respects with "carpal hair" units in the cat (Nilsson and Skoglund, 1965) which the latter appear to have confused with the slowly adapting "touch corpuscle" units (Type I). Whether the vibrissal units of FitzGerald (1940), the carpal hair units of Nilsson and Skoglund (1965) and the tactile hair follicle units described in this paper are identical and served by similar receptors and nerve endings must be left an open question.

STRUCTURE OF THE RECEPTORS

The receptive field of a Type I unit was invariably made up of a mosaic of sensitive spots, ranging in number from 1 to 5 for individual afferent

Slowly-adapting cutaneous units

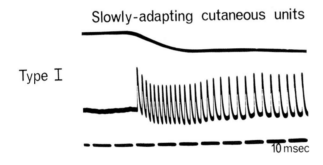

Type I

10 msec

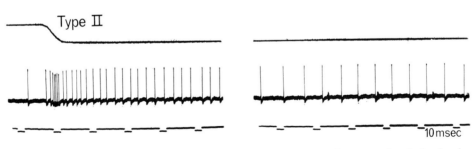

Type II

10 msec

Figure 5-5. Comparison of slowly adapting Type I and II units to mechanical stimulation. The Type I unit has no resting discharge which in the Type II unit is characteristically very regular but at low frequency (only a single impulse is seen at the beginning of the Type II trace). Both units fire at high frequency during mechanical displacement, but Type I at much higher frequency and for lesser displacements. Both adapt slowly, but the discharge in Type II settles down to a very regular rhythm.

units. At each spot the mechanical sensitivity was high and between spots no response could be evoked. Each spot in the cat was a roughly hemispherical dome (150μ to 300μ dia.), raised above the surrounding epidermis and was clearly visible on the surface of the skin on binocular microscopic inspection. Careful removal of the hair with a depilatory made the domes easier to see (Iggo, 1963). In the rabbit they are less distinctive as isolated domes and, almost invariably, are at the mouths of the tylotrich follicles (Brown, in press). Histologically, there is a thickening of the epidermis at each dome, with slightly different details in various species. The epidermis is always thicker than the adjacent epidermis, three to four cells compared with one or two, which sometimes forms a conspicuous plate of tissue, as in the guinea pig. The basal layer of cells is seen in the light microscope to form a flat sheet with a well-marked basement membrane. The myelinated axon which innervates the dome runs into the epidermis, usually after subdividing freely in the dermis subjacent to the thickened epidermis (Fig. 5-6). These histological features were first described by Pinkus (1902) and have since been reported by other histologists and dermatologists (Tamponi, 1939; Straile, 1960; Winkelman, 1960 who did not class it as a sense organ). They were originally called *haarscheibe* ("hair discs") by Pinkus because of their apparent association with hair follicles which suggested to the morphologists that the whole structure (follicle and dome) was a functional unit. The electrophysiological results presented above establish that this is not the case and that the afferent units comprising the Type T follicle unit and the Type I slowly adapting unit (dome) are quite distinct. For this reason, as well as the separate existence of the domes unrelated to tylotrich follicles in the cat and monkey, it is preferable to avoid the use of the misleading appellation, Haarscheibe, with its implication that the specialized structure of the dome has some functional relation to the hairs.

    The fine structure of these Type I spots is the subject of detailed examination in which I have been fortunate to secure the co-operation of Dr. Alan Muir. The basal layer of cells has proved to be the most interesting feature. Their structure is complex. The nerve ending expands to form a roughly circular disc parallel to the epidermal surface, about 10μ x 1.5μ dia., which is totally enclosed by a roughly spherical cell, (10μ to 12μ dia.) that I shall call the receptor cell (Fig. 5-7). The nerve ending expands from an axonal branch that loses its myelin sheath only over the terminal few microns, before it pierces the basement membrane of the epidermis to enter the enclosing cell. Within the nerve plate there is a very heavy concentration of mitochondria, some clear vesicles about 300 to 400 Å in diameter and, in the more recent preparations, structures similar to glycogen granules. The membrane of the nerve ending is closely apposed to the cell membrane and on its epidermal side there are morphologically distinctive regions, about

400 Å long, at which both membranes are parallel and thickened. In any section examined by electron microscope there were rarely more than one of these thickened regions.

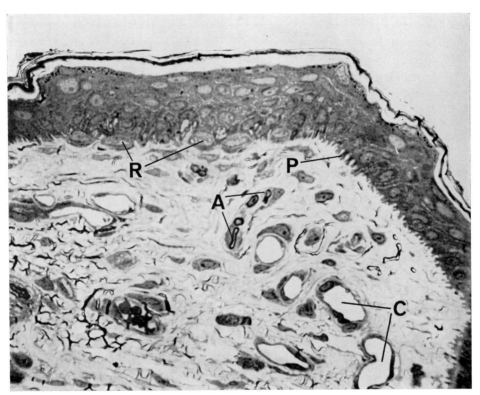

Figure 5-6. Light micrograph of a 1μ thick section through a dome-shaped swelling in the skin of the hind leg of a cat. The epidermis is thicker over the crest of the dome. At the sides, processes *P* from the basal layer of the epidermis extend into the fine collagenous core of the swelling. At the dermo-epidermal junction, five receptor cells *R* are seen. Their nuclei lie parallel to the surface and the whole cell bulges towards the dermis. A plexus of fine capillaries *C* and a myelinated axon *A* are present in the core of the swelling. Araldite embedding—toluidine blue pyronin staining (X 950).

The receptor cell that encloses the nerve ending has several distinctive features including a polylobulated nucleus and a zone of dense granular structures between the nucleus and the cell membrane adjacent to the nerve ending. These features have also been described by Cauna (1966) and Munger (1965) in glabrous skin and the snout of the opossum. The granular spheres vary in density and are separated from the cell membrane by a space of about 100 to 200 mμ, containing tubes. Opposite each thickened somatoneural junction the granular spheres are adjacent to the thickened membrane, an arrangement to which a functional significance could rather easily be ascribed. In some current experiments cats have been treated with reserpine in order to establish if the granules contain catecholamines, and if so, whether its removal modifies the functional behaviour of the receptors. The results indicate that the granules may not be catecholamines and that the functional behaviour of the afferent units is unaffected by this treatment with reserpine. Munger (1965), in PAS staining, reports that the area which in electron micrographs contains the granules, is PAS positive and diastase resistant. These observations could not be confirmed on our

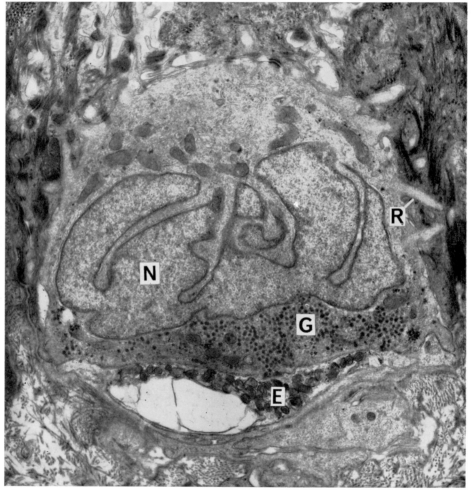

Figure 5-7. Low power electron micrograph showing a section through the center of a receptor cell in the cat. The nucleus *N* is multilobular, the whole cell is attached to the overlying epidermal cells by numerous desmosomes, cytoplasmic rods from the receptor cells *R* penetrate the epidermal cells. Beneath the nucleus, the cytoplasm contains a very large number of dark spherical granules *G* and it is this surface which is applied to the expanded nerve ending *E* containing many mitochondria and an artifactual dilation (X 16,000).

material. However, particles resembling glycogen (Revel, Napolitano, and Fawcett, 1960) are present in the cytoplasm, in electron micrographs, close to the poles of the nucleus of the receptor cell and adjacent to the nerve plate. The cytoplasm beneath the nerve plate (that is on the dermal side of the nerve plate) is an extension of the receptor cell and is in the form of a series of interdigitating processes. These processes, particularly on their dermal borders, contain numerous caveolae, which could indicate active regions of transmembrane movement. These indentations are less abundant in the membrane of the nerve plate.

The last feature to be commented on was noticed only very recently. The surface of the receptor cell facing towards the epidermis carries cylindrical, blunt-ended, rod-like extensions about 2μ long x 0.4μ dia. (Fig. 5-8). These processes pass into invaginations of the overlying cells and do not pass between the interstices of the contacts of overlying cells, which in any case contain many desmosomes. The cytoplasm in the rod process does not contain any organized or orientated material stainable with osmium. Instead the cytoplasm is clear and lacks both mitochondria and vesicles. The temptation to regard these processes as elements that aid or detect the degree of deformation of the overlying epidermal cells must be resisted in the absence of any evidence. Their location suggests some such function.

All these morphological features serve to distinguish the receptor cells very sharply from adjacent epidermal cells which have large spherical nuclei and numerous desmosomes. The distinctive structures are invariably associated with the presence of the nerve ending and the conclusion is inescapable that the whole complex forms part of a receptor that reveals a high degree of morphological specialization. The specialization is, moreover, restricted to the Type I units. The Type II slowly adapting are served by another kind of structure not yet examined in detail. Not only are the cells enclosing the nerve plate modified, in addition the whole region of epidermis is modified, to such a degree and with such uniformity in any species that the complete structure should be regarded as a morphological unit. Degeneration and regeneration experiments have established that the physiological properties of the Type I units depends on the presence of the receptor cells just described (Brown and Iggo, 1963).

The nerve endings just described can only be Merkel's discs, contained within Merkel's cells (Merkel, 1880). These discs in the hairy skin of all the species examined (rat, cat, monkey, rabbit) form a receptor which has a distinctive response to mechanical stimulation, and in an exhaustive analysis no other type of afferent unit has been found to be associated with the receptor. It is, therefore, logical to conclude that in this receptor the presence of Merkel's cells is a necessary prerequisite for the particular functional behavior. A reasonable generalization is that Merkel's cells and

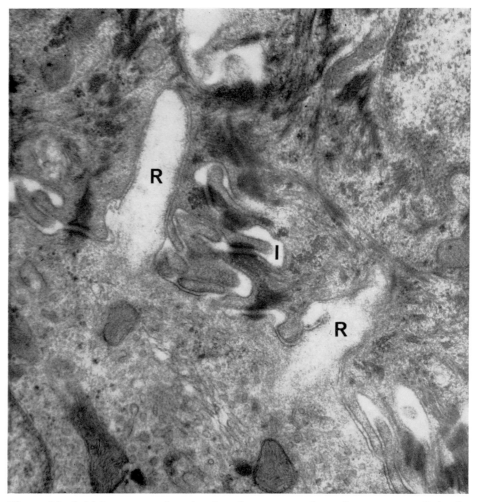

Figure 5-8. A higher power view showing the upper surface of a receptor cell in the cat. Cylindrical rods *R*, containing clear cytoplasm, penetrate the overlying epidermal cells. The two processes shown do not run in the intercellular cleft *I* (X 55,000).

disc function, wherever they are found, as slowly adapting mechanoreceptors. They have often been described as lying at the base of the epidermis in glabrous human and primate skin (Miller, Ralston, and Kasahara, 1958). There is also physiological evidence for highly localized, slowly adapting mechanoreceptors, excited by pressure on the ridges of glabrous skin (Iggo, 1963). If the mechanical sensitivity of the Merkel's discs is as highly restricted in glabrous, as it is in hairy skin then they could be part of the receptors that in the glabrous skin of the hand of the monkey, had the highly restricted sensitivity referred to above. This class of spotlike units were most sensitive to displacement of the epidermal papillary ridge. Miller *et al.*

(1958) found in human hand skin that Merkel's discs were present at the base of the epidermis only on the intermediate ridges, which are under the middle of the papillary ridge. The close structural linkage of the Merkel's cells to overlying epidermal cells by desmosomes may aid in the transmission of the mechanical displacement and thus preserve the fine discrimination that the receptors make possible.

The Type II slowly adapting afferent units, although they are a distinctive functional group, have not been accurately described histologically. In a number of combined electrophysiological-histological preparations a Ruffini-like nerve ending has been seen in the dermis beneath a sensitive spot in the skin of the cat. The location of the nerve ending in the dermis explains the high sensitivity of the afferent unit to stretching the skin and movement of hairs. The most widely studied receptor present in this skin is probably the Pacinian corpuscle. It is usually found in the dermis, particularly near the finger tips. This receptor has a highly distinctive structure as well as characteristic physiological properties which have been examined in visceral Pacinian corpuscles. There are a number of evident morphological differences from the slowly adapting mechanoreceptors that have just been described. First, each myelinated axon ends in one or a few pacinian receptors whereas each "touch spot" contains 30 to 50 Merkel's discs, all derived from one myelinated axon, and one dorsal root afferent fibre may supply up to five touch spots. Next, the nonmyelinated terminal in a Pacinian corpuscle is in the form of a long slender rod, 700μ x 20μ dia., of more or less uniform shape, whereas the Merkel's discs are expansions at the ends of fine nerves and are richly packed with mitochondria.

The importance of the accessory structure of a sense organ and its physiological properties has been considered in detail by Hubbard (1958) and Loewenstein (1966) as concerns the Pacinian corpuscle. Loewenstein has shown, experimentally as well as theoretically, that the lamellated structure of the corpuscle has an important function as a mechanical filter and restricts the range of response of the nerve terminal. The nerve terminal also imposes its own restraints on the frequency of discharge. It is clear, therefore, that the structure of this receptor is a determinant in its response. Loewenstein and Skalak (1966) go so far as to suggest that the nerve terminals of various receptors may differ very little in their properties, and that their differential sensitivity may be conferred by the accessory structures. This is an overgeneralization which can only be tested by further experiment. Such information as is available would suggest, on structural grounds alone, that there are great differences between even the different classes of mechanoreceptor. The time scales of the generator potential, or the afferent discharge, are also very different. The generator potential of a Pacinian corpuscle can be prolonged by removal of the lamellae and may

then last 70 msec compared with the normal 1 msec or less. Even this pro-
longation, however, is trivial compared with the duration of the response
from slowly adapting receptor units such as the muscle spindle or the cutaneous Type II units, which will discharge at a more or less fixed frequency
(therefore, with a constant generator potential) for 30 min or longer. The
accessory structure presumably adds to, rather than replaces, differences
which are already present in either the receptor cell, the nerve ending or the
preterminal nerve fibre.

EFFECT OF TEMPERATURE

The "specificity" or, as I prefer to call it, "selective sensitivity" of cutaneous afferent units has long been a matter for dispute, often, in my view, because of misunderstood or incomplete experimental evidence. One reason
for the long survival of the argument has been the difficulty of recording
from the finer afferent fibres which on psychophysical and differential nerve
block data were considered to include among their number the "thermal"
and "pain" fibres. The experiments of Iggo (1959), Hensel, Iggo and Witt
(1960) and Iriuchijima and Zotterman (1960) in the rat, cat, and dog,
established that the thermoreceptors in the skin covering the trunk and
limbs have nonmyelinated afferent fibres. These thermoreceptors had been
overlooked in most previous investigations because of their small size. The
primates (Boman and Hensel, 1960; Iggo, 1964) have thermoreceptors with
myelinated afferent fibres in addition to the nonmyelinated ones. This
absence of myelinated thermoreceptive afferent units from the skin of common laboratory animals has led to an interesting confusion which has arisen
from the effect of temperature on mechanoreceptors. This was first reported
in the tongue by Hensel and Zotterman (1951). In the past few years it has
become evident that the sensitivity of mechanoreceptors to temperature is
closely related to the rate of adaptation of the afferent unit, as well as to the
depth of the receptors in the skin. The slowly adapting Type II receptors
are the most obviously excited by a change in skin temperature (Fig. 5-9).
When the temperature falls these afferent units discharge at a higher frequency, especially if there is already a steady discharge. The resting discharge frequency is also affected by temperature, and at some value between
20° and 40°C, the resting discharge is maximal. Rapidly adapting receptors
are less easily affected, although some of the Type T and G hair follicle
afferent units are exicted by a steep fall in temperature. The Pacinian corpuscle, which adapts very rapidly, cannot be excited by steep changes in
temperature (Loewenstein, 1961).

This thermal sensitivity of the cutaneous mechanoreceptors can cause
uncertainty in the identification of afferent units especially in multi-unit
recordings, although less difficulty arises when single unit preparations are

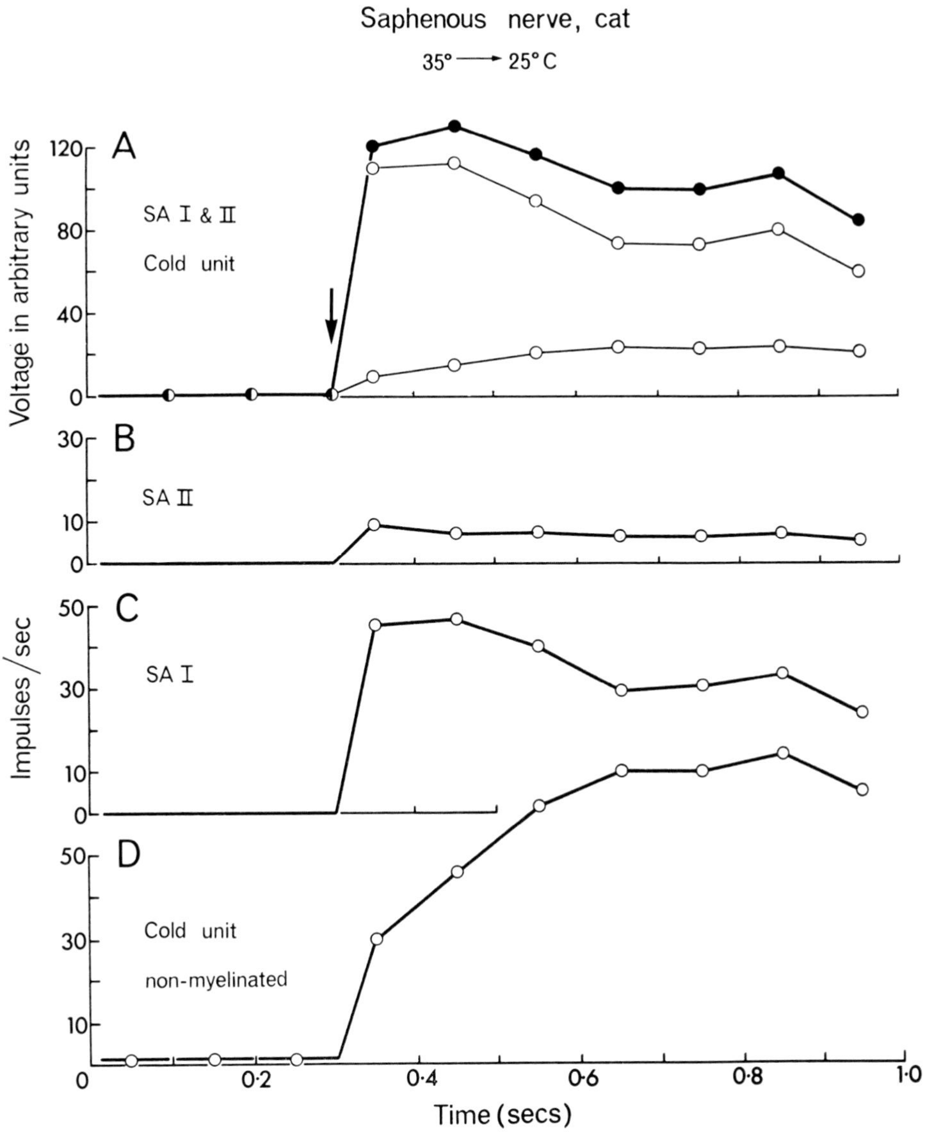

Figure 5-9. The effect of temperature of cutaneous afferent units in the saphenous nerve of the cat, plotted to show the contribution of three categories to an "integrated" potential record. *B, C,* and *D* show the frequency of discharge in single unit preparations; *B* a slowly adapting Type II unit, *C* a slowly adapting Type I, and *D* a nonmyelinated cold unit, to the same sudden change in cutaneous temperature from 35° to 25°C. *A* shows a computed voltage record calculated by multiplying the afferent discharges in *B, C,* and *D* by factors weighted for spike amplitude and relative proportions of the different classes of unit in the saphenous nerve of the cat. The three curves represent from the bottom upwards, the cold unit, the pooled responses of the mechanoreceptor units and (*heavy line*) the pooled response for all three categories. It is evident that the mechanoreceptors' contribution to the integrated record is much greater than the thermoreceptor.

used. The latter permit an exact and careful testing of the sensitivity of the receptor to thermal and mechanical stimuli.

The genesis of multi-unit and integrated (or instantaneous frequency) records is illustrated in Figure 5-9. The records are from preparations of the saphenous nerve supplying hairy skin of the leg of the cat and show the following: (a) a sensitive cold afferent unit with a nonmyelinated afferent axon; (b) a slowly adapting Type I unit; (c) a slowly adapting Type II unit, and (d) an example of each of the hair follicle units. With each afferent discharge is a plot of the frequency of discharge. These several curves are added together in the upper curve which is intended to indicate the response that would be recorded if the record was taken from a whole nerve or an intact fascicle. The addition has been scaled so that the contribution of each class of receptor is in proportion to the relative amplitude of the action potential spike (on an arbitrary scale, related to their heights in compound action potential records) , to the relative number of the different classes of unit and to the respective frequencies of discharge. It is at once clear that the background discharge in the myelinated axons (from Type I and II mechanoreceptors) dominates the record at any constant temperature, even though there is a persistent discharge in the thermoreceptors. The response of the mechanorecptors also dominates the potential record during the change of temperature. Thus, these integrated records display, for the greater part, the response of mechanoreceptors.

The second set of records is prepared from results of current experiments using the infraorbital nerve of the dog (Fig. 5-10) . The principal differences from the saphenous preparation are first the presence of Type III slowly adapting mechanoreceptors and, of particular significance, the presence of "cold" thermoreceptors with myelinated axons (Aδ). The figure was prepared in the same way as Figure 5-9. This time the higher frequency, larger amplitude, cold units make a significant contribution to the resting discharge and also to the response evoked by a change in skin temperature. By suitable adjustment of the stimulating conditions, and in particular, if the skin temperature is changed with a device that does not make physical contact with the skin, the records could be changed in one striking way. The resting discharge of the thermoreceptors would be less overshadowed by the mechanoreceptors. This would make little difference to the saphenous records in which the potential contribution of the nonmyelinated thermoreceptors is small. The mechanoreceptors, although for the most part silent at a constant temperature (except for some Type II units) , would still be excited by the fall in temperature. The infraorbital preparation would be different since the resting discharge in the myelinated thermoreceptors would now make a relatively greater contribution to the resting discharge which will disappear when the temperature rises and be strikingly enhanced when the temperature falls.

It is, therefore, possible to account for a variety of different kinds of integrated records only when the properties of at least the majority of the

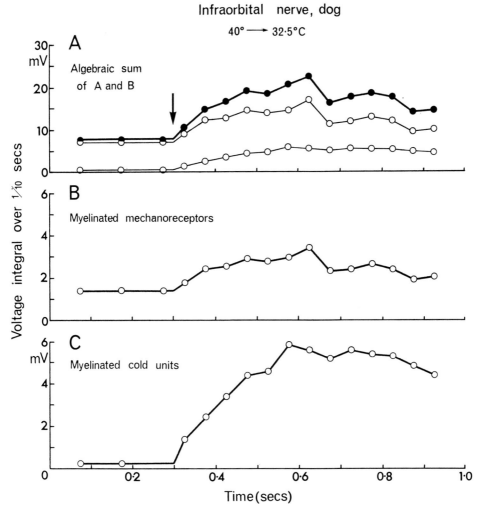

Figure 5-10. Like Figure 5-9 except that the nerve is the infra-orbital of the dog which contains myelinated cold afferent units. *A* shows the integrated response calculated for the whole nerve, obtained by adding the responses of the mechanical and thermal afferent units. *B* and *C* show pooled results from five slowly adapting units in *B* and three cold units in *C,* scaled according to the spike amplitude actually found for dissected strands of the nerve. As for the saphenous nerve, the "integrated" record is dominated by the mechanoreceptors, although the "cold unit" response is now proportionately larger. Both Figure 5-10 and Figure 5-9 analyze only one of a very large number of possibilities and make several assumptions about relative spike amplitudes and relative proportions of afferent units.

individual afferent units can be specified. Account must also be taken of the relative amplitudes and frequencies of discharge in the various units in order to arrive at an accurate assessment of the component contributions. The difficulties are multiplied if the recordings are taken from strands dissected from a nerve trunk, since the normal relation between diameter and recorded action potential may then be seriously distorted and potentials recorded from nonmyelinated axons may actually be larger than those from myelinated axons (Iggo, 1958).

REFERENCES

Boman, K. K. A., & Hensel, H. Afferent impulses in cutaneous sensory nerves in conscious human subjects. *J. Neurophysiol.*, 1960, **23**, 564.

Brown, A. G. Cutaneous afferent units associated with specialized hair follicles in the rabbit. *J. Physiol. (London)*, in press.

Brown, A. G., & Iggo, A. The structure and function of cutaneous "touch corpuscles" after nerve crush. *J. Physiol. (London)*, 1963, **165**, 28P .

Brown, A. G., & Iggo, A. Hair follicle receptors with myelinated afferent nerve fibers. *J. Physiol. (London)*, 1964, **172**, 33P.

Brown, A. G., & Iggo, A. Hair follicle afferent units with myelinated axons in the rabbit and cat. *J. Physiol. (London)*, 1966, in press. (a)

Brown, A. G., & Iggo, A. A quantitative study of a large somple of myelinated cutaneous afferent units. *J. Physiol. (London)*, 1966, in press. (b)

Brown, A. G., Iggo, A., & Miller, S. Myelinated afferent nerve fibers from the skin of the rabbit ear. *J. Physiol. (London)*, in press.

Cauna, N. The fine structure of the receptor organs and its probable functional significance. In O. E. Lowenstein (Ed.), *CIBA Foundation Symposium: Touch, Heat and Pain.* London: Churchill, 1966. Pp. 117-127.

FitzGerald, O. Discharges from the sensory organs of the cat's vibrissae and the modification of their activity by ions. *J. Physiol. (London)*, 1940, **98**, 163.

Fjällbrant, N., & Iggo, A. The effect of histamine, 5-hydroxytryptamine and acetylcholine on cutaneous afferent fibers. *J. Physiol. (London)*, 1961, **156**, 578.

Frankenhaeuser, B. Impulses from a cutaneous receptor with slow adaptation and low mechanical threshold. *Acta Physiol. Scand.*, 1949, **18**, 68.

Hensel, H., Iggo, A., & Witt, I. A quantitative study of sensitive cutaneous thermoreceptors with C afferent fibers. *J. Physiol. (London)*, 1960, **153**, 113.

Hensel, H., & Zotterman, Y. The response of mechanoreceptors to thermal stimulation. *J. Physiol. (London)*, 1951, **115**, 16.

Holmqvist, B., & Lundberg, A. Differential supraspinal control of synaptic actions evoked by volleys in the flexion reflex afferent in alpha motoneurones. *Acta Physiol. Scand.*, 1961, **54**, 51. (Suppl. 186.)

Hubbard, J. S. A study of rapid mechanical events in a mechanoreceptor. *J. Physiol. (London)* 1958, **141**, 198.

Hunt, C. C., & McIntyre, A. K. Properties of cutaneous touch receptors in cat. *J. Physiol. (London)*, 1960, **153**, 88.

Iggo, A. The electrophysiological identification of single nerve fibers, with particular reference to the slowest conducting vagal afferent fibers in the cat. *J. Physiol. (London)*, 1958, **142**, 110.

Iggo, A. Cutaneous heat and cold receptors with slowly conducting (C) afferent fibers. *Quart. J. Exp. Physiol.*, 1959, 44, 362.

Iggo, A. An electrophysiological analysis of afferent fibers in primate skin. *Acta Neuroveg. (Wien)*, 1963, **24**, 225.

Iggo, A. Temperature discrimination in the skin. *Nature (London)*, 1964, **204**, 481.

Iriuchijima, J., & Zotterman, Y. The specificity of afferent cutaneous C fibers in mammals. *Acta Physiol. Scand.*, 1960, **49**, 267.

Koll, W., Haase, J., Schütz, R.-M., & Muhlberg, B. Reflexentladungen der tiefspinalen Katze durch afferente Impulse aus Nochschwelligen nociceptivem A-fasern (post δ-fasern) und aus nociceptivem C-fasern Cutaner Nerven. *Pflüger Arch. Ges. Physiol.*, 1961, **272**, 270.

Loewenstein, W. R. On the "specificity" of a sensory receptor. *J. Neurophysiol.*, 1961, **24**, 150.

Loewenstein, W. R. The transduction process. In O. E. Loewenstein (Ed.), *CIBA Foundation Symposium: Touch, Heat, and Pain.* London: Churchill, 1966. Pp. 186-201.

Loewenstein, W. R., & Skalak, R. Mechanical transmission in a Pacinian corpuscle. An analysis and a theory. *J. Physiol. (London)*, 1966, **182**, 346.

Maruhashi, J., Mizuguchi, K., & Tasaki, I. Action currents in single afferent nerve fibers elicited by stimulation of the skin of the toad and the cat. *J. Physiol. (London)*, 1952, **117**, 129.

Melzack, R., & Wall, P. D. Pain mechanisms: A new theory. *Science*, 1965, **150**, 971.

Merkel, F. *Ueber die Endigungen der sensiblen Nerven in der Haut der Wirbeltiere.* Rostock: Schmidt, 1880.

Miller, M. R., Ralston, H. J., III, & Kasahara, M. The pattern of cutaneous innervation of the human hand. *Amer. J. Anat.*, 1958, **102**, 183.

Munger, B. L. The intraepidermal innervation of the snout skin of the opossum. *J. Cell Biol.*, 1965, **26**, 79.

Nilsson, B. Y., & Skoglund, C. R. The tactile hairs on the cat's foreleg. *Acta Physiol. Scand.*, 1965, **65**, 364.

Pinkus, F. Über einen bisher unbekannten Nebenapparat am Haarsystem des Menschen: Haarscheiben. *Derm. Z.*, 1902, **9**, 465.

Revel, J. P., Napolitano, L., & Fawcett, D. W. Identification of glycogen in electron micrographs of thin tissue sections. *J. Biophys. Biochem. Cytol.*, 1960, **8**, 575.

Straile, W. E. Sensory hair follicles in mammalian skin: The tylotrich follicle. *Amer. J. Anat.*, 1960, **106**, 133.

Tamponi, M. Nuove contributo alla conoscenza del "disco de pelo" (Haarscheibe di Pinkus), con particolare riguardo alla sua iconografia macroscopica. *Arch. Ital. Derm. Vener.*, 1939, **15**, 378.

Wall, P. D. Cord cells responding to touch, damage, and temperature of the skin. *J. Neurophysiol.*, 1960, **23**, 197.

Weddell, G. In O. E. Loewenstein (Ed.), *CIBA Foundation Symposium: Touch, Heat, and Pain.* London: Churchill, 1966. Pp. 359-360.

Werner, G., & Mountcastle, V. B. Neural activity in mechanoreceptive cutaneous afferents: Stimulus-response relations, Weber functions and information transmission. *J. Neurophysiol.*, 1965, **28**, 359.

Winkelmann, R. K. Similarities in cutaneous nerve end-organs. In W. Montagna (Ed.), *Advances in Biology of Skin. Vol. 1.* New York: Pergamon, 1960. Pp. 48-62.

Zotterman, Y. Touch, pain and tickling: An electrophysiological investigation on sensory nerves. *J. Physiol. (London)*, 1939, **95**, 1.

DISCUSSION

Dr. M. J. T. FitzGerald: There is one contribution which I would like to make to the structural background of the cutaneous receptors in the hairy skin. I recently examined the hairy skin of a number of mammals — rabbits, cats, guinea pigs, mice, and rats. All of these have encapsulated nerve endings in the interfollicular skin very close to the epidermis. This specimen (see Fig. 5-11) is from the dorsal skin of a mouse. You can see a hair shaft at the top and bottom of the field and a nerve fiber making an entry and broadening across the center of the field with the cellular thickening around it. Now, these corpuscles have the same structure in the five animals that I have mentioned, and they are undoubtedly bulbous corpuscles, or as Winkelmann calls them, the mammalian end-organs. They are quite difficult to find in spite of the fact that they are immediately subepithelial in position, and if one takes frozen sections in the plane of the skin surface, only the first section will have them and none of the others. To map these, it is necessary to take a single section, or perhaps two, from successive areas of skin. In the adult, there are about three per square centimeter, but in young animals, about a month to six weeks of age, they are much more densely crowded. If the section is taken in the appropriate plane, one can often see three or four in a single low-power field.

Dr. Iggo: What size are the afferent fibers?

Dr. FitzGerald: They are large.

Dr. Iggo: This is very interesting. I have been looking around for some structure that I can assign to the Type II slowly adapting response, the one which is excited by stretching the skin, and which has a lower sensitivity than the Type I unit. In some experiments I had marked the spot on the surface which showed the greatest sensitivity and then cut sections underneath. I did see structures which were rather vaguely like these, although I think they extended over a slightly greater distance than this one does, in between the hair follicles. I think this could be the same unit, again with the large myelinated fibers, which fits with what I saw.

Dr. FitzGerald: Yes. I think one should carry out a cholinesterase stain with a silver counterstain, in order to be quite sure of one's ground, because the sheath of the large fibers which approach the touch corpuscles may be quite thick and one could be deceived, though the sheath around the large fibers approaching the touch corpuscles is not cholinesterase-positive.

Dr. R. K. Winkelmann: Chu and Swinyard (1954) described corpuscles of this kind in the mouse some years ago, and I have yet to see a hairy mammal on whose back these end-organs were not present. They are not always present at the surface, however. Quite frequently when the hair follicles in a large animal extend deeply in to the subcutaneous tissue, you

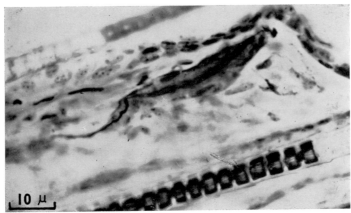

Figure 5-11. Encapsulated nerve ending in the hairy skin of a mouse. (Fig. 10, Fitz-Gerald, M. J. T., & Lavelle, S. M., *Anat. Rec.*, 1966, **154**, 629).

will find them around the middle or lower dermis. As Dr. FitzGerald says, in the young animal, they are quite dense, but in the adult animal or large animal they may be very difficult to find. This is why large frozen sections and the histochemical techniques are easiest to use in trying to find structures like these.

DR. IGGO: Can you in this preparation specify how many endings there would be per single fiber?

DR. WINKELMANN: I have never seen more than one per stem axon. That is really quite unique for this type of ending, I admit, because in the lip, for instance, there are usually quite a number of them per stem axon.

DR. IGGO: Because this would again fit with the slowly adapting Type II afferent unit, where there seems to be a single, most sensitive spot. On the other hand, there are also rapidly adapting spots, which show greater sensitivity to a rapid movement of a probe over the skin surface than of the hair follicle, but where the response is still rapidly adapting. This might be that type as well.

DR. WINKELMANN: May I make a comment about the problem that morphologists faced some years ago and ultimately decided that specificity of nerve morphology was not related to function and threw the problem back into the laps of the neurophysiologists. Dr. Iggo and his colleagues in neurophysiology have now begun to solve this problem properly from the physiological point of view. We can begin to associate some of this structure back with the types of stimuli tracings that he is developing.

DR. FITZGERALD: These endings do tend to occur in groups of three or four located quite close together. Whether they have a common parent axon, I do not know, but from their appearance and other situations, it seems likely that many would be derived from a common stem.

DR. Y. ZOTTERMAN: We should talk a little about the sensory function. Which of the types which you have described here have an after discharge?

DR. IGGO: These units do not have an after discharge unless they are the slowly adapting type, which has the regular background discharge, and that will then come back again. Otherwise, they are deadbeat in their response, but without after discharge. It is the nonmyelinated fibers that seem to have the after discharge.

DR. ZOTTERMAN: So, these are all myelinated fibers which you are working with here? They do not display any after discharge?

DR. IGGO: No.

DR. ZOTTERMAN: The after sensation which you have experienced after mechanical stimulation of the skin had nothing to do with these fibers. It must be smaller, nonmyelinated fibers.

DR. IGGO: It is very characteristic that if the preparation contains both myelinated and nonmyelinated fibers that in response to a short mechanical stimulus there is the brief deadbeat burst in the myelinated fibers and then, continuing for several seconds, the discharge in the nonmyelinated fibers.

DR. ZOTTERMAN: And I would emphasize this. This shows we have so many different kinds of end-organs that respond differently, but what we experience from our skin is so very different, subjectively, from the tickling sensation to a firm pressure, etc. This is the way of finding out what endings are participating when you produce these different sensations.

DR. H. DAVIS: Dr. Iggo, as an electrophysiologist I am very eager to know what the prospects are of moving in on these tactile endings with micro-electrodes to find out whether there are receptor potentials and whether they fit in the general scheme of our knowledge of other receptor end-organs. It certainly looks like a synaptic relation here, reminding us, perhaps, of Dr. Beidler's taste buds. Perhaps, if a Pacinian corpuscle can be skinned, you can also skin these and get in there.

DR. IGGO: Well, I have had that ambition for several years. I do not know quite why I have not done it.

DR. DAVIS: I do notice that there are capillaries in there which will undoubtedly make trouble for the microdissection, and this, I suppose, is related to the synaptic nature of the connection. Am I correct in guessing that if the blood supply is interrupted that the function of these fibers is blocked?

DR. IGGO: No, the evidence from Frankenhaeuser (1949) is that these slowly adapting discharges survive ischemia much longer than the rapidly adapting responses. We have some evidence that perhaps they might contain glycogen. This may provide these end-organs with a reserve of energy which will keep them going. There is not an immediate effect on the discharge if the blood supply is stopped.

DR. H. HENSEL: Dr. Iggo, you have shown two types of slowly adapting units, one with spontaneous discharge and another without spontaneous discharge. Could this depend on tension of the skin? Could you change, perhaps, one type into another type by changing the static tension of the skin?

DR. IGGO: I am afraid that the answer is no. Every attempt that has been made to convert one into the other has failed. Always the slowly adapting Type I response without the resting discharge has come from a little bump on the skin, whereas the other type which is excited by stretching the skin has never been found to be associated with the bump. It looks as though different structures are involved.

DR. HENSEL: What is the thermal sensitivity of these receptors, especially these endings with the spontaneous discharge?

DR. IGGO: Yes, they do display temperature sensitivity. They are silent, at least they are often silent, at about 40 °C and above, in my preparations. At lower temperatures they show a resting discharge related to the temperature, and then below 20 °C they cut off again. Within that range (40° to 20 °C), they are always excited by fall of temperature.

DR. J. D. HARDY: In characterizing the response of the fibers, in terms of the stimulus that you present to the receptor, you speak of rapidly adapting and slowly adapting fibers. Have you worked out the mechanics of the situation so that you can say what happens at the nerve terminal when you apply a measured force to the tissues? It might be that the rapidly adapting and the slowly adapting do not truly represent the characteristics of the terminals so much as the characteristics of the whole mechanical system. I am sure you thought of this.

DR. IGGO: Yes, but what experiment can you do to establish that it is not concerned with mechanical connections? Take the situation of the receptors which I have just described. The epidermis of the elevation is modified and thicker than the adjacent epithelium. The sensory endings consist of Merkel's corpuscles which hang along the lower border of the stratus basalis, being attached to this layer by many desmosomes. They are enclosed beneath by the basement membrane of the epidermis. The Merkel's corpuscle is approximately 10μ across and the nerve plate within the corpuscle is, perhaps, no more than 1 or 2μ thick. No matter how finely one does the microdissection, I think it is going to be very difficult, indeed, to remove that ending away from its mechanical associated structure.

DR. HARDY: So then, what one has to do is make a mechanical or electrical model of the whole system based on available data as to elastic, viscous and other coefficients of tissue and compute what the displacements may be at the nerve terminals as a function of time. This may be essential to a reasonable understanding of the neural responses.

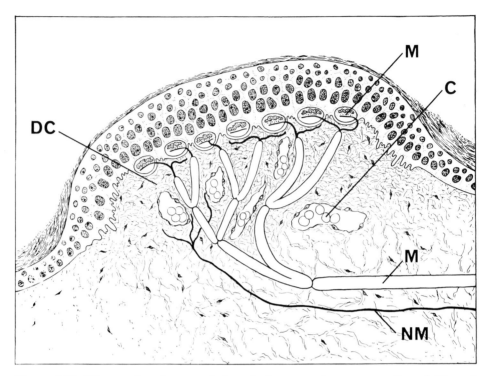

Figure 5-12. Diagram based on optical and electron microscope studies of Type I slowly adapting cutaneous mechanoreceptors ("touch corpuscle," Iggo, 1963). The diagram shows the basic structure of the cutaneous receptor with the afferent myelinated axon penetrating up through the dermis to end in Merkel's cells at the lower border of the epidermis. At this region the epidermis is thickened and the subjacent dermis is also much denser than in the adjacent region. Within the Merkel's corpuscle (M) the nerve ending forms an expanded disc of tissue about 10μ in diameter 1μ to 2μ thick. The nerve ending is totally encased by the enclosing cell, which is probably the Merkel's cell shown in an electron micrograph and described in detail in Figure 5-7 in the text. *C*—capillaries in the dermal core; *M*—myelinated axon; *NM*—nonmyelinated accessory axons; *D.C.*—dense collagen (Fig. 1a, Iggo, A. In O. E. Lowenstein (Ed.), *CIBA Foundation symposium: Touch, Heat and Pain.* London: Churchill, 1966.

DR. IGGO: The one piece of functional evidence, quite apart from computation, that for me provides support for the idea that there really are big differences between the nerve endings other than mechanical linkage is that the slowly adapting endings showed a discharge for 30 min. when the mechanical deformation was applied steadily all that time. This is to be compared with the Pacinian corpuscle where the discharge lasts for a few msec or for the hair follicles where, when they are moved, the discharge disappears after 5 to 10 msec. There is an enormous difference in the time scales here. This is perhaps not very logical evidence for the difference, but it would imply you have got to have some kind of mechanical linkage that continues to slip over many hours in order to account for the existence of this persistent discharge with the maintained displacement if the mechanical linkage determines the rate of adaptation.

DR. K. L. CASEY: The slowly adapting fibers have both a dynamic and a steady state of discharge. Is the dynamic aspect of the slowly adapting fiber also rate sensitive?

DR. IGGO: This really brings us back to one of the figures I showed, the rate sensitivity (Fig. 5-3). It really was the dynamic aspect which was displaying both rate and displacement sensitivity for the slowly adapting units, whereas for the rapidly adapting units there seems to be a rate sensitivity and no displacement sensitivity.

References

Chu, C. H. N., & Swinyard, C. A. Morphology and histochemistry of a veriform nerve end organ hitherto undescribed in mouse dermis. *Anat. Rec.* 1954, **118**, 287. (Abstract)

Frankenhaeuser, B. Impulses from a cutaneous receptor with slow adaptation and low mechanical threshold. *Acta Physiol. Scand.,* 1949, **18**, 68.

Iggo, A. New specific sensory structures in hairy skin. *Acta Neuroveg. (Wein),* 1963, **24,** 175.

Iggo, A. The perpheral mechanisms of cutaneous sensation. In D. R. Curtis, & A. K. McIntyre, (Eds.), *Studies in Physiology.* Berlin: Springer-Verlag, 1965. Pp. 92-100.

Chapter 6

QUANTITATIVE RELATIONS BETWEEN MECHANICAL STIMULI TO THE SKIN AND NEURAL RESPONSES EVOKED BY THEM*

GERHARD WERNER AND V. B. MOUNTCASTLE†

T HE TRADITIONAL CONCERN FOR the analysis of statements on sensory experiences consisted, in large measure, in the attempts to resolve the philosophically disturbing idea that the mental phenomena of sensation should be related, in an essentially predictable manner, to events in physical space and time. In the middle of the 19th century this problem, posed by dualistic thought, was cast into the form of the doctrine of the psychophysical parallelism. At that time the physiologists Helmholtz and Hering, the physicist Mach, and psychologist Wundt and the philosopher Lotze expressed the belief "that every mental process must be correlated with a process in the brain, and that the nature of the one must imply something about the nature of the other; at the very least, that change in one must mean change in the other" (Boring, 1941 p. 457). Fechner's program, on the other hand, marked a significant departure from dualistic philosophy. His idea was that sensations of differing degrees could be assigned numerical values, and that these sensation magnitudes would stand in a certain functional relationship to the magnitudes of the physical stimuli. In this manner physical and mental events were conceived to stand in a unique and characteristic quantitative relation, and this would imply that both are but appearances of the same underlying reality.

Almost 75 years elapsed after the publication of Fechner's *Elemente der Psychophysik* until one of the principal difficulties of his approach, namely the reliance on the introspective method, was circumvented. This became possible by bringing to bear on the problem of sensation two of the main streams of thought that had developed during this period, behaviorism and operationism. The implications were, first, the elimination of the contents of the mind from a study of psychophysical correlation. On the basis of these premises, studies of psychophysical correlation in animals and man, alike, aim at detecting quantitative correlations of objectively measureable magnitudes of physical stimuli with certain behavioral manifestations. Second, studies in animals and man could be viewed as expressing a biological

*This study was aided by grants from the Public Health Service, NB 01045 and MH 11682.
†V. B. Mountcastle is with the Department of Physiology, The Johns Hopkins University School of Medicine.

continuity, and the principle of evolution became applicable as a tool to seek order and lawfulness in otherwise isolated and anecdotal observations with different species. Furthermore, scientific parsimony suggested the postulate of psychoneural identity, that is, sensation is the neural activity, or some aspect of it, that is evoked by sensory stimuli. The question here is either to infer from psychophysical data, or to study directly in neurophysiological experiments, what features and relations of the impinging physical stimuli find a representation in neural activity, and in what quantitative relation.

Fechner's original approach to psychophysics introduced the fundamental and general problem of measurement to the study of sensation. The ramifications of this problem are as pertinent to the quantitative study of neural events in sensory systems as they are in psychophysics. In essence, this problem consists of the selection of certain features of sensory or neural responses, respectively, which are sufficiently characteristic and permit one to represent quantitative relations between them and corresponding stimulus parameters by one or another property of the real number system. The consequence of this for the study of neural activity in sensory systems is that the selection of scales for measuring this activity is not intrinsically determined, but open to experimental exploration. Accordingly, a primary concern in the quantitation of neural responses is the selection of scales which will set different neural responses in a monotonic functional relation to the corresponding stimuli of differing intensities which evoke them. On the basis of the principle of psychoneural identity, one might expect that there are some scales amongst these fulfilling this criterion which tally with psychophysical scales. This would tend to validate the relevance of the particular neural response scale to reflect the manner in which the nervous system "encodes" certain stimulus parameters.

Our investigations of neural activity in certain first-order cutaneous sensory fibers were undertaken with this general aim in view. We have sought, first, to determine quantitative characteristics of the neural activity elicited in these fibers by mechanical stimuli which mimic those encountered in normal life, but which could be precisely controlled in all parameters. Second, we related the magnitude of the responses in these fibers to the intensity of the stimuli used and compared the relations obtained with similar relations between tactile stimuli and subjective sensory experiences evoked by them in human observers. Thereby, we wished to determine whether, and to what extent, psychophysical and behavioral measurements of tactile sensation correspond to our measurements of neural responses in primary cutaneous afferents. We expected that these comparisons would reflect on the validity of the theory of psychoneural identity as a heuristical principle and would permit us to recognize the extent to which sensory phenomena can be determined by peripheral mechanisms.

Nature and Properties of Tactile Receptors Studied

The results of the present investigation were obtained, in part, from primary afferent nerve fibers innervating the mechanoreceptive endings which were studied in detail by Iggo (Iggo, 1963a; Iggo and Muir, 1963). He recognized as "touch spots" certain hemispheric, domelike elevations in the hairy skin of cats and monkeys. These elevations range in diameter from 150μ to 250μ, and are raised from the surrounding skin by about 150μ. It has been shown by Iggo (1963b) and Tapper (1964) that these corpuscles contain the endings of myelinated fibers which range from 7μ to 16μ in diameter, that the discharge rate of impulses elicited in these fibers by mechanical stimuli of their endings may decline only slowly, and that the effective stimulus for excitation at threshold may be as small as 10 mg of force, or 10μ of indentation. Activity in the afferent nerve fibers which end in "touch corpuscles" has probably been the subject of earlier studies (Marushi, Mizuguchi, and Tasaki, 1952; Witt and Hensel, 1959). The detailed examination of Hunt and McIntyre (1960) emphasized that responses in this class of fibers can be elicited from discrete spots and that their receptive fields are discontinuous, for each fiber branches and may end in several touch corpuscles.

A second series of experiments involved a study of the responses in cutaneous afferent fibers elicited by mechanical stimulation of the skin of the palm of hands in macaques. Two types of touch receptors are commonly associated with the papillary ridges of their distal glabrous skin, Meissner's corpuscles located in the dermal papillae of hairless digital, palmar and plantar skin, and epidermal nerve endings (Merkel's discs) related to the intermediary ridges and distributed through the hairless and hairy skin as well. The basal cell layer of the intermediary ridges contains rounded, clear cells in the neighborhood of which elongated nerve endings are found. Their diameter is considerably smaller (2μ) than is that of the terminal expansions of nerve fibers coursing towards the Meissner's corpuscles (Cauna, 1954).

Touch corpuscles in the hairy skin and tactile receptors in the glabrous skin of the palm differ with respect to some of their functional properties. The receptive fields of nerve fibers innervating the former are discontinuous, and the effectiveness of mechanical stimulation is limited to direct surface indentation of individual corpuscles, while lateral pressure or distension of the surrounding skin is largely ineffective for setting up discharges in the corresponding afferent nerve fiber. When the stimulus probe was placed lateral to a corpuscle so that as little as 200μ to 300μ intervened between the edges of the probe tip and the corpuscle, even extreme indentations (e.g., 1 mm or more) elicited only minimal responses, or none at all, even though the corpuscle could be seen to be displaced very markedly along the crater of skin indented by the movement of the probe. Furthermore, traveling waves set up in the skin in the neighborhood of a corpuscle produced by brief repetitive stimuli or sinusoidal deformation of adjacent skin areas are quite ineffective for excitation. On the other hand, Cauna's (1962) morphological investigations make it plausible that the sensory function of the epidermal nerve plexus underlying the intermediary ridges is closely dependent on structure and mechanical properties of the associated tissues of the skin, including the epidermis. The intermediate ridge is thought to follow and magnify movements anywhere on the surface of the corresponding papillary ridge, trading tactile sensitivity for tactile selectivity. The same mechanical arrangement is capable of producing an opposite effect on Meissner's corpuscle. Their location with respect to the papillary ridges is such that sensitivity is thought to be maximal when the direction of force acting on the corpuscle coincides with its longitudinal axis, with a considerable degree of selectivity.

Tactile receptors in the glabrous skin of the palm, unlike Iggo's touch corpuscles, permit one to map continuous receptive fields which were recently studied by Lindbolm (1965) in some detail. The intensity of responses to identical degrees of skin indentation varies greatly at different positions within the receptive fields. The family of response curves of Figure 6-1 shows this for the eight papillary ridges (numbered on the abscissa from 1 to 8) of a receptive field at the finger, in relation to different stimulus intensities. The stimulus-response relations described in what follows were, in all instances, obtained with the stimulus probe in what was judged to be the center of the receptive field for the afferent nerve fiber under study.

Metric of the Stimulus Intensity

These circumstances indicate the differences that are likely to exist in the quantitative manner in which equal degrees of identation at the skin surface excite different types of tactile receptors. Furthermore, the relation between skin surface displacement by the probe, its time course, and the forces acting at the effective stimulus site are complexly interrelated because of the elastic properties of the skin and the varying compliance, from place to place, of the tissues beneath it (Franke, 1957). In psychophysical studies in man the tactile stimulus has been scaled in a variety of static and dynamic dimensions by different investigators, the selection essentially being pragmatic, and determined by what was directly measurable and led to a consistent, monotonic and relatively simple relation between the stimulus and the observer's estimate of its magnitude (Renquist, 1933). For stimuli of brief duration, we have scaled the stimulus intensity in terms of skin indentation. The regularity of the stimulus-response curves we have obtained suggest the validity of this stimulus metric, while quantitative differences between the stimulus-response relations for the Iggo touch corpuscle on the one hand, and the tactile receptors of the glabrous skin on the other may reflect, at least in part, differences in the conveyance of the superficial skin dislocation to the underlying receptive structures.

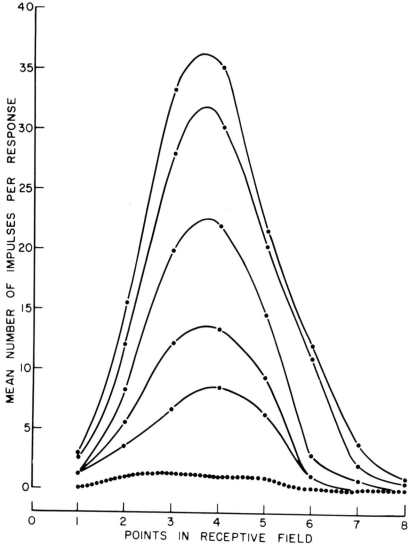

Figure 6-1. Results obtained in the study of a receptive field encompassing eight papillary ridges at the glabrous skin of the finger of a macaque. The points in the receptive field are numbered as consecutive ridges (*abscissa*). The response numbers for stimuli producing identical skin indentations are joined by curves, with the responses to the weakest stimulus represented as the lowest, and those to the strongest stimuli as the topmost, curve in the figure.

The electromechanical transducer used for stimulation of the skin was fully described in an earlier publication, as were the experimental preparation and the procedures for data acquisition and reduction (Werner and Mountcastle, 1963). The tip of the stimulus probe was turned from lucite, 1 mm in diameter, and its contacting surface smoothly rounded to 1/3 sphere. Smaller probe tips were found to injure the skin, particularly when fast-rising mechanical stimuli were used.

GENERAL CHARACTERISTICS OF THE RESPONSES OF TOUCH FIBERS TO MECHANICAL STIMULI

A general property of mechanoreceptors is that they respond to adequate stimuli of maintained intensity with an initial rapid discharge at onset which then declines to a more or less steady state of activity. Hunt and McIntyre (1960) and Iggo (1963b) have shown that the touch corpuscles are of this kind, especially if the quickly adapting hair fibers are taken for comparison. However, only a few of these fibers maintain rates of discharges of adequate stationarity when the stimulus persists beyond a few seconds. On the other hand, in what follows, it will be shown that the large majority of these fibers, and those innervating tactile receptors in the glabrous skin as well, exhibit a great regularity of discharge, in response to brief stimuli, of 1 sec or less in duration. For this reason, and because tactile acuity in humans is best when brief mechanical stimuli are applied repetitively (Katz, 1925), we have primarily studied the responses to the latter mode of stimulation.

Regularity of Number and Temporal Order of Impulses in Response to Brief Stimuli

The records of Figure 6-2 were obtained when stimuli of 400 msec duration were delivered to the touch corpuscle innervated by a single fiber in the saphenous nerve (fiber 16-3). These records are representative of those of all the fibers of this type we have studied, as are the records of Figure 6-3 for the responses in fibers innervating tactile receptors in the palm of the macaque. Inspection of these records shows that after the early onset transient during which the frequency of discharge changes rapidly, there follows a period of time (100 to 600 msec after stimulus onset) during which the frequency of discharge appears quite constant. With the very rapid rise rates of the mechanical stimuli used (100 to 200μ/msec) the initial displacement-rate sensitive period of the response is of negligible duration (Tapper, 1965).

In a previous publication (Werner and Mountcastle, 1965) we have documented for fibers innervating Iggo's touch corpuscles that the rate of discharge in the period following the onset transient is sensitively determined by stimulus intensity and that it is possible to delineate in this

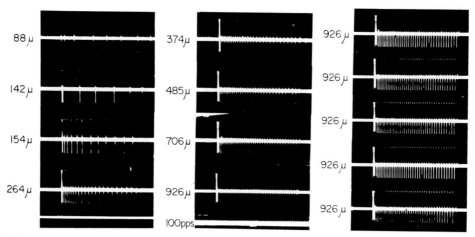

Figure 6-2. Nerve impulses evoked in a single fiber (16-3) of the saphenous nerve of a cat by mechanical stimulation of its corpuscular ending in the skin of the lower leg. Net skin indentation in microns is shown to the left of each record. Stimulus duration was 400 msec. The stimulus onset, arrival at plateau, and offset are indicated by the three code signals of the record to the lower left. Time line is 100 pulses/sec. The five records to the right display responses to stimuli of identical intensity, delivered at intervals of 3 sec.

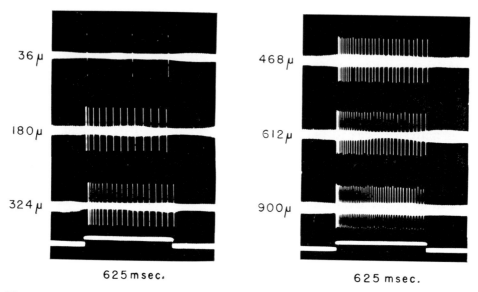

Figure 6-3. Nerve impulses evoked in a single nerve fiber of the radial nerve of a macaque by mechanical stimulation of the glabrous skin of the hand. The net skin indentation in microns is shown to the left of each record. Stimulus duration was 625 msec. The stimulus duration is marked in the bottom trace.

period an "early steady state" (Fig. 6-4). Evidence for the steady nature of this early response was obtained by the following analysis: 30 to 50 identical stimuli were delivered at intervals of 3 to 5 sec. Measurements were made of the intervals between impulses in the response train, and averages obtained for the duration of the 1st, 2nd, 3rd . . . nth intervals throughout the train until firing indices fell below 100 per cent. There results an accurate representation of the average sequence of the discharge intervals in the response to a stimulus. Figure 6-5 depicts the results obtained when this method of study was applied to activity elicited in fibers innervating tactile receptors in the glabrous skin.

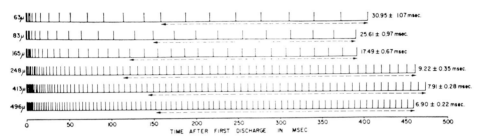

Figure 6-4. Graphical display of the averaged sequence of discharge intervals in 30 consecutive responses to skin stimuli at each of the intensities given to the left of each sequence. The intervals between the short vertical lines represent the means of the durations of the first, second, third. . .nth interval throughout the trains of nerve impulses, until firing indices fall below 100 per cent. The portions of the averaged discharge sequences delineated by the dashed lines indicate those periods of time after stimulus onset during which the cumulative poststimulus time histograms are linear. Mean interval and standard error (in msec) over these portions are given to the right of the discharge displays. Fiber 26-3.

Figures 6-4 and 6-5 illustrate, pictorially, what will be corroborated by additional evidence later on, namely that there exists in afferent fibers of Iggo corpuscles and tactile receptors in the palm of the hand a period of steady activity in responses to brief stimuli during which the frequency of discharge is remarkably constant and periodic. The period begins within 100 to 150 msec of stimulus onset and lasts for about 400 to 500 msec. This metronome like regularity of the temporal order in a major portion of the response train to brief stimuli may make one anticipate that the number of discharges at a given intensity of stimulation may also exhibit but little variation. That this is so is illustrated in Figure 6-6 for several afferent fibers from the glabrous skin. These results are representative of those obtained from all fibers studied in the former and the hairy skin, as well.

As a measure of the precision with which responses to identical stimuli replicate, we plotted (Fig. 6-6) the variability of the response number (expressed as S. D.) as function of its mean for several fibers. The variability was so low that for every fiber studied, at every intensity level tested, the true mean response number could be estimated with an error which commonly lay between 0.3 to 1.5 impulses and rarely exceeded three impulses (see right side of Fig. 6-5), even when the mean response number rose to as high as 120 impulses. In a few samples, this error was actually zero.

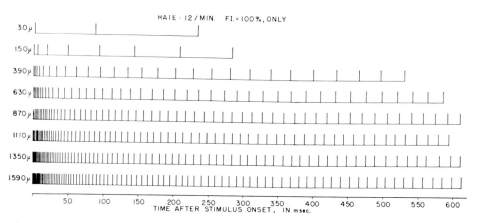

Figure 6-5. Graphical display of the averaged sequence of discharge intervals in 30 consecutive responses to skin stimuli at each of the intensities given to the left of each sequence. The responses were recorded from a single fiber in the radial nerve of a macaque, and the responses elicited by mechanical stimulation of the glabrous skin of the palm of the hand. For details of the analysis underlying this display, see legend to Figure 6-4. (Fig. 4, Werner, G., & Mountcastle, V. B., *J. Neurophysiol.,* 1965, **28**, 359) .

Additional studies were designed to determine whether individual components of the actually observed, total variability of responses could be singled out. The two components that were isolated will be designated as the "stimulus error" and the "time order error."

Stimulus Error

We noted from close inspection of the excursions of the stimulus probe that it did not consistently return to its starting position. This meant that the actual skin indentation was not always constant in a repetitive series of stimuli. To circumvent this, we determined the actual distance between initial and final position of the probe in each stimulus application. This was accomplished by an analogue-to-digital conversion of the electrical output from the stimulator's displacement indicator. It was then possible to calculate the mean response number, and its variability, elicited by *de facto* identical stimuli. The examples of results obtained in this manner are shown in the left panel of Figure 6-6 (units 6-5-13, 11-2-2, 6-4-7) and document that the "stimulus error," small as it was (10μ to 30μ), contributed

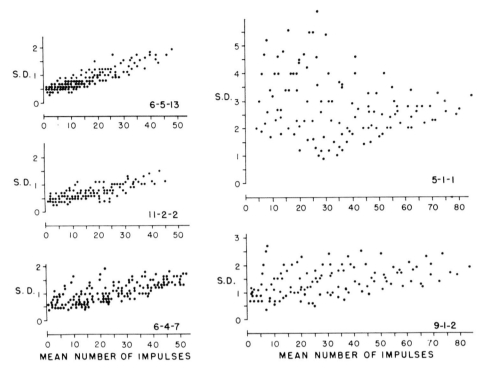

Figure 6-6. Graphs showing the relation between mean impulse number and variability for five mechanoreceptive fibers activated by brief stimuli delivered to their endings in the skin of the palm of the hand of a macaque. For each point the abscissa indicates the estimate of the mean number of impulses evoked by each of 30 to 50 stimuli, delivered at 3 sec intervals. In the right column of the figure (units 5-1-1 and 9-1-2), the responses were averaged for each set of stimuli with identical intensity setting of the tactile stimulator. The data points of the graph in the right column (units 6-5-13, 11-2-2, and 6-4-7) were obtained by measuring the actual displacement of the tip of the probe which was not always precisely identical with the nominal setting of the stimulator. The ordinate indicates the variability within each of the response populations. The reduction in the variability in the graphs of the right column as compared with those in the left is thought to be due to the "stimulus error," as described in the text.

markedly to the total response variability encountered in earlier experiments (Fig. 6-6, right panel).

The accurate estimation of the genuine response variability is of more than descriptive interest, for there is the possibility that the variability itself might be selected as the unit of measurement on the neural response continuum. A scale of this kind would fall under the category of what Stevens termed "confusion scale," and its implications will be discussed in the later section together with other derived analyses aimed at the quantitative appreciation of the discriminatory capacity in the tactile sensory system.

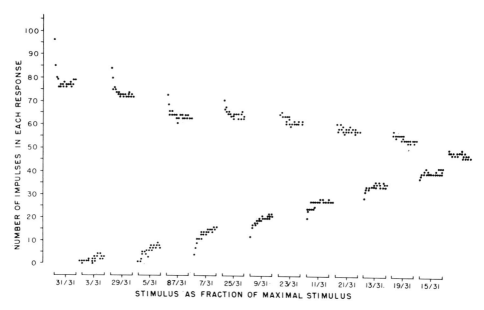

Figure 6-7. Graph showing the "time order error" (see text) Mechanical stimuli of relative intensities indicated along the abscissa are applied consecutively in the temporal order as depicted from left to right. The stimuli are applied at the rate of 12 per min, with the interval between stimuli identical within each train of equal intensity, and between the last stimulus of a preceding and the first of the next following intensity. The ordinate plots the number of impulses evoked in a single nerve fiber innervating a papillary ridge in the hand of a macaque.

Time Order Error

We have observed, as others have reported (Hunt and McIntyre, 1960) that when brief skin indentations are delivered more frequently, there occurs a regular decrease in the number of impulses per second for the first few stimuli of a series the diminution being greater the more frequent the stimuli are. Conversely, if stimuli of low intensity follow the series of strong stimuli, there is a gradual increase of the number of responses to the first few stimuli of the weaker series. Figure 6-7 depicts one characteristic example of the magnitude and time course of these changes which precede the leveling off to the relatively constant mean response number associated with different stimulus intensities. In this experiment the time interval between the last stimulus of the preceding intensity series and the first one in the next series of stimuli was 5 sec. The interval between the stimuli within each intensity series was also 5 sec. This "time error" is clearly present at stimulus rates as low as one every 5 sec and becomes more marked at shorter intervals between stimuli. We attribute this interaction between stimuli of different intensities largely to the slow time course of mechanical recovery of the indented skin. If the second stimulus is applied before the skin fully returns to its prestimulus position, a second identical movement of the stimulus probe will indent a lesser net distance from contact to end point than did the first.

The time order error has two immediate implications. First, its effect on quantitative stimulus-response studies may be minimized by applying stimuli of different intensities in a random sequence. In this way one would expect that the time order error cancels, at least partly. Second it reflects on the interpretation of the rate at which information can be transmitted and on stimulus discrimination in the tactile system. This aspect will be discussed in a later section of this paper.

STIMULUS-RESPONSE RELATIONS

Measurements of the stimulus-response relations were made in two ways. In what we term the "regular intensity series," trains of 30 to 50 stimuli of a given strength were delivered at intervals of 3 to 5 sec, and the responses recorded in a manner described in an earlier paper (Werner and Mountcastle, 1965). Subsequent series of stimuli of different intensities were then delivered, and so on until the physiological range of indentations (up to 800μ to 1500μ indentation) had been covered in a series of steps. Concern over the time order error made us also adopt a different strategy which we term the "random intensity series." In this, the intensity range was divided

TABLE 6-I

Fiber No.	O.T. msec	n	K	r	Fiber No.	O.T. msec	n	K	r	Fiber No.	O.T. msec	n	K	r
8-2	400	.387	1.56	.975	17-2	50	.666	.099	.949	24-3	20	.536	.171	.991
8-10	180	.603	.596	.996		100	.643	.190	.973		50	.479	1.00	.994
15-1	50	.718	.121	.995		250	.634	.354	.983		100	.499	1.44	.996
	100	.727	.184	.997	18-2	100	.988	.019	.993		250	.474	2.80	.997
	220	.801	429	.996		300	.967	.042	.998		500	.458	4.50	.996
15-2	50	.595	.635	.992		600	.929	.081	.998		750	.448	6.09	.995
	150	.546	1.64	.993	21-1	50	.897	.031	.985		1000	.444	7.00	.995
16-1	240	1.169	.006	.987		100	.899	.042	.986	25-1	20	.397	.588	.963
16-5	20	.459	.216	.976		200	.817	.102	.984		50	.400	.856	.973
	50	.561	.223	.998		350	.748	.218	.983		100	.404	1.31	.978
	100	.609	.251	.992	22-2B	450	.502	2.161	.985		250	.391	2.18	.973
	250	.587	.497	.988	23-2	400	.696	1.067	.949		400	.380	2.98	.975
	300	.588	.549	.989	26-3	500	.492	.664	.984		500	.378	3.42	.973
22-1	450	1.10	.163	.996	22-2a	450	.594	.200	.979	25-2	500	.269	10.3	.944
										26-2	500	.523	2.60	.976

in up to 31 steps and stimuli at the chosen intensity were delivered in a random order until about 30 of each had been given, using LINC to program the experiment. We have examined the results when total impulses were counted for successively longer periods of time after stimulus onset ("observation times" = OT), that is, the first 20, 50, 100 msec, etc.

We studied 21 mechanoreceptive fibers innervating Iggo's touch corpuscles, and 16 fibers activated from tactile stimuli to the palm of the macaque's hand in this way. The results with the former group of fibers are exemplified in Figures 6-8 and 6-9 with the data obtained from fiber 24-3, and summarized for 18 fibers in Table 6-I. These responses of fibers from the palm are illustrated with one characteristic example in Figure 6-10 and the data from all fibers in this category are displayed in Figure 6-11.

One characteristic difference between the two sets of results becomes

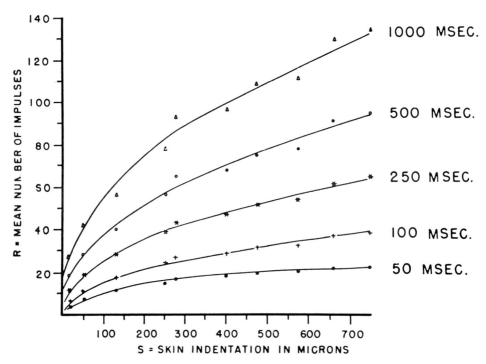

Figure 6-8. Stimulus-response relations for a mechanoreceptive fiber ending in an Iggo corpuscle of the skin of the inner side of the leg of a monkey. Single afferent fiber isolated for study by dissection of the saphenous nerve in the thigh. The fitted curves plot the S-R relation for a series of observation times, each of which begins with stimulus onset (all correlation coefficients of regression better than 0.991; all P < 0.005). Fiber 24.3. Thirty stimuli delivered at each intensity at repetition rate of one in 3 sec. Standard errors of the estimates of mean values varied from zero to 1.46 impulses. Skin temperature was steady at 34°C throughout (Fig. 9, Werner, G., & Mountcastle, V. B., *J. Neurophysiol.*, 1965, **28**, 359).

immediately apparent. The following can be seen from Figures 6-8 and 6-9, and Table 6-I: (a) the quantitative relation between stimulus and response number in the class of mechanoreceptive fibers innervating Iggo corpuscles can be identified as a power function of the general form $R = K \cdot S^n$ (R = response number, S = stimulus intensity, in microns) ; and (b) that the exponent n (i.e., the slope of the line fitted to the data points on log-log coordinates) is remarkably constant for each fiber when the response num-

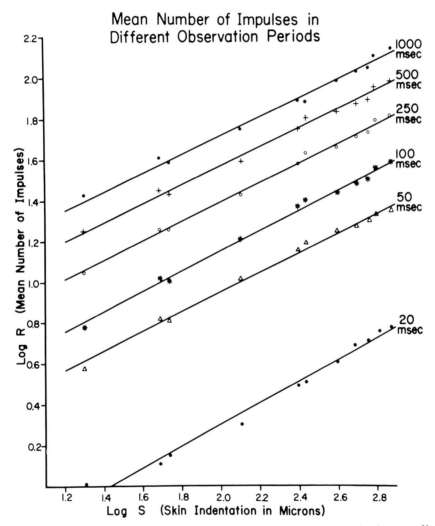

Figure 6-9. Re-plot of the data for fiber 24-3 given in Figure 6-8, on log-log coordinates with best fitting functions given as straight lines. The nearly parallel positions of the lines illustrates the near constancy of the value of the exponent n in the series of power functions; from below upward n = .536, .479, .499, .474, .458, .444 (Fig. 10, Werner, G. & Mountcastle, V. B., *J. Neurophysiol.*, 1965, 28, 359) .

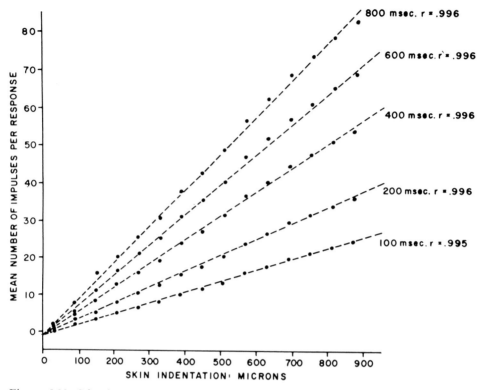

Figure 6-10. Stimulus-response relations for a mechanoreceptive fiber ending in a papillary ridge of the hand of a macaque. Single afferent fiber isolated in the radial nerve.
The fitted lines plot S-R relations for a series of observation times, each of which begins with stimulus onset. The correlation coefficients for the linear regression are shown
in the graph, to the right of the observation times. Thirty stimuli were delivered at each
intensity at a repetition rate of 6 per min.

ber is evaluated for different observation times. For fiber 24-3 this is reflected
in the nearly parallel position of the lines in Figure 6-9, and it can also be
seen from the numerical values of n determined for this and the seven other
fibers for which data at different OT's were evaluated (Table 6-I). For 16
of the 18 fibers studied, the values for n were less than 1 for 10 of them
less than 0.6. This indicates the negatively accelerating nature of the relation between stimulus and response for the large majority of the mechanoreceptive fibers of this class. The degree of this negative acceleration may
vary from fiber to fiber within considerable limits.

The results with fibers innervating tactile receptors in the distal glabrous skin of the macaque's hand were quite different. For them, the relation
between mean response number and skin indentation (in microns) was
accurately described by a linear function, with the slope for each fiber vary-

ing with the OT chosen (Fig. 6-10). The slopes also differed from fiber to fiber at equal OT's (Fig. 6-11). If one transforms the measures of stimulus intensity and response to their logarithmic values, it also becomes possible to express the stimulus response relation for this group of fibers as a power function, but this time with $n = 1$. This permits a more direct categorization of the two classes of fibers, depending on whether n is smaller than, or equal to one.

Regularity of Discharge Sequence in the Early Steady State

The logarithmic transformation of the coordinate axis converts the family of diverging stimulus response functions of Figure 6-10 in parallel lines similar to those depicted in Figure 6-9, except for the difference in slope. The implication is that, for fibers innervating Iggo corpuscles and tactile receptors in the glabrous skin, the exponent of the power function is practically invariant with respect to the OT, within the limits of the brief stimuli chosen for this study. If the slopes in the logarithmic display were exactly identical for any two observation times, t_1 and t_2, it follows from the power law that the number of discharges, R_{t_1} and R_{t_2}, evoked by a certain stimulus intensity and occurring within the two counting periods, would be linearly related. Departure from identity of the two exponents n_1 and n_2 of the power functions would result in a nonlinear relation between R_{t_1} and R_{t_2} according to

$$R_{t_2} = K_{t_2} \left(\frac{1}{K_{t_1}} \cdot R_{t_1} \right)^{\frac{n_2}{n_1}}$$

where K_{t_1} and K_{t_2} are constant for the power functions at t_1 and t_2 respectively. The relative constancy of the exponent n for the stimulus relationship measured for sequentially longer observation times gives, therefore, additional support for the statement, given in a preceding section, that there exists an early and very stable steady state in the response to stimuli of relatively brief duration.

DISCRIMINATION OF STIMULUS INTENSITY

Efforts to quantitate the intensity of sensory experiences in humans have led to various types of scales designed to show how sensation grows as a function of stimulus intensity. Amongst those most widely used are the scales which are based on the observer's ability to discriminate stimuli of different intensities. This approach led, at first, to the formulation of Weber's law, that the size of the discriminable stimulus increment at different levels of stimulus intensity is a constant fraction of that intensity $(\Delta s / s = C)$. While it is now established that Weber's law does not reflect

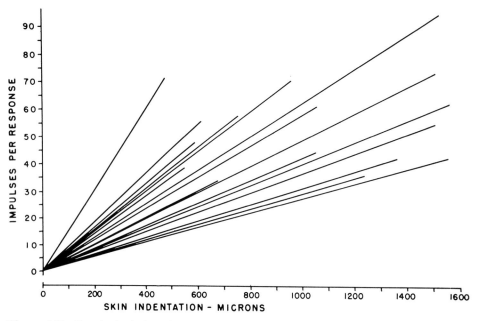

Figure 6-11. Graph depicting the stimulus-response relations for 16 afferent fibers, isolated from the radial nerve and ending in the glabrous skin of the palm of the hand of the macaque. The correlation coefficients of the linear regression between skin indentation (in microns) and the mean response numbers vary for the 16 fibers between 0.975 and 0.996.

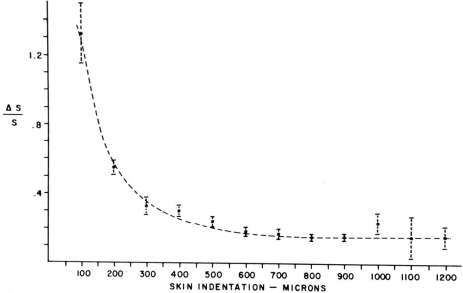

Figure 6-12. Graph of the Weber Function $\triangle S/S = f(S)$, calculated from the stimulus-response relations of 10 mechanoreceptive fibers ending in the skin of the palm of the hand in the macaque. The least discriminable response increment is assumed to be $R = 5$ impulses per response at any stimulus intensity. The data points in the graph are the means at each stimulus intensity; the vertical bars delineate a confidence region, three standard errors wide.

accurately the discriminating capacity of humans for tactile stimuli it is, nevertheless, always possible to determine experimentally the actual functional relation $\Delta s/s = f(s)$ (Weber function). We thought it of interest to derive from the experimentally determined stimulus-response relations various types of Weber functions for neural activity by selecting certain assumptions for the manner in which the nervous system might detect and measure just noticeable stimulus differences.

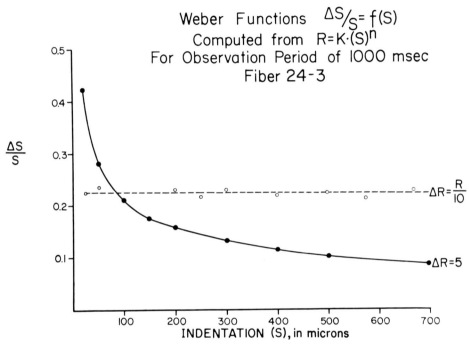

Figure 6-13. Graph of the two Weber functions $\Delta S/S = f$ (S) computed for the mechanoreceptor fiber 24-3 on the basis of the stimulus-response relationship determined at the observation time 1,000 msec (see Table 6-1): $R = 7.004 \times (S)^{.444}$. The solid points connected by the curve were obtained by assuming that the least discriminable response increment ΔR is 5 impulses/response, at any stimulus intensity. The open circles connected by the dashed line were obtained by assuming that ΔR is a constant fraction (i.e., 1/10) of the response at any stimulus intensity (Fig. 18, Werner, G. & Mountcastle, V. B., *J. Neurophysiol.*, 1965, **28**, 359).

First, we assumed that the critical neural response increment $(\triangle R)$ for "recognition" of a stimulus increment is a constant number of impulses, equal at any level for any comparison stimulus (S). Figure 6-12 shows the shape of the Weber function, averaged for 10 tactile fibers innervating the palm of the hand. It was assumed, in this case, that a discriminable response increment was $\triangle R = 5$ impulses per response. At stronger stimulus intensities this theoretical Weber function for neural discrimination is parallel

to the abscissa, and it departs from it at weaker stimuli, both being characteristic for the Weber function of tactile sensation in humans (Geldard,
1953).

This resemblance contrasts sharply with the Weber functions computed
from the stimulus-response curves of the same and other tactile fibers as well,
but assuming this time that the critical neural response increment is a
constant fraction of the response R elicited by the comparison stimulus (Fig.
6-13). This result might support the suggestion that stimulus discrimination
by the central nervous system of man may be based on equal increments of
neural activity rather than fractional increases in order to generate the type
of Weber functions established for him in psychophysical measurements.

Theoretical and experimental investigations in recent years have focused
on a signal detection model for stimulus discrimination (Barlow, 1957;
Swets, 1964; Treisman, 1964). The underlying concept is that when an
identical stimulus (S_1) is applied a certain number of times, it evokes
neural responses with a mean R_1 and a variance $\sigma_{R_1}^2$. A decision criterion
would be adopted such that, on application of stimuli S_1 and S_2, $(S_2 > S_1)$,
a false identification of the response R_1 and R_2 with their respective stimuli
would not occur in more than a certain, limiting proportion of the number
of stimulus repetitions. One of the possible decision criteria could be
satisfied by the relation $K = R_1 + k\sigma_{R_1}$ (k = decision criterion determined
by the acceptable probability of false stimulus identification; R_1 = mean
response number for stimulus S_1; σ_{R_1} = standard deviation of R_1). The implication is that the relation between $\triangle S = S_2 - S_1$ and S_1 can be interpreted
in terms of the stimulus-response relationship $R = f(s)$, and of the variability of R at different mean response levels. Assuming that this variability of
R is attributable to the occurrence of independent and randomly occurring
events, one would expect that $\triangle S \propto S^{1/2}$. On the basis of the experimental
data with the primary afferents from tactile receptors it is now possible to
test and reject this particular hypothesis. Figure 6-14 documents, for one
fiber, the departure of the relation between $\sqrt{S}$ and $\triangle S$ from the postulated
linearity, if the decision criterion is assumed to be $K = \overline{R}_1 + 2\sigma_{R_1}$. Similar
results were obtained for other fibers examined, and other multiples or
fractions of σ_{R_1} chosen.

This failure to conform with the theoretically predicted linear relation
between $\sqrt{S}$ and $\triangle S$ may be due to inapplicability of the assumption of
randomness, the failure of the Neyman-Pearson criterion to reflect the decision
process used by the nervous system or to the inapplicability of the decision
model in the first place. However, experiments with a large variety of stimulus situations have shown the usefulness of the latter in psychophysical
tests and, in at least one case, it yielded apparently meaningful results if

applied to the discrimination on the basis of the neural activity elicited in a central, sensory relay nucleus (Werner and Mountcastle, 1963). Moreover, detection and discrimination of visual stimuli in humans fulfill the condition of proportionality between $\sqrt{S}$ and $\triangle S$, at least in a certain range of stimulus parameters (Barlow, 1957; Treisman, 1964). This raises the question whether one of the most striking differences between peripheral and central nervous system, namely the increased variability of spontaneous and evoked activity and the convergence of afferent pathways in the latter, might not be the prerequisite for the applicability of the decision theoretical concepts, at least as a heuristic tool. For the response in cutaneous fibers from tactile receptors, the balance of evidence clearly favors the simpler

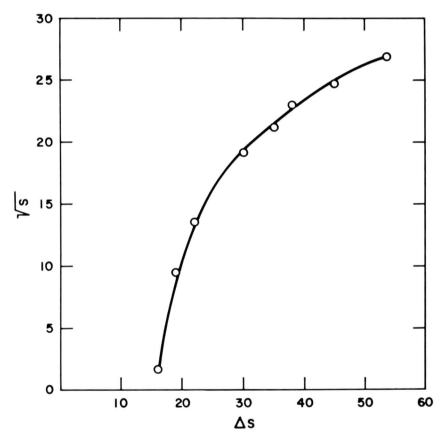

Figure 6-14. Graph depicting the relation between the least discriminable stimulus increment and the square root of the comparison stimulus. The discriminable stimulus increment is computed from the stimulus-response relation R = 0.05 x S, assuming that responses to stimuli of different intensities are discriminated on the basis of a statistical decision criterion of K = R + $2\sigma_R$. The variability of the responses to stimuli of identical intensity was determined after correction for the "stimulus error" (see text).

assumption of a constant additive response increment as the criterion for "recognition" of stimulus differences, at least among those few parsimonious assumptions tested.

CAPACITY OF AFFERENT TOUCH FIBERS
TO TRANSMIT INFORMATION

The idea of measuring in informational terms the accuracy of stimulus identification was introduced into psychophysics by Garner and Hake (1951) and Miller (1956). This approach has significant advantages, notably for quantitative comparisons of the sensory capacity in psychophysical tests with that studied in sensory neural systems, for it circumvents largely the problems posed by the stimulus and response metrics. In dealing with information transmission, we need not be metric in any sense, but merely employ a method of stimulus and response classification. This is of importance because, first, sensation magnitudes cannot presently be equated with any one specific measure of neural activity and, second, because of the inherent uncertainty as to the proper stimulus metric. In analogy to the more general considerations for information transmission between a source and a receiver, we have applied informational analysis to the stimulus-evoked activity in afferent mechanoreceptive fibers with the intention of comparing their information-transmitting capacity with that of humans measured in psychophysical tests for various modalities of sensation. The methods of applying the tactile stimuli in a random order as regards intensity, the collection of data and the considerations underlying the computation of the information transmitting capacity have been described earlier (Werner and Mountcastle, 1965).

In the subsequent graphs which depict our results, we plot on the abscissa the stimulus uncertainty. Its value depends on the number of discrete and equal intensity steps into which the stimulus continuum was divided, and on the relative frequency with which stimuli of each intensity occur in the total number of stimuli used, usually 600 to 1000. The ordinate plots the computed information transmission (in bits) for different values of stimulus uncertainty. For the computation of the latter we grouped the evoked neural responses according to the number of discharges in the given OT. In the analysis to be described we chose categories of two impulses each.

Figure 6-15 displays the calculated points for information transmission for a tactile fiber innervating an Iggo corpuscle. Information transmission remains in the order of one bit when only the first 20 msec of the responses are considered but increases conspicuously when OT is lengthened to 100 msec, and somewhat more to 400 msec. There is little further increase when the OT is lengthened to 500 msec. Different fibers behaved somewhat

differently in this respect, but common to all fibers of this class is the fact
that information transmission is low if only the response during the first
20 to 50 msec are considered, and that it reaches a maximum of 2.7 bits
(average of 14 fibers) when the impulses during the first few hundred msec
of the responses are considered. Therefore, maximal information transmission is attained when the OT's fall within that period of the responses
which we have defined as the early steady state.

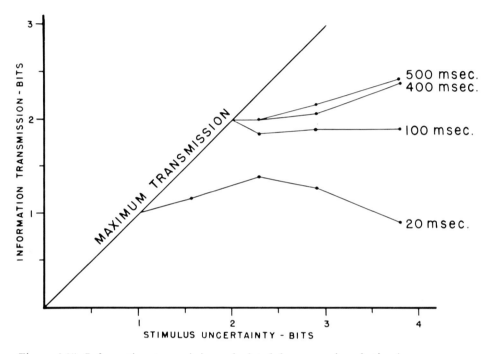

Figure 6-15. Information transmission calculated from a series of stimulus-response ma-
trice constructed for a mechanoreceptive fiber, for a series of successively longer observation times. Transmission increases very little beyond 400 msec of observation. Stimulus duration for this fiber 500 msec.

Maximum information transmission is somewhat higher in tactile fibers
innervating the palm of the hand. In 17 fibers of this group it reached a
value of 3 bits (on the average) for 500 msec OT and when the stimuli were
applied at the rate of six or twelve per minute (Fig. 6-16). The implication
is that inspection of the evoked-response number would permit one to
identify unequivocally, and without the use of comparison stimuli and a
metric scale, no more than $2^3 = 8$ discrete stimulus intensities although the
stimulus continuum was presented in as many as 32 discrete steps of equal
increments. For Iggo fibers the number of equivocally recognizable stimulus
intensities is slightly lower, between six and seven.

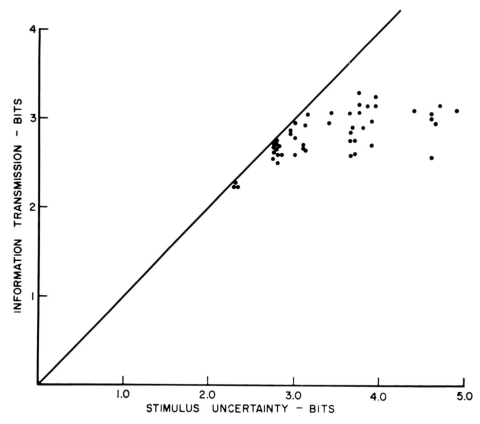

Figure 6-16. Information transmission calculated from a series of stimulus-response data obtained for each of 17 mechanoreceptive fibers ending in the palm of the hand (macaque). The stimuli were applied at a rate of 6 or 12 per min; observation times were 500 msec or longer, but not exceeding 1 sec.

There is a remarkable similarity between these results and the information transmitting capacities of humans determined by the method of absolute judgments. In a variety of sense continua the human capacity as regards stimulus intensity is between 2 and 3 bits of information (Miller, 1956). This suggests, that in principle, at least, the required information for the sensory judgment of intensity could be provided by a single afferent fiber.

In the context of characterizing the information handling capacity of a certain system the question also arises at what rate information can effectively be transmitted. In view of the time order error discussed earlier, this question assumes particular pertinence for the tactile system. Therefore, experiments were undertaken to apply sets of stimuli of identical stimulus uncertainty at different stimulus rates. Figure 6-17 summarizes the result

which is characteristic for all fibers studied in this regard. At a stimulus uncertainty of 3.75 bits, information transmission by this fiber from the palm
of the hand was 3.25 bits when the stimuli were applied once every 2 or 5
sec. It fell steeply to 2.6 and, even further, to 2.2 bits when the stimuli were
applied at shorter intervals (once every second, and twice a second, respectively). We believe that this fall of information transmission at high
stimulus rates reflects the failure of the skin at the site of stimulation to
return to its original distance from the stimulus probe, due to slowness of
mechanical "recovery" from the preceding indentation.

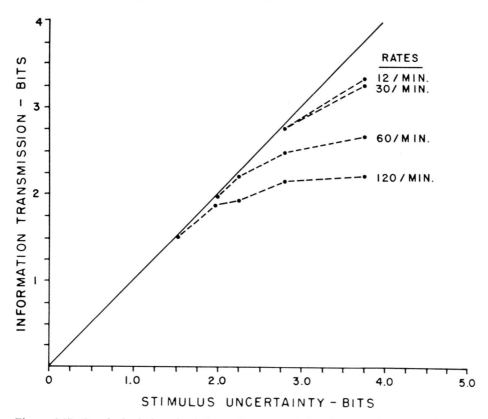

Figure 6-17. Graph depicting the information transmission in a mechanoreceptive fiber
from the palm of the hand (macaque), at different rates of stimulation. Observation
time: 200 msec.

CONCLUSIONS

Using mechanical deformation of the skin of controlled degree, the responses to relatively brief stimuli (less than one second) were studied in
detail for two classes of tactile fibers, those innervating Iggo corpuscles, and
those innervating tactile receptors in the glabrous skin of the hand. After

an early onset transient discharge which, at the rate of displacement used, is principally a function of the degree of skin indentation, the discharge continues in a highly periodic fashion during a period of time beginning at about 100 msec and lasting for about 400 to 600 msec after stimulus onset. We designate this period as the "early steady state."

The relation between stimulus and response is described with a high degree of statistical validity by a power function of the general form $R = K \cdot S^n$. Exponents are commonly less than one for tactile fibers of Iggo corpuscles and are equal to one for the fibers originating in the glabrous skin of the hand.

Certain aspects of the stimulus-response relation were explored in an effort to seek correlations between these physiological results and those of psychophysical studies in man. It was found that Weber functions resembling those for touch in man were obtained on the assumption that the detected difference in the neural responses is an absolute increase in the number of nerve impulses over the entire stimulus response continuum.

At low rates of stimulation, information transmission for stimuli of brief duration reaches a maximum of 3 bits in tactile fibers from the glabrous skin, and of 2.7 bits in the fibers from Iggo receptors. The information transmitted reaches its peak coincidentally with the early steady state period of the response and is of the same magnitude as that of human absolute judgments for various intensive stimulus continua. The rate with which information can be transmitted is thought to be limited by the slow time course of mechanical recovery of the skin after indentation. The results support the idea that the limiting link in the information transmission across the skin is at the level of the first order fibers and resides partly in the mechanical properties of the skin while central neural pathways preserve all or nearly all they receive as regards to intensity. On the other hand, it is thought that other aspects of the stimuli such as locus, contour and size of the stimulated peripheral field are more appropriately attributed to the spatial and temporal profile of activity in populations of neurons.

REFERENCES

Barlow, H. B. Increment thresholds at low intensities considered as signal/noise discriminations. *J. Physiol. (London)*, 1957, **136**, 469.

Boring, E. G. An operational restatement of G. E. Mueller's psychophysical axioms. *Psychol. Rev.*, 1941, **48**, 457.

Cauna, N. Nature and functions of the papillary ridges of the digital skin. *Anat. Rec.*, 1954, **119**, 449.

Cauna, N. Functional significance of the submicroscopical, histochemical, and microscopical organization of the cutaneous receptor organs. *Verh. Anat. Ges.*, 1962, **111**, 181.

Franke, E. K. Mechanical impedance of the surface of the human body. *J. Appl. Physiol.*, 1951, **3**, 582.

Garner, W. R., & Hake, H. W. The amount of information in absolute judgments. *Psychol. Rev.*, 1951, **58**, 446.

Geldard, F. A. *The Human Senses.* New York: Wiley, 1953.

Hunt, C. C., & McIntyre, A. K. Properties of cutaneous touch receptors in cat. *J. Physiol. (London)*, 1960, **153**, 88.

Iggo, A. New specific sensory structures in hairy skin. *Acta Neuroveg. (Wien)*, 1963, **24**, 175. (a)

Iggo, A. An electrophysiological analysis of afferent fibers in primate skin. *Acta Neuroveg. (Wien)*, 1963, **24**, 225. (b)

Iggo, A., & Muir, A. R. A cutaneous sense organ in the hairy skin of cats. *J. Anat.*, 1963, **97**, 151.

Katz, D. *Der Aufbau der Tastwelt.* Leipzig: Barth, 1925.

Lindblom, U. Properties of touch receptors in distal glabrous skin of the monkey. *J. Neurophysiol.*, 1965, **28**, 966.

Maruhashi, J., Mizuguchi, K., & Tasaki, I. Action currents in single afferent nerve fibers elicited by stimulation of the skin of the toad and the cat. *J. Physiol. (London)*, 1952, **117**, 129.

Miller, G. A. The magical number seven, plus or minus two. *Psychol. Rev.*, 1956, **63**, 81.

Renquist, Y. Das Messen auf dem Gebiete der Propriozeptic und Beruehrungsempfindung. *Ergebn. Physiol.*, 1933, **35**, 827.

Swets, J. A. (Ed.) *Signal Detection and Recognition by Human Observers.* New York: Wiley, 1964.

Tapper, D. N. Cutaneous slowly adapting mechanoreceptors in the cat. *Science*, 1964, **143**, 53.

Tapper, D. N. Stimulus-response relationships in cutaneous slowly adapting mechanoreceptor in hairy skin of the cat. *Exp. Neurol.*, 1965, **13**, 364.

Treisman, M. The discrimination of brightness and other dimensions. *Psychol. Rev.*, 1964, **71**, 314.

Werner, G., & Mountcastle, V. B. The variability of central neural activity in a sensory system, and its implications for the central reflection of sensory events. *J. Neurophysiol.*, 1963, **26**, 958.

Werner, G., & Mountcastle, V. B. Neural activity in mechanoreceptive cutaneous afferents: Stimulus-response relations, Weber functions and information transmission. *J. Neurophysiol.*, 1965, **28**, 359.

Witt, I., & Hensel, H. Afferente Impulse aus der Extremitätenhaut der Katze bei thermischer und mechanischer Reizung. *Pflüger Arch. Ges. Physiol.*, 1959, **268**, 582.

DISCUSSION

DR. R. H. GIBSON: Why do you choose mechanical, rather than neural, factors in the skin as your explanation of why information rates fall off with increasing rates of stimulation?

DR. WERNER: It seems the most plausible. I could not possibly exclude the basic uncertainty, which Dr. Hardy has brought up earlier, concerning tissue mechanics involved in mechanical stimulation of nerve terminals.

DR. GIBSON: You were watching these tissues, for example, under a stroboscope or something of that sort?

DR. WERNER: Yes, and you see that the residual indentation remains for some time after the probe is withdrawn. It seems the most obvious explanation.

DR. E. G. EIJKMAN: I think you have said that $\triangle S$ should vary as the root of S in applying the decision theory.

DR. WERNER: That is right, assuming randomness.

DR. EIJKMAN: I do not think that this is necessary. Decision theory does not predict how the neural activity changes with the signal.

DR. WERNER: I agree, but in the one particular form in which decision theory was applied, the independence assumption of randomness was made, and this requires $\triangle S$ to vary as the square root of S. It is not the decision theory was applied, the independent assumption of randomness was made, instance.

Chapter 7

A DUPLEX MECHANISM OF
MECHANORECEPTION*

Ronald T. Verrillo

IN THIS PAPER I SHALL ATTEMPT to demonstrate that at least two functionally distinct systems of nerve endings are involved in the reception of mechanical disturbances delivered to the skin. One of these systems is able to summate energy over time and space; the other system lacks this property. Implicit in this statement is the notion that neural endings exist in cutaneous tissue that are responsive to specific forms of physical energy.

The doctrine of specific nerve energies and its counterpart of modality specific nerve endings is still attended by considerable controversy. I shall not detail the history of that dialogue, since several scholarly surveys, as well as firm statements of position, have been documented (Geldard, 1940a; Melzack and Wall, 1962; Sinclair, 1955). Briefly stated, the classical position maintains that each sensory modality is mediated by a specialized, often encapsulated, receptor (von Frey, 1895). The dissenters from this position favor pattern theories in which complex spatial and temporal arrangements of impulses signal the "specific" sensation (Nafe, 1934; Sinclair, 1955; Weddell, 1955). Melzack and Wall (1962) have attempted a rapprochement between the two points of view by proposing that nonspecific fibers carry impulses encoded by specialized receptors.

The research reported in this paper has been carried out to investigate the effect of a variety of spatial and temporal stimulus patterns upon the threshold of vibration in humans. The results indicate that cutaneous tissue is host to a nerve ending specifically responsive to rapid, repetitive mechanical events.

APPARATUS AND METHOD

Two types of signal were used: sine waves and short mechanical pulses. In those experiments using sinusoidal signals, an electronic switch modulated the output of a sine wave generator so that the signal was on for 1 sec and off for 1 sec with a rise-fall time of 100 msec. The signal was preamplified and passed through a Békésy recording attenuator. After the final stage of amplification the signal was fed into the vibrator which was located within a sound-proofed booth.

*This work has been supported by contracts between the U. S. Office of Naval Research, the National Institutes of Health, U. S. Department of Health, Education and Welfare, and Syracuse University.

In those experiments involving mechanical pulses, three waveform generators and a pulse generator were used to produce a 1.0 msec rectangular pulse. The voltage pulses were passed through a manual attenuator and power amplifier before activating the vibrator. The response of the vibrator was a highly damped oscillation with a width of 1.0 msec and a 1.0 msec rise time.

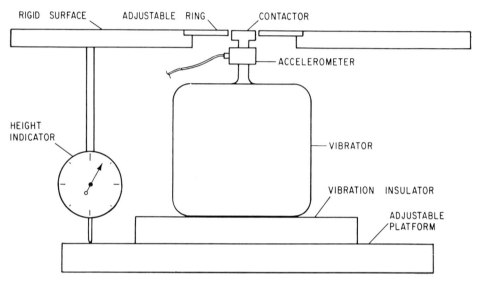

Figure 7-1. Diagram of the vibrator assembly (Fig. 1, Verrillo, R. T., *J. Exp. Psychol.*, 1966, **71**, 570).

The vibrator was mounted on the moveable platen of a drill press assembly (Fig. 7-1). This adjustable system was located so that the contactor protruded up into a hole in the rigid surface upon which the subject placed his hand, arm or tongue. The height of the vibrator could be adjusted to within 1/1000 of an inch. To insure that contact was maintained during stimulation the vibrator was raised 0.5 mm above minimum contact with the skin. By using a circuit consisting of a battery, the subject, the contactor and an oscilloscope, it was established that there was no loss of contact under the experimental conditions. Gluing contactors (0.02 and 2.9 cm²) to the skin did not produce any difference from those thresholds obtained with unglued contactors. The entire vibrator assembly and the subject were located within a booth in order to provide isolation from vibrations in the building. The subject wore earmuffs or earphones with a narrow-band noise centered at 250 Hz to mask the sounds from the vibrator which became audible at frequencies above 250 Hz.

Accurate measurement of the stimulus at the time of stimulation was accomplished by mounting a center-hole accelerometer directly on the moving element of the vibrator. Acceleration voltage readings were transformed to displacement in microns and then converted to decibels referred to 1 micron of peak displacement.* The accelerometer was calibrated against another accelerometer which serves as a laboratory standard. In addition, the accelerometer has been calibrated by direct measurement with a microscope (120×) under stroboscopic illumination. Measurements were obtained at four frequencies (40, 80, 160 and 320 Hz) under conditions of an unloaded contactor and with the subject's hand on the contactor using two sizes of contactor (.005 and 2.9 cm²). Direct measurements were consistent under all conditions and they agreed with the readings obtained through the accelerometer.

The contactors could be changed without disturbing this arrangement. The size of the free surround between the contactor and the rigid surface was kept constant at 1 mm by a series of interchangeable rings (see Fig. 7-1). This small gap served to confine the stimulation to the area of the contactor by preventing the spread of the disturbance along the surface of the skin (Eijkman and Vendrick, 1960). The reader is referred to previous publications for more detailed descriptions of the apparatus involved in the different experiments (Verrillo, 1963; 1965; 1966b).

ANATOMICAL SCHEMA

In order to provide the anatomical framework within which interpretations of the data are made, I shall begin by presenting in broad detail the neural innervation of skin. The schema follows, in essence, the outlines laid down by Winkelmann (1960), Cauna (1962) and Miller, Ralston, and Kasahara (1960).

Skin is classified into four basic types: glabrous, hairy, mucocutaneous, and mucous. Only the first three types will be considered in this paper. The nerve endings found in association with these skin types have been described as follows:

Glabrous skin
1. Dermal nerve network and its terminations.
2. Meissner corpuscles.
3. Pacinian corpuscles.
4. Merkel or hederiform endings.

Hairy skin
1. Dermal nerve network and its terminations.
2. Hair-follicle network.
3. Pacinian corpuscle.

*All thresholds in the present chapter are referred to 1 micron of zero-to-peak displacement. Previous publications by the author indicate a reference level of 1 micron RMS. This should have read RE 1 micron peak. The adjustment does not alter the slopes of the curves.

Mucocutaneous skin
1. Dermal nerve network and its terminations.
2. Mucocutaneous end-organ.

Some of you may object to the omission of Merkel disks in hairy skin. Winkelmann (1960) limits their distribution to glabrous skin; Cauna (1962) finds them also in hairy skin and Weddell, Pallie, and Palmer (1954) regard them as artifacts. I have adopted Winkelmann's position in order to keep the argument simple.

RESULTS

Frequency-Intensity Function and Spatial Summation

There are several consistent features of the frequency-intensity functions reported in the literature on vibratory sensitivity. Most striking is the difference in the shape of the function depending upon the size of the stimulating contactor. Those studies in which extremely small contactors were used yield threshold curves that are independent of frequency (Geldard, 1940b; Sherrick, 1960). On the other hand, a very pronounced frequency effect is produced when relatively large contactors are used to vibrate the skin (Békésy, 1939; Gilmer, 1955; Hugony, 1935; Knudsen, 1928; Setzepfand, 1935; Sherrick, 1953; Verrillo, 1962). It then appears that there is a very specific response on the skin to changes in stimulus frequency.

Another interesting feature of these data is the overall shape of the curve when thresholds are obtained with the larger contactors. In general, these curves are U-shaped and have a maximum of sensitivity in the region of 250 Hz. In the lower frequencies, however, the curves show a definite flattening (Békésy, 1939). As frequency increases, a pronounced break in the curves occurs in the region of 20 to 40 Hz. There is an apparent sudden increase in sensitivity from this region up to approximately 250 Hz. Békésy (1939) commented on this break in the threshold curve and suggested that two different processes may be involved. The slope of the curve in the frequency sensitive region is, in part, due to temporal summation. It has been shown that where temporal summation is found, there must be a dependence upon frequency (Zwislocki, 1960). Temporal summation will be discussed separately in the following section.

In order to investigate more thoroughly the interaction of temporal and spatial effects, a graduated series of seven contactors was tested at seven frequencies ranging from 25 to 640 Hz. The site of stimulation was on the fleshy pad (palmar) over the first metacarpal of the right hand. The results, plotted as a function of frequency, are shown in Figure 7-2. It is obvious that we are observing two distinct modes of response; one in which the receptor system is sensitive to changes in frequency, and another that is independent of frequency. The point at which the frequency-dependent system determines the shape of the curve is a function of the contactor size. For very small contactors the entire function is determined by those receptors not affected by frequency changes.

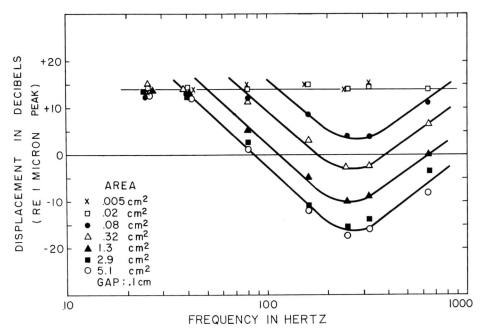

Figure 7-2. Vibrotactile thresholds as a function of frequency of vibration. The two modes of response are shown by the flat curve drawn through the data for the smallest contactors (.005 and .02 cm²) and the U-shaped curves described by the data of the larger contactors (Fig. 7, Verrillo, R. T., *J. Acoust. Soc. Amer.*, 1966, **35**, 1962).

The same data are replotted in Figure 7-3 as a function of contactor area. Again, the interaction of frequency and size is apparent. At frequencies higher than 40 Hz the slope of the curves is −3 dB per doubling of the contactor area indicating that a summation of energy is taking place over the area of the contactor. This result is consistent with comparable data for visual responses (Graham, Brown, and Mote, 1939; Weinstein and Arnulf, 1946) and for audition (Zwicker, Flottorp, and Stevens, 1957). There is no summation, however, at the two lowest frequencies (25 and 40 Hz). In addition, the area at which summation begins to become apparent is clearly a function of the frequency.

It is obvious that the data reflect two distinct modes of neural response. This can be explained by a single receptor system behaving in two different ways or by several systems, each functioning with its own characteristics. I think that the latter is a more reasonable position; that there exists in skin a duplex mechanism for mechanoreception. In order to narrow the number of possible anatomical structures involved, the same experiments were repeated on hairy skin which lacks Meissner corpuscles and Merkel disks. Testing was done on the volar surface of the forearm about 8 cm distal to the elbow. The results are essentially the same. Small contactors and low frequencies show no summation of energy, while the slopes of the curves where summation does occur are identical to those found in glabrous skin. It is obvious that neither the Meissner corpuscle nor the Merkel disk is involved in the summation of energy over space and time.

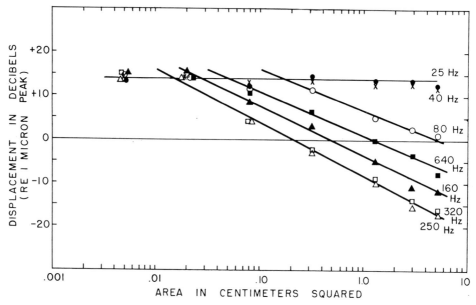

Figure 7-3. Vibrotactile thresholds as a function of contactor area. Spatial summation is clearly indicated by the -3 dB slopes of the curves at frequencies above 40 Hz. Summation does not occur at 25 and 40 Hz (Fig. 6, Verrillo, R. T., *J. Acoust. Soc. Amer.*, 1963, 35, 1962).

In Figure 7-4 the same contactor size is compared for hairy and glabrous skin. The upward shift in absolute threshold for hairy skin may be attributed to a difference in neural innervation. Another interesting feature of this comparison is that frequency at which the dependence upon frequency becomes effective. In glabrous skin the sensitivity to frequency starts in the vicinity of 50 Hz while in hairy skin the transition occurs at about 90 Hz. These differences are maintained when other contactor sizes are compared. This shift in the transition frequency suggests that there is a difference in the proportion of frequency dependent and frequency independent endings in hairy and glabrous skin.

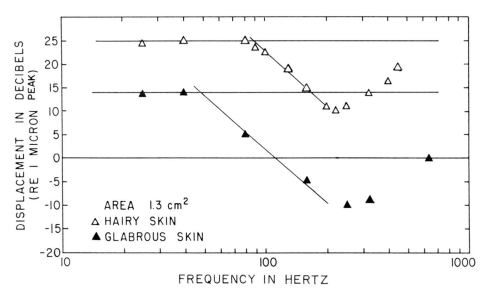

Figure 7-4. Comparison of vibrotactile thresholds measured on hairy and glabrous skin for a contactor 1.3 cm². The horizontal lines drawn through 14 and 25 dB represent the curves obtained using a contactor area of .02 cm². The two modes of response occur in both hairy and glabrous skin (Fig. 3, Verrillo, R. T., *J. Exp. Psychol.,* 1966, **72,** 47).

The process of elimination has left us with the choice of dermal nerve net endings or the Pacinian corpuscle as the receptor whose response is dependent upon frequency and area. (The hair follicle network is obviously eliminated by the U-shaped curves found on glabrous skin). The tongue (mucocutaneous tissue) is an ideal site for the next experiments since it contains the dermal nerve network and mucocutaneous endings, but the dorsal surface is devoid of Pacinian corpuscles. The mucocutaneous ending may be ruled out as it is not found in glabrous or hairy skin where frequency dependency is present.

Thresholds were determined on the dorsal surface of the tongue immediately posterior to the tip. The frequency functions obtained from the tongue and the hand for a single contactor size (1.3 cm²) are compared in Figure 7-5. It is quite obvious that there is no summation of energy in tissue which is lacking in Pacinian corpuscles. The endings of the dermal nerve network can be eliminated as a possible frequency follower since the curve for the tongue is flat.

The flat function for the tongue, shown in Figure 7-5, is at variance with the U-shaped curve obtained on the tongue by Sherrick (1953). A difference in the apparatus used in the two experiments may be shown to explain the different results. In these experiments the extent of free skin surrounding the vibrating contactor was limited to 1.0 mm by a fixed disk. Sherrick did not use such a disk to prevent the spread of the disturbance to other parts of the tongue. The principal nerves and blood vessels of the tongue run deep and toward the ventral surface and Pacinian corpuscles are reportedly found in close association to all major nerves and blood vessels (Winkelmann, 1960). The frequency function observed by Sherrick may have been due to corpuscles located in tissues near the undersurface of the tongue. This hypothesis is strengthened by the work of Spassova (1965) who founud many Golgi-Mazzoni bodies deep in the musculature and along nerve bundles in the tongue of the cat. The Golgi-Mazzoni corpuscles are regarded by Winkelmann and others at Pacinian corpuscles (Winkelmann, 1960). Spassova observed only mucocutaneous end-organs in the dorsal tissues. To test this hypothesis, Sherrick's experiment was repeated. Thresholds were determined on the dorsal surface of the tongue with no limiting disk. The resulting U-shaped curve verified Sherrick's results. If this result is in fact due to the spread of the vibratory disturbance over the tongue, thresholds obtained on the ventral surface should also produce a U function.

Thresholds were determined on the underside of the tongue using the rigid surround to prevent the spread of vibration. The results (Fig. 7-6) are very similar to those obtained on the dorsum when conditions permit

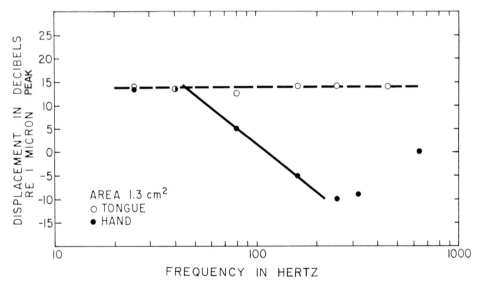

Figure 7-5. Comparison of thresholds obtained on the tongue and on the hand for a contactor 1.3 cm². The data for the tongue show no effect of frequency; they resemble the data obtained with the smallest contactors on the hand shown in Figure 7-2 (Fig. 1, Verrillo, R. T., *Perception Psychophys.*, 1966, **1**, 149).

the disturbance to spread beyond the intended locus of stimulation. The vibrotactile threshold is independent of frequency when the stimulus is confined to an area which does not contain Pacinian corpuscles.

The contention that the Pacinian corpuscle is the receptor responsible for summation is further demonstrated in Figure 7-7 in which absolute thresholds for the tongue and the hand are plotted as a function of area. The spatial summation observed on hairy and glabrous skin is absent in the responses determined on the tongue. The Pacinian corpuscle emerges as the most likely receptor responsible for frequency sensitivity and spatial summation in cutaneous tissue.

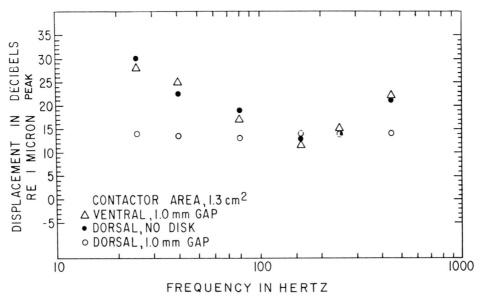

Figure 7-6. Comparison of measurements taken on the tongue with the limiting disk (1.0 mm gap) and without the disk (free surround) (Fig. 2, Verrillo, R. T., *Perception Psychophys.*, 1966, **1**, 149).

Temporal Summation

The next test of the hypothesis of a duplex mechanism is concerned with the time domain of the stimulus. The guide lines for these experiments were determined by Zwislocki's (1960) theory of temporal summation. This theory is a general mathematical model which describes the functional relationship between a variety of temporal patterns and the intensity level necessary to elicit a threshold response. The temporal patterns involved are the pulse repetition rate, pulse number, and the burst duration of sinusoidal signals.

In the first experiment thresholds were measured for varying pulse repetition rates. The results are shown in Figure 7-8 where threshold shift

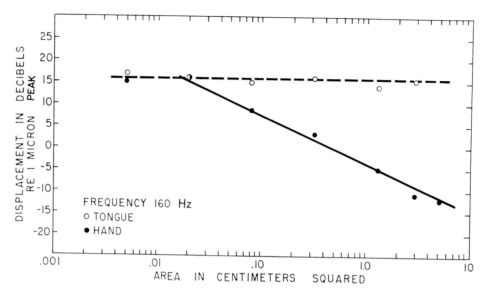

Figure 7-7. Comparison of thresholds obtained on the tongue and on the hand for a frequency of 160 Hz. There is no summation of energy over contactor area for responses determined on the tongue (Fig. 3, Verrillo, R. T., *Perception Psychophys.*, 1966, 1, 149).

referred to the threshold for one pulse is plotted as a function of pulse repetition rate. The heavy curve represents the theoretical predictions of the Zwislocki theory. It is clear that there are two modes of response, the largest area (2.9 cm²) produces complete summation, while the smallest area (0.005 cm²) produces no summation. The partial summation produced by intermediate sizes can be accounted for by a statistical overlap between the assumed populations.

Two modes of response are again apparent when threshold shift is measured as a function of pulse number at a constant repetition rate (100 pps). Figure 7-9 shows that the large contactor (2.9 cm²) summates energy increments over the number of pulses as predicted by the theory (*heavy line*). The curves become progressively flatter as the size of the contactor is reduced until summation can no longer be measured. This is reflected in the flat curve of the smallest contactor (0.005 cm²).

The final test of temporal patterns was performed by varying the burst duration of sinusoids. In this experiment the duration of the sine wave was varied from 10 msec to 2000 msec and the bursts were repeated at a rate of once every 2 sec. The results obtained on glabrous skin are shown in Figure 7-10. The two response modes are obvious. The Zwislocki theory of temporal summation (*heavy line*) predicts accurately the threshold as a function of the burst duration. Again, the curves become progressively flatter as the size of the contactor is reduced. For very small contactors the non-summating receptor system completely dominates the response and the resulting curve is flat.

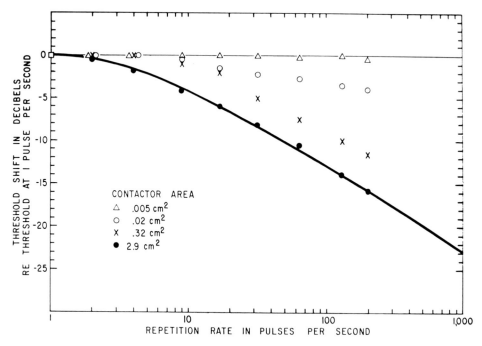

Figure 7-8. Vibrotactile threshold shift as a function of pulse repetition rate. The curve is theoretical. The largest contactor produces complete summation; the smallest contactor produces no summation at all (Fig. 2, Verrillo, R. T., *J. Acoust. Soc. Amer.*, 1965, **37**, 843).

It is clear that one of the receptor systems is capable of temporal summation while the other is not. It would seem reasonable to make the hypothesis that the receptors involved in temporal summation are those which account for the sensitivity to frequency changes, that is, the Pacinian corpuscle. A test of this hypothesis was made by measuring the threshold as a function of burst duration on the tongue. The results are compared in Figure 7-11 to data taken from the hand. The hand, rich in Pacinian corpuscles, follows the theoretical prediction (*heavy curve*) while the data from the tongue does not. Although the size of the contactor was large (2.9 cm²), the results obtained from the tongue resemble the data of the smallest contactor measured on the hand (see Fig. 7-10). It is very likely then that the Pacinian corpuscle is the nerve ending responsible for the observed temporal summation on glabrous skin.

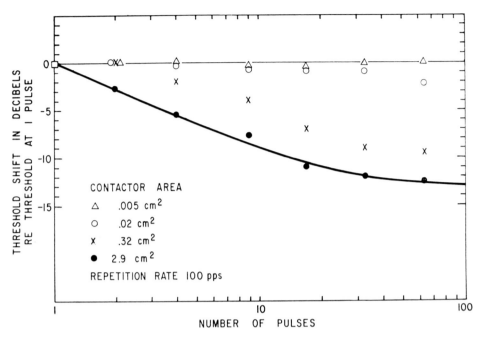

Figure 7-9. Vibrotactile threshold shift as a function of number of pulses. The curve is theoretical. The effect of summation is gradually diminished with the decrease in size of the contactor (Fig. 3, Verrillo, R. T., *J. Acoust. Soc. Amer.*, 1965, **37**, 843) .

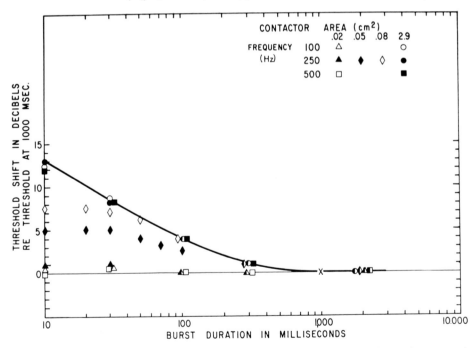

Figure 7-10. Vibrotactile threshold shift as a function of burst duration. The curve is theoretical. The effect of temperal summation decreases with the size of the contactor (Fig. 4, Verrillo, R. T., *J. Acoust. Soc. Amer.*, 1965, **37**, 843) .

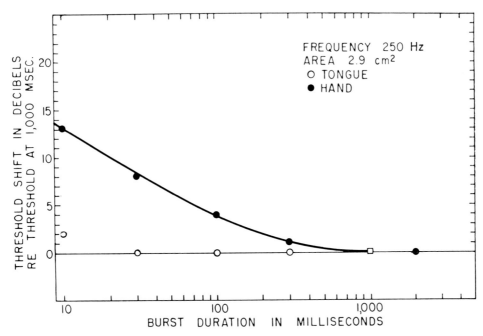

Figure 7-11. Comparison of threshold shift as a function of burst duration determined on the hand and on the tongue. The curve is theoretical. Measurements made on the tongue show no effect of temporal summation.

Contactor Height

Another line of evidence that supports the hypothesis of a duplex mechanism comes from experiments in which sensitivity to vibration is shown to increase as a function of the extent to which the contactor protrudes into the skin (Babkin, Rozen, Tumarkina, and Chernyak, 1961; Verrillo, 1962). This effect has also been observed on hairy skin (Verrillo, unpublished data). The Pacinian corpuscle is a deeply located receptor, so it is reasonable to expect a drop in threshold as the contactor is pressed closer to the sensitive unit. In addition, there is some compression of the tissue as the contactor presses into the skin which provides a better medium for the transmission of vibration to the corpuscle.

In order to test this hypothesis more systematically, threshold measurements were made on the tongue and on the hand. The resting level of the contactor was advanced in 0.5 mm steps into the skin and the thresholds were determined at each level for vibrations of 25 and 160 Hz. The results in Figures 7-12 and 7-13 are plotted as a function of contactor height. The resting level of the contactor is located deeper in the skin as the values along the abcissa go from — 1.0 mm through 0 to + 1.0 mm.

The Pacinian corpuscle responds to mechanical vibrations at 160 Hz in a ratio of 1:1 (Hunt, 1961; Loewenstein, 1958). The threshold level on the hand should therefore decrease as the contactor is pressed closer to the sensitive unit. The corpuscle is a velocity-sensitive receptor (Loewenstein and Mendelson, 1965) and will not fire easily at frequencies below approximately 40 Hz (Hunt, 1961; Sato, 1961) because the critical slope of the velocity is not reached at these low frequencies. Consequently, there should be no change in threshold at 25 Hz as the contactor presses more deeply into the hand. The threshold function for the tongue should remain flat at both frequencies since Pacinian corpuscles are not involved.

These predictions are verified in the results shown in Figures 7-12 and 7-13. The threshold for 160 Hz decreases as the contactor is pressed deeper into tissue containing corpuscles (hand). The tongue, measured at the same frequency, yields a flat curve (Fig. 7-12). There is no change in sensitivity on the tongue or hand when the measurements are determined at 25 Hz (Fig. 7-13). The corpuscles in the hand cannot respond and on the dorsum of the tongue they do not exist.

Comparison of Physiological and Psychophysical Results

It is infrequent that direct comparisons can be made between the results of physiological and psychophysical experiments. Such a comparison is

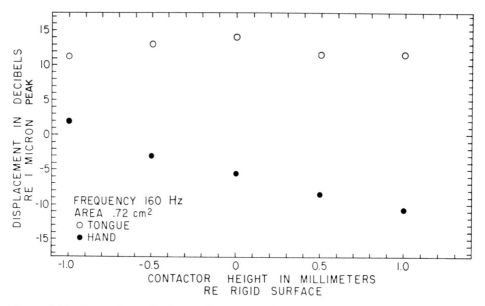

Figure 7-12. Comparison of vibrotactile thresholds measured on the tongue and the hand as a function of contactor height. The stimulus frequency was 160 Hz. Pressing the contactor into the hand results in a drop in threshold on the hand, but does not affect the threshold on the tongue (Fig. 4, Verrillo, R. T., *Perception Psychophys.*, 1966, **1**, 149).

possible in the case of responses to vibratory stimulation. Sato (1961) successfully measured the frequency response of Pacinian corpuscles. The
corpuscles were tested *in situ* in the mesentary of cat. The responses of two
corpuscles are compared in Figure 7-14 to the psychophysical threshold curve
obtained on the palm of the human hand. The physiological data have been
transformed so that they can be placed on the same coordinates with the
psychophysical results. The threshold values are absolute.

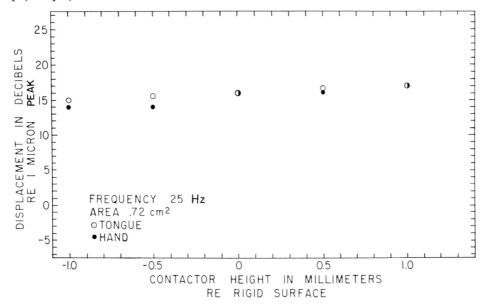

Figure 7-13. Comparison of vibrotactile thresholds measured on the tongue and the
hand as a function of contactor height. The stimulus frequency was 25 Hz. Neither
tongue nor hand thresholds are affected by protrusion of the contactor into the tissues
(Fig. 5, Verrillo, R. T., *Perception Psychophys.*, 1966, **1**, 149).

There is a striking similarity in the general shape of the functions for
the corpuscles and for the psychophysical thresholds obtained with a large
contactor (2.9 cm²). The slope of both functions (*solid lines*) is approximately — 12 dB per doubling of the frequency and each reaches a maximum
of sensitivity in the region of 250-300 Hz.

The dashed line is drawn through the psychophysical thresholds obtained with a small contactor (.02 cm²). Note that the data for the large
contactor follows this flat curve in the lower frequencies where it is extremely difficult to produce a discharge from the Pacinian corpuscle. A more
sensitive system determines the threshold response at lower frequencies. As
the frequency is increased there is a summation of energy by Pacinian
corpuscles and finally the downward slope of the curve is entirely determined by the response of the corpuscle.

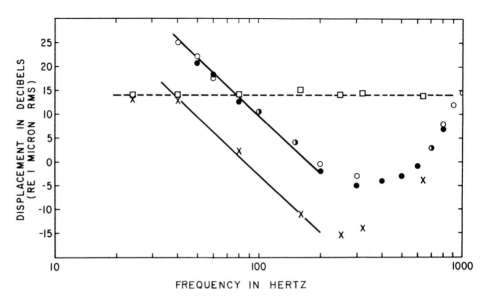

Figure 7-14. Absolute vibrotactile thresholds as a function of the frequency of vibration; O, ● — response of two Pacinian corpuscles in cat mesentery, tested electrophysiologically *in situ* (derived from Sato, 1961). □, X — responses of three human subjects, tested psychophysically on the glabrous skin of the hand. Contactor areas: X-2.9cm²; ● -.02 cm². The slopes of the curves for the two types of measurements are identical for the large contactor. The psychophysical data obtained with the small contactor is independent of frequency (Fig. 1, Verrillo, R. T., *Psychonom. Sci.*, 1966, **4**, 135).

SUMMARY AND CONCLUSIONS

Geldard noted the difference in shape between the threshold curves of large and "spot" contactors and commented: "The difference between the shapes of the curves . . . has never been satisfactorily accounted for, and further research along these lines is certainly indicated" (Geldard, 1953, p. 187). The results of a series of experiments have been presented which show that a satisfactory answer to the question may now be proposed. In these experiments vibrotactile thresholds have been determined as a function of a number of spatial and temporal parameters of the physical stimulus. A logical correspondence exists between the outcome of this research and the neural elements found in cutaneous tissue. The conclusions of this report may be summarized as follows:

1. Cutaneous tissue is innervated by at least two receptor systems involved in the transduction of mechanical disturbances.

2. One of the systems summates energy over time and space. It is this system that accounts for the frequency function obtained when large contactors are used to determine vibrotactile thresholds.

3. The other system is not capable of summation and it is this system that produces the flat frequency function when thresholds are determined with a very small contactor. It is this system, also, that accounts for the flat portion of the threshold curve that occurs at low frequencies. As frequency increases, summation occurs in the frequency-sensitive elements and this determines the downward slope of the curve.

4. By the process of elimination and by a direct comparison of physiological and psychophysical data it is shown that the Pacinian corpuscle is the nerve ending responsible for energy summation in cutaneous tissue.

ACKNOWLEDGMENT

I express my sincere appreciation to Dr. Jozef Zwislocki for his advice and suggestions throughout these experiments. My thanks go also to Robert Gardinier for the time and skill which he devoted to equipment problems. A note of thanks is due my colleagues in the laboratory for their willingness to listen.

REFERENCES

Babkin, V. P., Rozen, O. M., Tumarkina, L. N., & Chernyak, R. I. Investigation of vibratory sensitivity and factors affecting it. *Biophysics*, 1961, **6**, 39.

Békésy, G. von. Ueber die Vibrationsempfindung. *Akust. Z.*, 1939, **4**, 316.

Cauna, N. Functional significance of the submicroscopical, histochemical, and microscopical organization of the cutaneous receptor organs. *Verh. Anat. Ges.*, 1962, **111**, 181.

Eijkman, E., & Vendrik, A. J. H. Dynamics of the vibration sense at low frequency. *J. Acoust. Soc. Amer.*, 1960, **32**, 1134.

Frey, M. von. Beiträge zur Sinnesphysiologie der Haut. III. *Ber. sächs. Ges. Wiss. math.-phys. Cl.*, 1895, **47**, 166.

Geldard, F. A. The perception of mechanical vibration: I. History of a controversy. *J. Gen. Psychol.*, 1940, **22**, 243. (a)

Geldard, F. A. The perception of mechanical vibration: III. The frequency function. *J. Gen. Psychol.*, 1940, **22**, 281. (b)

Geldard, F. A. *The Human Senses.* New York: Wiley, 1953.

Gilmer, B. von H. The measurement of the sensitivity of the skin to mechanical vibration. *J. Gen. Psychol.*, 1935, **13**, 42.

Graham, C. H., Brown, R. H., & Mote, F. A., Jr. The relation of size of stimulus and intensity in the human eye. I. Intensity thresholds for white light. *J. Exp. Psychol.*, 1939, **24**, 555.

Hugony, A. Über die Empfindung von Schwingungen mettels des Tastsinnes. *Z. Biol.*, 1935, **96**, 548.

Hunt, C. C. On the nature of vibration receptors in the hind limb of the cat. *J. Physiol. (London)*, 1961, **155**, 175.

Knudsen, V. O. "Hearing" with the sense of touch. *J. Gen. Psychol.*, 1928, **1**, 320.

Loewenstein, W. R. Generator processes of repetitive activity in a Pacinian corpuscle. *J. Gen. Physiol.*, 1958, **41**, 825.

Loewenstein, W. R., & Mendelson, M. Components of receptor adaptation in a Pacinian corpuscle. *J. Physiol. (London)*, 1965, **177**, 377.

Melzack, R., & Wall, P. D. On the nature of cutaneous sensory mechanisms. *Brain*, 1962, **85**, 331.

Miller, M., Ralston, H. J., III, & Kasahara, M. The pattern of cutaneous innervation of the human hand, foot, and breast. In W. Montagna (Ed.), *Advances in Biology of Skin. Vol. 1.* New York: Pergamon, 1960. Pp. 1-47.

Nafe, J. P. The pressure, pain, and temperature senses. In C. A. Murchison (Ed.), *Handbook of General Experimental Psychology*. Worcester: Clarke Univer. Press, 1934. Pp 1037-1087.

Sato, M. Response of Pacinian corpuscles to sinusoidal vibration. *J. Physiol. (London)*, 1961, **159**, 391.

Stezepfand, W. Frequenzabhangigkeit der Vibrations empfindung des Menschen. *Z. Biol.*, 1935, **96**, 236.

Sherrick, C. E., Jr. Variables affecting sensitivity of the human skin to mechanical vibration. *J. Exp. Psychol.*, 1953, **45**, 273.

Sherrick, C. E., Jr. Observations relating to some common psychophysical functions as applied to the skin. In G. R. Hawkes (Ed.), *Symposium on Cutaneous Sensitivity*. Ft. Knox: U. S. Army Med. Res. Lab., 1960.

Sinclair, D. C. Cutaneous sensation and the doctrine of specific energy. *Brain*, 1955, **78**, 584.

Spassova, I. On the structure of encapsulated nerve endings in tongue of the cat and its functional significance. *Z. Mikr. Anat. Forsch.*, 1965, **72**, 366.

Verrillo, R. T. Investigation of some parameters of the cutaneous threshold for vibration. *J. Acoust. Soc. Amer.*, 1962, **34**, 1768.

Verrillo, R. T. Effect of contactor area on the vibrotactile threshold. *J. Acoust. Soc. Amer.*, 1963, **35**, 1962.

Verrillo, R. T. Temporal summation and vibrotactile sensitivity. *J. Acoust. Soc. Amer.*, 1965, **37**, 843.

Verrillo, R. T. Vibrotactile sensitivity and the frequency response of the Pacinian corpuscle. *Psychonomic Sci.*, 1966, **4**, 135. (a)

Verrillo, R. T. Effect of spatial parameters on the vibrotactile threshold. *J. Exp. Psychol.*, 1966, **71**, 570. (b)

Verrillo, R. T. Stimulus specificity in a cutaneous receptor. *Perception Psychophys.*, 1966, **1**, 149. (c)

Verrillo, R. T. Vibrotactile thresholds for hairy skin. *J. Exp. Psychol.*, 1966, **72**, 47. (d)

Weddell, G. Somesthesis and chemical senses. *Ann. Rev. Psychol.*, 1955, **6**, 119.

Weddell, G., Pallie, W., & Palmer, E. The morphology of peripheral nerve terminations in the skin. *Quart. J. Micr. Sci.*, 1954, **95**, 483.

Weinstein, C., & Arnulf, A. Contribution a l'etude des senils de perception de l'oeil. *Comm. Lab. Inst. Opt.*, 1946, **2**, 1. Cited by Y. Le Grand, *Light, Colour, and Vision*. London: Chapman & Hall, 1957. Pp. 242-243.

Winkelmann, R. K. *Nerve Endings in Normal and Pathologic Skin*. Springfield, Ill.: Thomas, 1960.

Zwicker, E., Flottorp, G., & Stevens, S. S. Critical band width in loudness summation. *J. Acoust. Soc. Amer.*, 1957, **29**, 548.

Zwislocki, J. Theory of temporal summation. *J. Acoust. Soc. Amer.*, 1960, **32**, 1046.

DISCUSSION

DR. R. H. GIBSON: I have several comments. First, you mentioned that absolute sensitivity on the fingertips was greater than that on hairy tissue because of greater innervation density, and I think it is not quite that simple because there are other factors to be considered. For example, the eye has a much greater absolute sensitivity in the periphery than it does in the fovea, yet the innervation density is just the reverse. Second, I wonder whether it is not possible, though certainly I don't know how, to invoke other factors than a separate receptor population, perhaps mechanical features in the tissues, to explain failure to follow frequency with small contactors. It certainly would be of interest to investigate mechanical characteristics of the skin in order for you to rule them out as a possibility.

DR. VERRILLO: Factors other than density of innervation may be involved in the upward shift in threshold from the palm to the arm. As to the second part of your question, I do not understand just how the mechanical characteristics of tissue could account for the differences observed when small contactors are used.

DR. GIBSON: Perhaps you have to move a certain amount of tissue in order to get sufficient spatial summation to show certain frequency effects. The tongue is not only anatomically different; it is also physically and structurally different. It is soft, and I am not sure that I feel perfectly comfortable that there is not some physical property of the stimulus or of the tissue that can account for these differences. It is possible, on the tongue at least, that you could move very small areas without actually doing much violence to the population that has to be moved.

DR. VERRILLO: Using several different-sized contactors on the tongue produced no effect.

DR. GIBSON: I have one more point I would like to present. There is another way, than by mechanical stimulators, that the effects of frequency on sensitivity may be investigated. If one uses brief electrical pulses of constant width and varies the interpulse interval, one can investigate the effect of frequency upon sensitivity. If this is done, using three contactor sizes which span yours, one gets a threshold curve which slopes sharply negative for the smallest contact area; for the next smallest contact area the slope of the threshold response is less negative; while the largest contact area gives a curve which is linear and has a more shallow slope. Not only do we not get a U-shaped function, unlike your data obtained with mechanical stimuli (with electrical pulses we get a continuous temporal integration), we also get an ordering of the effect of electrode sizes which is the reverse of what you would expect if it were simply the size of the area stimulator.

DR. VERRILLO: It is difficult to say just what receptors are being stimulated when electrical pulses are being used.

DR. R. K. WINKELMANN: I want to point out that we did study the tongue in forty biopsies of human individuals, and in a comparison of anterior, posterior, dorsal, and ventral surface, we did find that there is some kind of encapsulated ending which is not like the ending we term "mucocutaneous" down in the gutter, under the tongue. We have not studied that area with silver techniques extensively, but enough to know that this is an encapsulated mammalian type of Vater-Pacini corpuscle type ending, which is something that Dr. Verrillo did predict. However, the thing that disturbs me most about this is the fact that, in the comparison of the dorsal and ventral surfaces of the tongue, the skin is so different that, really, the mechanical results of stimulating these two surfaces should be different. I would feel a great deal happier in ascribing this all to a difference in receptors if the dorsal and ventral surfaces of the tongue were identical types of skin with different receptors, but they are definitely, as we can all feel, different types of skin. It seems to me that a good deal of this difference on dorsal and ventral might be ascribed to physical qualities of the skin surface as Dr. Gibson suggested.

DR. VERRILLO: [Ed. note — Dr. Verrillo wishes to use the following as a replacement for his comment in the discussion.] I do not see how this would make a difference in the threshold curves. The probability of the mechanical characteristics of tissue producing these curves is extremely remote. Tissue differences would alter the threshold level, but it is very unlikely that these differences would alter the shape of the curve that drastically, if at all.

DR. GIBSON: What happens when you soften the heel of the hand with glycerine, for example, to change the properties?

DR. VERRILLO: I have never done it, but I have placed a piece of felt between the skin and the contactor and have observed no difference in slope.

DR. WINKELMANN: Have you stripped off the stratum corneum and have you seen that this made any difference?

DR. VERRILLO: No, I have not done that. I have tested children, though, where the skin is much softer and the stratum corneum thinner and I also find -12 dB slopes to the curves.

DR. WINKELMANN: Let me put it in another way; what we think of in terms of skin is not always just epidermis and nerves but the thickness of the dermis and the dermis underneath the tongue is almost nonexistent. It is a thin submucosal layer overlaying the muscular and other tissues. On the dorsum of the tongue, there is quite a definite papillary and reticular dermis and I think there is a different mechanical bed which is receiving this stimulus. As I say, morphologically, I agree with your results, but I would feel happier if the skin were comparable.

DR. ROSNER: I just wanted to comment on the result with repetitive electrical stimulation. After a good deal of experience with it, I think it is quite likely you are not stimulating mechanically receptive terminals all the time when you use that kind of stimulation; therefore, I would expect, on the basis of very simple principles of peripheral nerve physiology that your result would appear with electrical stimulation. I think your population of excited nerve fibers could be very different with the two types of stimulation.

Chapter 8

PSYCHOPHYSICAL PROPERTIES WHICH CAN BE RELATED TO ELECTROPHYSIOLOGICAL DATA

E. G. EIJKMAN AND A. J. H. VENDRIK

A REWARDING RESEARCH IN SENSORY communication problems is the attempt to find connections between electrophysiological observations and psychophysical measurements. Establishing these connections yield, on the one hand, a better comprehension about the meaning of observed electrical phenomena, and on the other, it points to a nervous structure probably responsible for mediating the investigated aspect of a sensory stimulus to consciousness.

CHRONAXIE

Let us see if we can find some examples of corresponding measurements in psychophysics and electrophysiology. It is, for instance, quite simple to measure the chronaxie of fibers in the skin, stimulated by square pulses of electrical current. Hahn (1958) found, with psychophysical methods, a chronaxie of 0.2 msec which indicated that A fibers were involved. The experimental method used in electrophysiology and psychophysics to find the chronaxie are the same except for the response measured. In both cases a current of variable duration is applied to the nerve and the amplitude for some threshold is determined. In psychophysics a specified small sensation is used as a criterion and in electrophysiology a minimum number of spikes. Despite this difference results are comparable.

CONDUCTION VELOCITY

An old and seemingly simple example is found in the determination of conduction velocity in peripheral nerves. The electrophysiologist displays the passing action potential at two points. By measuring the time of passage and the length between the measuring points, the conduction velocity can be calculated. There seems to be little difficulty in doing the same psychophysically in man. With little effort it can be shown that reaction times of human subjects are in the range of 0.1-0.4 sec while stimulating the distal part of the leg by deformation or electrical pulses. Reaction may be elicited by mere detection of the stimulus, by a particular location stimulated or by simultaneity of two stimuli. The short reaction times found indicate that C fibers do not play a significant part in (a) detection of the stimulus; (b) indication of site of stimulation, and (c) indication of simultaneity.

This is, of course, not a surprising result but it indicates the way in which psychophysics and electrophysiology may interact.

Now consider an experiment where two sites on the leg are stimulated by a suitable pulse-shaped touch stimulus. After a stimulus the subject is asked to push a button as quickly as he can. The difference in reaction times corresponding with two places is measured. This difference will be the time needed for the action potentials to travel from one site to the other provided that the central processing takes the same time for both stimuli.

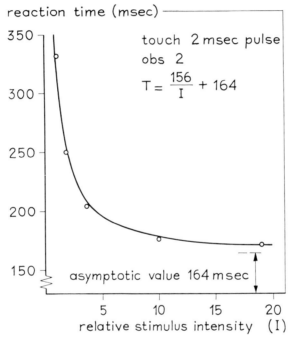

Figure 8-1. Stronger stimuli produce shorter reaction times. The relation is approxi-mately hyperbolic $T = \frac{a}{I} + b$. The asymptote is a time quantity independent of I.

The calculation of the conduction velocity from psychophysical measure-ments is complicated by the fact that reaction times are, for a great part, determined by the central nervous process which produces the right re-sponse. Also, the fact that reaction times are strongly dependent on the strength of the stimulus is probably a central phenomenon. Comparable reaction times would demand equal stimuli at the two different sites. As skin sensitivity on different locations differs considerably, this poses a problem. Fortunately the dependence of the reaction time on stimulus in-tensity decreases with increasing intensities. In Figure 8-1 this dependency appears to show a hyperbolic shape. Assuming a hyperbolic relation one can calculate the horizontal asymptote and so acquire a reaction time that is independent of a particular intensity. By subtracting two averaged reaction times for two locations on the leg and dividing the known distance between the two points by the time difference, a conduction velocity is found. We have reached an accuracy of 10 per cent of the conduction velocity when 1200 reaction times are involved in the calculation. The two stimulated points were inside dermatome L5 in the leg. In six subjects the velocities found were in the range from 13 m/sec to 35 m/sec. These are rather low values compared with many electrophysiological observations (e.g., Gasser and Grundfest, 1939; Lindblom, 1965). As far as the authors know, neither the anatomical situation with respect to the length of the nerve between two points nor electrophysiological measurement should cause one to expect that intraindividual differences would be so large. Moreover, with averaging techniques, the time of arrival of the primary response of the evoked potential has been measured with the same subjects and the same kind of stimulus. From the difference in arrival time after the stimulus at the two points on the leg a conduction velocity between 35 and 45 m/sec is now found. This is in accordance with other electrophysiological data.

What is the cause of failure of the psychophysical method compared with the more direct electrophysiological measurements? As stated before, the only assumption made is that the central processing of the neural activity coming from the two spots has the same duration. This assumption may prove to be false as a result of the comparison of the two methods.

DYNAMIC BEHAVIOR — TIME CONSTANT

Our third example is concerned with a very marked property of skin receptors with respect to their dynamic response. It is well known that, after a step-like stimulus, the response of skin receptors show an overshoot. There may be only a short-lived response which can be characterized by a time constant τ (see Fig. 8-2; total adaptation). There may also be a steady state discharge after the overshoot, in which case another quantity $A/B = \beta$ can be attached to the receptor system. This quantity describes the height of the overshoot with respect to the resting discharge, as can be seen in Figure 8-2. Note that, for characterizing the dynamic properties of a receptor system, only two quantities are used. For systems displaying an overshoot and incomplete adaptation, $\beta < 1$. Total adaptation is represented by $\beta = 0$. The duration of the overshoot is described by τ.

Our problem is to develop a psychophysical method in order to measure the quantities τ and β. The steplike stimulus is not well suited for this purpose. A much better form of stimulation is a linear increasing stimulus, which is stopped after different times t_e. To clarify this point consider

Figure 8-3, where a displacement is shown which is linear with respect to time. Immediately below, the response of a touch receptor is depicted. The response may be thought of as a graded receptor potential or as a frequency of action potentials. This response is derived from the transient response after a step. The linear function is the integral of the step function and similarly, the response to a linear function is the integrated step-response, provided that the receptor system equation is reasonably linear. It may be said in a less exact way, that the receptors are sensitive to velocity and a linear deformation provides a constant velocity after an initial increase.

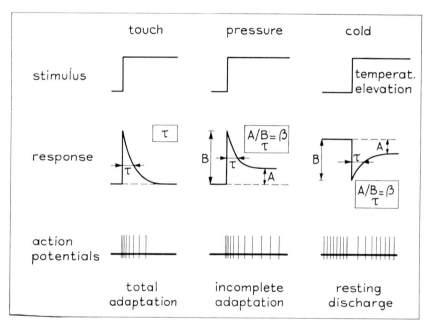

Figure 8-2. The dynamic response after a steplike stimulus is described by a time constant τ which is a measure of the duration of the overshoot and by a quantity β.

Now consider what happens if the stimulus is stopped at different times t_e. It depends on the slope of the linear displacement whether the receptor response surpasses a criterion value or not (Fig. 8-3). With small rates of displacement the criterion value is never reached. In the right part of Figure 8-3 the deformation which corresponds to some threshold criterion is depicted as dependent on the exposure time t_e. In this figure the experimental points, corresponding to a psychophysically defined threshold criterion, are represented rather well by a line through the origin, which is typical for a total adapting receptor system. The stimulus in this case was applied to the inner side of the forearm. Despite the fact that the adapting nature of the touch receptor system comes out clearly, a time constant cannot be derived from these measurements. This derivation should require the use of t_e smaller than 0.1 sec. With these small durations the integration-time (Verrillo, 1965) of the central nervous system will play its role and obscure the adaptation effect of the receptor. From the need of a small t_e it can be concluded that the time constant must be considerably smaller than 1 sec.

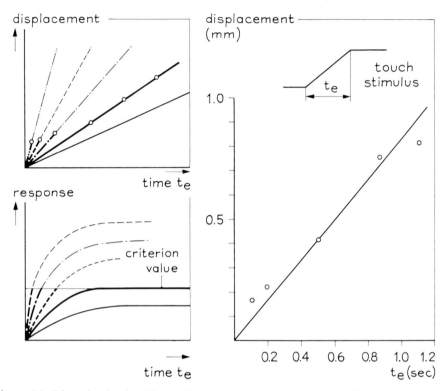

Figure 8-3. The stimulus is a linear displacement with duration t_e. The response of the receptor system is derived from the total adaptation after a step (Fig. 8-2). The result of an actual psychophysical experiment at the right half of the figure appears to be in accordance with this.

Sinusoidal stimulation yields the means to test the time constant of the receptor system using stimuli of longer duration. It is clear that higher frequencies produce faster displacements. A touch system which is sensitive to velocity should display a smaller threshold amplitude for higher frequencies (Fig. 8-4). Such is indeed the case as is shown in the right part of Figure 8-4. This curve contains the information of the time constant τ which appears to be 0.03 sec (Eijkman and Vendrik, 1960a). The mathematics involved have been compiled in the appendix.

The dynamic behavior described here approximates very closely the results obtained with touch fibers in the cat. It appears that linear displacements yield, after a short transient, an approximately constant frequency of discharge (Lindblom, 1965; Eijkman and Vendrik, 1960b). Psychophysical experiments show that the touch receptive system, as a whole, is approximately as sensitive to pulling out as to pushing in. In accordance with this, spike discharges appear on the ingoing and outgoing phases of the sinusoidal displacements. The phase of the occurrence of action potentials is another quantity that can be used to calculate τ (see appendix). Low frequencies produce action potentials at moments of maximum velocity. High frequencies tend to produce spikes at the tops of the sine waves (Fig. 8-4).

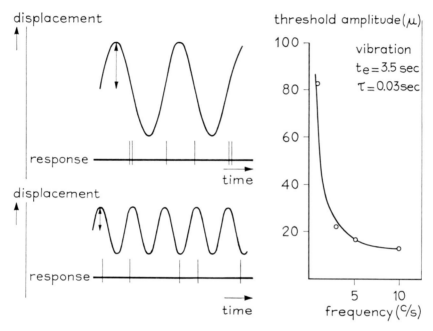

Figure 8-4. Sinusoidal stimulation. Note that higher frequencies have steeper slopes and have smaller threshold amplitudes. Action potentials are displaced to the top at higher frequencies. At the right are measured thresholds with different frequencies. This curve contains the information of time constant τ.

After consideration of the totally adapting touch system we turn now to receptors notably having a resting discharge. It has been shown (Hensel and Zotterman, 1951) that temperature receptors in mammals show a resting discharge dependent on temperature and an overshoot in their discharge response pattern after a steplike change in temperature. Our reasoning is the same as with the touch receptor system. The stimulus is a linearly increasing temperature. During the experiments a radar wave guide was placed against the inner side of the forearm. The skin was irradiated with

10 cm waves which penetrate deeply into the skin and warm the superficial layers uniformly. During the first 7 sec a linear increase of the temperature of the skin is ensured, in this way eliminating the unknown depth of the receptor as a disturbing factor.

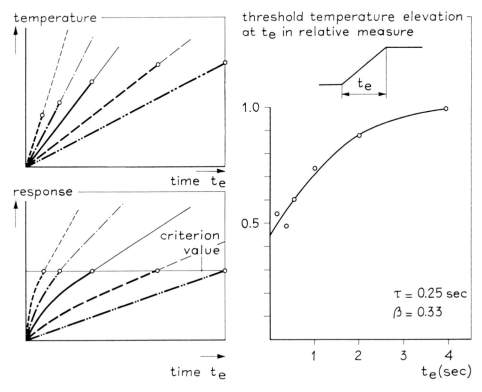

Figure 8-5. The stimulus is a linear increase in temperature with duration t_e. The response of the receptor system shows a sharp initial increase due to the overshoot character of the dynamic response. At the right are measured thresholds which are typical for a partial adapting system. $\tau = 0.25$ sec $\beta = 0.33$.

In Figure 8-5 the linear increase in temperature is shown together with the presumed response of the thermoreceptors. This response is again derived from the integrated response after a step function. The initial sharp increase in frequency corresponds with the overshoot depicted in Figure 8-2. Because of the resting discharge component, the response continues to increase in contrast with the touch receptor system (Fig. 8-3). We may consider now an experiment where stimuli of duration t_e and different slopes of increase are used. The threshold slope is determined and the total temperature elevation is recorded for different t_e's. The result is shown in the right part of Figure 8-5. The flattening of this curve is characteristic for incompletely adapting receptor systems. The time constant τ appears to be 0.25 sec while the quantity β equals 0.33. With different subjects it was found that $0.2 < \tau < 0.4$ sec and $0.2 < \beta < 0.35$. These properties are comparable with electrophysiological findings in the cat (Hensel and Zotterman, 1951) and rat (Iriuchijima and Zotterman, 1960). It must be stressed, however, that psychophysical results have been acquired with small temperature elevations ($<1°C$) and normal skin temperatures.

We will consider now what happens if the exposure time is increased. For instance, with greater times of exposure, there must be a point where a slowly increasing displacement is finally perceived. A feeling of pressure is emerging when a little piston pushes slowly into the skin of the forearm for more than 1 mm. By extending the experiment of Figure 8-3 to longer t_e and greater displacements, the result of Figure 8-6 is obtained. It is conceivable that with greater deformations a pressure receptor comes in, which shows the characteristics of an incompletely adapting receptor. It is not possible to estimate the constant β and τ for the pressure system from the measured curve.

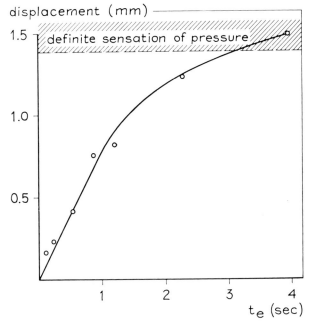

Figure 8-6. Extension of the measurement shown in Figure 8-3. With greater displacements of the skin a feeling of pressure emerges which does not adapt completely.

When exposure times for warmth stimulation are extended beyond 4 sec a result is obtained that is contrary to the one just described. In Figure 8-7 the threshold increase in temperature is shown for longer irradiation times. The curve now exhibits the character of a complete adapting system as threshold increases linearly with exposure time. Judging from electro-physiological evidence receptor adaptation is not responsible for this phenomenon. In view of the known properties of thermoreceptors (Hensel and Zotterman, 1951) it is likely that an additional adaptation is intro-duced, which may be called central adaptation (Eijkman and Vendrik, 1961). This adaptation is a slower process than receptor adaptation and it is complete, at least, in a limited temperature region. While the resting discharge might be used for thermoregulation, central adaptation is very useful as it prevents the lasting perception of temperatures not of interest for perceptual purpose.

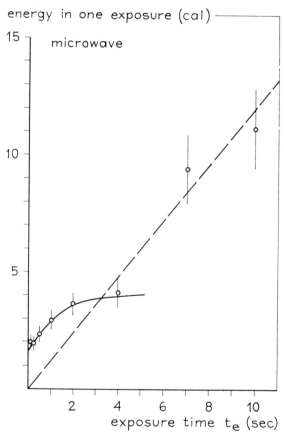

Figure 8-7. Threshold temperature elevation for long irradiation times. For $t_e > 4$ sec the system shows a complete adaptation which is presumed to be of central nervous origin. Accuracy of measurement is indicated by vertical lines.

Turning to the touch system, it may be asked if it shows a central adapta-tion. Experimentally, a sinusoidal stimulus can be applied which generates a discharge of long duration. It is found then that sensation decreases somewhat during the first few seconds, but a complete central adaptation does not occur here.

In summary, the results are tabulated in Table 8-I, which show that the receptor constants τ and β and the central adaptation are useful means for identification and characterization of the sensory systems involved.

TABLE 8—I
THREE CHARACTERISTICS DESCRIBING DYNAMIC BEHAVIOR

Quality	τ (sec)	β	Central Adaptation
warmth	0.2 - 0.4	0.2 - 0.35	complete adaptation after delay
cold		very similar to warmth	
touch	0.03	0	limited
pressure	<1	>0	limited

INTERNAL NOISE

Our last problem is one that is of prime importance to psychophysics. It was implied before that a threshold sensation results when the sensory activity considered surpassed a criterion value. The existence of a threshold has long been cherished in psychophysics. Recently, however, serious doubt has been cast upon the validity of this threshold concept. Many experimental results invalidate the existence of a stimulus level above which a perception of some kind always results. It is not necessary to go into details here (see e.g., Swets, 1964). Instead we will consider a particular experiment in which a subject is asked to state whether or not a stimulus is applied in a certain well-defined observation interval. In our case the stimulus is a cold stimulus which can have one of four different strengths. The smallest of the four has zero amplitude which means, in fact, that there is no stimulus. The different stimuli are intermingled at random, and the subject is asked to indicate whether or not the stimulus has been present. We may refine our experiment and ask the subject to give graded responses by stating one of the alternatives: (a) stimulus not present; (b) stimulus might be there but I am not sure at all; (c) rather sure that stimulus was present; or (d) confident that stimulus has been given. In Figure 8-8 three curves are given, each corresponding to the detection of the cold stimulus with a high level of confidence, a medium level of confidence and the lowest level of confidence. It is seen that the curves shift to the left in the order just mentioned. It means that with lowering the demand of confidence a particular probability is reached at a comparatively lower stimulus level. It is difficult to interpret these findings with a fixed threshold. Another interpretation is better suited to explain the results.

Consider a center in the brain where peripheral messages are received. There is very probably a lasting sequence of discharges, so-called spontaneous discharges. When a small activity of peripheral origin is added to the already existing 'spontaneous' activity, the detection of the peripheral signal must be dubious. The smaller the signal the more uncertain will be its detection. The possibility of detecting a signal falsely after a "stimulus" of zero intensity is clearly included. This response is often called a false alarm. At a lower level of confidence, smaller amounts of activity are included within the criterion resulting in a higher probability of detection and, of course, a higher probability of false alarms.

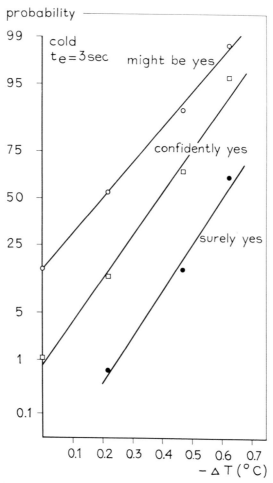

Figure 8-8. Probability of positive response after cold stimuli of four different strengths, of which one is zero. Note that the vertical scale is divided according to normal distribution. There are three levels of confidence used by the observer.

    In detection and decision theory an exact theoretical treatment can be found, provided the experimental conditions are sufficiently specified. In terms of detection theory an observer samples the output of his receiver during a well-defined observation interval. If the observer is to make a decision whether or not his sample contains a signal, he has to transform the received noisy sample into a single number of merit. When this number exceeds a criterion value the observer chooses for the signal to be present. If the number does not exceed the criterion then the observer decides the signal not to be present. There may be more than one criterion, of course, each corresponding with a particular response (Fig. 8-8) .

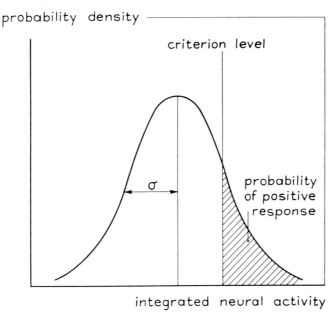

Figure 8-9. The integrated neural activity shows fluctuations despite constant stimulation. The distribution of the possible values of this activity are shown together with a criterion level. When the activity exceeds the criterion, a positive response is given.

Applying this to our psychophysical experiment it means that a stimulus has a fluctuating result in the brain center considered. The integrated nervous activity needed to weigh against the criterion thus fluctuates despite a constant stimulus. The consequence of such fluctuations are depicted in Figure 8-9. Horizontally, the integrated neural activity after a well-defined stimulus is plotted, and vertically, the probability density that the activity shows the magnitude indicated. The position of the criterion level on the horizontal axis has also been indicated. When the neural activity exceeds this level, the decision is made that the signal is present. The proportion of positive decisions can be read from the figure as the shaded area in respect to the total area under the probability density curve. Stronger stimuli displace the probability curve to the right and yield a greater proportion of positive decisions.

What is the advantage in the application of this theory? In the first place, it is recognized, from Figures 8-5, 8-8, and 8-9, that the unknown criterion level of the subject can be eliminated by measuring the probability of positive responses after a zero stimulus, the false positive rate, and secondly, by doing so, one is able to obtain a number for the magnitude of the neural activity with respect to its fluctuations, the so-called detectability index d'. In this way, the detectability index yields a measure for the magnitude of the stimulus independent of the criterion level of the subject (see Vendrik and Eijkman, this volume).

If this picture is the correct one, it must be understood that many psychophysical experiments which measure the probability of perception are, in fact, measurements of neural noise expressed in physical stimulus magnitudes. Furthermore, the sensitivity of a sense system can be expressed as the standard deviation of the internal noise (Eijkman and Vendrik, 1963).

Some important questions arise when the sources of neural noise are questioned. Some of this noise may be conveyed by the peripheral inflow or may be generated by the brain centers themselves. One should expect that totally adapting systems do not contribute to the neural noise, which causes false alarms, because there is no activity inflow when the stimulus is not present.

Werner and Mountcastle (1963; 1965) conducted important experiments which are, in some ways, electrophysiological counterparts of the psychophysical experiments just described. The results of these experiments suggest that a better understanding of the processing of signals in the midst of noise by the brain is at hand.

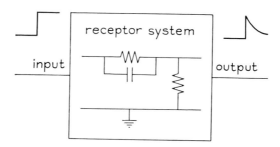

Figure 8-10. Diagram of receptor system showing an overshoot in the response after a steplike stimulus. An electrical analog is shown. The differential equation is given in the text.

APPENDIX

A differential equation describing a simple system that is not completely adapting (Fig. 8-10) is the following:

$$\frac{dI}{dt} + \frac{\beta}{\tau} I = \frac{dO}{dt} + \frac{1}{\tau} O \tag{1}$$

where I = input

O = output

β = the quantity $^A/_B$ shown in Figure 8-2.

τ = time constant of the system.

A total adapting system is acquired from (1) by putting $\beta = 0$. Equation (1) offers a solution for O with a given input I. The output O may be proportional to a graded potential or to the frequency of firing. The input I being a unit step-function (1) yields the solution

$$O = \beta + (1 - \beta) \ e^{-t/\tau} \tag{2}$$

Now take I to be a linear increasing function $I = vt$, v = velocity. The solution of (1) is now

$$O = v\beta t + v\tau \ (1 - \beta) \ (1 - e^{-t/\tau}) \tag{3}$$

The output is predicted when the two constants of the system β and τ are known. Now suppose that the firing frequency f in the nerve is proportional to O,

$$f = \alpha O$$

and that the actual f has at least to equal f_s to obtain a sensation which falls within the criterion, then the boundary frequency f_s can be predicted with the exposure time t_e as parameter.

$$f_s = \alpha v\beta t_e + \alpha v\tau \ (1 - \beta) \ (1 - e^{-t_e/\tau})$$

In that case the stimulus at time t_e will have the value

$$I = vt_e = \frac{f_s}{\alpha\beta + \alpha\tau/t_e \ (1 - \beta) \ (1 - e^{-t_e/\tau})} \tag{4}$$

For $t_e = 0$ $\qquad vt_e = \dfrac{f_s}{\alpha}$

$t = \infty$ $\qquad vt_e = \dfrac{f_s}{\alpha\beta}$ the asymptotic value of Figure 8-5.

By dividing the two values for vt_e, β is found. Totally adapting systems are described by putting $\beta = 0$. Then with $t_e \gg \tau$

$$vt_e = \frac{f_s}{\alpha\tau} t_e$$

which describes a straight line through the origin (Figure 8-3).

When sinusoidal stimulation is used the input is of the form $I = Ce^{i\omega t}$ and the output can be written $O = \gamma Ce^{i(\omega t - \phi)}$.

The differential equation (1) yields the solution:

$$\gamma = \frac{\sqrt{\omega^4 \tau^4 + \omega^2 \tau^2 (\beta^2 + 1) + \beta^2}}{1 + \omega^2 \tau^2}$$

which in case of a total adapting system $(\beta = 0)$ simplifies to

$$\gamma = \frac{\omega \tau}{\sqrt{1 + \omega^2 \tau^2}} \tag{5}$$

Again the frequency of firing is proportional to O: $f = \alpha O$. Then the amplitude of the output $\alpha \gamma C$ must at least equal f_s: $\alpha \gamma C \geqq f_s$ to get a sensation which falls within the criterion. With (5) the critical stimulus amplitude will then be

$$C = f_s/\alpha \sqrt{1 + 1/\omega^2 \tau^2} \tag{6}$$

which is the curve shown in Figure 8-4.

For electrophysiological purpose the phase ϕ of the output will be of importance because this can often be measured more conveniently than an amplitude diagram. It appears that

$$\mathrm{tg}\ \phi = \frac{\beta/\omega \tau - 1/\omega \tau}{1 + \beta/\omega^2 \tau^2}$$

which again in case of $\beta = 0$ simplifies to

$$\mathrm{tg}\ \phi = -\frac{1}{\omega \tau}$$

Eventual rectifying properties of the system may be incorporated without much change in the formula above (Eijkman and Vendrik, 1960a).

REFERENCES

Eijkman, E., & Vendrik, A. J. H. Dynamics of the vibration sense at low frequency. *J. Acoust. Soc. Amer.*, 1960, **32**, 1134. (a)

Eijkman, E., & Vendrik, A. J. H., Time constant of touch fibers in the cat. *Acta Physiol. Pharmacol. Neer.*, 1960, **9**, 461. (b)

Eijkman, E., & Vendrik, A. J. H. Dynamic behavior of the warmth sense organ. *J. Exp. Psychol.*, 1961, **62**, 403.

Eijkman, E., & Vendrik, A. J. H. Detection theory applied to the absolute sensitivity of sensory systems. *Biophys. J.*, 1963, **3**, 65.

Gasser, H. S., & Grundfest, H. Axon diameters in relation to the spike dimensions and the conduction velocity in mammalian A fibers. *Amer. J. Physiol.*, 1939, **127**, 393.

Hahn, J. F. Cutaneous vibratory thresholds for square wave electrical pulses. *Science,* 1958, **127**, 879.

Hensel, H., & Zotterman, Y. Quantitative Beziehungen zwischen der Entladung einzelner Kältefasern und der Temperatur. *Acta Physiol. Scand.*, 1951, **23**, 291.

Iriuchijima, J., & Zotterman, Y. The specificity of afferent cutaneous C fibers in mammals. *Acta Physiol. Scand.*, 1960, **49**, 267.

Lindblom, U. Properties of touch receptors in distal glabrous skin of the monkey. *J. Neurophysiol.*, 1965, **28**, 966.

Swets, J. A. (Ed.) *Signal Detection and recognition by Human Observers.* New York: Wiley, 1964.

Verrillo, R. T. Temporal summation and vibrotactile sensitivity. *J. Acoust. Soc. Amer.*, 1965, **37**, 843.

Werner, G., & Mountcastle, V. B. The variability of central neural activity in a sensory system, and its implications for the central reflection of sensory events. *J. Neurophysiol.*, 1963, **26**, 958.

Werner, G., & Mountcastle, V. B. Neural activity in mechanoreceptive cutaneous afferents: Stimulus-response relations, Weber functions and information transmission. *J. Neurophysiol.*, 1965, **28**, 359.

DISCUSSION

DR. H. HENSEL: Is this the time constant of warm responses for electrophysiological responses or for sensations?

DR. EIJKMAN: In the psychophysical experiments, it is the time constant of sensations, but we feel that there is similarity with the time constants found in electrophysiological experiments.

DR. HENSEL: This means that if central adaptation occurs, the time constant is not longer than the time constant in the periphery, is that right?

DR. EIJKMAN: Yes, that is right. That is just what I mean.

DR. HENSEL: Secondly, I think you have difficulties with the response curve (Fig. 8-2 of text) to rising temperatures. The shape of this curve depends on the temperature of the skin from which the warming started.

DR. EIJKMAN: Yes.

DR. HENSEL: If this static discharge of cold receptors is such that the maximum frequency occurs at a skin temperature of about 30°C and falls off to zero at both 15° and 32°C, then the change in frequency due to sudden warming is very different, depending on the temperature of the skin at which warming commenced [Ed. note: See Hensel, 1952]. When you start warming from temperatures below 30°C, the steady state before warming is much lower than after warming, but when you start warming from temperatures above 30°, just the reverse occurs.

DR. EIJKMAN: We were only concerned with normal skin temperature, about 28° to 30°C.

DR. HENSEL: Yes, I see. I would like to ask you about internal noise. Did you do some experiments with touch receptors also?

DR. EIJKMAN: They were psychophysical experiments.

DR. HENSEL: Did you find that these results indicated a probability curve for detection? Or was there some indication of an "all or nothing" response?

DR. EIJKMAN: Professor Vendrik will tell you about that in the next presentation.

DR. J. A. B. GRAY: I wanted to raise a point about errors in systems of rapidly adapting receptors. We have been looking at the information transmitted by a whole population of rapidly adapting receptors in the footpad of cat (Fuller and Gray, 1966). We are looking at the primary nerve population and here, as you say, there is no background activity, so that noise cannot be thought of in terms of unwanted impulses. But, there is still a considerable error component in the transmission of information. In this system, and it may be typical of other systems of rapidly adapting receptors, the main factor in the transmission of information is the pattern of activity between different units; not the time distribution in any one unit, but the number of units which are active and which units are active and which are not. In other words, you get a spatial representation of the stimulus rather than a temporal one. At each receptor there is a certain element of error in the threshold. This can be seen directly by looking at receptor potentials or measuring thresholds. When one reconstructs, in a way which I cannot go into now, the patterns of impulses which result from stimuli of various displacement amplitudes and various positions, you do get errors. If you repeat a stimulus many times, you will get a variation in the responses. Looking only at the responses, these variations could be interpreted as a shifting size of the stimulus or a shifting in position of the stimulus. You can now apply confidence limits to the stimulus predicted from having seen a single response. The 68 per cent confidence zone in our system gives steps of about 10 per cent increments in magnitude; that is, you can distinguish one stimulus from another with a 68 per cent probability, provided that they differ by more than 10 per cent. This variability is introduced by fluctuations in threshold.

DR. EIJKMAN: Yes, but this is a case of differential sensitivity and not so much a matter of absolute sensitivity. Besides the noise which we find is of an additive kind.

DR. J. D. HARDY: Dr. Eijkman, I just want to say for the record that we could not confirm your results with the microwave stimulation of the skin. Now the reasons for this, I think, are pretty detailed, but they have to do with the way the experiments were done, the precision of measurement, the microwave intensity, its distribution over the skin surface, the temperature changes at the skin surface and beneath the skin. I think that this may explain the differences in our results; this, however, cannot be discussed in detail here.

As far as the "noise level" is concerned, it might be worth mentioning that there are spontaneous changes in skin temperature even in the absence of any thermal stimulus and these temperature changes may be associated with thermal sensations. We have studied the effects of this "internal noise" by placing a subject in a neutral environment and following the thermal sensations and also the changes in forehead temperature with a very sensitive radiometer. When the skin temperature was constant, the subject reported "neural," "slightly warm," and "slightly cool" with equal frequency. If the skin temperature happened to be falling slightly (0.005° C/sec), reports of "slightly cool" were almost three times as great as those for "slightly warm." If the skin temperature happened to be rising (0.001° C/sec), the reports of "slightly warm" were fifteen times as numerous as those for "slightly cool." In this sense, sensations of warmth and cold are appreciated without external stimulation and perhaps one could agree that for these sensations there is no threshold for external stimulation. On the other hand, it seems to me that this definition of threshold is a little too restrictive inasmuch as one can establish operational thresholds for skin temperature as related to sensation (for example, a 3 to 1 frequency of reports of "slightly cool" over "slightly warm" might be called the "cold" threshold) whether one is observing the effects of the internal "noise" or is actually applying a stimulus. Would you permit this, Dr. Eijkman?

DR. EIJKMAN: There may be a threshold, for instance, in regulation systems or, of course, in single nerves. I do not think, however, that thresholds like these determine the detectability in sensory systems. There are too many experiments which are in favor of the signal-in-noise model. Not only the experiments I told you about. More complete discussions can be found in a book by Swets (1964). I fully agree with you that spontaneous changes of temperature cannot account for the "internal noise" especially not for smaller areas. Finally I think the disagreement about the microwave stimulation was not so much a difference of results but more a difference in interpretation. The microwave results I have seen fit very well with the scheme of receptor adaptation.

References

Fuller, D. R. G., & Gray, J. A. B. The relation between mechanical displacements applied to a cat's pad and the resultant impulse patterns. *J. Physiol. (London)*, 1966, **182**, 456.

Hensel, H. Physiologie der Thermoreception. *Ergebn. Physiol.*, 1952, **47**, 166.

Swets, J. A. (Ed.) *Signal Detection and Recognition by Human Observers*. New York: Wiley, 1964.

Chapter 9

PSYCHOPHYSICAL PROPERTIES DETERMINED WITH INTERNAL NOISE

A. J. H. Vendrik and E. G. Eijkman

In the preceding paper of this symposium the detection model of sensory perception has been introduced. The main point of this model is that perception of a stimulus by a subject is the detection of a signal in noise. Also, when no external noise is present during the observation period, the detectability of a signal is determined by noise generated in the sensory system itself. This internal noise is a fluctuating neural activity which is always present and which cannot be distinguished qualitatively by the observer from the neural activity evoked by small physical signals. The experimental evidence for the applicability of this model will not be discussed here (Swets, 1964). We will start by accepting this model. We will discuss whether the concept of internal noise can be used for obtaining insights on some aspects of the information processing in the sensory systems.

PROBABILITY DISTRIBUTION OF INTERNAL NOISE; STIMULUS-NEURAL ACTIVITY RELATIONSHIP

The probability distribution of the internal noise is of great importance. In every quantitative application of the detection theory this distribution should be known. Working with external physical noise this distribution is known, but with internal noise matters are considerably complicated.

Although electrophysiological experiments have been performed in determining the statistics of the firing of action potentials (Fitzhugh, 1957; 1958; Siebert, 1965; Werner and Mountcastle, 1963; 1965) these experiments do not permit a decision on the distribution of the internal noise which is relevant in psychophysical experiments. It is not known where in the sensory system the noise is generated which limits the signal detectability. But even if we assume that the electrophysiologically measured fluctuations are also the psychophysically relevant fluctuations, we still do not know how many elements (receptors, peripheral and central neurons) are involved in a particular sensory observation and how the information processing takes place. If the stimulus causes a change of the activity of a large number of these elements, the total activity change will approach a normal distribution regardless of the distribution of the activity of each separate element. This is a consequence of the central limit theorem of statistics. Moreover, averaging procedures which presumably occur in the processing

of the information by the central nervous system also results in a distribution approaching the normal one.

Probability distributions are sometimes plotted as a probability density
function f (x) and sometimes as the probability P. If the statistical quantity
is denoted by x the probability that x lies between x and x+dx is f (x) dx.
And by P is meant the probability that x is equal to or smaller than
x:P (x ≦ x). If the distribution is normal, f (x) has the well-known bell-
shape and P the sigmoid shape (Fig. 9-1 a and b). The P-curve is derived
from the f-curve by taking the area under the f-curve, as indicated in Figure
9-1. When working with normal distributions the P-curves are often plotted
on so-called normal coordinates. The ordinate is scaled in such a way that
the sigmoid shape becomes straight (Fig. 9-1c). By doing so one can easily
see if the measured statistical quantity is normally distributed.

In psychophysical experiments we only know the strength of the given
stimuli and the frequencies of the responses by the subject. If the number

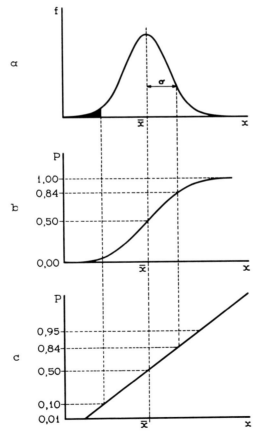

Figure 9-1. Normal distribution. (a) Probability density f with mean value $\overline{x}$ and
standard deviation σ; (b) probability P; (c) P plotted on normal coordinates.

of observations is large enough these frequencies can be considered as probabilities. But then we have only probabilities as a function of stimulus
strength and not as a function of the relevant neural activity. This cannot
be remedied. Therefore, we will start to investigate the distribution of the
noise expressed in terms of signal strength. After that we shall see that some
valuable information about the relationship between neural activity and
signal strength can be obtained.

The probability distribution of the internal noise could be determined
if the observer could shift his detection level at will over a known amount,
and the probability of yes or no responses would be measured at each position of the detection level. The observer can, indeed, shift his detection level
but the magnitude of such a shift is not known. It can be shown that it is
equivalent if the observer shifts his detection level while the signal is held
constant, or if he holds his detection level constant and the signal strength
is varied (Eijkman and Vendrik, 1963). An experiment is done as follows:
In each observation interval a signal is presented, which is randomly chosen
from a series of five signals of different strengths. One of these five signals

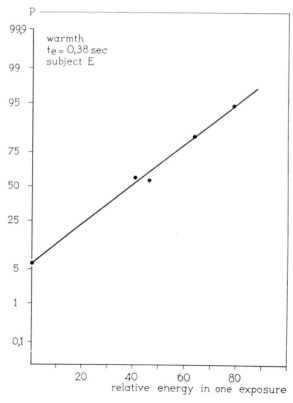

Figure 9-2. Relative frequency of positive responses versus signal strength, plotted on
normal coordinates, for warm stimuli.

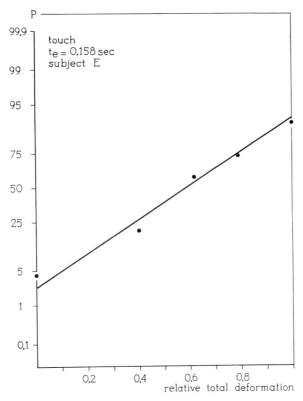

Figure 9-3. The relative frequency of positive responses versus signal strength, plotted on normal coordinates, for light touch stimuli.

has zero strength, which means that if this signal is chosen, no signal is applied. The subject answers by "yes" or "no" indicating whether he thinks a signal was given or not. The subject adopts, in this simple experiment, only one detection level, which is used independent of which signal will be applied. The frequency of yes responses is plotted on probability paper versus signal strength. These experiments have been done with warmth, cold, touch, and electrical stimuli. Signal strengths are, respectively, temperature increase, temperature decrease, displacement, and current. Figures 9-2 and 9-3 show some typical experimental results. As can be seen, the experimental points lie in good approximation to a straight line. Some deviations will be discussed later on in this paper. This means that the neural activity expressed in terms of stimulus strength is approximately normally distributed.

The simplest assumption is that the relationship between stimulus strength and relevant neural activity is linear and that the probability distribution of the neural activity, plotted against magnitude of this activity, is normal. We shall see below that this assumption can be experimentally verified.

Some interesting deviations from linearity of the probability graph have been measured. With touch, the experimentally determined frequencies at small stimulus strengths are too high. This cannot be judged from the curve in Figure 9-3, but the effect turns out to be significant when all measurements are taken into account. The experiments with electrical stimuli show this effect quite markedly, as is shown in Figure 9-4. It means that either the relationship between signal strength and neural activity is nonlinear or the distribution of the neural activity plotted against magnitude of this activity is not normal or both. Some information on this problem can be obtained by asking the subject to adopt not one but three different detection levels, e.g., c_1, c_2 and c_3, as has been explained in the preceding paper. The answer of the subject is now one of four different responses, indicating if he finds the observed stimulus to exceed the highest level c_3, to lie between the highest, c_3, and the next one c_2, etc. Measuring the response frequencies similar curves, as in Figures 9-2 and 9-3, can be

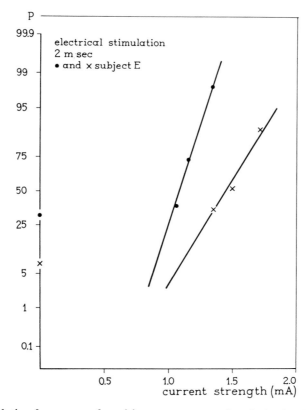

Figure 9-4. Relative frequency of positive responses to electrical stimulation. At small stimulus strength a marked deviation from linearity occurs.

plotted but now for every detection level another curve is obtained, as shown in Figure 9-5.

If the detection level, which is a particular value of the relevant neural activity, has a linear relationship with stimulus strength, a shift of the detection level would be equivalent to a shift in the stimulus strength, equal for all stimuli. This means that adopting another detection level causes the curve to shift in horizontal direction. On the other hand if the experimentally found deviation is due to a nonlinear relationship between the neural activity and stimulus strength, while the distribution of the neural activity is normal, it can be easily proved that the shift in the detection level will cause a shift of the curves in vertical direction. The transformation of neural activity to stimulus strength causes a nonlinearity of the probability curve which is the same for the various detection levels. Therefore, the deviation from linearity occurs for the various curves at the same value of the stimulus strength. The experiments are quite conclusive. The curves

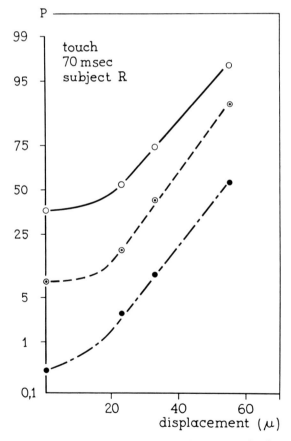

Figure 9-5. Experiment with four response categories on touch. Curves are shifted in vertical direction.

for the various detection levels are mutually shifted in vertical direction (Figs. 9-5 and 9-6). Of course this can only be observed if a marked deviation of linearity occurs. The experiments can be described by assuming that the neural activity is normally distributed and that for the warmth and cold system a linear relation exists between this neural activity and temperature change, while for touch and electrical stimulation the neural activity and stimulus strength are nonlinearly related. The stimulus-neural activity relation in the latter two cases has a shape as depicted by the solid line in Figure 9-7. The approximation by the broken line shows the tendency clearly that the neural activity does not change its average magnitude up to a certain stimulus strength. One could say then that there is a threshold, but in another sense, than commonly used. Here the noise concept is an explanation of the probability curve, while the older threshold theory cannot explain the frequency of positive responses for signal strengths below threshold.

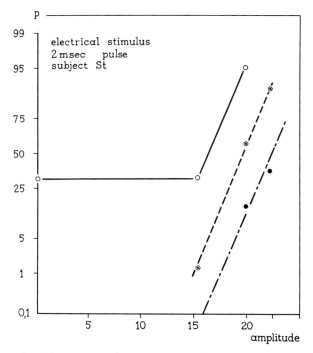

Figure 9-6. The same as Figure 9-5, now with electrical stimulation.

It is tempting to speculate about the reason why the temperature sensory system does not have a measurable threshold in contrast with the touch system and with the system stimulated by electric current. As discussed in the preceding paper, temperature fibers have a resting discharge while touch fibers have not. Generating an action potential in a touch fiber will be a threshold phenomenon. Stimulating a temperature fiber means changing intervals between the spikes which may be a continuous process without threshold. This may be the basis of the difference between these two sensory systems. But it should be stressed that the explanation may very well have to be sought in the behavior of central nervous processes instead of peripheral ones.

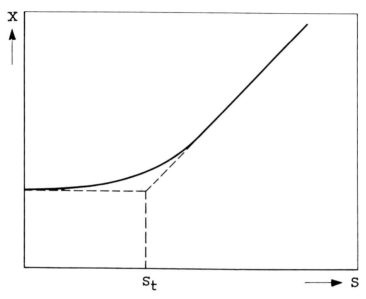

Figure 9-7. Solid line represents the nonlinear relation between neural activity x and signal strength s. The broken lines represent the course with a threshold stimulus s_t.

INTERACTION AND CORRELATION

By means of the detection model some aspects of the organization of the sensory part of the nervous system can be studied. We have in mind the problem of interaction between different sensory channels and the investigation of the correlation of the noise of different sensory channels. We will define a sensory channel as that part of the living system that transmits information on a property of the signal to the final center where perception of that property occurs.

Let us consider an example. Temperature increase and temperature decrease evoke sensations of warmth and cold, respectively, which can be well distinguished. The question arises as to whether the channels which convey both types of information are entirely separate or whether they have a part in common. Do these channels interact in one way or another, i.e., is there facilitation, inhibition, funneling or summation? Furthermore, both channels have internal noise which limits the detectability of temperature changes. If the noise of the two channels is correlated it can be said that these channels have a part in common.

These problems can be investigated by detection experiments in which two different stimuli are applied both separately and simultaneously. The idea is quite simple. The detectability is measured in both situations. If the detectability of a stimulus applied alone is different from the detectability when another stimulus is applied simultaneously, one or another type of interaction exists. An analysis of the experimental results allows one to find which type of interaction occurs and to what extent. However, these experiments require a good reproducible measure of the detectability. The detection model provides such a measure, the detectability index d'.

Detectability Index

The sensitivity of a sensory system is limited by the noise. Therefore the best way to express the sensitivity is by the value of the standard deviation (σ) of the noise. This suggests that the detectability of a signal S can be very well characterized by the ratio S/σ. In detection theory this ratio, called the detectability index d', is used. An important fact is that d' is independent of the height of the detection level. Hence, if two experiments are carried out successively with the same signal and the subject uses different detection levels in these two experiments, the same value for d' will be found.

The sensory systems we are interested in display internal noise which is approximately normally distributed, as we have seen. The whole distribution is known if we know the probabilities of detection for two signal values. In psychophysical experiments, mostly, the frequencies of positive responses are determined when a signal of known strength and when no signal (signal of zero strength) are presented. These two values are sufficient for the determination of the detectability index d' for signals of other than zero strength.

Types of Interaction

The interaction can be facilitation, inhibition, funneling, and summation. These concepts are often used in the literature but not always in the same sense. For our purpose we need an exact definition. We say that stimulus A facilitates stimulus B if the detectability of stimulus B is enhanced by the simultaneous presentation of stimulus A. If only this occurs, the detectability of A is not influenced by the presence of B. If, however, the detectability of A is also enhanced by B, mutual facilitation takes place. If, instead of enhancement, a diminution of detectability occurs, it is called inhibition. Again, inhibition can be single sided or mutual. If, in presenting the two stimuli simultaneously, the detectability of stimulus A is enhanced and that of stimulus B is diminished, compared with the detectabilities when the stimuli are given separately, we use the word funneling. This term was introduced by von Békésy (1958). In terms of nervous channels this means that the activity of one channel is partially funneled into and added to the activity of the other channel. If the funneling is complete, all the activity is poured into one channel. This can be called complete funneling. It is effectively the same as summation with respect to signal magnitude.

Experiments on Interaction

A 'basic experiment' can be designed to investigate the interaction between two stimuli, A and B. In an observation interval one of four possible signals is presented to the subject, that is, a stimulus of zero strength (0), stimulus A, stimulus B or stimuli A and B simultaneously (AB). The subject is asked to respond by o, a, b, or ab, according to the stimulus he thinks is given. The frequencies of the responses are measured. If the number of trials is sufficiently large, these frequencies are equal to the probabilities. The various probabilities are written in the usual way, for example, the probability of the response ab after presentation of stimulus B is written by $P(ab|B)$. The matrix of the probabilities resulting from this experiment is shown in Table 9-I. The use of the matrix in the calculations can be clarified by an example. The detectability index of stimulus B, when presented alone $(d'_B(B))$ is calculated from the frequencies of false positives and the frequency of correct positive responses. The probability of responding b when B is given, is $P(b|B) + P(ab|B)$; the probability of responding b when zero stimulus is given, is $P(b|0) + P(ab|0)$. The detectability index of stimulus B when presented simultaneously with A $(d'_{AB}(B))$ is calculated from the same probability of false positives and from the probability of correct positive responses $P(b|AB) + P(ab|AB)$. If for example, $d'_{AB}(B) > d'_B(B)$ stimulus B is facilitated by A or activity evoked by A is funneled into channel B. Whichever of the two occurs can be decided by calculating from the same matrix the detectability indices of A when presented apart $(d'_A(A))$ and simultaneously with B $(d'_{AB}(A))$. A whole system can be made for determining the type and the magnitude of the interaction (Eijkman and Vendrik, 1965).

TABLE 9—I
MATRIX OF PROBABILITIES OF A "YES" RESPONSE TO THE PRESENTATION
OF NO STIMULUS OR STIMULUS A, B, OR AB

Response	*O*	*A*	*B*	*AB*
o	$P(o|O)$	$P(o|A)$	$P(o|B)$	$P(o|AB)$
a	$P(a|O)$	$P(a|A)$	$P(a|B)$	$P(a|AB)$
b	$P(b|O)$	$P(b|A)$	$P(b|B)$	$P(b|AB)$
ab	$P(ab|O)$	$P(ab|A)$	$P(ab|B)$	$P(ab|AB)$

Experiments of this type have been carried out with two warmth stimuli applied on different sites of the skin with a warmth and a cold stimulus and a warmth and a touch stimulus. The stimulator is shown in Figure 9-8. A thin metal strip stuck to a perspex block can be warmed by an electric current. The Peltier element produces a temperature increase or decrease, depending on the direction of the electric current. Touch stimuli can be given by means of the piston. The shape of the stimulator was chosen in this way because we wanted one stimulated area to be surrounded by the area excited by the second stimulus. All experiments have been done on the inner side of the forearm. Each subject performed ten series of observations, each consisting of sixty trials.

Warmth — Warmth Stimuli

Experiments of another type had been performed previously in our laboratory to investigate the ability to recognize two warmth stimuli as a function of distance. It appeared that for small stimuli (probability of correct positive responses markedly smaller than 1.00) the subject is not able to distinguish between two stimuli applied on the inner side of the forearm up to a distance of at least 15 cm. Therefore, carrying out the basic experiment with the stimulator shown in Figure 8 we expected that summation, with the absence of recognition, would be found. This appears to be the case. The values of the detectability indices calculated from the experimental results are in agreement with the hypothesis that summation of the neural activities evoked by both warmth stimuli occurs.

Warmth — Cold Stimuli

This experiment is of more interest than the preceding one because the result cannot be predicted. This experiment has been carried out with three subjects. The general result is that there was only surprisingly small interaction. It should be noted that the distance between the sites on the skin where the two stimuli were applied was equal to the distance between the two warmth stimuli in the preceding experiment. The two warmth stimuli showed a very marked interaction. After close inspection of the results, the only effect appeared to be that the detectability of the cold stimuli decreased somewhat by the application of the warmth stimuli while the detectability index of the warmth stimuli was somewhat increased by the simultaneous application of the cold stimulus. According to our definition that is funneling of activity of the cold channel into the warmth channel. The changes of the detectability indices caused by this funneling were, on the average, only about 20 per cent. On *a priori* grounds one could have expected inhibition between cold and warmth stimuli. But on this part of the skin and with this distance this appears not to occur.

Warmth — Touch Stimuli

The "basic experiment" has been carried out with warmth and touch stimuli using the stimulator of Figure 9-8. The result was that there appeared to be no interaction between the warmth and the touch stimuli. A small, hardly significant interaction was found. The detectability index of the touch stimulus was lowered a bit by the simultaneous application of the surrounding warmth stimulus, and the detectability index of the warmth stimuli was increased somewhat by the touch stimulus. This means that a small funneling of the activity of the touch channel into the warmth channel existed. The changes in the detectability indices were only of the order of 10 per cent.

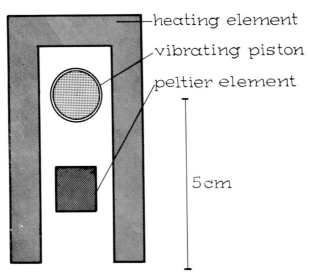

Figure 9-8. Stimulator used in the interaction and correlation experiments.

Correlation of the Noise

In electrophysiology, the measurement of the correlation between the electrical activities of two groups of neurons as a function of time is often used for investigating whether these activities have a common origin. The same idea can be applied to the study of the correlation of the internal noise of different sensory channels. Again, the experiments involve the measurement of the detectability of stimuli, when applied simultaneously, as compared with the detectability when applied separately. The same basic experiment as described above can be used.

A value of the correlation coefficient ρ can be calculated from every vertical column of the probability matrix of Table 9-I. Consider, for example, the probabilities of responses after the presentation of stimulus A.

If no correlation exists, that is, if $\rho = 0$, the probability of responding ab is simply the product of the probability of responding a and the probability of responding b. Hence P (ab|A) =[P (a|A) + P (ab|A)] [P (b|A) + P (ab A)]. If complete correlation exists, that is, if $\rho = 1$, the probability of responding ab is equal to the smaller of the probabilities of responding a and of responding b. Without further mathematical derivations it can be understood that a value of ρ can be calculated from the measured values of P (0|A), P (a|A), P (b|A) and P (ab|A) (Eijkman and Vendrik, 1965). In the same way a value of ρ can be obtained from the probabilities of responses on stimulus 0, B and AB. Thus every experiment yields four values of ρ.

The experiments with warmth and touch stimuli gave values of ρ, which are, on the average, not significantly different from zero. Hence, a correlation of the noises in the warmth and touch channels can be considered to be absent. The correlation coefficient calculated from the results of the experiments with cold and warmth stimuli was, on the average, slightly positive, but the difference from zero is hardly significant. Hence, the correlation of the noises of the cold and warmth channels is, at best, small. Concluding, the correlation of the noises shows that if the warmth, cold, and touch channels have a part in common, it cannot be any part that generates an appreciable portion of the internal noise.

Simultaneous Observation

It has been tacitly assumed that the subject is capable of observing two stimuli simultaneously. However, it could easily be that observation of one type of sensory information is hampered by the simultaneous observation of another. By an extension of the basic experiment the ability of simultaneous observation can be studied. For the sake of brevity we will not treat this problem (Eijkman and Vendrik, 1965). This has been investigated by us for the warmth, cold, and touch stimuli and we have found that the subject is able to observe two of these stimuli simultaneously.

DISCUSSION

On the basis of the detection model, psychophysical methods have been developed which allow an investigation of interesting aspects of the sensory system. The distribution of the internal noise and the relationship between the stimulus strength and the neural activity, which is relevant for the perception, the magnitude and type of interaction between these various sensory channels, and the correlation of the noise of these channels can be studied by these methods. It has been shown that the experimental data can be described by assuming a normally distributed noise and a stimulus-neural activity relation which is linear for the warmth and cold sensory systems, slightly nonlinear for the touch system and markedly nonlinear for the system stimulated by electric current. Moreover, a surprising absence of interaction and correlation have been found of the warmth, cold and touch systems.

Can these results be connected to electrophysiological data? The difficulty of relating the distribution of the noise with electrophysiological fluctuation measurements has already been discussed. This difficulty, however, is not essential. If more electrophysiological and psychophysical data on noise become available it will be possible to find the desired relations.

One would be inclined to relate the results of the interaction and correlation experiments with the often discussed question of the specificity of the sensory skin fibers. Are there separate warmth, cold and touch fibers or are two or all three modalities mediated by the same fibers? The absence of interaction and correlation form an argument against the hypothesis that the same fibers are used for the transmission of the information on more than one modality. Unfortunately, however, these experimental results do not prove beyond doubt the specificity of the fibers.

One of the results of our experiments is that warmth, cold, and touch stimuli can be easily recognized by the observer even at threshold. This means that in the central nervous system different warmth, cold, and touch centers exist. Hence, even if the same peripheral fibers carry the information on the three kinds of stimuli, somewhere in the nervous system the information must be sorted out and fed into the three different centers. If the relevant noise is generated not peripherally but centrally to this branching point of the information paths, the noise of the three systems can very well be uncorrelated.

As regards the interaction, let us consider the most surprising result. This is the absence of inhibition between the warmth and cold system. The warmth and cold stimuli were applied within the summation area of the warmth stimuli. One would be tempted to state that information on cold cannot be transported by the same fibers as warmth because cold stimuli give the opposite change of the frequency of action potentials as warmth stimuli. Again the argument is not conclusive. It might be possible that the peripheral fibers carrying information on cold and warmth are identical but that the cold and warmth centers sort out both types of information by a kind of rectifier action, one center accepting only increase, the other center only decrease of frequency of action potentials. The only conclusion which can definitely be drawn is that central adaptation (see preceding paper) takes place before the center where summation is affected.

More arguments are available for the existence of separate temperature and touch fibers. The properties of dynamic behavior such as time constants of peripheral adaptation and central adaptation show large differences. Also the notion of a temporal pattern of specificity brings about some difficulty. Vibratory touch stimuli give sensations which show very little adaptation as compared with warmth and cold stimuli. The complete adaptation of the latter is very likely of central origin. Vibratory stimuli can give a pattern of action potentials which cannot be well distinguished from the resting discharge of warmth and cold fibers. If warmth, cold, and touch were mediated by the same fibers one cannot see how confusion between these modalities could be avoided.

SUMMARY

An important point of the detection model used in this paper is that the detectability of small signals by a human observer is determined by internal noise, that is, fluctuations of the relevant neural activity. A method is described for investigating the distribution of this noise and the relationship between the stimulus strength and the neural activity. This method has been applied to the warmth, cold, and touch sensory system and to the sensory system stimulated by electric current. It is shown that the experimental data can be described by assuming a normally distributed noise and a stimulus-neural activity relation which is linear for the warmth and cold systems, slightly nonlinear for the touch system and markedly nonlinear for the system stimulated by electric current. Furthermore, interaction between the various skin sensory channels and correlation of the noise of these channels have been studied. A surprising absence of interaction and of correlation of noise has been found in the warmth, cold, and touch systems. This result is discussed in relation to the specificity of the sensory nerve fibers.

REFERENCES

Békésy, G. von. Funneling in the nervous system and its role in loudness and sensation intensity on the skin. *J. Acoust. Soc. Amer.*, 1958, **30**, 399.

Eijkman, E., & Vendrik, A. J. H. Detection theory applied to the absolute sensitivity of sensory systems. *Biophys. J.*, 1963, **3**, 65.

Eijkman, E., & Vendrik, A. J. H. Can a sensory system be specified by its internal noise. *J. Acoust. Soc. Amer.*, 1965, **37**, 1102.

Fitzhugh, R. The statistical detection of threshold signals in the retina. *J. Gen. Physiol.*, 1957, **40**, 925.

Fitzhugh, R. A. statistical analyzer for optic nerve messages. *J. Gen. Physiol.*, 1958, **41**, 675.

Siebert, W. M. Some implications of the stochastic behaviour of primary auditory neurons. *Kybernetik*, 1965, **2**, 206.

Swets, J. A. (Ed.) *Signal Detection and Recognition by Human Observers*. New York: Wiley, 1964.

Werner, G., & Mountcastle, V. B. The variability of central neural activity in a sensory system, and its implications for the central reflection of sensory events. *J. Neurophysiol.*, 1963, **26**, 958.

Werner, G., & Mountcastle, V. B. Neural activity in mechanoreceptive cutaneous afferents: Stimulus-response relations, Weber functions and information transmission. *J. Neurophysiol.*, 1965, **28**, 359.

DISCUSSION

DR. G. WERNER: Do your subjects know the *a priori* probabilities with which the different stimuli are presented?

DR. VENDRIK: Yes.

DR. WERNER: If you change this *a priori* probability, would you change the interaction or absence of interaction patterns?

DR. VENDRIK: We did not try it in these kinds of experiments. We have done this in other experiments, and it is well known that it results in a shift of the detection level which does not influence the detectability. I would not expect any effect, and that is also the reason why we did not do these experiments which would be quite elaborate. You have to have quite a large number of trials before you have a reasonably accurate probability.

DR. H. HENSEL: Did you conduct any experiments with systematic shifts of the attention of the observer?

DR. VENDRIK: No.

DR. HENSEL: And if I understood, you had considerable summation of warmth plus warmth.

DR. VENDRIK: Yes, that is correct.

DR. HENSEL: Did you observe the correlation between cold and touch?

DR. VENDRIK: No, we did not do that; that was because these experiments had been done in the last month, and we did not have time to complete it.

DR. A. IGGO: When you were looking for these interactions between thermal stimuli, did you work over a range of temperatures or did you arbitrarily select certain preset temperatures for the cold stimulus and for the warm stimulus? The reason I ask is that depending on the temperatures chosen you may, in some situations, select conditions in which an increase in temperature will alter the activity of both cold and warm receptors, whereas the increase in temperature over another range may alter the activity of only the warm receptors. I would expect that it would be possible for you in one particular range of temperatures to cause a diminution in the rate of firing of the cold receptors at the same time that you were causing an acceleration in the rate of firing of warm receptors. For this reason, I would think that the possibility of an interaction between warm and cool sensations would depend on the base temperatures from which you choose to work.

DR. VENDRIK: We did not change the skin temperature purposely. It has all been done in a couple of months in the same season of the year and with the same room temperature. Therefore, the skin temperature will not have been varied in these experiments by more than about two degrees.

DR. IGGO: You are starting with your subject at some neutral temperature and then changing it?

DR. VENDRIK: Yes, the stimulus is an increase or a decrease from the neutral temperature. You could raise the temperature, that is what you are suggesting, then wait until the subject adapts to it, and then present the warm and cool stimuli, again measuring the probabilities of these responses.

DR. IGGO: This would require that you held the temperature at some fixed value before you started and then moved away from it. There are two possible situations. In the first, you could select an adaptive temperature in which there was a resting discharge in cold fibers but no resting discharge in warm fibers. When the temperature was raised the cold fiber discharge would disappear and warm fiber discharge would appear. The second set of conditions would be where you were working at a different adaptive temperature, where there was no discharge from the cold fibers. When you alter the temperature to a new level, then you have only a discharge in the warm fibers. I was wondering where this would lead — possibly to interaction?

DR. VENDRIK: Have you any idea what temperature you should have before you should have these two extreme situations? Perhaps Dr. Hensel knows.

DR. HENSEL: I think about 20°C.

DR. IGGO: Yes, I would think that the first set of conditions would occur in the range of temperatures of about 33° to 36°C; it is still possible to get a steady discharge in cold receptors, but it depends on the animal. If you are working on a monkey, then you are more likely to have a steady discharge at 36° than you are in a cat. The second set of conditions would occur in the range of temperatures of, perhaps, 38° to 40°C.

DR. VENDRIK: That is uncomfortably high, isn't it?

DR. IGGO: If you hold to that temperature.

DR. VENDRIK: In order to do these kinds of experiments, complete adaptation to the base temperature — what we call central adaptation — has to occur, but it does not occur along the whole temperature range and, I think, 39°C is about the upper boundary for the areas stimulated in our experiments.

Chapter 10

INTENSIVE AND EXTENSIVE ASPECTS OF TACTILE SENSITIVITY AS A FUNCTION OF BODY PART, SEX, AND LATERALITY*

Sidney Weinstein

THE MOTIVATION FOR THE INITIATION of the present study derived from frequent reference to a well-known textbook of physiology, the past several editions of which have shown an intriguing illustration in the chapter on somatic sensation (Ruch, Patton, Woodbury, and Towe, 1965). Depicted is the figure of a supine, hairless male with protruding tongue, staring at superior bar graphs showing two-point thresholds for various parts of his anatomy (see Fig. 10-1).

The legend specifies that the data are from Weber, cited by Sherrington (1900, in Schäfer's *Text-book of Physiology*). We traced Weber's quotation to *Muller's Archives,* published in 1835. The figure, therefore, is Ruch's interpretation of Sherrington's translation of Weber's observations made 131 years ago.

We were curious about these data in view of their age. We questioned whether the values were based on males or females, whether the right or left sides of the body had been tested, and what the size, age, and other characteristics of the group studied were.

Weber said that he had conducted a great number of such experiments upon himself and others. He wrote, "I begin to distinguish between stimuli at the following distances between points. I believe that these observations, selected from a number of others, will suffice to indicate how extremely different the sensitivity of touch is to various parts of the body." The data, therefore, seem to have been selected by Weber from observations on himself or on others, and are probably not averages, but "representative" thresholds. The number and sex of the others tested, and whether right or left sides were tested or both averaged, are among the questions which remain unanswered.

Weber's observations demonstrate the inhomogeneity of the body surface for one form of tactile sensitivity. From these data, two phenomena seem evident: (a) a proximal-distal gradient of sensitivity, and (b) a tendency for motile parts to show greater sensitivity than the nonmotile.

Recent studies have also shown a disparity between sides of the body for

*The research reported in this chapter was supported by NASA and VRA through the following grants to the author: NsG 489 and RD 1495M, respectively.

The Skin Senses

sensitivity, with the left demonstrating superiority in a majority of dextral subjects. The significance of this finding to cerebral dominance and the genetics of dextrality and sinistrality have recently been explored (Ghent, 1961; Semmes, Weinstein, Ghent, and Teuber, 1960; Sersen, Weinstein, and Vetter, 1960; Weinstein, 1962a; 1962b; 1963; 1964; Weinstein and Sersen, 1961) but only for a few body parts and not generally for spatial measures of sensation.

Contributions to the understanding of somatic sensation have also derived from more direct physiological sources such as studies involving the cerebral cortex. Thus, Penfield and his associates (Penfield and Jasper, 1954) have frequently recorded sensations from conscious patients whose cerebral cortex was electrically stimulated during craniotomy for relief of epilepsy. As a result of numerous observations, they have developed a sensory homunculus, a topographic representation of the areas of the cortex which subserve regional somatic sensation.

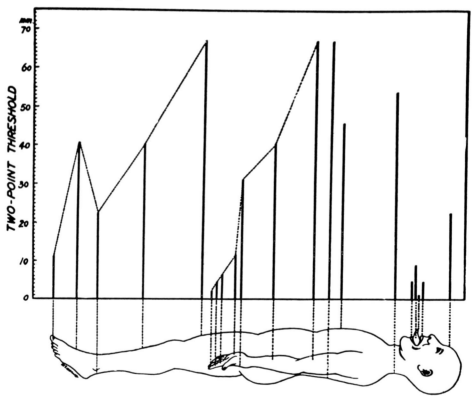

Figure 10-1. Regional variation in two-point threshold for touch. Length of vertical lines is approximately equal to magnitude of two-point threshold. Data are from Weber cited by Sherrington in Schäfer, *Text-book of Physiology*. Edinburgh, Young J. Pentland, 1900 (Fig. 12, Chapt. 14, Ruch, T. C., Patton, H. D., Woodbury, J. W., & Towe, A. L. [Eds.], *Neurophysiology* [2nd ed]. Philadelphia: W. B. Saunders, 1965).

From the sensory homunculus it can be seen that the "leg area" is at the vertex of the rolandic fissure, the "trunk area" is more lateral, the "hand area" more lateral still, and the "face area" is located near the sylvian fissure. A second fact worthy of note is that these areas are neither equal in size, nor proportional to the cutaneous areas of the structures they serve. Thus, the cortical area serving sensation of the thumb is much larger than that serving sensation of the entire trunk. Findings such as these have yielded the hypothesis that the larger the cortical area serving a given body part, the more sensitive the part. However, no previous quantitative studies have ever tested this hypothesis to the writer's knowledge.

One observation by the present writer has questioned the universality of this hypothesis, at least for pressure sensitivity. Thus, the cortical area serving sensation of the nose is smaller than that serving sensation of the thumb. Yet the peripheral sites are approximately the same size; indeed, despite the fact that the surface of the nose is slightly larger than that of the thumb, initial observations seem to indicate much greater pressure sensitivity of the nose. Experimental confirmation of this observation would question the generality of the hypothesis that size of cortical area and somatic sensation of a part are positively related. An empirical question derivable from the foregoing concerns the relationship between body parts for spatial as well as for intensive measures of sensitivity. We, therefore, decided to study the sensitivity of the body surface on right and left sides, in relatively large groups of men and women, using a variety of objective tactual measures.

METHOD

Subjects

The subjects were 24 dextral men and 24 dextral women ranging in age from 19 to 37; the mean age of the males was 22.2, and that of the females 22.0. Most were college students while others were skilled or semiskilled workers.

Sensory Measures

The three measures of sensitivity employed were the following: (a) pressure sensitivity; (b) two-point discrimination, and (c) point localization. Pressure sensitivity was measured with a set of modified von Frey-type filaments, consisting of nylon monofilaments calibrated on a chemical balance for the force exerted. The two-point aesthesiometer consisted of a pair of machinist's calipers, with two points on the jaws that could be separated from one to 120 mm. It also contained a single point whose total hemispherical surface area at the tip (3.2 mm^2) totalled that of the areas of the tips of the two single points. The final test was that of point localization. For this measure a Y-shaped grid, with the arms diverging at 120° and the tail oriented proximally, was stamped on the surfaces of the skin to be tested. There were two grids employed, one with arms marked in 1 mm, the other in 2.5 mm gradations. The single point used for two-point discrimination was also employed as the stimulus in this test.

Body Parts Tested

The parts, in one order of testing, were the pads of the distal phalanges of the fingers (little, ring, middle, index, and thumb), center of palm, volar surface of the forearm, lateral surfaces of the upper arm and shoulder, supraorbital surface of the forehead, perioral surface of the cheek, lateral surface of the nostril, nonpigmented upper lip, breast 1 cm above the areola, subscapular area of the dorsal trunk, belly lateral to the navel, ventral surface of the midthigh, dorsal surface of the midcalf, center of the sole, and the volar surface of the distal phalanx of the hallux. This order of testing was reversed in half of the group.

Experimental Design

Homologous regions of the right and left sides of the 20 body sites were studied. In half of the subjects the left side was tested first; in the other half the right was tested first. Each subject was classified according to whether the right or left side was to be tested first, and which of the two orders (of body parts) was to be employed. The order of tests was balanced, using all permutations among subjects but a constant order for each one. Each pair of body parts was completely tested in the designated order, that is right-left, or left-right for each test before the next test was employed. After completely testing a body part for all three tests, the second body part in the designated order was then tested.

Testing Procedures

For each measure of sensitivity, a modified method of limits was employed. For pressure sensitivity, six alternating ascending and descending determinations were made at each site. The mean of these six determinations comprised the pressure threshold for that site. For two-point discrimination the subject had to identify, at each separation of the two points, two double and two single stimulations randomly presented. Changes in separation of the points were dependent upon the sensitivity of the parts tested. Thus, for the facial parts and fingers the points were separated (or brought together) in 1 mm steps. For the other parts 2.5 mm steps were employed. All thresholds were determined along the longitudinal axis. The mean of six alternating ascending and descending series constituted the two-point threshold for each site. For point localization, the Y-shaped grid was stamped on each body part tested, the center of the grid was firmly touched with the above-mentioned point, and the subject was asked to use that site as the point of reference. Following stimulation of the center (reference) point, the comparison points of the arm of the Y being tested were touched with the point and the subject asked whether or not that point was the reference point. For the smaller body parts (facial, fingers) the grid with 1 mm gradations was employed; the grid with 2.5 mm gradations was employed for all others. Alternating series of stimulation, proximal and distal to the reference point were employed for each arm of the Y. The point most distant from the reference point that the subject identified as the reference point for each arm of the Y, was the error of localization for that arm. The mean of these three values was the error of localization for that body part.

Each part was carefully examined for the presence of hair, which, when present, was cut close to the skin with scissors. Testing of body parts above the waist was done while subjects were seated; for testing parts below the waist, they were supine or prone. The testing required from five to eight two-hour sessions. Subjects were paid by the hour.

RESULTS

A separate analysis of variance was computed for the data of each test. For each analysis, the "between" variable was sex; the "within" variables were the twenty body parts, and laterality. A series of rank-order correlations was also computed.

Let us first consider the results in general (Table 10-I). As a primary variable, sex was significant only for pressure, with women demonstrating

TABLE 10—I
SUMMARY OF ANALYSES OF VARIANCE FOR PRESSURE SENSITIVITY,
TWO-POINT DISCRIMINATION, AND POINT LOCALIZATION AS A
FUNCTION OF BODY PART, SEX, AND LATERALITY

Source of Variance	df	Pressure MS	Pressure F	Two-point MS	Two-point F	Point-Loc. MS	Point-Loc. F
Subjects (S)	47						
Sex (MF)	1	186.96	63.45†	236.67	<1	1.27	<1
S within MF	46	2.95		515.67		150.99	
Laterality (RL)	1	1.27	4.82	33.00	1.10	.02	<1
Body part (BP)	19	19.02	6.79†	27,745.61	151.59†	1,574.74	54.94†
RL x BP	19	.16	4.58†	29.89	1.62*	2.30	<1
S x BP	893						
BP x MF	19	2.80	9.49†	183.03	1.80*	28.66	1.78*
BP x S within MF	874	.30		101.81		16.14	
RL x S	47						
RL x MF	1	.26	4.49*	.28	<1	4.58	1.15
RL x S within MF	46	.06		23.87		3.99	
BR x RL x S	893						
BR x RL x MF	19	.04	1.04	10.05	<1	2.19	<1
BP x RL x S within MF	874	.03		18.47		4.86	

*p<.05
†p<.01

significantly greater sensitivity than men. In addition, for all three sensory measures there was a body part × sex interaction. For all three measures of sensitivity, body part was a highly significant variable. For none of the measures was laterality a significant primary variable, that is, there were no overall differences between right and left sides for any measure. However, for pressure sensitivity, laterality interacted significantly both with body part, and with sex. For two-point discrimination, laterality interacted with body part. For point localization laterality did not interact significantly.

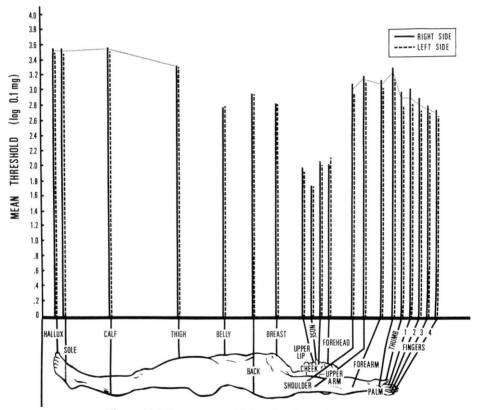

Figure 10-2. Pressure sensitivity thresholds for males.

Figure 10-2 gives the pressure sensitivity thresholds for the right and left sides of the body for male subjects. It can be seen, first of all, that the most sensitive part is the face. The trunk tends to rank next in sensitivity, followed by the fingers and upper extremity, in general. Finally, the least sensitive body parts tend to be those of the lower extremity. Laterality differences will be considered below.

Figure 10-3 gives the data for pressure sensitivity of the female. Essentially the same results were obtained. That is, the facial parts were most

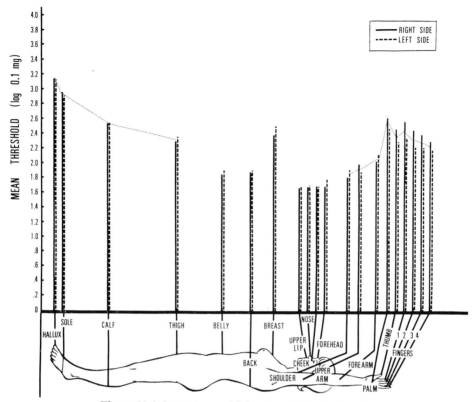

Figure 10-3. Pressure sensitivity thresholds for females.

sensitive, the trunk and upper extremity parts next most sensitive, and the lower extremities least sensitive. There was a general female superiority for pressure sensitivity as well as a significant body part × sex interaction, which we will discuss below.

Figure 10-4 gives the data for two-point discrimination on right and left sides for each body part for the males. For this measure, body part was a significant variable, as were the body part × laterality, and body part × sex interactions. Here, it can be seen that the most sensitive body parts were the fingers, and next the face and feet.

The data for the females (Fig. 10-5) tend to parallel those of the males. However, there were sex × part, and laterality × part interactions. The specifics of these interactions will be considered in the figures concerned with the statistical comparisons.

For the final measure of sensitivity, point localization, it can be seen (Fig. 10-6) that body part was a highly significant variable. The most sensitive parts were the fingers, the face, and the hallux. The rest of the upper and lower extremities, and the trunk were less sensitive than these parts.

The data on the females for point localization (Fig. 10-7) are quite similar to those of the males, with several specific differences for various parts.

The next series of figures are concerned with the statistical significance of the analyses. Figure 10-8 shows the rank order of sensitivity of the 20 body parts for each measure, regardless of sex or laterality, with the most sensitive part at the top. First note the low, nonsignificant correlations between pressure and each of the spatial measures, and the high (.92) correlation between two-point discrimination and point localization.

The bracketed parts do not differ significantly from each other; all parts which are *not* included within the *same* bracket differ significantly. The horizontal, dotted lines indicate significant differences between all parts separated by them. Thus, for pressure, note that the four facial parts differ significantly from all others. For two-point, the hallux and all parts above it are significantly more sensitive than the forehead and all parts below; the sole and all parts above it are significantly more sensitive than the belly and all parts listed below it.

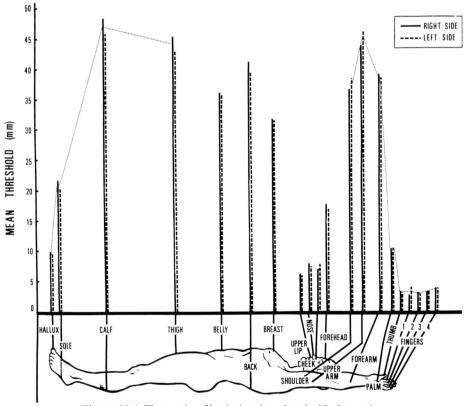

Figure 10-4. Two-point discrimination thresholds for males.

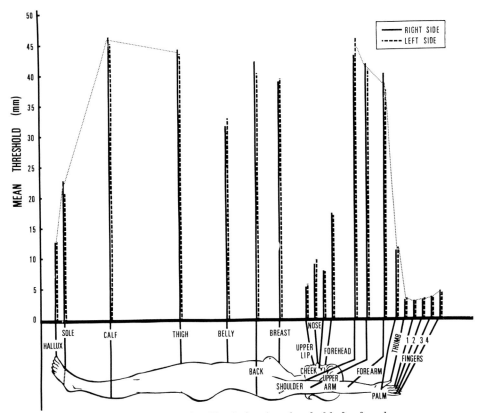

Figure 10-5. Two-point discrimination thresholds for females.

For point localization the forehead and all points listed above it are significantly more sensitive than the palm and all parts below it. It is interesting to note that whereas the forehead is significantly more sensitive than the palm for both pressure and point localization, the opposite relationship is significant for two-point discrimination, demonstrating a double dissociation of body parts for these measures.

The forehead and hallux also demonstrate a double dissociation. The forehead, one of the more sensitive areas of the body for pressure (rank 4) significantly exceeded the hallux (rank 20) in sensitivity. However, these parts are not only adjacent in rank for the two spatial measures (10 and 11 for two-point, and 9 and 10 for point localization), but the relationship is significantly reversed for two-point.

A converse relationship held for the forehead and sole. For these two parts all three measures yielded the same results. The forehead was more sensitive, and significantly so, for pressure and point localization. This similarity of the relationship held despite the disparity of their relative

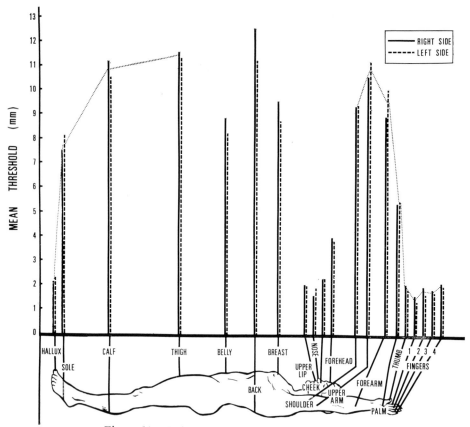

Figure 10-6. Point localization thresholds for males.

ranks. Thus, the forehead ranked 4th, and the sole 19th for pressure; the same parts had adjacent ranks (11 and 12) for two-point and almost adjacent ones (10 and 12) for point localization.

In view of the theoretical consequences raised earlier concerning the nose and thumb, it is worthy of note that the nose is a great deal more sensitive for pressure than the thumb (rank 1 versus 13). For two-point, however, the data show a double dissociation, with the thumb significantly better (rank 3) than the nose (rank 8).

Another disparity in relative sensitivities is that of the index finger and lip. These ranked 1 and 2 respectively for point localization but showed a significantly opposite relationship for pressure (ranks 15 and 2).

The thigh and the sole are among the least sensitive of all parts for all measures. Yet, here too, a double dissociation occurred. The thigh (rank 16) was significantly better than the sole (rank 19) for pressure. However, it was significantly poorer than the sole for the two spatial measures.

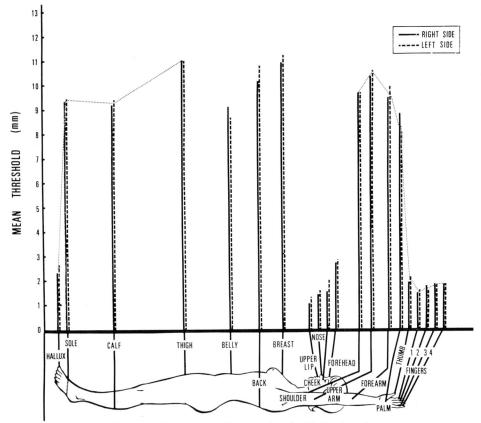

Figure 10-7. Point localization thresholds for females.

Despite great differences in the relative sensitivity of a given part for different measures, it frequently maintained its relative superiority to other body-parts on all measures. A case in point is that of the index finger, which ranked 2 and 1 for two-point and point localization respectively and only 15 for pressure. However, despite the large disparity of its relative rank difference between measures it maintained the same (significant) superiority over parts such as the calf, sole, and hallux. An example of significant identity of relationships between body parts for sensitivity across all measures is that of the forehead and belly. The former was significantly superior for all three measures.

Figure 10-9 deals with the sex × body part interaction for pressure sensitivity. For this measure, the rank-order correlation between the male and female means was .73 (p <.001). The first two columns are organized with the most sensitive parts for each sex at the top. The column of differences at the right gives increasingly greater differences at the bottom. It can be seen that the females were significantly more sensitive than the males on all parts except the nose. The facial parts showed the smallest, and the upper and lower extremities and the trunk the greatest female superiority.

Rank Order of Body Parts

for Three Measures of Tactual Sensitivity

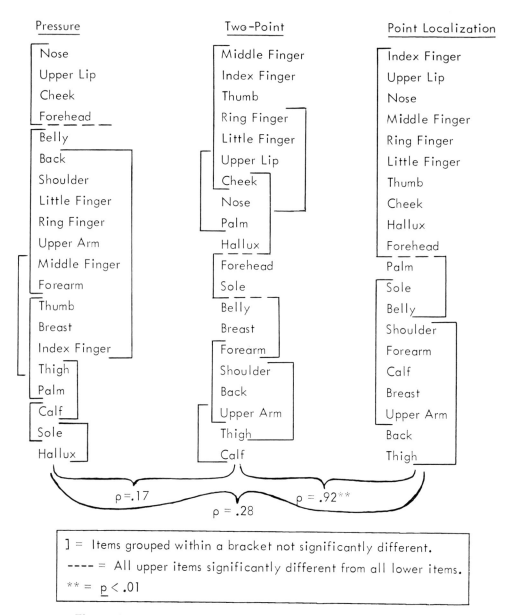

Figure 10-8. Rank order of body parts for three measures of sensitivity.

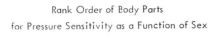

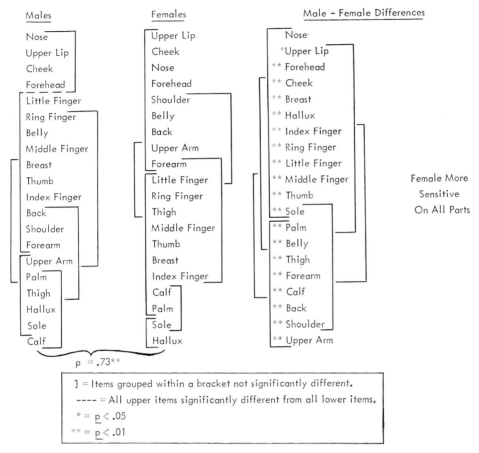

Figure 10-9. Rank order of body parts for pressure sensitivity as a function of sex.

Figure 10-10 deals with the sex × body part interaction for two-point discrimination. The correlation between the means of the body parts was .96, indicating very little difference in rank orders for the sexes. Quite unexpectedly, the males were superior to the females on a majority of parts for this measure, with the breast and shoulder showing the greatest (significant) male superiority.

Figure 10-11 concerns the sex × body part interaction for point localization. The rank-order correlation between the sexes was .89. Unexpectedly, the males showed significantly greater superiority over the females for the palm and the breast for this measure. In general, however, neither sex showed greater sensory superiority.

Rank Order of Body Parts
for Two-Point Discrimination as a Function of Sex

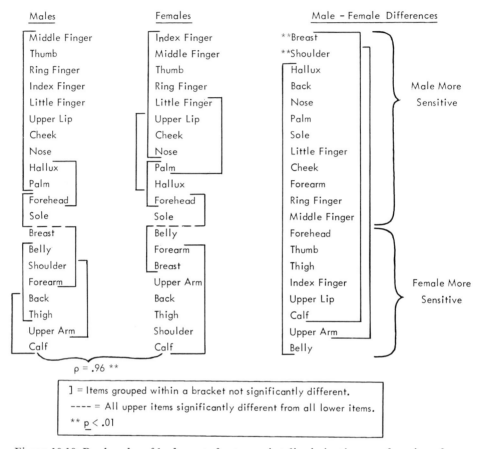

Figure 10-10. Rank order of body parts for two-point discrimination as a function of sex.

The next two figures deal with the interaction of body part × laterality. Figure 10-12 shows the interaction for pressure. Note first of all that the correlation between the sides is .96, indicating extremely close correspondence between sensitivity of the sides, and also, incidentally, extremely good reliability for this measure.

It should also be noted that with the exception of two facial and two truncal parts, all body parts were more sensitive on the left side. The final figure (Figure 10-13) concerns the laterality × body part interaction for two-point discrimination. Again, note the extremely high correlation (.99) between the rank orders of sensitivity of the two sides. For this measure, the sides tend to be equally divided in terms of sensitivity. However, five of the differences favored the left side significantly.

In the final series of analyses, rank-order correlations were computed between the body parts ranked for sensitivity on each measure versus various rankings of gross anatomy (rostral-caudal, medial-lateral, and body-surface area) and neuroanatomy (cortical homunculus area, corrected and uncorrected for size of body part, dermatomal position, and cortical locus). (See Table 10-II.)

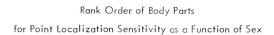

Rank Order of Body Parts

for Point Localization Sensitivity as a Function of Sex

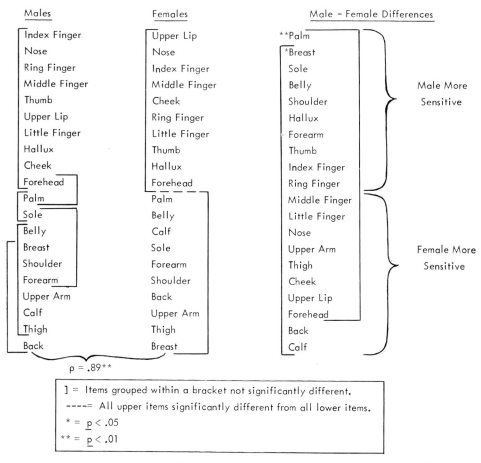

Figure 10-11. Rank order of body parts for point localization as a function of sex.

Table 10-II is organized so that the left column indicates the anatomical variable being related to the sensory measures in the column to its right. The two right columns contain the rank-order correlations between the anatomical and sensory measures for males and females.

TABLE 10—II
RANK-ORDER CORRELATIONS BETWEEN SENSITIVITY
AND ANATOMICAL MEASURES

Anatomical Measures	Sensory Measures	Male	Female
Rostral to caudal	Pressure	.67†	.83‡
rank of body parts	2-pt	−.05	−.06
(forehead to hallux)	Point Loc	.01	.09
Dermatomal	Pressure	.66†	.73‡
rank (rostral to	2-pt	.28	.30
caudal)	Point Loc	.35	.42
Medial to	Pressure	.54*	.83†
lateral	2-pt	−.30	−.30
rank	Point Loc	−.21	−.03
Cutaneous surface	Pressure	.51*	.03
area rank (lip to	2-pt	.83‡	.80‡
back)	Point Loc	.88‡	.81‡
Homunculus	Pressure	.07	−.14
(total	2-pt	.52*	.56*
area)	Point Loc	.51*	.52*
Homunculus	Pressure	.36	−.003
(area corrected for	2-pt	.71‡	.70‡
body part size)	Point Loc	.76‡	.77‡
Cortical locus	Pressure	.81‡	.57†
(vertex to	2-pt	.64†	.67†
lateral)	Point Loc	.65†	.72‡

*$p<.05$
†$p<.01$
‡$p<.001$

The first set of correlations concerns the rostral-caudal ordering of the body parts. It can be seen that for pressure sensitivity, the more rostral the body part, the greater the sensitivity. This was true for males and for females. However, the correlations with this anatomical variable and sensitivity were consistently of zero magnitude for both sexes on both spatial measures.

When dermatomal rank, rather than gross anatomical rank, was related to the sensory measures, pressure sensitivity, again, was highly significantly related to the rank along the rostral-caudal continuum. For this measure, although the spatial measures did not yield significant correlations, they were not of zero magnitude as for the gross ranking of the parts. Instead, the correlations for both sexes and both spatial measures ranged from .28 to .42.

The third anatomical variable related to sensation was medial-lateral ranking. Here the parts were organized along a continuum from the center of the body to the periphery. Again the correlations with pressure sensitivity were significant for both males and females, with females showing the greater correlation. Unlike rostral-caudal ranking which had zero magnitude correlations for the spatial measures, or dermatomal ranking with which the spatial measures correlated positively and low, the medial-lateral ranking correlated consistently low and negative with the spatial measures.

The next anatomical measure studied was total cutaneous surface area

Rank Order of Body Parts
for Pressure Sensitivity as a Function of Laterality

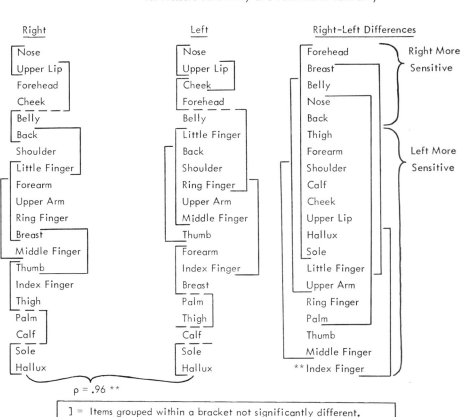

Figure 10-12. Rank order of body parts for pressure sensitivity as a function of laterality.

for each body part. Here the parts were ranked from the smallest in surface area (lip) to the largest (back). Unlike the previous measures, it can be seen that the two spatial measures correlated from .80 to .88 for both sexes. Also, this time, the sexes showed different correlations for pressure sensitivity; the males had a moderately high significant positive correlation (.51) whereas that for the females was .03.

The next two sets of correlations involved aspects of the sensory homunculus of Penfield (Penfield and Jasper, 1954). Measures of the cortical area subserving each body part studied were made directly from the published figure. These areas were ranked from largest to smallest, and correlated with the sensitivity ranks of the sensory measures. It can be seen that cortical

Rank Order of Body Parts

for Two-Point Discrimination as a Function of Laterality

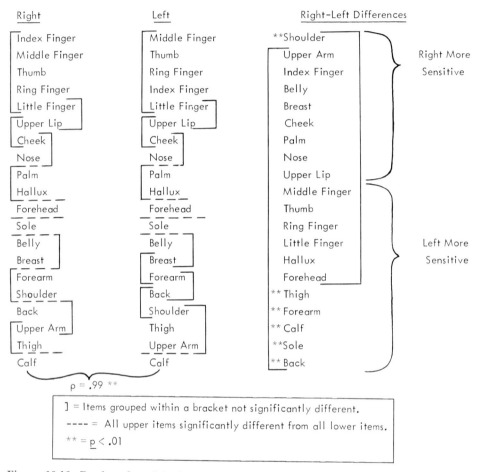

Figure 10-13. Rank order of body parts for two-point discrimination as a function of laterality.

size was correlated significantly and positively with the two measures of spatial sensitivity for both sexes, but not for pressure for either sex.

Since the body parts are extremely disparate with regard to their cutaneous surfaces, measures of cortical area subserving each part do not give an indication of the relative proportion of cortical neurons subserving a given unit of cutaneous surface. To achieve such an index, some ratio of both the cortical and the cutaneous areas should be made. We corrected the ranking of the cortical areas to compensate for disparities between relative body part size and size of cortical representation by dividing the homunculus area serving each body part by the rank of the cutaneous area of the body part in question. Thus, the lip had the largest homunculus area and ranked first for body surface area; its rank for the corrected homunculus was therefore also first. The sole had the second largest homunculus area; however, its cutaneous body area ranked twelfth, bringing its corrected homunculus area down to fifth.

When the corrected homunculus was correlated with the sensory measures, the correlations with the spatial measures increased about .20, on the average, over those for the uncorrected homunculus for both sexes. The correlation with pressure for the females remained negative and quite low; the correlation for the males increased from .07 to .36, but remained nonsignificant.

The final series of correlations concerned the position of the cortical representations of the body parts along the lateral surface of the cortex from vertex to the sylvian fissure. Here, for both sexes, significant positive correlations were obtained with all three measures of sensitivity, indicating that sensitivity increases as the representation of the part goes from the vertex, caudally along the lateral cortical surface to the sylvian fissure.

DISCUSSION

There were several hypotheses that were considered in this study. Probably the major one predicted a proximal-distal gradient of sensitivity on all limbs, with the more distal regions being the more sensitive.

With regard to the two spatial measures of sensitivity, it can be said that moderately good confirmation of this hypothesis was obtained, with some exceptions. However, for the intensive measure, pressure sensitivity, quite the reverse findings were obtained.

For two-point discrimination there was fair confirmation for the hypothesis. The proximal-distal gradients were maintained for the upper extremities. That is, the fingers were significantly more sensitive than the palm, which was significantly more sensitive than the forearm, shoulder, and upper arm. This order maintained the gradient with only one reversal. For the lower extremities essentially the same result was obtained. That is, the hallux was significantly more sensitive than the sole, which was significantly more sensitive than the thigh and calf. However, the latter two parts were reversed in order of sensitivity although they did not differ significantly. For point localization, the hypothesis was also fairly well confirmed. For the upper extremity, the fingers were significantly more sensitive than the second most sensitive part, the palm, which was significantly more sensitive than the shoulder and the forearm in that order. The least sensitive part was the upper arm. This part did not differ significantly from the forearm and shoulder although, according to the hypothesis, it should have been more sensitive than either. For the lower extremities, the hallux was significantly more sensitive than all the other parts. The remaining order was sole, calf, and thigh. Although the sole was significantly more sensitive than the thigh, neither sole nor thigh differed significantly from the calf.

For pressure sensitivity, a good argument could be made that the data were opposite to the predictions of the gradient hypothesis. That is, with regard to the upper extremities, the most sensitive part was the shoulder and the least sensitive part the palm. The order of sensitivity from highest to least was not consistent. For the females, the forearm was slightly better than the fingers, although the tendency for the reverse was true for the males. For the lower extremities, the obtained order was exactly opposite to that predicted. That is, the thigh was more sensitive than the calf, which was more sensitive than the sole, which was, in turn, more sensitive than the hallux.

In a previous study (Weinstein, 1962b) dealing with pressure sensitivity of the digital phalanges, the second most sensitive tended to be the proximal, rather than the middle phalanx, although the distal phalanx was generally found to be the most sensitive.

The second hypothesis proposed a superiority of the left side of the body for each measure of sensitivity. This hypothesis was also partially confirmed and partially rejected. It was rejected for point localization, and only partially confirmed for pressure sensitivity and two-point discrimination. The left side tended to be more sensitive than the right in a majority of parts for the latter measures. These laterality differences tend to confirm the results reported by Semmes *et al.* (1960), Weinstein (1962a; 1962b; 1963; 1964), Weinstein and Sersen (1961), Ghent (1961) and by Sersen, Weinstein, and Vetter (1966) on the extremities. The expected generality of the left-sided superiority, however, was not extended to the head and trunk. The discrepancy between the results for the extremities, and those for the head and trunk cannot be explained at present. The hypothesis that callus could account for the laterality differences between the parts has already been rejected in the studies of Weinstein and Sersen (1961), and Ghent (1961). The reason for the similarity in this respect, of pressure and one of the spatial measures (two-point discrimination) but not the other is also a matter for conjecture at this time.

The third hypothesis predicted a significant, positive relationship between the size of the primary projection cortical region subserving a given part and the sensitivity of that part. This hypothesis was confirmed for the two spatial measures, but not for pressure sensitivity. When the cortical areas were correlated with the rank order of the parts according to sensitivity, pressure sensitivity failed to yield a significant relationship, in contrast to the spatial measures. In fact, for the example discussed above, the nose, which ranked first for pressure sensitivity, ranked ninth in size of homunculus area; the thumb, which ranked thirteenth in sensitivity, ranked third according to size of homunculus. The results, taken in conjunction with correlations of pressure sensitivity with gross anatomical measures and with dermatomal rank, seem to indicate a greater dependence of spatial resolution, and relative independence of intensity on size of cortex.

The fourth hypothesis proposed that the rank order of sensitivity of the two sides of the body would be significantly the same for all measures. This hypothesis was well confirmed, since the correlations between the sides for all measures ranged from .96 to .99, indicating that despite any absolute laterality differences, the relationship among the parts on any side tended to remain relatively constant for both sides.

Of interest, too, were the unexpected sex differences. Thus, whereas the females were more sensitive than the males on *all* body parts for pressure, they were only more sensitive than the males for ten of the twenty body parts for point localization, and were more sensitive on only eight parts for two-point discrimination. Thus, the female breast was more sensitive than the male breast for pressure, but *less* sensitive for the two spatial measures. Although these data are derived from sex differences in sensitivity, they may reflect actual size differences for the body parts between the sexes. Thus, we have seen that the large truncal parts (belly, back) were more sensitive than all nonfacial parts. It would appear that the size of the cutaneous area of a part may be positively related to intensive and negatively to extensive measures of sensitivity.

A related finding was obtained for the palm for which the size relationship between the sexes is opposite to that for the breast. That is, the female palm (the smaller) was more sensitive than the male palm for pressure, but less sensitive for point localization. Here, a tenable hypothesis which might be offered is that of practice; the experience which thickens the male skin may facilitate its spatial resolution.

An interesting observation concerning the differences between the males and females is derived from the correlations in Table 10-II. With very few exceptions the correlations between the anatomical measures and spatial measures of sensitivity were very similar for males and females, frequently approaching identity. However, when pressure sensitivity is considered, the females showed greater correlations than the males for the body-surface measures, and the males greater correlations for the cortical measures. These differences between the sexes cannot be presently explained. Possibly, differences in body size, hormonal concentrations, or their interaction may play some role in these relationships.

The empirical finding that proximal-distal gradients of sensitivity hold only partially, and only for spatial measures, is more than balanced by the new finding that cortical locus is positively related to both intensive and extensive measures, and that this neuroanatomical measure may enable a partial prediction of those sensory gradients which exist. Sensitivity, in general, increased as the cortical representation for the body part was located more laterally from vertex to sylvian fissure. It might be hypothesized that the more lateral the presentation the more sensitive the part since the more lateral, rather than the rostral cortex, may be more closely and more densely integrated with subcortical, possibly thalamic, structures.

The possible concomitance of cortical locus and cortical size of the representation also cannot be ignored. Reference to the relative rank orders of cortical locus and cortical representation size (Appendix) shows that these ranks are somewhat similar (mdn rank difference = 4.0).

Of great interest were the differences and similarities obtained between the intensive and extensive measures of sensitivity. Firstly, there were body part × laterality interactions for pressure and for two-point discrimination, with general superiority of the left side. This laterality difference was not obtained for point localization. Secondly, although some proximal-distal gradients of sensitivity were found to exist for the spatial measures as well as for pressure sensitivity, they were actually opposite in direction. That is, whereas the more distal parts were more sensitive than the proximal for the spatial measures, the proximal parts tended to be more sensitive than the distal for pressure. Thirdly, although the extent of cortical area serving the part was strongly related to its sensitivity for the spatial measures, it was unrelated to pressure sensitivity. The rostral-caudal and dermatomal ranks, on the other hand, were strongly related to pressure sensitivity but not to the two spatial measures. Finally, the various double dissociations between the two types of sensory measures (forehead versus hallux, palm, and belly; thigh versus sole; and nose versus thumb) demonstrate clearly the independent nature of the sensory measures.

The similarities between intensity and extensity are found essentially in the positive correlations of both sets of measures with cortical locus. Other similarities are found, e.g., in the identical dissociations of forehead from palm, belly, and sole and index finger from leg parts for pressure, and at least for one of the spatial measures.

The obtained similarities and differences between the data for the spatial and the intensive measures would seem to indicate certain similarities as well as differences in the modes of sensory organization of the nervous system. From our data it would seem as though cortical size may play a greater role with regard to spatial measures, subcortical or spinal cord structures a greater role with regard to pressure sensitivity, and cortical locus an equal role for both types of sensitivity.

The differences between the sides of the body for pressure sensitivity, and for two-point discrimination but not for point localization seem somewhat paradoxical. If the spatial measures are relatively more dependent upon cortical organization than pressure sensitivtiy, one would expect that the known differences between the two hemispheres for complex measures such as speech would result in differences in sensitivity for the spatial measures but not for intensive measures. The fact that the opposite relationship tended to be true seems to indicate that interaction with subcortical structures may be responsible for the difference between the sides of the body for pressure sensitivity.

In any event, regardless of which hypothesis may be confirmed in the future, it appears safe to say that no longer can studies dealing with somatic sensation fail to specify the nature of the sensory measure employed, nor ignore the locus or laterality of the body part, nor the sex of the subject.

SUMMARY

1. Somatic sensation is not a unitary function with regard to sex, laterality, body part, or intensive versus extensive measures.

2. Body parts may be sensitive on either, neither, or both the intensive and extensive measures of sensitivity.

3. Women were significantly more sensitive than men for pressure sensitivity. This superiority did not hold true for the extensive measure of sensitivity.

4. Depending upon whether the measure is intensive or extensive, males and females may show significantly opposite sensitivities for the same body parts.

5. Significant laterality differences were obtained for the intensive and one of the extensive measures of sensitivity. Some body parts were significantly better on the right, others were significantly better on the left for these measures.

6. Significant relationships were obtained between sensitivity and both size and position of the cortical representation in the cortex, and between sensitivity and the size and position of the body part. Some of these relationships were true for the intensive measure, some for the spatial measures, and some for both sets of measures.

ACKNOWLEDGMENT

The author is grateful to Deanna Weinstein and Solomon Steiner for testing the female and male subjects, respectively.

REFERENCES

Ghent, L. Developmental changes in tactual thresholds on dominant and nondominant sides. *J. Comp. Physiol. Psychol.*, 1961, **54**, 670.

Penfield, W., & Jasper, H. *Epilepsy and the Functional Anatomy of the Human Brain.* Boston: Little, Brown, & Co., 1954.

Ruch, T. C., Patton, H. D., Woodbury, J. W., & Towe, A. L. (Eds.), *Neurophysiology.* Philadelphia: W. B. Saunders, 1965.

Semmes, J., Weinstein, S., Ghent, L., & Teuber, H. L. *Somatosensory Changes after Penetrating Brain Wounds in Man.* Cambridge: Harvard University, 1960.

Sersen, E. A., Weinstein, S., & Vetter, R. J. Laterality differences in tactile sensitivity as a function of handedness, familial background of handedness, and sex. Paper presented at East. Psychol. Assoc., New York, 1966.

Sherrington, C. S. Cutaneous sensation. In E. A. Schäfer, (Ed.), *Text-book of Physiology.* London: Young J. Pentland, 1900. Pp. 920-1001.

Weber, E. H. Uber den Tastsinn. *Archiv. fur Anatomie, Physiologie, und Wissenschaft-liche Medicin.,* 1835, 152.

Weinstein, S. Differences in effects of brain wounds implicating right or left hemispheres: Differential effects on certain intellectual and complex perceptual functions. In V. B. Mountcastle (Ed.), *Interhemispheric Relations and Cerebral Dominance.* Baltimore: Johns Hopkins University, 1962. Pp. 159-176. (a)

Weinstein, S. Tactile sensitivity of the phalanges. *Percept. Motor Skills,* 1962, **14,** 351. (b)

Weinstein, S. The relationship of laterality and cutaneous area to breast-sensitivity in sinistrals and dextrals. *Amer. J. Psychol.,* 1963, **76,** 475.

Weinstein, S. Functional asymmetries of right and left cerebral hemispheres. Presidential address to Division of Physiological and Comparative Psychology of Amer. Psychol. Assoc., Los Angeles, 1964.

Weinstein, S., & Sersen, E. A. Tactual sensitivity as a function of handedness and laterality. *J. Comp. Physiol. Psychol.,* 1961, **54,** 665.

APPENDIX
RANK ORDER OF BODY PARTS ACCORDING TO VARIOUS CLASSIFICATIONS

Rank	Rostral-Caudal	Derma-tomal	Medial-Lateral	Body Surface Area	Homun-culus Area	Corrected Homun-culus	Cortical Locus
1	FH	FH	No	Li	Li	Li	Li
2	No	No	Li	No	So	No	Ch
3	Li	Li	FH	LF	Thu	Thu	No
4	Ch	Ch	Ch	Thu	MF	LF	FH
5	Sh	Sh	Be	Ha	RF	So	Thu
6	Br	Ua	Ba	IF	FA	RF	IF
7	Ua	FA	Br	RF	LF	MF	MF
8	Ba	Thu	Sh	MF	IF	IF	RF
9	Be	IF	Ua	FH	No	Ha	LF
10	FA	Pa	Thi	Pa	Ha	FH	Pa
11	Pa	MF	FA	Ch	Thi	Ch	FA
12	Thu	RF	Ca	So	Ca	Ca	Ua
13	LF	LF	Pa	Br	Thi	Ua	Sh
14	IF	Br	Thu	Sh	Pa	FH	Br
15	RF	Ba	LF	FA	Ua	Ch	Ba
16	MF	Be	IF	Ua	FA	Ba	Be
17	Thi	Thi	RF	Ca	Sh	Sh	Thi
18	Ca	Ca	MF	Thi	Ba	Pa	Ca
19	So	Ha	So	Be	Br	Br	So
20	Ha	So	Ha	Ba	Be	Be	Ha

Note. Abbreviations are defined as follows: lip (Li), nose (No), little, ring, middle, and index fingers (LF, RF, MF, IF), sole (So), hallux (Ha), forehead and forearm (FH, FA), thumb and thigh (Thu, Thi), cheek (Ch), calf (Ca), palm (Pa), upper arm (Ua), shoulder (Sh), back (Ba), belly (Be), breast (Br).

DISCUSSION

Dr. R. T. Verrillo: Has the two-point threshold picture changed significantly in the past 130 years?

Dr. Weinstein: No, I should have pointed out that, in spite of this bemusement about the figure based on Weber's data, our data are in good agreement with his.

Dr. C. E. Sherrick: My question has to do with the rank order of the body parts for pressure sensitivity. Did you use a masking noise when you tested the face areas for pressure sensitivity? There are indications that an individual may respond to a sound and think he is responding to a pressure.

Dr. Weinstein: We are aware of this. We have been testing pressure sensitivity using these devices for about fifteen years. The first time that we became aware that this was a very relevant point was when we put on starched white coats. As soon as we rustled a little bit the subjects would claim that they felt a sensation. We wondered about this. We might have postulated ESP, etc. but finally concluded that it was obviously an auditory cue. We now routinely introduce sham stimulations among the measurements so that we think we are getting a pretty reliable indication of tactual, not auditory, sensitivity. As a matter of fact, I think the extremely high correlations are an indication that they are quite reliable, unless you think it indicates high auditory reliability.

Dr. Sherrick: No, the point I am making does not have to do with the auditory stimulation that comes in connection with the movement of the experimenter, but with the actual touching of the face; in other words, by bone conduction.

Dr. Weinstein: We are concerned here with absolute pressure sensitivity, which means that for the face we are using something like 3 or 4 mg of force. You could not possibly get a sound from that. Stimulation is from small filaments which require only a few mg of force to bend them. Even with the filaments which require 5 gm of force to bend, there is no sound. Actually, even with the largest filaments, the most that would occur would be for them to penetrate the tissue, very much as a pin would; we would not have any sound from that either.

Dr. R. Melzack: Could you tell us something about the individual differences? There is an interesting paper by Halnan and Wright (1960) on tactile localization as a function of experience and use of different body parts, and I was wondering if that might not account in part for the differences between the males and the females. Also, I wonder if your method might not be useful for looking at individual differences among people who have certain kinds of skills, to see whether the rank order might not differ as a result of that experience.

DR. WEINSTEIN: We did not look at individual differences in this investigation. We have, in the past, done things like testing different occupational groups. The first thing we did, in the attempt to establish a normative group, was to use the psychologists, neurologists, and psychiatrists around the hospital as subjects. Then, of course, we raised the question, "Are they representative of the general population?" and the answer is, "They are not." They are much more sensitive than the general population. As for employing individuals with specific skills, aside from the fact that there may be possible intellectual differences which help the person establish a criterion, I do not think that their experience really helps them. There was a dissertation done several years ago by Axelrod (1959) who used these devices to test blind and sighted children. There was no particular superiority of the blind children on these measures, in spite of the fact that they used their hands to read braille. So I would tend to doubt whether you would get a specific occupation or group which shows a superior tactual sensitivity. The superiority of the group of highly educated subjects which I mentioned earlier is probably related to their ability to define a criterion more easily than the average person.

DR. A. IGGO: I think it is possible to suggest at least one group which might have some variation in its sensitivity. This is the group of people who test woolen fabrics. Their job is to run their fingers under these fabrics which are passing by in a roll. They eventually wear thin the epidermis of their fingers and there is a very considerable increase in sensitivity in that group.

DR. WEINSTEIN: In a study of texture discrimination we developed a test comprising eighteen textures, running from silk and satin all the way to burlap. We had, as one subject, a textile salesman who amazed us because he got a nearly perfect score. It turned out, of course, that he did this sort of thing daily. Interestingly enough, though, his sensitivity on the psychophysical measures was not any better than the mean of the group. I think what happens here is that these people use experience to pick up certain cues. For example, in rubbing your hand along burlap, there might be a degree of friction which would resist finger movement, more so than with the smoother ones. I think one of them — silk or satin — also tends to produce a cooler sensation. Apparently there must be some form of thermal conduction. I think it is rather more the use of experience to evaluate subtle cues than a basic change in the absolute pressure sensitivity levels. Although we have not done this systematically, the one case does seem to indicate that experience does not improve absolute sensitivity as measured by psychophysics.

DR. MELZACK: It seems possible that the texture itself could serve as a basis for discrimination. I am thinking here of Diamond and Neff's work

(1957) on discrimination of auditory signals in the monkey. Cortical ablation fails to affect the discrimination of single tones, but disrupts pattern discrimination, in which cortex plays a more important role. Why was this man unable to make the two-point discrimination, but perform so well on the basis of tactual texture?

DR. WEINSTEIN: You are asking why he did not perform well on these tests using the same cues he used for the texture discrimination?

DR. MELZACK: Yes.

DR. WEINSTEIN: Well, it is quite different; I think that these are highly specific abilities. For example, in being tested many times myself, I developed a rather good threshold for pressure sensitivity only because I became aware of the different qualities of sensation that could be present when one is touched with a light filament. For example, you often feel a slight coolness; you learn that this is correlated with the touch and this helps you reduce your threshold. However, this is something that you have to develop on the individual tests. We found no one, regardless of any particular skill with his hands, with any unusual abilities on these psychophysical measures.

DR. IGGO: Could I cite one other example? This is a bank clerk who had the misfortune to have damage to his median nerve and, to all of these tests employed by the neurologists, he had recovered perfect cutaneous sensibilities in his hands, but he could no longer count bank notes. This presumably was due to the fact that the testing did not have the level of discrimination which was required to do the ordinary, everyday tasks. What I am really suggesting is that the tests that you employ are not sufficiently discriminative.

DR. WEINSTEIN: With regard to the median nerve, is that not a mixed nerve and might this therefore not have been a motor impairment?

DR. IGGO: There were no tests which revealed any disturbance.

DR. W. A. ROSENBLITH: I wonder whether we are really communicating with you. What you have shown is that in your populations there do not seem to exist large individual differences in tactile sensitivity.

DR. WEINSTEIN: I did not say that. I said that I do not know what the individual differences are.

DR. ROSENBLITH: Well, they were not so striking that you specifically investigated them. You tested practically everything else. What has been said here is that there are more sophisticated discriminations, multidimensional discriminations if you will, which may constitute a sensory capacity like the ones you have been testing but for which the generality of your conclusions might be only very partially confirmed.

DR. WEINSTEIN: It would depend on what your criterion of somatic sensation is. If we are going to deal with the term *sensation,* it is incumbent upon us to rule out factors which obviously relate to training. We have tested any number of discriminations, two-dimensional and three-dimensional, size discrimination, pattern discrimination, three-dimensional shape discrimination, texture discrimination, roughness discrimination, weight, etc., possibly thirty different types of discrimination. We never got very much of a correlation between these measures and the more primary indexes, e.g., absolute and two-point sensitivity. Somehow, training does seem to help these learned abilities, but if you want to consider performance on that basis as a criterion for sensation, you would have as many operational definitions of sensation as you could devise tests. It must be pointed out that these are first, classical measures; second, they seem to be as simple as we could get them. Even an earthworm will respond to a slight touch, but you cannot ask him to discriminate burlap from wool. I consider the former, but not the latter, sensation.

References

Axelrod, S. Effects of early blindness, performance of blind and sighted children on tactile and auditory tasks. *Amer. Foundation for the Blind, Research Series,* 1959, **1**, 1.

Diamond, I. T. & Neff, W. D. Ablation of temporal cortex and discrimination of auditory patterns. *J. Neurophysiol.,* 1957, **20**, 300.

Halnan, C. R. E., & Wright, G. H. Tactile localization. *Brain,* 1960, **83**, 677.

Chapter 11

ELECTRICAL STIMULATION OF
PAIN AND TOUCH*

ROBERT H. GIBSON

Various attempts have been made over the past century to devise cutaneous communication systems as visual and auditory supplements, but none has provided speed or complexity comparable to information transmission through visual channels. Major progress in cutaneous communication requires knowledge of perceptual properties of touch. The presently limited nature of cutaneous communication reflects the failure to make effective use of these properties, rather than reflecting any inherent limitation of the touch sense.

To find whether cutaneous channels are effective for receiving more than simple, unidimensional warning information or slow speech transliteration, it is essential to determine perceptual properties of stimuli varied systematically along temporal and spatial dimensions. Large, artificial tactile displays are needed, composed of many stimulus elements capable of complex variation over space and time. One impediment to acquiring knowledge of perceptual properties of touch has been poor stimulus control. For example, vibrators are bulky and inconvenient to couple to the body in a manner which successfully avoids intensity variation with body movement. Even good cutaneous vibrators do not respond well to rapid changes in the temporal characteristics of the stimulus, which limits the potential complexity of the stimulus used.

Unlike mechanical stimuli which are impeded in their movement by their own mass and by tissue factors, certain electrical stimuli are capable of a wide range of temporal variation. Electricity shares this desirable property with light and sound stimuli. Also, electrical stimuli provide flexibility in the control of spatial factors, since approximately two square yards of skin are available (Rothman, 1954), and electrodes are easy to attach.

Under suitable conditions, direct electrical stimulation of the skin will arouse touch sensations similar to those from vibration or brief contact. With the appropriate electrode size, certain electric waveforms at three times threshold require an average power expenditure of 50 milliwatts,

*This work was supported in part by the National Science Foundation (B 15440), the National Institute of Neurological Diseases and Blindness (NB-06304), The American Foundation for the Blind, The Seeing Eye, and an institutional grant to the University of Pittsburgh from the National Aeronautics and Space Administration.

less than 1 per cent of that used by an efficient mechanical transducer set to the same apparent intensity (Gibson, 1963d). Furthermore, electricity is measured in physical units relevant to the characteristics of the nervous system.

However, pain and discomfort are often associated with cutaneous electrical stimulation. Max von Frey wrote that the weakest effective electrical stimuli excite only burning pain on the hairy skin surface (von Frey, 1915). Recently, procedures were developed for painless electrical stimulation of touch on most body surfaces (Gibson, 1963a; 1965a; 1965b). In part, this was accomplished by obtaining knowledge of the stimulus conditions relevant to pain-free electric touch stimulation over a series of experiments (Gibson, 1960; 1962a; 1963a; 1963b; 1963c; 1963d; 1964; 1965a; 1965b). In these experiments, brief pulses were used to define the boundries of a "region" of reliably pain-free electrical stimulation of touch, based partly on the notion that touch and pain thresholds respond differently along several dimensions of electricity.

TEMPORAL FACTORS IN THE STIMULUS

Temporal properties of an electrical stimulus determine, in part, whether it arouses touch or pain. Both touch and pain thresholds rise at different rates with an increase in ac frequency in the audio range (Hahn, 1957; Hawkes and Warm, 1960; Schöbel, 1936; Schwarz, 1944). Thus, threshold stimulation that is reported only as painful at 100 Hz may be well above touch threshold and still not painful at 10 Hz. Hahn (1957) has pointed out that three properties of the stimulus vary with an increase in sinusoidal frequency: (a) frequency increases; (b) current per half-cycle decreases, and (c) the rate increases at which current changes each half cycle. The effects of these stimulus properties of sinusoidal energy cannot be assessed separately because they vary jointly with frequency. However, when electrical stimuli are presented as brief dc pulses, all three properties plus the effects of polarity can be measured separately, since each property can be varied independently. Brief pulses also have the advantage of being relatively free of accommodatory effects produced by electrical stimuli of greater duration.

Pulse Width and Polarity

Hahn (1957) reported that the fingertip electrical touch threshold varied with pulse width and was independent of repetition rate within the range 60-1000 pulses per second (pps). In the present experiments the pulse width was varied first at several interpulse intervals to determine the width that would provide the greatest current ratio between pain and touch thresholds. Long pulses ranging from 10-50 msec readily produced pain on hairy tissues and frequently sensitized the region temporarily. Occasionally a slight increase in peak current of the brief (0.1 msec or less) pain-free pulse produced a sudden stinging pain considerably above a threshold pain sensation. This pain, which sometimes remained after the current was reduced, was usually localized at a point under the electrode, and a spot of redness appeared occasionally at this point. Since brief pulses required high-peak current to stimulate touch on hairy tissue, an accompanying high-peak voltage across the epidermal layer was developed. Such voltages may have exceeded the dielectric breakdown voltage of the skin, thereby stimulating pain by high current density through a small area.

Since pain from brief pulses may have resulted from sudden tissue breakdown, several methods were tried in order to lower tissue impedance and, in turn, reduce the voltage developed across the normally high resistance skin layers. The epidermis was sanded, sliced laterally, stripped away layer by layer with cellophane tape, or ground off with a diamond studded dental burr. The affected area was kept reasonably large to ensure sufficient electrode area. In every instance pain sensitivity increased, and the pain-to-touch threshold current ratio sharply fell. Since the drop in pain threshold probably resulted from the tissue treatment, the question of possible effects of skin impedance reduction was left unanswered.

An increase in pulse duration to about 0.5 msec lowered the peak current considerably. This value, 0.5 msec, is slightly greater than that for touch chronaxie. Consequently, although an increase beyond 0.5 msec did not further lower touch threshold current significantly, it did reduce pain threshold current in most tissues. Thus, a pulse duration of about 0.5 msec represents a useful compromise of high pain-to-touch threshold current ratio. All pulses in the present experiments were 0.5 msec in duration at half peak. Since this pulse duration is shorter than the time constant of human skin (1 to 4 msec), the stimuli can be handled as approximations to square waves. Thus, stimulus intensity is measured as the peak current through the tissues.

The polarity of the applied current affected threshold values at low repetition rates. Cathodal threshold currents were one-half to three-fourths the anodal values. At the same touch sensation intensities, however, anodal stimulation was definitely less painful than cathodal stimulation. After long-term anodal stimulation on the chest, the tissue area under the electrode was less reddened and less uncomfortable than with cathodal stimulation at the same subjective intensity. Stimulation with bidirectional pulses resulted in still less reddening and discomfort than with either of the unidirectional stimuli. In the first two experiments of the present series, the anodal pulses were accompanied by a low cathodal current of opposite polarity to limit accumulation of polarization products (see Fig. 11-1).

PEAK MILLIAMPERES

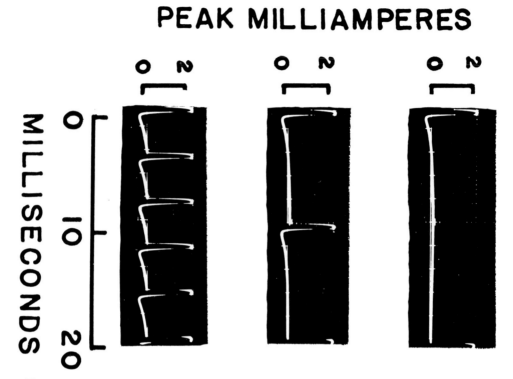

Figure 11-1. Sample stimuli. Photographs from an oscilloscope displaying the voltage across a resistor in series with the tissue.

Figure 11-1 shows oscillographs of three sample stimuli measuring the current going into the tissue. Each pulse is about 0.5 msec in duration and is separated from the following pulse by three different time intervals. As already discussed, pulses much briefer or longer than 0.5 msec increase the likelihood of pain.

Number of Pulses

To find whether touch and pain differ in their response to basic temporal properties of the electric stimulus, touch and pain thresholds were determined in two experiments as a function of the number of brief pulses and the rate of pulse repetition. Thresholds, measured as peak current, were obtained singly for eight body regions selected both for anatomical differences and for differences in pain sensitivity relative to touch sensitivity. Anodal pulses were delivered through a 10 mm diameter active electrode with a large, indifferent electrode placed on the sole of the foot.

Four subjects were well trained as psychophysical subjects for a minimum of 20 hours. As a result of the training procedures (Gibson, 1962c;

1963b), the effects of pain reaction were functionally separated from effects of actual cutaneous pain. This contributed to the surprising reliability and reproducibility of the pain threshold data.

In the first experiment the number of pulses was varied at a single rate of pulse repetition. The method of limits was used, ascending series only; that is, the current was increased incrementally until the observer reported pain. At this point the spot was retired for two or three minutes rest. Both the times between stimuli and for recuperation on a given spot of hairy tissue are important to pain threshold stability. These times need to be long to avoid sequential effects of stimulation.

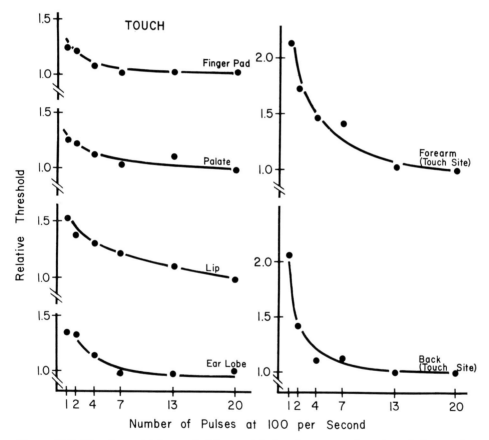

Figure 11-2. Touch sensitivity on hairless and hairy tissues as a function of the number of pulses per stimulus. Threshold values are expressed in sensation units relative to peak threshold current with 20-pulse stimuli. (The *abscissa* is a linear scale.)

The graphs of Figure 11-2 show the mean touch thresholds, for six of the eight body areas studied, as relative peak current plotted against the number of pulses per stimulus with a constant pulse repetition rate of 100

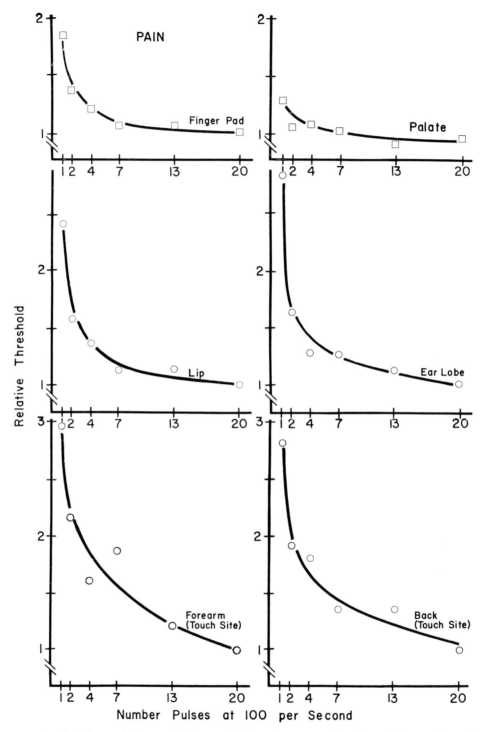

Figure 11-3. Pain sensitivity on hairless and hairy tissues as a function of the number of pulses per stimulus. Threshold values are expressed in sensation units relative to peak threshold current with 20-pulse stimuli (The *abscissa* is a linear scale.)

pps. Touch thresholds are a decreasing function of the number of pulses, and the shift is greater on hairy tissues than on hairless regions. On hairy tissue, the threshold for a 20-pulse stimulus is about half that found for a single pulse, while the corresponding ratio on hairless regions is about 1.3 to 1. The first five points of the touch threshold curve on hairy tissues can be fitted with a rectangular hyperbola, which indicates perfect linear integration of current by the touch system. Between the first and fifteenth pulses, doubling the number of pulses at the uniform repetition rate of 100 pps roughly halves the difference between threshold current for a single pulse and for a 15-pulse stimulus.

As with touch thresholds, pain thresholds fall at different rates in hairy and hairless tissues (Fig. 11-3). A difference between the touch and pain thresholds is that the latter summates over a greater number of pulses than does threshold touch. Figure 11-4 shows extensive temporal summation for pain thresholds on hairy tissue locations which were especially selected for high (insensitive) touch thresholds in order to free the longer pain threshold stimuli from touch sensations. (On the other sites having low touch threshold relative to pain threshold, touch partly masks the pain sensation and pain temporal summation is reduced with longer stimuli.) The threshold current ratio of the one-pulse to the 20-pulse stimuli is five to one on touch-free sites and less than three to one on the other sites. Were a stimulus to be chosen largely on the basis of a maximum ratio between pain and touch, a good choice, particularly for hairy tissue, would be a stimulus with only a few pulses.

A single pulse stimulating touch on hairless tissues feels somewhat like a light tap from the blunt end of a fountain pen. With single pulses from moderately sized electrodes, the apparent area stimulated can be smaller than the electrode and easily localized. With the same size electrode on hairy tissues, the apparent area is more diffuse. This subjective area decreases with an increase in the number of pulses per train set to the same apparent intensity. When the train is sufficiently long, the perception takes on a temporal character, and the apparent area decreases with an increase in repetition rate.

Repetition Rate

In the second experiment, repetition rate was varied in order to discover the extent to which the pain and touch systems respond differently to the time between pulses. Stimuli with four and with 20 pulses were presented at five repetition rates ranging from 10 to 250 pps. This range includes the maximum absolute sensitivity to mechanical vibration and most acute sensitivity to changes in repetition rate. Threshold touch stimulation on hairy tissues requires roughly twice the touch threshold current of hairless tissues. On the dorsal forearm, for example, a peak current of about 2-3 ma can stimulate moderately strong touch with 0.5 msec pulses, whereas a current of approximately 1-1.5 ma is required to produce the same sensation magnitude on hairless skin (Gibson, 1962b) .

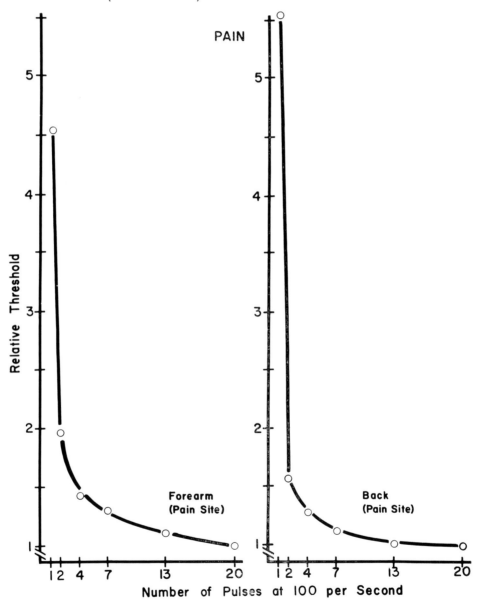

Figure 11-4. Pain thresholds on hairy sites selected for high pain sensitivity coupled with low touch sensitivity. Values are expressed in sensation units relative to peak threshold current with 20-pulse stimuli. (The *abscissa* is a linear scale.)

Pain thresholds are more sensitive to changes in repetition rate than are touch thresholds. At low repetition rates pain thresholds are quite high. Furthermore, the difference between the pain and touch thresholds at a given repetition rate increases as the number of pulses in a train decreases. In short, the influence of repetition rate is greater on the pain than on the touch thresholds when few pulses per stimulus are used.

Both experiments indicate a time constant of integration of approximately 30 msec for the touch sense on hairy tissues. Thus, the total amount of current within this period determines sensation. Because the corresponding value for pain is considerably higher, it becomes possible to stimulate painlessly at low repetition rates and few pulses but not at high rates with many pulses. A long time constant for threshold touch integration in hairy tissues, i.e., the failure of a sensory system to integrate energy quickly, may relate to the relative diffuseness of excitation. Support for this view was provided when the various body regions used were ranked in order of increasing temporal summation. They were arranged roughly by decreasing density of neural innervation.

It may also be that the neural pathways for touch are not the same for brief pulses as for longer trains. Short "cutaneous clicks" may travel via "through" pathways to the higher centers of the nervous system without being inhibited through lateral connections that do not fire sufficiently rapidly to have effect. By analogy, acoustic clicks are readily located in the auditory cortex, but pure tones are not. Consequently, the neural pathways are not necessarily the same for the two kinds of signal.

A final comment concerns anatomical differences and possible similarities between the palate and fingertip. The sensation which results from single pulse electrical stimulation of the palate is sometimes described as a light, dull "thud" and is not unpleasant once it becomes familiar (Gibson, 1962c; 1963b). Such stimulation of the palate (a) "feels" rather like that on the fingertip, and (b) has a high electrical pain threshold relative to its touch threshold. Unlike the finger pad, the hard palate is not equipped with a thick layer of protective horny tissue and it lacks perspiration ducts. These anatomical differences do not appear to be able to account for the fact that the touch sensation obtained from the palate is like that obtained from the finger pad and that it is, generally, pain free. Rather, these sensory observations suggest that the palate is well supplied with the neural elements involved in touch sensation. And, like the finger pad, the palate lacks the small nonmyelinated fibers (Winkelmann, 1960) which may be responsible for the pain signal from relatively low intensities of electrical stimulation of hairy skin.

MULTIPLE DIMENSION STIMULUS CONTROL SYSTEM

So far the research of this laboratory has mainly been designed to provide data on the static state of cutaneous perceptual phenomena. These have usually employed one and seldom more than two sites of electrical pulse stimulation of the skin. Yet, the perceptual nature of absolute location phenomena, apparent motion, etc., all may change markedly in a dynamic situation where spatial and temporal patterns are changed rapidly and repeatedly over time. As a result, we have devised a system to control multiple dimension stimuli (Fig. 11-5).

Figure 11-5. Stimulus control system console. The optical block tape reader programs combinations of brief direct current pulses, delivered by any combination of six independent channels to as many as 48 total locations. (Thus, for example, a matrix of 6 x 8 electrodes on the back might be used for experiments on spatial and temporal aspects of cutaneous pattern perception.)

This system uses a photo-block paper tape reader which can control and deliver, by means of computer modules and banks of reed relays, combinations of multiple electric stimuli to several locations on the body. The general problem is to transmit a number of preprogrammed cutaneous electrical stimuli, which differ on several stimulus parameters, to a number of electrode locations either simultaneously or in rapid succession. These parameters include stimulus duration, pulse repetition rate, time delay among locations, and intensity. The optical block tape reader reads 96 bits of information each step, at a maximum rate of 10 steps per sec. Six independent channels, each multiplexed to eight electrodes, make a total of 48 possible attachments to the body (Gibson, 1965a).

Figure 11-6 shows a transistorized, portable three-channel model. Stimulus delay, duration, and pulse amplitude are independently variable for each channel. Two concentric electrodes are in front of the stimulator.

SPATIAL INTERACTION

Two electric touch stimuli, individually suprathreshold, may arouse only a single phantom touch when simultaneously applied to separate body sites. This phantom touch is felt between the sites of stimulation, and its position varies with the relative stimulus intensities. Successive electric stimulation of two or more separated sites, under certain conditions, will bring reports of apparent movement of the touch from one site to the other.

Apparent Location

Observers were asked to point to the phantom touch sensation aroused by simultaneous, 0.5 msec pulse stimulation at two sites, 12.5 cm apart, on the lower dorsal forearm. The observers pointed with pencils to a ruled grid on that length of the arm. Figure 11-7 shows the position of a phantom touch at various levels of peak current delivered to the forearm site of one observer. The peak current of the pulses delivered simultaneously to the wrist site was fixed at 14 ma. The points on the graph show the position of the phantom with different intensities of current ranging from 5 to 11 peak ma applied to the forearm site. Note that a phantom position halfway between the two sites required an intensity ratio of nearly two to one, wrist to forearm site. When the intensity at both sites was 14 peak ma, the phantom was located nearly at the forearm site, not near the middle. This asymmetry was reliable across several observers and occurred on all limbs.

The variables which best arouse such phantom sensations are not well determined as yet. At times, under seemingly the same stimulus conditions, the phantom was diffuse and poorly localized. It could be located at both electrodes, at one side of the line connecting the two electrode sites, or at both electrode sites as well as between them. Repetition of the single pulse,

Figure 11-6. Transistorized (battery powered), three-channel constant-current stimulator. The concentric electrodes in front are stainless steel with nylon insulators.

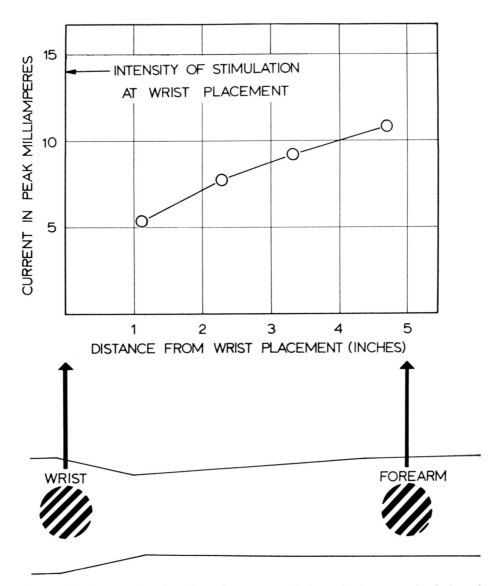

Figure 11-7. Apparent location of a "phantom" touch from simultaneous stimulation of two sites; intensity was varied at the forearm site, fixed at the wrist site. The values of current shown on the ordinate are not correct. It was later observed that when the observer placed his arm on or near a metal equipment shelf, some of the current was capacitively coupled to ground, i.e., to the equipment cabinet. The peak current actually led through the tissues was therefore less than the values displayed. The shape of the curve was not affected; the proper values of current would be obtained by dividing by a constant. The correct values are probably about two-thirds of those shown.

simultaneous stimulation once a second, up to five times, markedly improved the perceptual clarity of the phantom as long as the stimulus rate remained low. The phantom was clearest with intensities ranging from two to three times threshold current. The likelihood of a clear phantom with little or no perceived stimulation at the electrodes themselves fell off on either side of this intensity range. The clarity increased with stimulus duration (or more accurately, pulse number per train at medium to high repetition rates) and with repetition rate at least up to 100 pps.

When the intensity difference between two sites or among three or more sites was modulated at a slow rate, the phantom moved from one locus to another. Neither the best conditions for moving a phantom, nor the rates for perceiving motion have been established. This arrangement provided apparent movement without the usual successive stimulation; only the intensity differences among loci changed over time. It should be feasible to trace geometric patterns on the skin by modulating only relative intensity.

Apparent Movement

The purpose of these experiments was to determine conditions for the optimal arousal of cutaneous apparent movement with electric stimuli and to state these conditions quantitatively. Although other investigators have reported tactual apparent movement aroused by simple tactile or vibrating stimuli (Sumby, 1955), they have not used electrical stimulation, despite its measurement and control advantages. In fact, there has been little agreement on the stimulus properties which are optimal to arouse cutaneous apparent movement, and the quantitative description of the properties of the stimulus dimensions involved has been insufficient.

Apparent movement in the present sense may be considered, theoretically, as a special case of movement perception. A pencil point dragged over the skin surface at a rate of 25 cm/sec sequentially excites receptors and groups of laterally connected receptors. No one knows what the upper speed limit is beyond which the perception of motion no longer changes; little is known about the lower limit. It would also be useful to know the transformations across stimulus dimensions that leave invariant a vivid perception of motion where, in fact, no motion occurs in the stimulus. Such knowledge would increase our understanding of the mechanisms by which motion on the skin is perceived. The fundamental properties that characterize and distinguish the skin and eyes as spatial receptor systems may be reflected in the extent to which their apparent motions correspond as to effects of variation in the same physical dimensions.

For these experiments, five paid, male observers were selected on the basis of intelligence and their status as upper-class, undergraduate engineering students accustomed to working with numbers and familiar with imposing-looking electrical apparatus. They showed a low initial responsiveness to electrical stimulation of the skin.

The effects of three variables on the magnitude of perceived movement were determined in two experiments. These variables included the following: (a) distance on the body between two electrode sites; (b) stimulus duration (pulse train length), and (c) time between stimulus onsets. Direct estimation scaling procedures were used. Observers were instructed to judge directly the magnitude, or strength, of perceived movement from a given stimulation and to report their estimates as a ratio to the amplitude of movement from the standard stimulus, called "10." Prior to the first session observers were familiarized with several of the stimuli to be presented and received samples of stimuli reflecting the extremes of the range of movement. The standard was presented several times at the beginning of each session and also presented and identified after every five judgments.

Electrodes arranged vertically from the shoulder down the right side of the back delivered the stimuli. Stimulation, from trains of pulses with 5 msec separations, was delivered through two 15-mm diameter active electrodes with a common large indifferent electrode on the right foot pad. The "standard" movement was obtained by stimulation of the right dorsal forearm, using the same arrangement of two active electrodes and one indifferent electrode employed on the back.

In the first experiment four interelectrode distances (5-40 cm), four stimulus durations, and three interstimulus intervals were employed. The results of this experiment indicated that interstimulus interval, measured as onset time difference, had little effect on the strength of the movement illusion. This surprising result was contrary to effects reported from the use of vibrotactile stimuli (Sumby, 1955; 1965). As a result, in the second experiment, seven interstimulus intervals extended and covered the appropriate range; the range and number of stimulus durations were increased, and two interelectrode distances were selected which had been found to represent the extremes of the effect in the first experiment. All stimuli used at all loci were adjusted by each observer to be equal in apparent intensity to single pulse stimulation at the shoulder site. Single pulse stimuli were set at triple the intensity of the absolute threshold at that locus, producing a "moderately" loud stimulus. In each of three sessions all possible combinations of the three variables were presented randomly to each observer with the restriction that all combinations appeared in each third of the session. Means of each observer's median estimates were plotted separately on log-log coordinates as a function of each variable.

Figure 11-8 shows the effect of the linear distance between two sequentially stimulated sites on the vividness of the perceived movement. As the distance between electrode sites increased beyond 10 cm, the amplitude of the movement decreased. The data in this range were fitted by a linear function on these logarithmic coordinates with a slope of less than −1.0. Thus, to a first approximation, this curve is a power function. From 10-40 cm, doubling the distance between electrodes decreased the amplitude of movement by a proportion that was less than the physical decrease. The impressiveness of the apparent movement was little changed with a decrease in the distance to less than 10 cm, which is roughly the value of two-point threshold on this body region with these electrical stimuli.

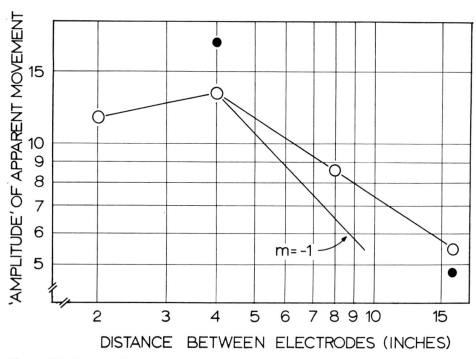

Figure 11-8. Direct estimates of apparent motion amplitude as a function of distance on the back between two electrodes. Open circles are means of five observers' median judgments, Expt. 1. Closed circles are values from Expt. 2, same O's summed across a greater range of stimulus duration and interstimulus interval. The line with a slope of −1 is for ease of visual comparison.

Figure 11-9 shows how the amplitude of apparent movement varied with stimulus (train) duration. Beyond roughly 20 msec, an increase in the stimulus duration increased the amplitude of the movement. A portion of these data are also fitted by a power function. A decrease in the train length from 10.0 to 0.5 msec of stimuli that were equally intense did not affect the amplitude of the movement. This feature of the curve is supported by the fact that 10 msec represents the limit of the critical integrating interval for the skin; successive events separated by less than about 10 msec are perceived as single events.

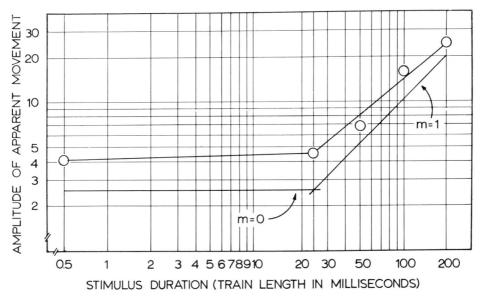

Figure 11-9. Direct estimates of apparent motion amplitude as a function of stimulus duration (measured as train length). Points are means of 5 observers' median judgments. Lines with slopes of 0 and of 1 are for ease of visual comparison.

Figure 11-10 shows the effect of time-between-stimulus onsets on judgments of the impressiveness of the apparent movement. Within the range of times used, the time between stimuli was obviously not a variable with a simple major effect. Although this result is contrary to Sumby's findings with vibrotactile stimuli (Sumby, 1955) and disagrees with one of Korte's laws for visual apparent movement, it is reliable with these procedures.

Since each of the five observers received every combination of delay, distance, and duration, an analysis of variance appropriate for such a repeated measures design was performed.* The significance of each treatment and interaction was tested against its interaction with subjects. There are two principal aspects to the analysis. (a) Interelectrode distance, stimulus duration, and their interaction accounted for the major portion of the variance. Considering Figures 11-8 and 11-9, this result is not surprising. (b) The effect of interstimulus onset delay was not found to be statistically significant.

As shown both graphically and statistically, broad variation in interstimulus time intervals apparently had little influence on the strength of the

---

*The analysis was kindly performed by K. Kotovsky, Carnegie Institute of Technology.

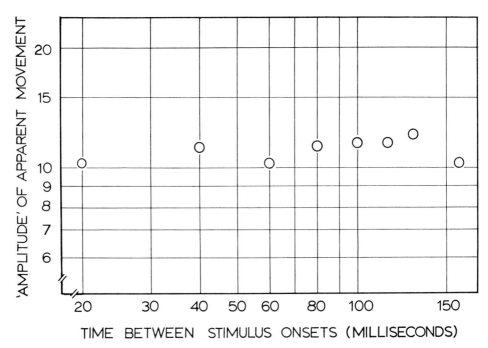

Figure 11-10. Direct estimates of apparent motion amplitude as a function of time between stimulus onsets. Plotted points are means of 5 observers' median judgments.

movement illusion; this behavior may be explained by examining the nature of the interactions between interstimulus delay and the other variables. The interaction was significant between distance on the body and the time delay between stimulus onsets. The interaction between stimulus duration and interstimulus delay was also significant, although its contribution to the variance was small. Thus, over small distances with long duration stimuli, conditions optimal for a strong illusion of motion, the impression of motion remained strong within a wide range of interstimulus delays.

When the duration and distance become marginal for good motion, then the value for delay is more critical to the strength of the illusion. However, even with short stimulus durations and/or larger distances on the body surface, the range of acceptable delay during which motion is perceived is quite broad. Moreover, the interstimulus interval optimal for motion perception varies with duration and distance, being greater for longer durations and distances. With small interelectrode distances and/or long stimulus durations, the impression of motion remains strong within a wide range of stimulus onset delays. When the duration and distance become marginal for good motion, the value selected for interstimulus delay is more critical. However, even with shorter stimulus durations and/or larger distances on

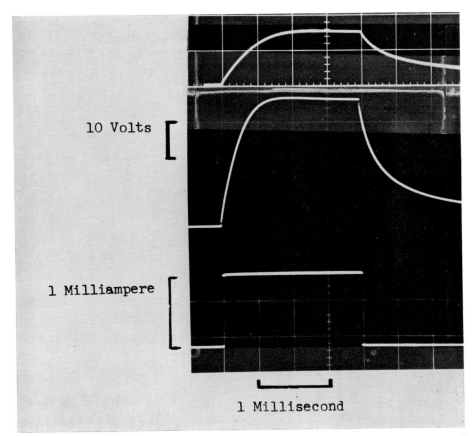

10 Volts

1 Milliampere

1 Millisecond

Figure 11-12. Oscilloscope photograph showing voltage and current during the course of stimulation by a 2 msec rectangular electrical pulse from high-impedance constant-current stimulator. Bottom sections show current pulse and accompanying voltage pulse; top shows increased voltage rise-time from a current of reduced amplitude.

voltage and the time constant of voltage growth were measured as a function of the three variables.

Figure 11-12 shows a rectangular 1 msec, 1 ma current pulse applied to the palm through a 16-mm-diameter electrode. The bottom trace shows the stimulus current. The center trace shows the voltage developed between the two electrodes by the constant-current pulse. The top trace shows the voltage from a lower amperage pulse. Notice the onset-rise-time differences between the two voltage pulses.

Pulse width was increased substantially to permit the voltage of low current pulses to reach peak, owing to their long rise times. Figure 11-13 displays voltage pulses from five constant current pulses of different durations, ranging from 0.5 to 2.5 msec. It is clear that voltage onset times do not vary with pulse duration.

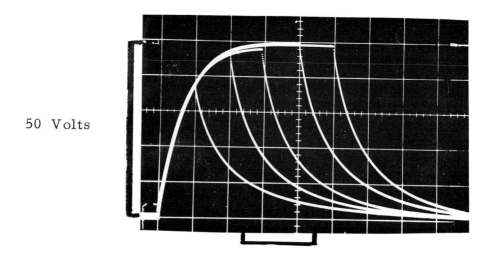

50 Volts

1 Millisecond

Figure 11-13. Time-lapse oscilloscope photograph showing voltage pulses from constant current pulses of five different durations.

Effect of Current Amplitude on Tissue Resistance

As current increases from 0.05 to 5.0 peak ma, peak tissue resistance decreases rapidly at first, then more slowly with further increase in current. Figure 11-14 shows tissue resistance separately for hairy and hairless forearm tissue under the roughly nickel-sized active electrode with the large indifferent electrode under the sole of the foot. The time constant of the voltage rise (Fig. 11-15) falls with an increase in peak current in the same manner as peak resistance. The greater the current, the lower the tissue resistance, and the shorter the time for voltage to reach its peak. (One testable implication is a possible interaction between pulse repetition rate and peak current on pain thresholds measured as pulse train length.) Low peak currents mean long voltage rise and fall times. Because the tissues have insufficient offtime to fall to zero, low current pulse trains of short interpulse times might summate to pain rapidly as successive single voltage pulses become additive in the tissues. Figure 11-16 shows one function from each of the previous two graphs plotted on log-log coordinates. Each is linear to a first approximation in these coordinates. The lines were fitted by eye. The relation between peak resistance and peak current is hyperbolic with an exponent of near unity. When the current was doubled, the peak resistance was nearly halved. The time constant fell similarly, although with a slightly greater exponent. The variation in time constant can be accounted for largely in terms of the fall in peak resistance. Consequently, the small difference between the two slopes is attributable to tissue capacitance.

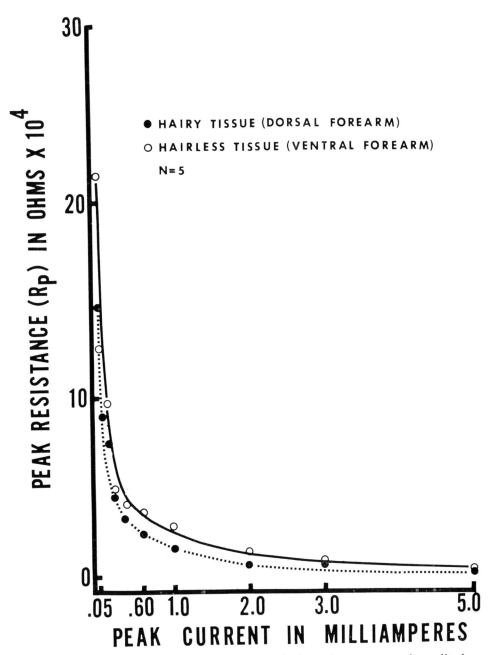

Figure 11-14. Tissue peak resistance as a function of stimulating current peak amplitude.

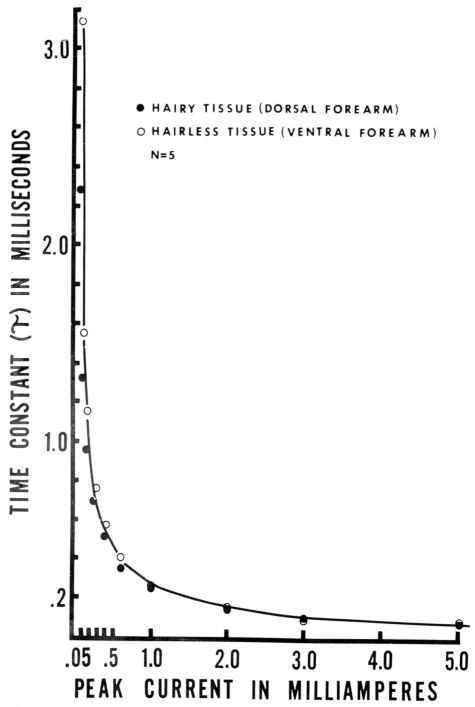

Figure 11-15. Time constant of pulse voltage rise, as a function of stimulating current peak amplitude; high output impedance constant-current amplifier.

Tissue resistance primarily, not membrane capacitance, is affected by the passage of current. Most of the resistance change may be assumed to be in the surface layers which represent a large percentage of the total inter-electrode resistance. In a more practical vein, it is clearly not safe to stimulate human tissue with electricity for either touch perceptual research or therapeutic purposes without using constant current stimulators or rapidly acting current limiters. Peak voltage requirements are such that satisfactory constant current operation in the 0.1 to 5.0 ma region is clearly possible with an available maximum of less than one hundred volts, owing to the large decrease in tissue resistance with the passage of, for example, currents even as small as 100 peak microamperes for one msec. This property of tissue makes transistorized constant current units feasible for portable communication devices.

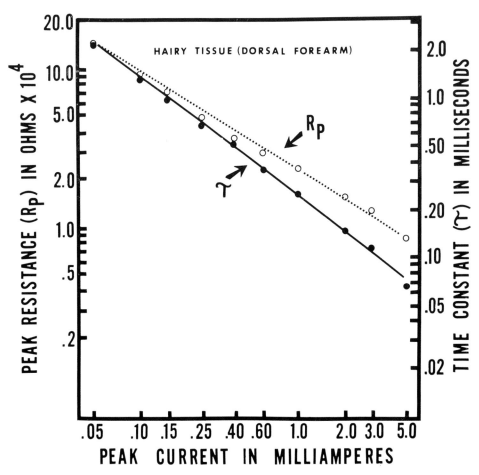

Figure 11-16. Tissue resistance and voltage rise time constant, as a function of stimulating current peak amplitude; log-log coordinates.

Tissue Resistance and Electrode Temperature

In four experiments on pain and touch sensitivity, effects of skin surface temperature were found to be ambiguous (Gibson, 1965a). These experiments were part of a larger effort to determine factors that underlie cutaneous electrical stimulation so as to separate sensory properties from tissue properties. Touch and pain thresholds were obtained from several observers under a variety of controls and conditions which increased the measurement precision.

An electrical thermode was constructed similar to that described by Kenshalo (1963). A thermoelectric element, using the Peltier effect to generate rapid temperature change proportional to the quantity of electricity passed through a junction, was attached to a machined brass electrode and built into a calibrated beam balance to control electrode pressure. The proper heat sink on the upper plate of the element enabled a 55°C temperature difference between upper and lower plates. Rough calculations showed that, at room temperature, a 7-watt heat load was supplied by the tissues of the dorsal forearm to a one-square-inch stimulator area. This electrical thermode had sufficient temperature capacity so that, despite the load, the temperature could be varied (15 sec/°C) from cold, through neutral, to warm, without being moved on the skin, a distinct advantage for threshold reliability.

Skin surface temperature was varied by means of the electrical thermode attached to a brass electrode (2 cm in diameter) and measured with a small thermistor contacting the skin under the electrode. The thermistor, situated in the electrode flush with the stimulating surface, was insulated thermally and electrically from the electrode by a silicone rubber compound. Temperature was displayed digitally with a system temperature time constant of 2.5 secs.

Effects of temperature variation of 15°C to 45°C, the tolerable range, on electrical touch sensitivity were found to be slight or nonexistent. The rate of increase of a receptor potential with a constant amplitude stimulus varied directly with temperature. Two explanations for the failure to observe a temperature effect on electrical touch are either (a) the site of excitation of the touch system by electricity is directly at the nerve itself, beyond this potential, or (b) the temperature change for this and previous similar studies (e.g., Hawkes, 1962) was not reaching the "receptor." There is evidence (e.g., Hensel, 1950; Stolwijk and Hardy, 1965) that such a temperature change applied to a limited region of otherwise room temperature tissue may not simply be mirrored over time in subcutaneous tissues, and certainly will be well reduced in amplitude. The heat rise within the tissue itself probably grows over time as the square root of the surface temperature.

Our own experiments indicate the steepness of lateral surface temperature gradients. With a 15-mm-diameter thermode maintained as 18°C (15°C below normal surface temperature), the temperature only several millimeters from the thermode edge was within 2.8°C of normal. In short, effects of moderate temperature change on electrical touch sensitivity are probably not yet known.

Contrary to expectations from the preliminary work, the results with stinging pain on hairy tissue suggested an approximately U-shaped function relating pain threshold (measured as peak current) to temperature, with maximum sensitivity to pain near room temperatures. However, pain thresholds were highly variable, despite precautions in several experiments to obtain regularity by reducing effects of extraneous variables. This implies either a basic instability in the pain mechanism, or further variables for study. Several observations suggested the latter, that thresholds vary from tissue properties independent of sensory mechanisms.

Tissue electrical resistance was determined in the present experiment as a function of temperature, at different current levels. Figure 11-17 shows peak tissue resistance, as a function of electrode-skin interface temperature at four single-pulse current levels, under a dime-sized area on the palmar base of the thumb. At low currents, with tissue-resistance high, a 30°C increase in skin temperature halved skin resistance. At higher current levels, tissue resistance driven to lower values was less affected by a rise in electrode temperature. Above 5.0 ma peak current, electrode temperature in the tolerable range had little influence on skin resistance under this electrode area. The extent to which perspiration is involved has not been determined.

Tissue Factors in Electrical Stimulation of Pain

Occasionally, with no obvious change in stimulus properties, painless electrical touch stimulation suddenly stings. This happened more frequently on hairy than hairless tissues. Sometimes the pain did not disappear when the peak current was quickly reduced to one-fifth the value at which pain first appeared. Tripling the current upon the sudden appearance of pain may render the region relatively painfree for 5 minutes. At other times, only a slight increase in the current levels increased the sting intensity. The irregularity of sting in our laboratory on any given trial has a long history with regard to the control by stimulus factors. This time we tried to determine the likelihood that tissue breakdown underlies the stimulation of stinging pain.

Under 7.5-cm-diameter electrodes on the back with long trains of pulses, the sting was usually reported as a "point" which could sometimes be located tactually with a pencil point. Although a small, red spot occasionally appeared (usually near the edge of the area under a large, disc electrode),

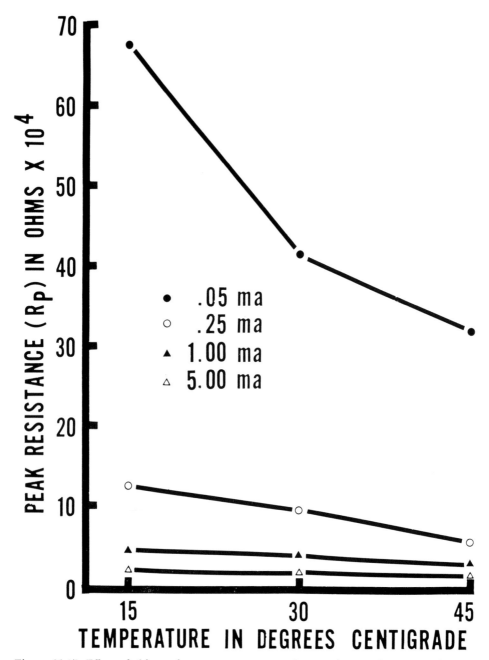

Figure 11-17. Effect of skin surface temperature on tissue resistance. Parameter is peak current. Peak final voltage measured at each current to obtain resistance values. The 1 cm- diameter electrode-thermode was located at the palmar base of the thumb.

often nothing untoward was visible in the area under the electrode even with a low power (20 X) microscope.

The four-sectioned electrode, pictured in the left foreground of Figure 11-18, was used. Current, displayed on a separate oscilloscope trace for each of the four parallel wedge-shaped electrode sections, was increased in small steps. One stimulator fed all (parallel) active electrode elements; the one large indifferent electrode was located on the sole. At several current steps prior to pain threshold, the current display for one segment would increase slightly. At pain threshold, the current through one electrode segment would sometimes be several times the peak values of a portion of the current in each of the other three.

Figure 11-19 shows a photograph of current through four parallel segments at the pain threshold. Three small current steps prior to this photo-

Figure 11-18. Polished stainless steel electrodes embedded flush into machined plexiglas are arranged into three groups by function. At the top right are flat and concave electrodes of different sizes, used, for example, in the equal loudness contour study. At the top left are electrodes of different linear areas with different degrees of curvature, to be used in the pressure, curvature, and area experiments. At lower left are samples with multiple conducting areas. The concentric and bat-wing shapes are two of several electrode pairs currently being tested to replace, for some purposes, the single active electrode and foot ground. In the foreground is shown a four-section stainless steel electrode for use in the tissue properties experiments.

graph, the heights of the four traces were within 10 per cent of each other. It is difficult to read the photograph because of the rise-time differences among channels. Spread out from left to right, the traces, top to bottom, would look roughly like Figure 11-20. Note in these figures that the current pulse first rose quickly to nearly the same value through all four electrode sections. The current then flowed primarily through one section, and was reduced through the three other segments by the action of the stimulator maintaining the total current constant. During the pulse, the third trace

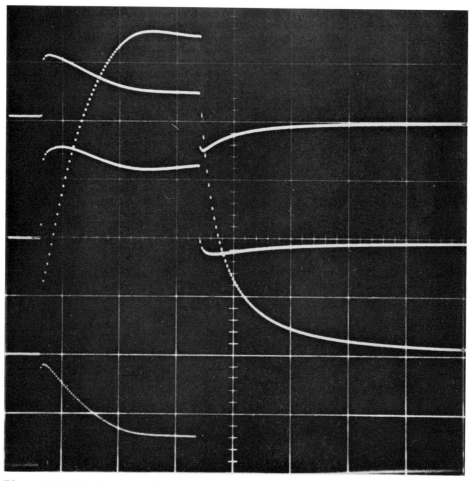

Figure 11-19. Oscilloscope photograph of current pulse from a single stimulator, split through four electrically parallel electrode segments, taken at the first report of pain. The single common indifferent electrode was on the sole of the foot. Moments before, at 0.3 ma lower intensity, all four pulses were rectangular and the same size. Notice that the peak current through one segment is several times higher than that through the others, indicating tissue breakdown under one electrode segment on the dorsal forearm as the cause of the stinging pain.

increased to four times the peak values in the other channels. The sudden swift flow of current at pain threshold does not always go through the same electrode segment. This shows that the increase resulted from tissue properties, not electrode properties. Rather, tissue resistance under a small segment of the electrode seemed to be reduced substantially, allowing current to be diverted from other areas under an electrode to a small percentage of the total electrode-skin surface. This resulted from the constant current nature of the stimulator.

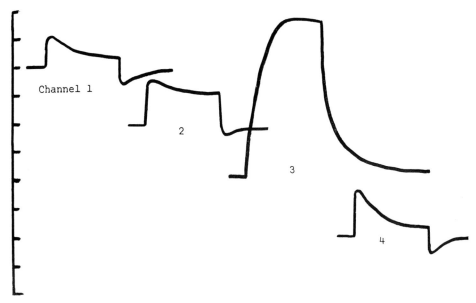

Figure 11-20. Drawing of the four traces in Figure 11-19, spread out horizontally for clarity.

COMPUTER SIMULATION OF TISSUE VOLTAGE RESPONSE

The nature of the voltage rise from a rectangular step of current and its dependence on current, electrode size, temperature, and certain polarity effects not discussed here, imply a dynamic electrical circuit with resistance and capacitances varying nonlinearly over time. Such circuits are difficult to solve with simple circuit theory. As a beginning, however, two computer programs were written to produce output plots of voltage versus time. One program produced an approximation to our oscilloscope photograph of pulse voltage by plotting the appropriate exponential growth. The more promising of the two programs used the SCADS subroutines at Carnegie Tech's computation center (SCADS = Simulation of Combined Analog Digital Systems) . The next version of this program set up an analog circuit that approximates a parallel R-C network with a large variable series resistor to assure constant current. The satisfying output of this program is a figure closely resembling some of our oscilloscope photographs (Fig. 11-21).

SUMMARY

Temporal Factors and Pain-free Stimulation

Major progress in cutaneous communication requires knowledge of perceptual properties of touch. Adequate study of touch perception requires complex tactile displays composed of many stimulus points which are variable on temporal and spatial dimensions. The primary impediment to such a stimulus array has been the lack of control of an adequate tactile stimulus. Electricity can be controlled and measured, as can light and sound, with a precision greater than the discriminatory power of the sensory system. Brief (0.5 msec) pulses of anodal direct current can reliably arouse pain-free touch when delivered through sufficiently large electrodes by a constant current stimulator to ensure that current intensity does not vary with tissue impedance. Such pulses may effectively stimulate touch without pain when combined in short trains at low pulse repetition rates, because the temporal integration time is shorter for touch than for pain. Pulse repetition rates can be readily manipulated at low values (5-50 pps) within the region of highest sensitivity to rate changes. Finally, electricity is measured in units relevant to the characteristics of the nervous system. Thus, stimuli adequate to the problem are available for the study of touch perception.

Multiple Dimension Stimulus Control System

A system which uses computer logic modules was designed around a photo-block paper tape reader to control and deliver combinations of multiple electric stimuli to several locations on the body surface.

Apparent Motion

Conditions for optimal apparent motion include close interelectrode spacing (near the two-point threshold), long stimulus durations, and any moderate interstimulus interval from 50 to 150 msec. Beyond the two-point threshold, the magnitude of the movement illusion is a decreasing power function of the distance, with an exponent less than minus unity. Beyond the critical integrating temporal interval for touch (10 msec), the magnitude of motion is an increasing power function of stimulus duration, with an exponent of less than one.

Figure 11-21. Computer program and printout of simulated voltage pulse. This is output from a rectangular, 0.9 msec, 1 ma current pulse delivered to a circuit simulation with equations paralleling electrical properties of human tissue.

```
AN USER G446.119; PROGRAM 1/5;
AN RUN,ALGOL,TAPE; DONE;
```

GIBSON, R. H.
TIME: 00:00:03
'AND' RECORD SOURCE   21:54:59
00:00:05

```
AL      15710   BEGIN INTEGER X,Y,Z; Y←0;
AL      15713   FOR X←0 STEP 1 UNTIL 50 DO BEGIN
        15734   IF X=10 THEN Y←10; IF X=30 THEN Y←0;
        15750   PRINT (<1C>,→8<'|',9R>);
        15772   IF ↓(X/10)=(X/10) THEN PRINT (<1C>,→71<'-'>);
        16024   IF X>29 THEN BEGIN
AL      16031   PRINT (<1C>,
        16036     →$(40/(((X/3)-9)*((X/3)-9)))$<R>,<'*',E>);
        16067   GO SKIP; END;
        16071   IF X>9 THEN
AL      16076   PRINT (<1C>,
        16103     →$↓(40-(40/(((X/3)-3)*((X/3)-3))))$<R>,<'*',E>);
        16136   SKIP; END;
        16137   END;
```

00:00:03

TIME USED: 00:00:13   PAGES USED: 21:55:09
22:02:22   END OF RUN

Within the range of times used, the time between stimulus onsets was obviously not a variable with a simple major effect. The effective inter-stimulus time intervals covered a broad range (greater than 50 to 150 msec) under distance and duration conditions conducive to movement. The range of effective times was narrowed when distances and/or durations were used that were less likely to produce good movement.

Electrical Properties of Tissue

Electrical properties of tissue were investigated with pulses of direct current in order to relate tissue properties with sensory events. The time properties of voltage-current relationships within tissue were determined by recording the voltage response to current pulses of 1.0 to 50 msec duration delivered by constant current stimulator with high output impedance (ef-fectively 200 megohms).

It was found that the current rises nearly instantly to maximum; how-ever, the voltage lags as in a capacitive circuit. Both the rate of voltage rise and the peak voltage at any given current were a function of the variables investigated. Therefore, (a) the peak voltage, and (b) the time constant of voltage growth were measured from enlargements of the oscilloscope photo-graphs as a function of the three variables.

Results were as follows: (a) as current increased from 0.05 to 5.0 peak milliamperes, tissue peak resistance decreased, precipitously at first, then more slowly with further current increase. The decrease was from greater than 250 kohms to less than 10 kohms, with 0.05 ma to 5.0 ma peak current increase. The relation between peak resistance and peak current is hyper-bolic with an exponent nearly unity; that is, if the current is doubled, the peak resistance is nearly halved. (b) When the peak current increased, the time constant fell in the same manner as peak resistance (although with a slightly greater exponent). The variation in time constant can be accounted for largely in terms of the fall in peak resistance. Tissue resistance primarily, not membrane capacitance, was affected by the passage of current. It is reasonable to assume that most of the resistance change is in the surface layers, which represent a large percentage of the total interelectrode resistance.

Computer Simulation of Tissue as Electrical Network

Increases both in temperature and in current reduce tissue resistance. A computer program was written to simulate time properties of voltage and current relationships within tissue; computer printout of simulated voltage pulses closely approximated oscilloscopic photographs of actual tissue stimu-lation, emphasizing the dynamic, rapidly changing resistive-capacitive nature of electrically stimulated human tissue.

REFERENCES

Frey, M. von. Physiologische versuche uber des vibrationsgefuhl. *Z. Biol.*, 1915, **65**, 417.

Gibson, R. H. Conditions of painless electrical stimulation. *Report No. 42: O.N.R. Project NR 140-598*. Charlottesville: University of Virginia, 1960.

Gibson, R. H. Conditions of painless electrical stimulation of touch. Paper presented to Eastern Psychological Association, April, 1962. (a)

Gibson, R. H. Electrical stimulation of the skin. In J. W. Linsner (Ed.), *Proceedings of the Mobility Research Conference*. New York: American Foundation for the Blind, 1962. (b)

Gibson, R. H. Temporal factors in electrical stimulation of pain and touch. Doctoral dissertation, University of Virginia, 1962. (c)

Gibson, R. H. Electrical stimulation of pain and touch systems. *Nature (London)*, 1963, **199**, 307. (a)

Gibson, R. H. Requirements for the use of electrical stimulation of the skin. In L. L. Clark (Ed.), *Proceedings of the International Congress of Technology and Blindness*. New York: American Foundation for the Blind, 1963. (b)

Gibson, R. H. Tactile perception by electrical stimulation of the skin. Paper presented to the Psychonomic Society, August, 1963. (c)

Gibson, R. H. Tactile perception with electric stimuli. Invited paper presented to Living Systems Section, WESCON, August, 1963. (d)

Gibson, R. H. Effects of temperature on touch, pain and on tissue electrical properties. Paper presented to the Psychonomic Society, Niagara Falls, Canada, October, 1964.

Gibson, R. H. Communication by electrical stimulation of the skin. *Space Research Coordination Center, Report No. 21*, 1965. (a)

Gibson, R. H. Cutaneous perception of apparent movement from electric stimuli. *Research Bulletin, American Foundation for the Blind*, 1965, **9**, 13. (b) (Paper presented to Eastern Psychological Association, April, 1963.)

Hahn, J. F. Cutaneous vibratory thresholds for square-wave electrical pulses. *Science*, 1958, **127**, 879.

Hardy, J. D., Wolff, H. G., & Goodell, H. *Pain Sensations and Reactions*. Baltimore: Williams and Wilkins, 1952.

Hawkes, G. R. Effect of skin temperature on absolute threshold for electrical current. *J. Appl. Physiol.*, 1962, **17**, 110.

Hawkes, G. R., & Warm, J. S. The sensory range of electrical stimulation of the skin. *Amer. J. Psychol.*, 1960, **73**, 485.

Hensel, H. Die intracutane temperaturbewegung bei einwirkung ä usserer temperatureize. *Pflüg. Arch. Ges. Physiol.*, 1950, **252**, 146.

Kenshalo, D. R. Improved method for the psychophysical study of the temperature sense. *Rev. Sci. Instr.*, 1963, **34**, 883.

Rothman, S. *Physiology and Biochemistry of the Skin*. Chicago: University of Chicago, 1954.

Schöbel, E. Experiments on intensity discrimination by electrical touch of various frequencies. *Z. Sinnesphysiol.*, 1936, **66**, 262.

Schwarz, F. Über die reizung sensibler nerven des menschen durch mittel-frequente wechselstrome. *Pflüg. Arch. Ges. Physiol.*, 1944, **247**, 405.

Stolwijk, J. A. J., & Hardy, J. D. Skin and subcutaneous temperature changes during exposure to intense thermoradiation. *J. Appl. Physiol.*, 1965, **20**, 1006.

Sumby, W. H. An experimental study of vibrotactile apparent motion. Master's thesis, University of Virginia, 1955.

Sumby, W. H. An experimental study of vibrotactile apparent motion. *Research Bulletin, American Foundation for the Blind,* 1965, **9,** 71.

Winkelmann, R. W. *Nerve Endings in Normal and Pathological Skin.* Springfield: Charles C Thomas, 1960.

DISCUSSION

Dr. H. Davis: Dr. Gibson has really given us two interesting papers, one in biophysics and the electrical properties of tissue and another in psycho-acoustics where he gets into judging magnitudes of sensation. These are the two ends of the story and perhaps there are some questions as to what goes on in the middle.

Dr. Y. Zotterman: Your presentation is a beautiful demonstration of both of these things. They leave quite a number of questions to correlate with electrophysiology as well as other studies. Your work reminded me of a piece of research which I did about 40 years ago, in London, with Sir Thomas Lewis (Lewis and Zotterman, 1927). We were studying the reaction of minute vessels of the skin and we became interested in the skin resistance. We found out that even the slightest little crack in the skin, like a pin prick which you could hardly see without looking very sharply, changed the resistance of the skin. The main resistance of the skin is in the horny layer and may be changed by just the smallest crack in that layer. You work with unmolested skin, I suppose. How do you test this and how do you control the condition of the skin?

Dr. Gibson: I agree that skin cracks make the great difference in the physical properties of the skin, but I do not think that they necessarily matter to sensory properties, provided you do not produce a sting.

Dr. Zotterman: The next question is, have you tried to molest the skin or anything like that?

Dr. Gibson: In very many ways, for example, we have used a highspeed drill with a diamond-studded dental burr and tried to just touch it to the skin to get down below the horny layer. It really did not help reduce the likelihood of pain at a given intensity. Probably the best preparation to produce good pain-free stimulation from a short-term standpoint, is to use slightly convex stainless steel electrodes which have been encased in some insulator, so that the bend in the skin is well away from the electrical area, and to rub some electrode paste into the skin, wash the skin, then rub in some more and use it.

Dr. R. K. Winkelman: Dr. Gibson, in measuring the electrical resistance and capacitance of the skin, we found that the barrier seemed to be always at the keratin layer, the so-called keratinization layer of the skin, and I wonder if you are not measuring the electrical properties of this barrier of the skin rather than measuring the sensory correlates of it. It seems to me that all your curves change rather abruptly at one point and then trail off. I am wondering if this may be because you have suddenly exceeded the electrical barrier properties of the skin and, from that point on, then the neural correlates or the sensory correlates are rather uniform. If you could explain how this is due to the sensory and not the electrical properties of the skin that you are measuring, I would be obliged.

Dr. Gibson: The leading question was, "Why pain?" Now we are doing something to the skin so we should investigate the physical and electrical properties of the tissue to see if we can understand what happens when it is stimulated electrically. We have not yet completed that. We have found that electricity itself drastically reduced the tissue resistance, within a 100 msec, to less than one-fifth of its former value. If you strip off the surface layers, the amount of change in current required for a given intensity of touch is small, suggesting that a good part of the resistance change is in the surface horny layers rather than in the deeper layers. We discovered that there are likely to be holes or breaks produced in the surface continuity when the voltage is high enough. We have not yet formally determined whether we are summating voltages over repeated pulses. For example, the trailing edge of an electrical pulse delivered to the skin is not vertical but trails off like a capacitor discharge. If a second pulse follows the first sufficiently rapidly, the second may be added to the after effects of the first. We know this occurs with brief interpulse intervals. We have not yet made formal measurements.

Reference

Lewis, T., & Zotterman, Y. Vascular reactions of the skin to injury. Part 8. The resistance of the human skin to constant currents, in relation to injury and vascular response. *J. Physiol. (London)*, 1927, **62**, 130.

Chapter 12

RESPONSE OF THE SOMESTHETIC SYSTEM TO PATTERNED TRAINS OF ELECTRICAL STIMULI
An Approach to the Problem of Sensory Coding*

William R. Uttal and Madelon Krissoff†

THE RELATIONSHIP BETWEEN discriminative psychophysical reactions and the underlying neurophysiological mechanisms has been one of the major scientific problems of the second half of the 20th century. The classic "mind-body" problem has taken this direction for many reasons, including some technical (the accessibility of the receptors and occasionally even their afferent pathways) and some conceptual (the relatively well-ordered neural structures and the well-defined nature of physical stimuli). The inquiry into the nature of this relationship should ideally embody experimental investigations which compare directly some manipulation of the external environment with both the resulting psychophysical and electrophysiological responses. Nevertheless, creative ideas resulting from purely psychophysical studies and from purely neurophysiological investigations have also contributed greatly to the development of our knowledge of information coding and processing in the various sensory systems.

The philosophy underlying current psychophysiology is a supremely mechanistic one, which assumes that there is a mappable correspondence between the psychological and the electrophysiological realms of discourse. We have evolved a specific statement of what we mean by the "relationship between mind and body" in terms of the concept of a code due, in part, to the influence of recently developed information theories. A code has been defined as a set of symbols and transformation rules which allows us to represent informational patterns economically. The mapping of the external stimulus onto the pattern of nerve impulses (the symbols) according to a logarithmic compression (the transformational rule) in a peripheral nerve is one code; the same external stimulus may be mapped in a totally different code at other synaptic levels of the nervous system. Two coded representations of the same stimulus pattern at two levels of the nervous system, although transformed into different sets of symbols, must contain at least the

*The research reported in this paper was supported, in part, by a grant (MH-8786-01) from the National Institutes of Health and, in part, by a grant (GB-2000) from the National Sciences Foundation.

†Madelon Krisshoff is with the Mental Health Research Institute, University of Michigan, Ann Arbor, Michigan.

critical features of the original external stimulus pattern. Indeed, these two coded representations can also be considered to be transformations of each other. The main limitation of this generalization is that not all features of the original pattern may be retained throughout the sequence of transformations — later stages may contain less of the original pattern than earlier stages. Nevertheless, the important point is that at each stage in the chain of nervous transmission, the same information* may be represented by almost unrecognizably different patterns of physical and electrochemical energies. Thus, when we talk about "the" nervous code, it is absolutely critical to define the transmission link or level about which we are speaking. In general, the second law of thermodynamics requires that there be degradation of the information content at each stage of neural transmission and at each sequential recoding stage. A main function of the nervous system, as is clearly evident from many kinds of investigation, is to accomplish that reduction in a selective fashion, gleaning from among the environmentally- or evolutionary-irrelevant only those patterns which are biologically useful.

To reiterate, the code for a single parameter of stimulation may be quite different in two sequential neural links or even in different parts of the same link. The code must be broken individually for each of the separate recoding stages. In this particular set of studies, we will be uniquely concerned with the code in the long axons of peripheral somesthetic nerves.

There have been two principal approaches toward determining the codes for sensory processes: the neurophysiological approach, which uses electrical recordings of the evoked neural activity, and the psychological approach, with its statistical analysis of subjective responses to simple, almost unitary, stimuli. Each of these approaches has a number of limitations. The neurophysiological approach, until recently, has only infrequently been applied to human subjects, and even then usually under the constraints of pathological patient conditions. The specific level of code under investigation in the neurophysiological laboratory is simply a function of where the electrode is placed; thus, coding may be investigated at many different levels. This advantage is offset, however, by the fact that the animals on which neurophysiological experiments are usually made cannot possibly be expected to give the same richness of subjective reports available from a human subject. Unfortunately, cross-species comparisons between humans and animals make assumptions of similarities in the perceptual and neural processes of each, which have not yet been adequately proven.

The psychophysical approach is also limited in its range of applications. Peripheral stimulation through normal receptors evokes unknown trains

---

*"Information" is used here in its informal sense as a symbol of order, rather than its formally defined sense.

of neural activity which are not generally observable. By simply comparing the input stimulus pattern and the subjective response, no direct information may be gained about any specific stage of neural encoding. Rather, only an overall statement of the limitations of the total human sensory-integrative-motor system obtains.

The limitations of the two independent approaches suggest that a third combined approach would add valuable insights toward the solution of the coding problem. It would be desirable to be able to record nerve impulses from intact and normal human subjects while simultaneously collecting subjective data. Dawson and Scott's (1949) techniques for recording compound action potentials percutaneously have provided one opportunity for this combination. In recent years, several of us have combined these techniques with various psychophysical procedures, as an additional way of studying the coding problem in human subjects.

Our procedure is generally one in which electrical pulses are used to stimulate the somesthetic system. Electrical pulse stimuli have been chosen because of the high degree of control which can be exerted over the parameters of stimulation. Particularly, it has been possible to stimulate with pulses which are of a shorter duration than the nerve impulse itself. Since these electrical currents pass easily through the skin, another important advantage is gained. Axonal fibers may be stimulated directly, without the intervening transformations introduced by the specialized receptor organs. Thus, by electrical pulse stimulation of peripheral nerves, we are able to set up in those nerves a sequence of compound action potentials which are on a one-to-one correspondence with each external stimulus pulse. By patterning the stimuli we are, therefore, able to pattern the sequence of compound nerve impulses in the large nerves of the arm, in a fashion impossible to duplicate with the more natural stimuli of mechanical displacement or temperature. Specific inquiries may, therefore, be made into the effects of specific variations in the nerve impulse pattern on the sensations experienced by the subject. This is an approach which we feel adds a valuable supplement to the determination of the pattern of stimuli evoked by the natural or quasi-natural stimulus. In fact, specific sensitivities to microtemporal fluctuations that have no quantitative analog in the pure electrophysiological or psychophysical experiment can be measured by this technique.

Though this technique adds an important tool to our repertoire for the study of coding problems, it, admittedly, does also have its limitations. The most important of these limitations is the fact that rather than dealing with fine single axons, we are synchronizing the response of the total population of nerve fibers in the nerve trunk being stimulated. By so doing, we obliterate any chance of studying the individual responses of individual places within the nerve tract. A recent paper by Casby, Siminoff, and Houseknecht (1963) suggests that for some neural dimensions this may not, however, be a crucial limitation, since the activity evoked by natural activity in peripheral nerves of the cat, when analyzed by their technique, was shown to be of the same general form as that produced by pulse electrical stimulation.

The somesthetic system has been singled out for this series of investigations for two reasons. This system is, of course, intrinsically interesting, but it also should be admitted that the topology of the peripheral somesthetic nervous system has provided opportunities for investigation that are unmatched by any of the central senses. The optic, auditory, olfactory, vestibular, and gustatory pathways all lie deeply buried in the bony superstructure of the head inaccessible to recording or stimulating electrodes and, for the most part, preceded by complex peripheral analyzers whose complete functions are still a matter of active inquiry.

THE NATURE OF THE CODING PROBLEM

Many recent studies have shown that the problem of somatosensory coding is a far more intricate and multifaceted one than the simple duality of quality and quantity that has usually been emphasized. It is our intention in this section to present a schema to organize the problem by explicitly stating the dimensions of stimuli and the possible neural symbols into which they may be encoded. The first part of this schema deals with the physical dimensions of stimuli and is a compendium of those stimulus variables which have been shown to be effective in eliciting discriminable psychophysical or electrophysiological responses.* Two stimulus patterns which are not discriminated by the organism are, for the purpose of this biological discussion, identical even though they may be represented very differently in the pattern of nerve impulses.

The second part of the discussion deals with those parameters of the neural responses which have been observed to vary during either spontaneous or evoked activity. This part of the discussion will have a dual air of uncertainty. One reason for this uncertainty arises because the more complex patterns of neural activity have, as yet, not been observed due to the known limitation of the neurophysiological technique. Another reason stems from the fact that, even though we may observe a pattern, there may be more than one way for this pattern to exert its influence on subsequent neural stages, and the crucial experiments for distinguishing between two alternative decoding processes may not have been attempted yet.

---

*The idea of such a categorization is drawn from the organization of the book, *The Sensations*, by Pieron (1952) and by a recent, similar analysis by Rosenblith and Vidale (1962) which concentrated mostly on the visual and auditory sensory processes. The former work, though infrequently cited in American literature, has apparently had an important influence on the development of the concept of sensory codes.

Discriminable Dimensions of the Physical Stimulus

Quantity

The intensity or amplitude of a physical stimulus has long been an area of concern to the psychophysiological cryptographer. Yet since a different physical measure is involved in the definition of the intensity of each different kind of stimulus, the term *quantity,* defined independently of a specific quality, is spurious. For example, the specific physical dimension of quantity for touch may be a gradient of displacement through which the skin is distorted by an externally applied force. For vision, as another example, the quantity dimension must be defined in terms of the number of quanta of a given color of light. If one considers the electrical stimuli used in the experiments reported in this paper, then the amount of charge per unit time (current) passing through the skin (or more specifically, that portion of the current which passes effectively through the nerve bundle) defines stimulus quantity. It should be noted, however, that even in this relatively well defined case, the temporal relations among a group of pulses determine whether a simple statement of the peak current of a single pulse is adequate to specify the stimulus quantity. Temporal interactions such as those occurring within refractory periods can grossly modify effective stimulus quantity.

Nevertheless, we prefer to define stimulus intensity in terms of the physical energy measured exterior to the organism. This is in context with most modern experiments and has a certain methodological efficiency. Alterations prior to the neurological transduction by some biological medium must be considered in the same way as any other information link. This allows one to retain the advantages of a well-defined stimulus amplitude, while still not losing sight of the fact that the "most proximal stimulus" may be a highly altered form of the incident physical stimulus.

Quality

The kind of stimulus is, of course, the other classical area of sensory research. Yet again, there is an ambiguity in the interpretation of this term or of its closely related biological equivalent, modality. At its most gross level, the problem of modality is trivial. It is clear that the receptor organs make an initial analysis of incident physical energies by virtue of a lowered threshold to one kind of physical stimulus. There is no question that the human eye is best able to detect radiant energy between 4000 and 8000 angstroms, or that, among the sense organs, the ear responds maximally to pneumatic pressure fluctuations within the range of 30-15,000 Hz. This is the concept of the "adequate simulus" basis of gross "place" coding of the senses.

The second part of this dual interpretation is not trivial and has been the major point of attack of sensory theoreticians for the past century. The problem in this case concerns those different kinds of stimuli discriminable within a given modality. The nature of color vision and pitch perception, each representing families of micromodalities within vision and hearing, respectively, are problems of this level.

In the case of vision and hearing, the specifications of the physical stimulus are very highly developed. We have a single physical dimension in each case, which can be systematically varied to alter the microquality of the visual or auditory sensation. However, when one deals with senses such as somesthesis, olfaction and gustation, another complication arises. The separation of the various modalities into their families of micromodalities is based upon popular, historic and nonscientific traditions. We feel that the complexities of subjective quality in the cutaneous senses are not adequately described by a statement mentioning only the classic categories of touch, pain, pressure, warmth, and cold, and an open-ended group of "derived" sensations. The electrical stimulation of the skin gives rise to sensations, some of which mimic some of these qualities, but also some for which these older classification schemes have no descriptive term.

It may be noted that in the studies we will report in this paper, as elsewhere, the issue of quality has been, so far, carefully avoided. This was not an oversight. It was, rather, an expression of the ill-defined nature of the sensations associated with the family of somesthetic modalities. What, then, can be made of experiments in which the "tickle of a camel hair brush," the "cutaneous pinch," or the "pain-producing burn" are compared with the evoked nervous activity? Nevertheless, the problem of quality coding is an important one and if there is more than a single somesthetic modality (this is synonymous with saying less than an infinite number, each dependent upon a different spatiotemporal pattern of neural activity), some set of differential transformation rules must be present which we hope will ultimately succumb to a more systematic attack.

Temporal Parameters

We now leave the classic problems of quality and quantity and move into an area of discussion which is far less familiar to most students of sensory coding. There appear to be many different time senses, some within a given modality, and some common to many modalities. For very long durations and intervals, the temporal judgments made by an observer may almost be considered to be modality-independent, since the stimulus events merely serve to delimit some other internal timing process. On the other hand, for very short times, within a modality, timing considerations are critical. For example, the ability of the nervous system to use a frequency code for intensity is bounded at the upper end by the threshold for temporal acuity. Thus, there are significant differences between the temporal characteristics of each of the senses (see, for example, Gescheider, 1966). Fraisse (1963) has recently published an important volume dealing with the perception of time. Beyond the presentation of a wealth of studies on the time senses, his main contribution is an elucidation of the complexity of the family of time senses. Our categorization includes the following temporal subsenses.

RELATIVE TEMPORAL ORDER. The ability to determine which of two different stimuli arrived first is of a high level of biological significance. This parameter of the stimulus may be dealt with in purely temporal terms but surprisingly it is more often interpreted spatially. One of the most familiar of this latter class of discriminative abilities is the auditory system's use of differential time of arrival (and to a lesser degree, relative intensity) to localize a sound source in space. The timing precision of binaural localization is astonishingly high, corresponding to only a few tens of microseconds of difference in the arrival times.

Relative temporal order can also be a major determinant of spatial localization of thermal, tactual, and gustatory sensations. Békésy (1963) has demonstrated a wide variety of these effects and has shown the very slight difference in relative temporal order which can substantially change the apparent position of a resultant fused sensation. He has interpreted these slight differences in terms of nerve conduction times which, he speculates, may be as great as 800 m/sec in the case of tactual nerves. We do not believe this interpretation to be justified for the complexity of the central interpretive mechanisms allows many alternative explanations. In addition, peripheral nerve velocity measurements have been made on man (see, for example, Uttal, 1959) which place the conduction velocities well within the range found in other mammals. It is also interesting to note that a closely related experiment (Efron, 1963), testing the temporal conditions of apparent simultaneity, showed little or no compensation for these more moderate conduction times for nonfused sensations. This apparent contradiction in results remains to be resolved.

TEMPORAL ACUITY. Temporal acuity is defined as the ability to distinguish two stimulus events, sequential in time, as being separate, rather than a single event. As we indicated above, measurements of temporal acuity are very important, for the threshold of temporal acuity defines the upper bound of the simple frequency coding possibilities of the nervous system. Temporal acuity is, of course, directly related to the relative temporal order sense, for to specify one stimulus as having preceded another they must have been distinguished as separate events, temporally as well as spatially, or qualitatively. Yet, we believe that these two capabilities are distinguishable from each other, since the former capability requires an ordinal judgment, in addition to the more primitive resolution capability of temporal acuity. Hirsh and Sherrick (1961) demonstrated just such a distinction in their study of temporal order by showing situations in which acuity obtained even though the subject was confused about relative temporal order.

TEMPORAL DURATION OR INTERVAL. Another temporal sense involves the ability to replicate the sustained duration of an event or the interval between two events. This sense requires the organism to be capable of clocking time. How this is accomplished is a problem of much current speculation, since there are many biological rhythms which could serve as bases for the clocking operations. It is clear that there is probably no reason to distinguish between a marked interval and a continuous event, since the true stimulus information is only that included in the initiation and termination of the interval or event.

All three of these temporal discriminative abilities probably play an important role in what might be called complex temporal pattern recognition. Whether there are other temporal abilities which must be added to fully explain all aspects of temporal discrimination is yet to be determined.

Spatial Parameters

The recent research of Hubel and Wiesel (1959), Maturana, Lettvin, McCulloch, and Pitts (1960), and of Barlow and Hill (1963) have emphasized the importance of special codes for dynamic spatial parameters. In each case, stimuli were shown to produce different nerve messages when the stimulus pattern differed geometrically, even though all other stimulus dimensions were held constant. On a simpler level, it is clear that spatial localization of stimuli applied to different points of the receptor fields must be accounted for, and although we have a good deal of evidence to suggest that this is carried out by a corresponding place code within the nervous tissue, there still remain two other major problems. First, how does one explain the pseudolocations made of interacting patterns, such as those summarized in Békésy's (1958) paper on funneling? Second, how does the mapping of spatial localization by a place code overlap with those theories of quality coding or of other stimulus dimensions which also require spatially distributed codes?

In the study of interactions between different spatial areas, a great deal of progress has been made. Ratliff (1965) reviews the work of the last century describing not only the spatial codes for contours, but also gives a detailed electrophysiological analysis of the transformation processes which lead from the original spatial stimulus pattern to the evoked pattern of neural signals.

These, then, are among the most prominent of the stimulus dimensions which we know to be discriminable, and which must be accounted for in defining the complete neural code. We shall now consider the possible dimensions of nervous activity which provide symbols for the representation of these stimulus variables.

Possible Dimensions of the Neural Code

The key problem in the study of sensory coding is the determination of which of the possible dimensions of variation of the nerve response represent which dimensions of the stimulus. To associate stimulus dimensions accurately with neural response dimensions, one must be cognizant of as many of the likely neural dimensions as possible. The purpose of this section is to list and describe the more important of these dimensions without either resorting to a meaningless class of all classes, such as "the spatiotemporal pattern", or to biologically unlikely possibilities.

Place

By "place" in a nerve tract or a ganglion, we are referring to the constituent parts which are activated by a given input. There are many conceivable ways in which one particular neuron or group of neurons might be selected for the transmission of information by an incident stimulus. Lowered thresholds to particular types of physical energy or significantly specific temporal pattern inputs are among the most interesting possibilities. Throughout much of modern sensory neurophysiology, we find the assumption that quality, in particular, is mediated by some sort of place code. This assumption is a basic foundation of many of the major theoretical expressions. For the cutaneous senses, however, as Melzack and Wall (1962) have pointed out, this is not very clear in spite of the persistency of the classical special receptor notion. Place may, therefore, be available for the representation of other stimulus dimensions.

Number of Activated Units

Another possible dimension of neural coding is, simply, the number of activated fibers in a given nerve tract or ganglion. Intensity coding is the stimulus dimension which is most often considered to be mapped, at least in part, by the number of responding neural elements. Since an increase in the number of responding units also means that more places must have been activated, it is expected that there would be strong interactions between stimulus dimensions which are coded by place and those which are coded by number.

Neural Event Amplitude

The all-or-none law has effectively removed the amplitude of the response of a single axon from among the possible coding dimensions. It appears certain now that the all-or-none law is acceptable, and that the amplitude of the individual nerve impulse is related to metabolic features of the neuron, which are independent of stimulus dimensions. However, it should be remembered that in other parts of the neuron it has been clearly established that slow potentials of graded amplitude and elongated duration are the significant information symbols. In general, as we shall show, when we refer to the amplitude of compound action potentials, we are actually dealing with an indirect measure of the number of nerve cells which are firing. The amplitudes of compound action potentials are meaningful only in this latter frame of reference.

Temporal Pattern

Defining temporal pattern as one of the dimensions of neural coding is almost as weak a statement as defining a class of "spatiotemporal patterns." In the following paragraphs, we strive for more precision by specifying the definite dimensions under consideration.

FREQUENCY OF FIRING. While place and the number of activated neural elements are relatively unambiguous measures which can be evaluated without confusion (even though the technical details may be cumbersome), frequency is an ambiguous dimension of neural activity. Frequency, or the number of responses per unit time, may be evaluated in one of two different ways by a subsequent decoding mechanism. The first way is one in which time measurements are made of the intervals between each pair of sequential responses. The alternative form of decoding possible for frequency is one in which a count is made of the number of neural events occurring within some basic integrating unit of time. As Anatol Rapoport (1962) pointed out, the interval-sensitive procedure would be essentially an analog process, since the range over which the interval varied could be continuous. On the other hand, the counting procedure is essentially a digital process dealing only with integral values of the number of events.

MACROFLUCTUATIONS IN FREQUENCY PATTERN. Wall and Cronly-Dillon (1960) have suggested that a specific code for somatosensory quality, at certain levels, might be the macropattern of the frequency of neural discharge in afferent pathways. Thus, a frequency pattern in which the nerve impulse rate goes from a minimum level to a higher level very rapidly and then slowly diminishes would be perceived differently than a signal in the same pathway and with the same average frequency, but whose frequency pattern slowly increases and then rapidly diminishes. These macrofluctuations are regularly observed in many types of neurophysiological recordings from single cells and might be of significance in the encoding of stimulus dimensions other than quality. The serious question concerning macrofluctuations in frequency is whether the nervous system is able to differentially respond to different macropatterns, or whether these patterns are examples of irrelevant concomitancies. We shall deal later with both of these alternatives. Time of occurrence, of course, is also a macrofluctuation which is of obvious significance in the representation of very long term events.

MICROFLUCTUATIONS IN FREQUENCY PATTERN. An important related question is whether or not the nervous system is able to detect microfluctuations in frequency which are of significance for neural coding. There have been few studies which have specifically asked whether two mixed frequencies of neural discharge give rise to sensations which are related to one or the other of the two frequencies, or whether a beat, additive, or some other mixed sensation obtains. This experiment is quite different from those seemingly related auditory and visual studies in which the stimulus may be well controlled, but the nerve impulse pattern is unspecifiable because of the transducer action of the receptor organs. In this categorization of the possible codes of afferent activity, transient fluctuations in an otherwise regular sequence of nerve impulses may, therefore, be considered as a distinct coding possibility. Several of the studies we report later in this paper are directly aimed at resolving these questions.

TEMPORAL COMPARISONS BETWEEN TWO OR MORE PLACES. Another important possibility for a coding dimension is one in which comparisons are made in some neural center between temporal patterns, which arrive on spatially different neural channels. The spatial localization phenomena in hearing, somesthesis and gustation certainly operate in some fashion which takes into account the phase and amplitude differences of the stimuli applied to the receptor surfaces. Mountcastle, Poggio and Werner (1963) have reported such a spatial integration in the position indicators of the cat thalamus. Pfaffman (1959) has also suggested such a spatial comparison for gustatory quality coding. A somewhat different expression of a related idea is the volley principle which has been invoked to explain high frequency following by the auditory system. According to this principle, spatially-separate neural structures are capable of cooperatively conveying a frequency which exceeds the capacity of any individual neural structure. Such a process would require a high degree of synchronization among the neurons involved and a precise comparison of their firing rates. In any of these cases, the important fact is that the temporal coding dimension is not limited to a single channel of information, but that cooperative or comparative processes among various channels can play an important role as codes in a sensory system.

DERIVED STATISTICAL MEASURES. When we spoke of macrofluctuations, we were referring to relatively continuous changes in the frequency pattern. When we spoke of microfluctuations, we were referring to almost immediate evaluations of transient changes in the frequency pattern. There is, however, another possibility. There may be long-term fluctuations in the statistical characteristics which depend upon an evaluation of the microtemporal fluctuations, but in a summarized fashion over long periods of time. Thus, the standard deviation and the range of the interval histogram of individual units in the cochlear nucleus of the cat have been shown to exhibit a specific signature. This was accomplished by Rodieck, Kiang, and Gerstein (1962). Mountcastle, Poggio, and Werner (1962) have shown similar effects in thalamic cells representing joint position and have given an interesting analysis of how this information could be used as a code. The critical test of such a hypothesis, though, must be a maintained sensitivity to the derived statistical measure throughout the entire sensory process up to and including the perceived experience itself.

Some Cautions

Before we discuss our specific experimental results, it would be desirable to point out a number of potential pitfalls in the search for codes. These are simple and yet subtle traps which might confuse many of the specific issues of sensory coding.

Concomitant But Irrelevant Changes

Is it too obvious to point out that an experiment might lead to several correlated functional changes in the output pattern of a given neural structure, and yet only one of these might have any effect on the neural coding at any subsequent level? The changes which have no effect, even though they are concomitant, are thus not codes. They neither convey information nor alter the signal in any way. They may, of course, be signs of the input, useful at this stage, but are not participants in the information system with which we are concerned.

Dimension Alterations

It must be expected, from what we already know of the coding of sensory information, that there will be very drastic changes in the dimensions of stimuli as they are encoded at various stages of the afferent nervous system. For example, the most current theory of auditory encoding assumes that there is a transduction from temporal (frequency) to spatial dimensions in the form of a place localization of different frequencies. It is not too surprising, therefore, when we hear of other specific neural structures which respond spatially to a specific temporal pattern of stimulus input. Segundo, Moore, Stensaas, and Bullock (1963) have reported the existence of such temporal "keys" in the nervous system of the gastropod mollusc *Aplysia*. On the other hand, MacKay (1961) has also reported several instances of spatial patterns which give rise to flickering changes in the visual field.

Thus, we should expect spatial-to-temporal, as well as temporal-to-spatial transformations. The caution inherent in these results is that we should not demand dimensional constancy throughout the afferent pathways.

Boundary Condition Results

Another caution relates to the fact that many of our results are significant only in the sense that they represent limiting cases or boundary conditions. The determination of a threshold in a psychophysical experiment is a case in point. The threshold may impose a limit on the availability of a certain dimension to serve in some particular coding operation, but it does not necessarily completely define the functional variability of such a dimension as the corresponding stimulus dimension is altered.

Multiple Coding in Two or More Dimensions

The old slogan, "spatiotemporal pattern," naive and ill-defined as it was, did reflect a certain problem. Many complex stimulus patterns are not unidimensional and it is sometimes difficult to determine which of the stimulus dimensions are associated with which of the nerve signal dimensions. In fact, such a separation may not be possible without considering interdimensional interaction, since some temporal dimensions may act to modify some other dimensions. Thus, it would probably be misleading to presume a one-to-one relationship between a given stimulus dimension and a given neural code. As we shall see, there appear to be relatively large numbers of redundancies in the coding schema. Anatol Rapoport (1962) discusses some related cautions in an excellent discussion of the coding problem.

SOME PSYCHOPHYSIOLOGICAL RESULTS FROM THE HUMAN SOMATOSENSORY SYSTEM

The previous section has described the general nature of the neural coding problem. It may be summarized as a search for a translation matrix relating the dimensions of the stimulus to the dimensions of the coded signals transmitted through the afferent nervous system. A number of our earlier papers dealt with specific aspects of this general problem. They (Uttal, 1959; 1960a; 1960b; Uttal and Cook, 1964) have been reported elsewhere. The purpose of this section will be to present some newer results which, in general, use patterned trains of stimuli, rather than single, double, or triple stimuli, as an approach to the coding problem. The first study in this section uses electrophysiological recordings to define the nature of the nerve impulse generated by our patterned pulse electrical stimulation. The others use psychophysical responses to determine the effect of the patterned train of nerve impulses on the subject's perceptions. These latter studies will be specifically concerned with the effect of the temporal pattern of the stimulus on the temporal acuity of the subject.

Before presenting the details of these studies, we would like to make a purely methodological comment. This comment concerns the control of psychophysical experiments in particular, but may also be relevant to the problems of the electrophysiological laboratory. Smith (1961) has pointed out the extreme efficiency introduced into a psychophysical experiment when one selects each subsequent stimulus on the basis of some criterion of likelihood calculated from the preceding data. In some simple psychophysical techniques, this can be simply accomplished by increasing the stimulus along the dimension of interest if the stimulus was below the instantaneous threshold and by decreasing it if it was above. More sophisticated statistical techniques can be used; but then the resetting of stimulus parameters may become a complicated process, and automated assistance will be necessary to avoid elongated delays between stimulus presentations. The answer, of course, to these requirements is to build into one's experimental system a digital computer. This is no longer a preposterous suggestion, since small and very inexpensive computers are now commercially available, and purchase prices often are less than the alternative manual costs of data processing. The advantages are manifold, but this is hardly the place to list fully the delights of the automated laboratory. Rather, we would prefer to mention one subtle, but important, advantage for psychological research. This is a relationship which develops between the experimental subject and the computer, which we have seen occur, and which Amnon Rapoport (1964) has also reported. Subjects dealing with computers seem to give more stable responses, and they report that it is a more "satisfying" experience to deal with a dependable and impartial mechanical device than with a fallible and perhaps biased human experimenter. The objective reasons for this phenomenon are, one would imagine, related to the stability of response timing and the associated rhythm which develops in the experiment.

We have used a digital computer to control several of the experiments which are described below. In each instance, the experiment was done more easily and, we believe, more economically than would have otherwise been possible. We now feel that the automated laboratory is an essential part of our research operation.

Let us now consider our experimental work in detail. The first study, electrophysiological in design, is a precautionary one in which it is shown that there is a kind of preprocessing in peripheral nerves, which may qualify our confidence in a one-to-one correspondence between stimulus pattern and compound action potential pattern. The rest of the studies presented are primarily psychophysical and show the effects of stimulus pattern on temporal acuity. Temporal acuity is used as a convenient probe which is demonstrably sensitive to microfluctuations in the temporal pattern of the nerve impulses.

Oscillations in the Amplitude of Human Peripheral
Nerve Action Potentials During Repetitive Stimulation

Oscillatory phenomena produced by impulsive stimulation of sensory systems have been observed by a number of investigators. Central nervous system structures seem to show these effects most clearly (Keidel, Keidel, and Wigand, 1961; Rosner, 1956). Recovery functions in presynaptic peripheral nerves following electrical stimulation have also been shown to display oscillatory behavior (Gasser and Grundfest, 1936). Larrabee and Bronk (1947) have also shown that oscillations in the amplitude of the compound action potentials occur in postsynaptic nerve tracts in the sympathetic nervous system. However, the response amplitude of presynaptic compound action potentials seems generally to be considered to decrease without oscillation or not to change at all during repetitive stimulation. (See Fig. 5 in Gasser and Grundfest, 1936; Fig. 12 in Keidel *et al.*, 1961; Fig. 3 in Larrabee and Bronk, 1947). These results suggest that oscillations in response amplitude are introduced into the response waveform by synaptic action.

Some earlier work in our laboratory with widely separated stimulus doublets (Brown, 1960) suggested that there may be long-term effects generated by two-pulse stimulation of human peripheral nerves *in situ*. In the present studies, oscillations in the response amplitudes are shown to occur when the ulnar nerve is stimulated by trains of electrical pulse stimuli. Our results deal particularly with functional relation of this oscillation to variations in stimulus amplitude and interpulse interval.

The data reported are for three male Ss. The two superficial points of the ulnar nerve on the left arm were located as described in our previous paper (Uttal, 1959). Stimulus pulses in the train were .5 msec in duration and the interval between pulses and the amplitude of each pulse varied according to the designs of the experiments described below.

The first experiment we performed investigated the effects of variation of the magnitude of the repetitive stimulus pulses on the envelope of response amplitudes. The second experiment investigated the effects of variation of the frequency of the stimulus train on this envelope.

In the first experiment, the Ss were stimulated with a train of constant current pulses which were separated by 12 msec intervals for a period of 200 msec. The amplitude of the pulses in a given train was varied to include the following current levels: 1, 2, 3, 4, 5, 6, 7 and 8 ma. One set of records was taken for each of the Ss for each of the current levels.

In the second experiment, the Ss were stimulated with a train of constant intensity stimuli. The particular value of the constant current varied for each S, but was in the range of 2.5 to 3.5 ma. The parameter varied in this experiment was the interval between the sequential pulses. A given train would have an interval selected from the following set: 8, 10, 12, 16, 18, 20, 25, 30, and 40 msec; but, as in the first experiment, the total duration of the sequence of pulses was limited to 200 msec. One set of records was taken for each of the Ss in this experiment for each interval.

The records were measured directly from Polaroid oscillograms by hand. Several different measurements were taken, as indicated in Figure 12-1 which shows a diagrammatic sketch of the typical response. A_1 was the amplitude of the largest spike in the initial part of the response, and varied from record to record as a measurement of the first, second, or third response, depending upon the stimulus interval. A_2 was the amplitude of the smallest spike in the first trough of amplitude. T_1 was the time from the beginning of the stimulus train to the minimum of the envelope. A pulse may or may not have been present at this minimum, depending upon the intervals of the pulses in the stimulus train.

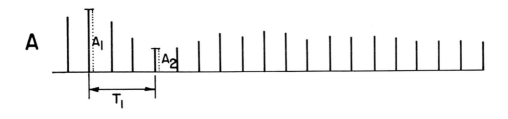

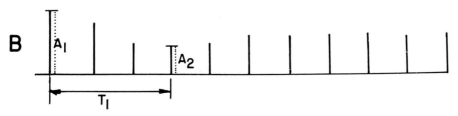

Figure 12-1. Schematic drawing of the oscillatory response showing the two different measurement criteria used for the two different types of response.

An important derived measure was the peak-to-trough ratio which was defined at A_1/A_2, and which is independent of the amplitude of the response. Thus, a high peak-to-trough ratio indicated a considerable swing in the amplitude of the response, but would not necessarily differentiate between large or small absolute amplitudes.

Figure 12-2 shows a 200 msec sample of the series of responses to a repetitive train of stimuli. The upward going spikes are the nerve responses and the lower the stimulus artifacts. It can be seen that there is an oscillation of the amplitude of the responses as a function of serial position which lasts for a considerable period of time. In some records, this oscillation may appear to continue for 300 or 400 msec, but, like many damped oscillations, it appears that the first few amplitude swings are the largest.

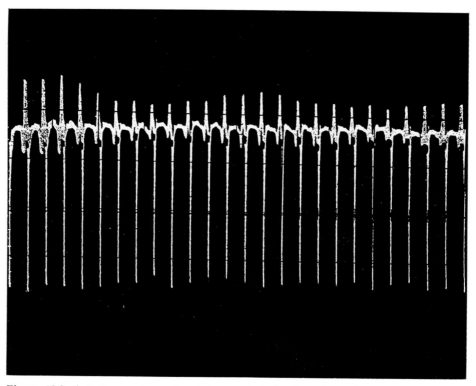

Figure 12-2. A 200 msec long stimulation period showing the oscillations (200μV full scale vertical) generated by repetitive stimuli.

As the stimulus amplitude is increased, the following sequence of events was exhibited by all subjects. Responses cannot be distinguished from noise for stimulus amplitudes of 1 and 2 ma, but begin to emerge at 3 ma. At 4 ma, all responses were clearly visible and the oscillation peak-to-trough ratio was most clear. Above this stimulus intensity, the size of the responses continues to increase, but the ratio of peak-to-trough amplitudes decreases. Therefore, peak-to-trough ratios are maximum for the lowest effective stimulus currents. In general, there appeared to be no change in T_1, the time at which the first trough appears. All Ss showed this same pattern. Differences between Ss were, however, observed in the stimulus intensity at which the responses appeared. The steady increase of A_1 as stimulus intensity is increased and the steady decrease in A_1/A_2 during this same variation is plotted in Figure 12-3 with data pooled for all Ss.

Because of the variation in threshold at which the responses emerge, stimulus intensity in the second experiment was adjusted individually for each subject. Figure 12-4 shows the pooled data for all subjects in all trials in which the stimulus interval was varied and the amplitude held constant.

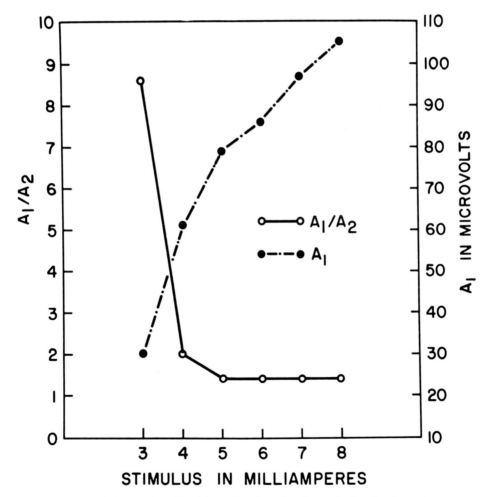

Figure 12-3. Pooled data for all subjects showing the effect of stimulus intensity increase on the absolute amplitude A_1 and the peak-to-trough ratio A_1/A_2.

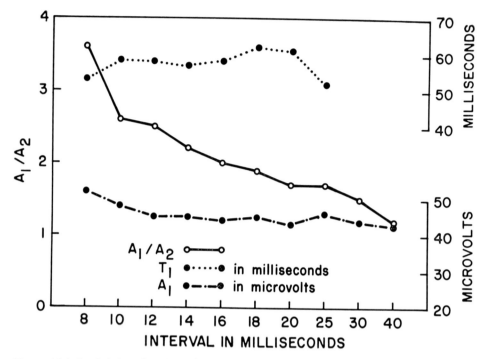

Figure 12-4. Pooled data for all subjects showing the effect of increasing stimulus interval on the peak-to-trough ratio A_1/A_2, the time to the first trough T_1, and the absolute amplitude A_1.

Thus, each plotted point represents the average of six measurements. The amplitude of A_1 remained relatively constant over the entire range of intervals studied. The peak-to-trough ratio A_1/A_2, however, showed a gradual decline as the interpulse interval was increased. This decline, however, did occur for a trough with an essentially constant T_1 regardless of interpulse interval, as can be seen from the other curves in Figure 12-4.

Inspection of the responses revealed no change in the latencies of the responses during the repetitive stimulus burst.

In this experiment we are dealing with an oscillation of response amplitude which occurs during tetanic stimulation, rather than the recovery effects which follow the tetanus. It is this latter set of problems involving post-tetanic effects to which most of the attention of neurophysiologists has been directed. It is for this reason that the phenomenon reported in this paper has not, to our knowledge, been observed. Larrabee and Bronk's (1947) study of sympathetic ganglia is the only other observation of oscillation during a tetanus to have come to our attention. Their study shows a similar oscillation, but only when the stimulus is applied to the presynaptic neurons and the response recorded from postsynaptic ones. If the stimulator is then moved to the postsynaptic tract, the responses are flat during the tetanus and the post-tetanic potentiation (PTP) is absent. This suggests that these oscillatory phenomena may be related to synaptic action.

We are, therefore, faced with the question of the origin of the oscillatory potentials in our records. There are two principal hypotheses which remain once we exclude artifacts of technique, and accept these oscillations as true neurophysiological events. The first assumes that the oscillation is due to the changes in the nerve membrane potentials which occur during tetanic stimulation. Thus, the oscillation could reflect the collective "hunting" of the involved nerve membrane potentials for new equilibrium levels. This is a response typical of lightly damped systems. The oscillation would be related, in this case, to refractory periods and a nonmonotonic accumulation of afterpotentials during the repetitive train of stimulations.

The second hypothesis assumes that the effect is not a function of the nerve membrane dynamics of the stimulated nerves, but, rather, is a result of centrifugal activity which is reflexively generated by spinal or higher centers. Thus, in this case, efferent activity would be assumed to be interfering with the compound action potential amplitude by some as yet unidentified mechanism and the oscillations would indeed be phenomena associated with synaptic activity.

There is evidence which supports the idea of a central feedback as the source of the oscillation. Toennies (1938) observed a reflex nerve impulse which is carried on the afferent fibers, which usually carry information through the dorsal roots to more central regions. Eccles and Krnjevic (1959) have shown that these dorsal root reflexes can be carried in exactly the same individual axons which carry the afferent activity. Thus, a site of interaction is suggested for the orthodromic and antidromic responses, which could lead to the oscillation observed in human peripheral nerves.

The basic characteristics of the response also argue strongly for a feedback explanation of this phenomenon. The insensitivity of the wavelength of the response to stimulus interval variation suggests that a constant factor, such as transmission time from point of stimulation to the CNS back to the point of interaction, is involved. A nerve membrane hypothesis would certainly involve a frequency sensitivity as more and more frequent stimuli produced a greater and greater decrement in the recovery state of the involved neural elements.

The fact that the response is most enhanced at low stimulus intensities is, although a less conclusive argument, also a sort of evidence towards a feedback hypothesis. Dawson (1956) has shown that the sensory fibers in the mixed ulnar nerve have lower thresholds than the motor fibers in the same nerve at the same anatomical point. Thus, it might be suggested that, at low stimulus intensities, we are dealing primarily with the sensory fibers in which the dorsal root reflex might be operating. This specific conclusion is, however, equivocated by the fact that we may be dealing with a delicate effect which is washed out by high stimulus intensities.

Because of this indirect evidence, we are tempted to suggest that the oscillation observed in the percutaneous peripheral preparation is a phenomenon generated by feedback effects from the CNS. Thus, we may indeed be dealing with a synaptic effect, even though the stimulating and recording electrodes are both apparently presynaptic.

This, then, is the qualification which we referred to earlier. Although our stimuli are known to each produce a single compound action potential, it may be that some processing involving feedback from synaptic relays is already operating to modify the signal characteristics. We have not yet been able to determine if the oscillations are psychophysically effective. That is, is the subject able to perceive the waxing and waning of the train of nerve action potentials? Another problem which is raised is whether or not the perceived timing relations, apparently well controlled by our stimulus pattern, are also disrupted by such antidromic activity. Apparently they are not, for as we shall see in the next set of experiments, there is a delicate discrimination of the temporal properties of the stimulus train.

Effects of Stimulus Pattern on Somesthetic Temporal Acuity

Acuity, the ability to distinguish adjacent stimuli, is, in many situations, a very delicate measure of sensory capacity often exceeding the precision of absolute judgments. Pieron (1955) has suggested the term "temporal acuity" for the ability to distinguish between two stimuli presented sequentially, such that an observer reports two successive events, rather than a single temporal experience. The distinction, however, is rarely complete for closely spaced stimulus doublets. The observer, therefore, reports that there are two events if he detects a sufficient modulation in the intensity of the stimulus pattern. Somesthetic temporal acuity may be considered to be an extremely effective measure of the information characteristics of both the transmitting and analyzing properties of sensory mechanisms. As such, it can be expected to be sensitive to the temporal organization of a stimulus train. This section of the paper describes four separate studies which were carried out by respectively exploring the effects of intensity, interval, numerosity, and position on the detection threshold of a gap in a train of electrical pulse stimuli.

Stimulus trains were composed of 0.5 msec isolated constant current electrical pulses with intervals and amplitudes varied in accordance with the specific design of the experiments described below. The stimuli were fed into two glass test tubes, which were filled with normal saline solution. The subject inserted the index and middle fingers of his left hand, up to the first joint, into the saline solution. The stimuli were experienced as buzzes or tingles without noticeable motor involvement. Contingent upon the S's responses, the stimulus patterns were altered in accordance with an up-and-down method of limits. An initial stimulus pattern would be presented by the computer and if a discontinuity were detected by the subject, the gap size would be automatically shortened. If it were not, it would be automatically lengthened. The experiment usually began with a gap size well above the threshold, and in the first few responses the S brought the gap into the region of the threshold by a sequence of positive responses. A block of trials consisted of 100 estimates by the S of whether a gap was present or absent. Estimates were indicated by the S depressing a Yes or a No key. The computer acquired these responses and stored them in the magnetic core memory. At the end of the block, the computer branched into an analysis program which computed the mean gap of all except the first 12 presentations in the block. It also computed the standard deviation, the range and a new step size to be used in the next block. At the completion of a block, the computer paused and the S was given a 30-sec rest before the next block was initiated.

In each experiment, the task of the S remained the same, that is, to report whether a gap in a train of pulses was detectable. The computer-controlled stimulus programming procedure described earlier was used in all experiments. Under each condition, each value of the independent variable was presented once each day in a block of 100 trials. The order of experimental blocks was varied in a constrained random order over successive days.

The first experiment was designed to determine the effect of stimulus intensity on the detection of a discontinuity in a series of nine pulses, with four pulses preceding and five pulses following the gap. Except for the gap itself, each stimulus in the train was separated from its neighbors by an interval which remained constant at 16 msec throughout the entire experiment. The S was presented with the following current levels: 2, 3, 4, 5, and 6 ma with the selected current held constant during each block. Each block was presented once each day for five days. Five Ss were used in this experiment.

The second experiment was designed to determine the effect of variation of interpulse interval on the detection of a gap. There were five stimuli on either side of the gap and the stimulus intensity was held constant at 4 ma. The intervals used were 8, 12, 15, 20, 30, 40 and 50 msec. The experiment was repeated for seven days for each of the four Ss used.

Experiment 3 was designed to determine the effects of numerosity of the stimulus pulses on the ability of the S to perceive gaps in trains. The stimulus patterns used included bursts of 2, 4, 6, 8, 10 and 12 pulses with the gap always placed centrally in the burst. The current was again held constant at 4 ma and the intervals other than the gap itself were constant at 16 msec. In this experiment, each of four Ss was used for six days.

The fourth experiment was designed to determine the effects of the location of the gap within a pulse train on its detectability. The number of pulses in each sequence was 8, with a uniform spacing of 16 msec and a constant current level of 4 ma. Thus, the gap might come after the first, second, or after any sequential stimulus up to the seventh, while all the other parameters remained constant. Each of four Ss was run on each of seven days.

The results of the four experiments are presented in Figures 12-5 through 12-8. In each case, the horizontal coordinate represents the inde-

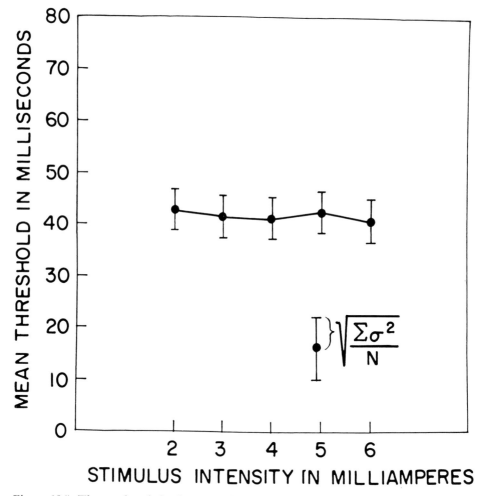

Figure 12-5. The results of the first experiment on gap detection showing lack of variation in the threshold for the gap as the stimulus intensity is varied.

pendent variable of the experiment and the vertical coordinate represents the gap threshold averaged over all Ss for all days. The mean value for a block was based on an N of 88. Therefore, each point on the curve represents the average of $88nd$ estimates of the gap threshold, where n is the number of Ss, and d is the number of test days. The number of observations represented by each point of Figures 12-5 through 12-8 are 2200, 2464, 2112, and 2464 respectively. The square root of the average of the variances of each point have also been drawn in each case to display a measure of variability. In a sense, this variance measure is also a measure of the difficulty of making a given decision.

Figure 12-5 displays the results of Experiment 1 in which the amplitude of the stimulus pulses was the independent variable. Clearly, both the

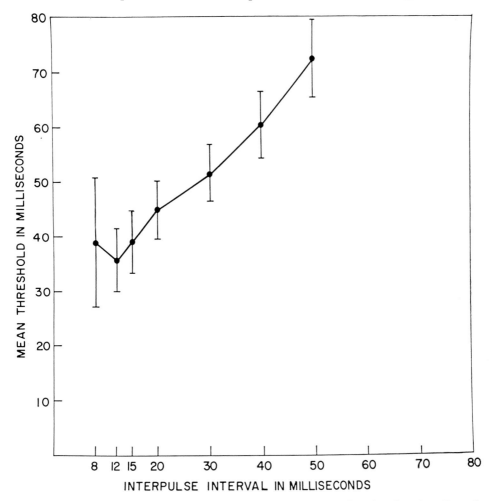

Figure 12-6. The results of the second experiment on gap detection showing the effect of varying the interval between electrical pulse stimuli on the threshold for the gap.

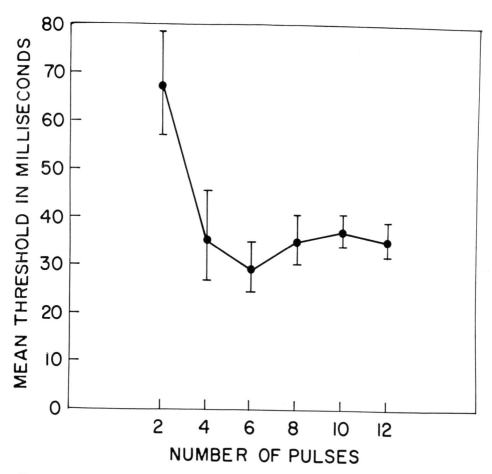

Figure 12-7. The results of the third experiment on gap detection showing the results of varying the number of pulses in which the gap was embedded.

threshold value and the measures of variance do not show any appreciable effect as a function of this parameter.

Figure 12-6 displays the results of Experiment 2 in which the independent variable was the interpulse interval between the stimuli surrounding the gap. Figure 12-6 shows that the effect was considerable. As the interpulse intervals increase, the threshold for the gap monotonically increases. The one exception to this rule is the result for the shortest interval, 8 msec, which is slightly elevated over the result for 12 msec. It should be noted also that the difference between the mean gap size at threshold and the interval between the other stimuli varies little over the range of intervals used in this experiment. This result suggests that the j. n. d. for gap interval is nearly constant over the range used.

Inspection of the variances shows that the elevated point at 8 msec is associated with a large increase in the variance, thus indicating the increased difficulty of making the discrimination at this interval.

Figure 12-7 displays the results of Experiment 3, in which the independent variable was the numerosity of the stimulus pulses. The results of this experiment demonstrate emphatically the importance of considering the total temporal pattern as a significant parameter, rather than dealing strictly with stimulus doublets. By far, the largest threshold was obtained for the simple doublet situation. For other multiple pulse patterns, the thresholds are seen to be relatively constant. The variances, though, tell an additional and interesting story about the difficulty of making the discriminations. The variances decrease almost monotonically with increase in numerosity, thus indicating that the Ss were able to make the discrimination more consistently for stimulus patterns in which the pulses were more numerous.

Figure 12-8 shows the results of Experiment 4 in which the position of the gap within the pattern of stimuli was varied. A bow-shaped curve is obtained with maximum sensitivity for symmetrically placed gaps with increasing thresholds for greater imbalance between the preceding and following bursts. Inspection of the variance measures shows that it was more difficult for the S to deal with stimulus patterns which consisted of a single pulse or a double pulse in the following burst, but that otherwise the decisions appear to be equally difficult.

The results of these studies have shown that the threshold for gap detection is functionally related to the pattern of the stimulus train in which the gap is imbedded. The quality of the evoked sensations has been ignored so far, but it is an important aspect which deserves discussion. For all except the shortest intervals, Ss reported that the "buzz" was a series of more or less discrete events, and thus their criterion for a gap was a just-noticeable difference between the gap and some function of the intervals of the preceding and following bursts. On the other hand, the situation in Experiment 3 in which the gap was preceded and followed only by a single pulse represents a very special case in which the S was probably being called upon to make a different discrimination, that different discrimination being a judgment of the "oneness" or the "twoness" of the doublet. There was some suggestion that the elevation of this point was a context or instructional set effect since naive Ss usually reported a much lower threshold for simple acuity tests with doublets, and this two-pulse threshold is higher than that reported elsewhere. Similarly, the slight elevation of the shortest interval in Experiment 2 is, we believe, an effect of a quality change for there is evidence that at this interval, we may well have been above the fusion frequency.

The results of Experiment 4 indicate that there is a considerable effect on the threshold as the numerical imbalance between the bursts on either side of the gap increases. There are two major hypotheses explaining the elongation of the threshold for a gap when only a small number of pulses are present on one or the other side. The first suggests that the perception of the burst with fewer stimuli is inhibited or masked by the presence of the longer burst. Both backward and forward masking effects would have to be involved, but both have been demonstrated in one or another sense modality. Thus, according to this hypothesis, the elevation of the threshold of the gap would be due to the fact that the less numerous burst is not perceived by the subject. On the other hand, an explanation is also possible in terms

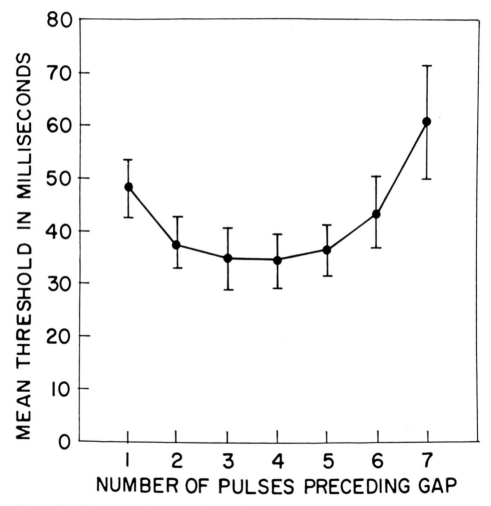

Figure 12-8. The results of the fourth experiment on gap detection, showing the effect of altering the position of the gap in an otherwise constant stimulus pattern.

of a disruption in the temporal discrimination ability of the S independent of the subjective amplitude. This second hypothesis suggests that the S perceives both of the stimuli, but that his ability to deal with them in a temporal way is inhibited by the imbalance between the two, or perhaps even by the simple numerosity of the stimuli in the bursts. However, in Experiment 3, we see that it is only at the extreme condition of only two pulses that the threshold is so elevated. Thus, the systematic elevation of the threshold as the imbalance is increased may be due exclusively to the imbalance, rather than the numerosity. The one exception to this rule may be the situation in which there is only a single pulse at either end, a situation in which the numerosity effect is more effective. Since the stimulus intensities are so high, it is our belief that the effect is chiefly due to the disruption of the time sense rather than masking.

Closely analogous to our experiments are those studies concerning the perception of rhythm. As Pieron (1952) points out, "There is a particularly high sensitivity to frequency variation." This statement, of course, is the precursor of the idea that repetitive stimulation may generate sensitivities which are superior to those measured for simple doublets. Knudsen (1928) and Perilhou (1947) have studied the differential threshold of vibratory stimuli and have found differential sensitivities as small as 2 to 10 per cent. In their experiments, the differential threshold was measured for a periodic waveform which shifted frequency *in toto*. In our experiments, the frequency shift is for a single cycle only, and probably represents a different discriminative task. Pieron and Segal (1938) have reported that for electrical stimulation of the fingers the fine discrimination evidenced for total frequency is degraded and differential thresholds of 50 per cent were more common. Such values are more in accord with the data of the present experiments.

Effect of Unequal Intervals on Somesthetic Temporal Acuity

In spite of the fact that electrophysiological evidence is accumulating that stimuli do produce statistically different distributions from different cells, and that these different statistical patterns can differentially affect at least some synapses in certain invertebrate nervous systems, there is as yet no direct evidence that these derived statistical properties can be discriminated by the total sensory system of a human subject. The study described in this section was our first attempt to determine whether differences in derived statistical measures can, in fact, be detected by the human somatosensory system.

The test chosen for this study utilized temporal acuity as the dependent variable. In this case, this choice is even more appropriate than previously, for it is in context with related experiments in vision (see, e.g., Forsyth and

Brown, 1959) in which flicker thresholds were measured with a related form of unequal interval stimulus train. There is a fundamental difference, however, between the two experiments. As emphasized earlier, electrical stimulation of the somesthetic system is unique in that the pattern of peripheral compound action potentials is completely defined. In the case of the visual flicker experiments, however, we are more probably dealing with effects reflecting the integrative properties of the visual photochemical. This transducer function completely distorts the actual temporal pattern of the nervous response before it is transmitted centrally. It is, therefore, not surprising that the results of this first attempt at determining what, if any, derived statistical properties of the action potential train could be discriminated, resulted in a set of data which was quite different from that obtained in the visual system. Our results do indicate that there is a derived statistical interpretation of the stimulus patterns being made; however, it is not one in which the sum of the intervals is the determining relationship, but rather the differences between the two unequal intervals.

The procedure in this experiment was essentially the same as that described in the previous section. The subject inserted the index and middle fingers up to the first joint into two test tubes filled with saline solution. The electrical stimulus pattern was once again generated by the computer which also controlled the timing of the stimulus presentations, the generation of the next stimulus pattern and the collection and analysis of the data. In this experiment, however, stimulus patterns different from the preceding set were used. In general, they are described by the diagrammatic sketch in Figure 12-9. In each stimulus train the x value defines the six intervals within the six pairs of stimuli and the y value defines the larger intervals between the pairs. The subject's task remained the same, to report whether or not a discontinuity had existed in the stimulus train.

The design of this experiment included random order of presentations of the blocks within a given daily session for each subject. Within a block, however, since the computer-controlled method of limits was used to track the threshold, the stimulus sequence was dependent upon the responses of the subject. A set of x values was selected which covered the range we felt most likely to show the effects of the unequal stimulus intervals. These x values included 12, 14, 16, 18, and 20 msec. Each of these intervals was then paired with all of the set of y values (12, 14, 16, 18, 20, 25, 30, and 40 msec) which were equal to or larger than the given x value. The stimuli were presented in blocks of presentations, with the y value presented in a constrained random order. The different x values were also run in a random order. Since each block allowed 65 estimates to be made, was presented once on each of eight days, and the data of each of five subjects were pooled to give our final results, each point of Figure 12-10 represents the average of

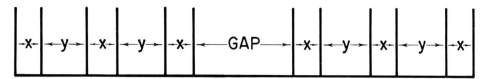

Figure 12-9. A diagrammatic sketch of the stimulus pattern used in the unequal interval experiment.

2600 estimates. In some cases, there were fewer blocks possible because the high value of x eliminated all but a few of the y values. In these cases, the few acceptable combinations of x and y values were repeated sufficiently often so that there were eight blocks in each experimental session. The additional blocks given to keep the daily number of blocks constant were eliminated from the final data, so that all points of Figure 12-10 represent the same number of estimates.

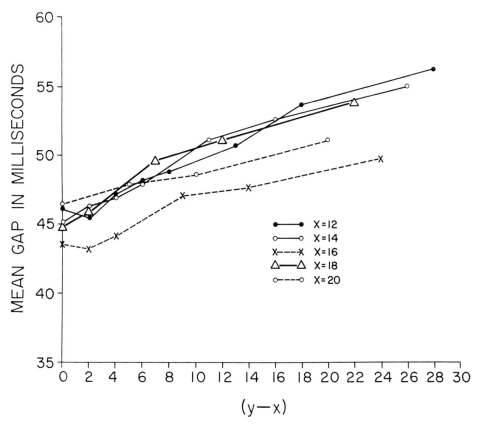

Figure 12-10. The results of the gap detection experiment with unequal intervals plotted as a function of the difference between the two intervals.

The data obtained in this experiment were first plotted as a function of the largest interval (*y*) parametric in the smallest interval (*x*). In this manner, a family of curves were obtained which, though generally approximating the equal interval function, was sufficiently scattered so that no systematic effect was apparent. These data were then replotted as shown in Figure 12-10, where the horizontal axis is the difference between the two intervals. In this case, the family of parametric curves can be seen to overlap very closely. This suggests that the remaining variance is now well accounted for on the basis of the difference in intervals. Because of the great amount of data summarized on each of the curves, the variances for each data point have not been plotted. The curve of this parametric family corresponding to an *x* value of 16 msec is slightly divergent from the others. This is, we believe, a sampling error, since the same population of subjects was not used for this part of the experiment.

Thus, in this experiment, using temporal acuity as our probe of the perceived temporal environment, we have shown that there is, in fact, a statistical effect maintained throughout the entire sensory chain. We do not, as yet, know what the critical dimensions of this statistical process are. For example, how many times must the signal be repeated before the statistical analysis becomes effective? There is also the suggestion that the reduction in the spread of the data is not quite as effective for larger values of the differences. This adds vigor to the notion that the effect we have observed is a second order one, a perturbation of the dominant effect of the absolute value of the largest interval (*y*). We hope to explore these and related issues in the future.

It is interesting to note the differences between this experiment and the apparently analogous study of Forsyth and Brown (1959). In their experiment, the fundamental frequency defined by the sum of the two intervals (as well as the duration of the two light flashes) was the derived statistical measure which dominated the perception of flicker. In later papers they interpret this result in terms of a low pass filter effect which we feel is most likely, caused by the sluggish dynamics of the visual photochemical. In our experiments, the derived statistical effect was, however, the difference between the two intervals and it was, we believe, only a perturbing factor in specifying the sensory experience. When a similar plot is made of the sum of the intervals, this sum is actually negatively correlated with the average size of the just detectable interval when compared across parametric curves.

Thus, we believe that Forsyth and Brown were not studying a neural coding phenomenon, but rather a gross temporal effect in the most peripheral portion of the transducer. On the other hand, the somatosensory experiment described here is sensitively exploring the critical features of the nerve impulse pattern itself.

One final detail should be noted. The values on the parametric curves with a difference of zero represent a replication of the equal-interval experiment of the preceding experiment. In addition, we also separately replicated this equal-interval curve with the same set of subjects used in this experiment. Though these two forms of replication agreed with each other, the values obtained were somewhat higher than those found in the preceding experiment. The general form of the results was the same, but the careful reader may be interested in comparing these two figures for an estimate of the size of the sampling error possible with different small groups of subjects for this type of experiment.

SOMATOSENSORY CODES FOR PERIPHERAL TRANSMISSION

It should now be clear that the cutaneous electrostimulation-psychophysical response technique is conceptually different than either the conventional psychological or neurophysiological approach. The usual psychological approach is to compare the external stimulus and the psychological response. The usual neurophysiological approach is to compare the stimulus and the pattern of responses generated in the nerve elements. On the other hand, electrical stimulation sets up nerve response patterns which are so specific that, in fact, the significant comparison is being made between the message in the peripheral nerve and the psychophysical response. This is true in spite of modifications such as the oscillation phenomenon, since such modifications can be monitored by the Dawsonian electrophysiological techniques.

We feel that this difference allows this approach to make a useful additional contribution to the theory of sensory coding. Yet, even by combining all three approaches, we do not yet know enough to make a comprehensive statement which could be dignified by the phrase, *theory of somatosensory coding.* We, at most, can begin to fill in some of the relations on a matrix such as that shown in Table 12-I, which summarizes the stimulus dimensions and neural response parameters discussed earlier.

It is, however, important to emphasize one of the cautions we made earlier. The primitive theoretical comments which we shall make and the associations between stimulus and neural response are defined only at a single level of the neural transmission and processing system. Our attention has been focused entirely on codes for peripheral transmission. At higher levels, undoubtedly, additional recodings of the transmitted information occur which may completely alter the symbols used for a given stimulus dimension. This discussion, then, is a preliminary statement of what we believe are the significant facts of peripheral somatosensory neural encoding. The matrix itself, defining the various possible neural symbols which might be used, would, however, still be valid for higher levels of the ascending pathways although conceivably with different associations possibly being made between different combinations of stimulus and neural parameters.

TABLE 12-I

SOME NECESSARY STIMULUS-RESPONSE RELATIONSHIPS IN FORMULATING A THEORY OF SOMATOSENSORY CODING

Stimulus Dimension		Place	Number of Activated Units	Response Amplitude	Frequency	Frequency Macrofluctuations	Frequency Microfluctuations	Temporal Comparison between 2 places	Derived Statistical Measures	
						Temporal Parameters				
Quantity			*		*[1]					
Quality		?				?				
Temporal Parameters	Relative Temporal Order					*				
	Temporal Acuity						*		*	
	Duration					?				
Spatial Parameters	Spatial Localization	*						*		
	Spatial Interaction and Patterns	*	?	*		?		?		

* relatively well-established relation
? relatively poorly-established relation

[1] as reflected in the number and not the temporal characteristics of the sequence of nerve impulses.

It should also be remembered that there may be overlaps in the code since one or another neural parameter may serve more than a single stimulus dimension. Thus, the spatial distribution of nerve responses, which at least contributes to spatial localization, may also contribute to quality coding. Because of this overlap, various columns of the matrix will be seen to have multiple entries. Similarly, some of the stimulus parameters may be represented by more than a single neural dimension. This results in multiple entries in the rows as well. It may be suggested that we come perilously close to losing all organization as these multiple entries proliferate. Our analysis would then be degraded to the level of the meaningless "spatio-temporal pattern" warned against earlier in this paper. Fortunately, although there are multiple entries, it does not appear that all stimulus dimensions are represented by all neural parameters and vice versa.

Now let us consider the problem in detail. We will suggest a preliminary set of associations organized about the stimulus dimensions on the basis of recent research in our laboratory, and in those other laboratories whose results we believe to be pertinent.

Quantity

When appropriate stimuli impinge upon receptors, almost all micro-electrode studies have shown that there is a functional relationship between the quantity or intensity of the stimulus and the frequency of firing of the individual activated fiber, which is generally (though not exclusively) mono-tonic. As we pointed out earlier, this result is an ambiguous one, for either a counting or a clocking process may be used to decode the information.

Yet, because of the nature of intensity as a controllable and testable parameter, and because of the research which has been carried out on this part of the problem, we can be more confident about this aspect of the coding problem than about any other. We have concluded that the code for stimulus quantity is exclusively a function of the number of nerve impulses which occurs both on a single fiber and collectively on a group of fibers within some critical period of time. During this critical integrating period, it seems (Uttal 1959; 1960a) that the temporal pattern does not significantly affect the subjective magnitude of the sensation. Thus, the increase in frequency serves only to increase the number of impulses available for counting, in the same way that the recruitment of additional activity in nearby fibers would also provide additional impulses to be counted.

One of the most important related result was the observation that subjective magnitudes were nearly linearly related to the actual measured milli-voltage of the nerve impulse. This suggests that it is at the receptor itself that the logarithmic or power conversion is made. Some of our other work (Uttal, Cook, and Kasprzak, 1964) on arthropod photoreception also suggests that it is, indeed, the receptor that is responsible for most of the stimulus compression properties of the nervous system which are required for increasing the dynamic range of various receptors. Similarly, Mount-castle, Poggio, and Werner (1963) have shown a complete compression of the neural signal according to a logarithmic transform at the level of the thalamus. Since almost all of the variability involved in this compression can be accounted for at the periphery, there is no need to require or search for further transformations at higher levels of the afferent pathway. On the other hand, since linearity of the coded representation is not a requisite of psychophysiological processing, we should also not be surprised to find other transformations imposed at these higher levels.

We now confidently associate stimulus intensity with two of the neural parameters in our matrix, that is, number of responding fibers and frequency of firing in a given fiber, specifically, as the latter reflects the number of impulses per unit time. We feel that it is very improbable that there is a place code for different intensities and that temporal dimensions in general are not significant factors in quantitative estimates, except as they may, on a more gross level, indicate the initiation and cessation of the stimulus itself. Because of the dominant influence of number, quantity should tend to interact with the spatial distribution of the stimulus in significant ways. Zotterman (1959) discusses just such effects in his review of the thermal sense. Similarly, much of Békésy's work (1958) on funneling is concerned with the phenomenon of spatial interaction and its modulation of response amplitude for mechanical and electrical stimuli. Finally, the close association between the nerve response amplitude and the psychophysical threshold, as shown in another study from our laboratory (Uttal, 1964), also supports the contention that "number" of responses is the key variable for the coding of stimulus intensity.

Quality

We have pointed out that our current experiments do not bear at all upon the issue of quality. When one considers current research, in general, the problem of somesthetic quality coding appears to be seen from two very vigorously defended and, at first glance, contradictory points of view. The older view maintains that there are special receptors for the cutaneous and proprioceptive modalities, and that these receptors (usually encapsulated nerve endings) are associated with the classic stimulus modalities of pressure, cold, warmth, and pain. This theoretical orientation grew from the observations that these senses appeared to be punctate and that histological examinations of the skin showed the presence of a wide variety of encapsulated nerve endings in a similar punctiform arrangement. Other, more recent studies relating thermal threshold differences to differences in the average depth of certain types of endings (Hensel, Strom, and Zotterman, 1951) also continue to support this point of view. A corollary to this specific receptor notion is that information associated with touch and pressure is transmitted by larger nerves and that smaller nerves mediate thermal and painful sensations. Thus, a very specific place code is invoked to account for quality coding by the holders of this theoretical outlook.

An alternative view has grown up in the last few years which states that the apparent presence of specialized receptors is a false concept which has arisen due to a misinterpretation of the punctate sensitivity experiments and the coincidence of the presence of a vaguely defined family of encapsulated endings. The mobility of psychologically-determined sensory spots, the lack of a statistical correspondence between specific encapsulated endings and specific spots, and the apparent success of at least the Pacinian corpuscle at retention of its function, despite the complete destruction of the encapsulating corpuscle, all argue strongly against the special receptor theory. According to this second point of view, all somatosensory stimuli can be effective in activating any cutaneous or proprioceptive receptor and the critical factor in their encoding becomes the spatial or the temporal pattern in which they do so. Weddell (1955) champions this theoretical orientation. The specific suggestions of Wall and Cronly-Dillon (1960) associating specific patterns with specific modalities also explicitly make this assumption at the spinal level.

One of the major difficulties in resolving this conflict is that the cutaneous senses do not fall neatly in place on a physical continuum as do the varieties of photic stimuli. There is still some question of what the actual stimulus conditions are, and the many ambiguities of complex qualities, synthetic qualities and paradoxical qualities in the somatosensory system all contribute to a poorly defined statement of the actual sensations with which we are dealing.

Furthermore, even when we are dealing with a single physical stimulus continuum, such as temperature, are the various means of stimulation identical? Do, for example, differential thresholds for thermal convection and conduction correspond exactly to those for radiant stimulation? We are now studying the skin's sensitivity to low levels of radiant thermal stimulation in an attempt to answer this and related questions.

The difficulties of going beyond these seemingly conflicting theoretical viewpoints are illustrated very well in the thoughtful paper of Melzack and Wall (1962) on the nature of cutaneous quality coding. In this paper they attempt to resolve the controversy between the two major theories by analyzing the basic assumptions of each and merging those surviving into one set of supplementary propositions. Nevertheless, their propositions, while integrating much of the new electrophysiological knowledge of synaptic action into this psychophysiological problem, do not specify the coding processes, but only a general framework within which they can work. This is not a criticism of their work, but rather a reflection of the complexities described above which are certainly also reflected in our present paper.

In this light, it may not be too extravagent to propose that a third possibility for somatosensory quality coding might exist. According to this point of view, there is but one somatosensory stimulus, a mechanical distortion or displacement of any of the nerve endings making up the plexus of the nerve net in the skin and body. Pressure or touch would certainly fall within this framework. The thermal senses might also work indirectly through the mechanical medium by a transduction performed by the circulatory vessels. This latter idea is one suggested by Nafe (1936) many years ago. In addition, the psychological complexities of the "sense of pain" suggest that it may not be necessary to account for it as a separate somesthetic modality (see Melzack and Wall, 1965), but rather as a gated or modulated form of almost any sensory experience.

Even though only a single kind of stimulation may actually underlie somatosensation, the fact that one can discriminate between so many sensations leads us to conclude that different stimulus energies must be coded differentially. Perhaps this differentiation is effected by the overall geometrical pattern of the mechanical distortion which thus leads to different spatial patterns of activity in the neurons. On the other hand, we may also accept the suggestion by Wall and Cronly-Dillon that macrotemporal fluctuations might be a key code for somatosensory quality.

We feel the question of quality coding is very much an open one with seemingly contradictory results forthcoming from different experiments. The two specific codes which have been suggested for quality coding, place (size and selection of fibers) and macrotemporal pattern, may or may not individually be valid and overlapping with other dimensions. We have indicated them both on our tentative matrix of somatosensory coding.

Temporal Parameters

A single sense for all kinds of relative temporal order probably does not exist. Rather, it seems that there are at least two different subsenses involved. The first subsense is one in which the two stimuli appear to be fused into a single sensation which is perceived along a dimension other than time. Thus, as we have mentioned, binaural sound location and the analogous effects on the skin are examples of this sort of interaction. The second subsense is a macrotemporal discrimination which is made between stimuli separated by a considerable amount of time, yet impinging upon the same sensory receptors. The temporal acuity demonstrated in our gap detection study is probably an example of this sense of relative temporal order.

Similarly, we feel that the estimates of duration of long-term intervals are coded by the macrofluctuations of neural activity and, as such, represent phenomena which almost go beyond our interest in peripheral coding. Indeed, the information is hardly encoded at all in the sense that the critical information, time of occurrence, is still in the same form, along the same dimension, as it was when it stimulated the organism.

Our experiments on the effect of stimulus pattern on temporal acuity, however, are relevant to this problem of temporal discrimination in the nervous system. An estimate of temporal acuity is important in defining the limits of integration of higher frequency signals which might be used to encode other stimulus dimensions.

On the microtemporal level there is, so far, a scarcity of information which suggests true temporal discrimination. The greater or lesser degree of fusion of stimulus doublets results in a temporal acuity measure which can be interpreted in terms of an amplitude discrimination by the subject. Similarly, there is an insensitivity of quantity codes to the temporal pattern as indicated in some of our earlier studies. On the other hand, the positive results of the search for an effect of a derived statistical measure of the temporal pattern with the unequal interval experiment suggest that a temporal code for macropatterns of this scale may be somewhat effective. These patterns, however, lie on the borderline between what we have come to believe are two different time regions, microtime and macrotime. This fact may explain the secondary nature of the influence of the unequal intervals.

Spatial Parameters

On a gross level, there seems little doubt that spatial localization is encoded by place. Certainly the neurons which carry impulses signifying stimulation of the skin of the forearm are the nerves of the arm. The retention of localization in a topologically constant fashion at the cortex suggests that the spatial map of the body remains very constant throughout the ascending pathway. Yet the spatial code is not completely unaffected by its temporal environment. Ethel Schmid (1961) has shown that the time between spatially-separated masking and test stimuli was a critical factor in determining the amount of inhibitory masking. We have already pointed out that the perceived localization of a fused sensation produced by two spatially disparate stimuli depends to a large degree upon the timing relations of the two stimuli. Thus, space is, in a way which we do not yet completely understand, closely related to time in the somatosensory nervous system. This relativistic notion is reflected in the psychophysical results of many experiments.

An Interim Summary

As we look over the stimulus variables and the possible neural parameters, it appears that there are (a) many overlaps in the code, and (b) many lacunae in our knowledge which prevent the presented schema from being exhaustive. It would be presumptuous to consider this outline as anything more than a statement of a problem and very tentative approach to a general theory of somatosensory coding. Yet, there has been some progress, and although we have emphasized our own point of view in the presentation of this paper, many other researchers have been evolving their own. Unfortunately, almost all of these separate points of view represent partial theories dealing with but one aspect of the stimulus domain.

If there is anything which is clear from the outline we have presented, it is that there are many interactions between the various dimensions; a discussion of quantity, for example, is not complete without consideration of both the spatial and temporal aspects which modify quantitative judgments by the subject. A second point which is suggested is that neither the microscopic approach of the electrophysiologist nor that of the psychophysicist leads to a complete solution to the problem of somatosensory coding. Both approaches may be insufficient when we are dealing with the complex interactions of space and time, as well as of quality and quantity. The specification of a particular coding relationship for some sensory experience at a particular level of the nervous system requires a number of proofs, none of which is sufficient itself to allay completely the cautions we described earlier. First, the stimulus must be shown to produce the suggested pattern of activity in the neural tissue. Second, the particular pattern must be shown to be influential on at least the next link in the neural transmission chain, and preferably on all subsequent links including the subjective response. That is, fluctuations in that dimension must be discriminable by subsequent synaptic levels. If at any point a given dimension does not meet this test, it is no longer of interest in terms of the coding problem since it has been either transformed into another coded form or has been proven to be an irrelevant, though persistent, concomitant.

The type of test we have advocated, which uses human subjective response as a test of this influence, is adequate only when the nerve-response pattern can be very precisely determined at a given level. In that case it is perhaps the most powerful, for in addition to allowing precise control of the pattern, this test also provides an intrinsic check that the effects of the dimension variation are being reflected throughout the entire system in some interpretable code. This latter advantage may be a practical impossibility in the purely electrophysiological case, in which, at best, the input and output dynamics of only a single synaptic stage can be explored. Another important advantage of the experimental procedure of "forcing" the desired pattern of nerve impulses by an appropriate pattern of electrical stimuli is that the effects of redundant codes can be separated.

A model of the organization of the somatosensory system begins to emerge from the few insights we have. We are beginning to see a peripheral nervous system in which a manifold of separate yet interacting channels convey information about the stimulus to a central interpreting mechanism. This information is carried in patterns of nerve impulses which vary specifically in accord with the incident stimulus. The dimensions of the stimulus and the dimensions of the neural code appear to be more plentiful than the classic analysis would have led us to believe. Some response dimensions such as frequency, which may have seemed to be monolithic, can probably be analyzed into significantly different subdimensions in various parts of their range. At the very least, we should distinguish between macro- and micro-time, on the one hand, and macro- and microspace on the other. We have already noted how macrospatial interactions can grossly modify the quantitative perceptions of stimuli in spatial proximity; however, little is known about microspatial properties of the somatosensory system, and it appears that such knowledge may be basic to an understanding of quality coding. This is true whether quality ultimately is shown to be encoded by place or by time, or by some combination of the two. Our studies, which have shown critical points of discontinuity in the frequency domain, in addition to similar studies, play the important role of defining the boundaries between these different regions of macro- and microtime.

Another important approach to the problem of sensory coding is to examine the nature of the interactions between the various dimensions. The fact that area and intensity interact suggests an overlap between these two dimensions. Similarly, intensity and time seem, in some instances, to interact while in others to operate independently. Explorations of these sorts of phenomena can also help in filling in all of the points on our matrix, thereby creating a truly comprehensive theory of somatosensory coding for each level of nervous transmission.

ACKNOWLEDGMENT

This paper was written while the senior author was a visiting professor in the 1st Department of Physiology of the Kyoto Prefectural University of Medicine; Kyoto, Japan. He would like to express his appreciation for the cordial hospitality of Professor Hisato Yoshimura and for the support of an N. I. H. Special Post-doctoral Fellowship which made this experience possible.

REFERENCES

Barlow, H. B., & Hill, R. M. Selective sensitivity to direction of movement in ganglion cells of the rabbit retina. *Science,* 1963, **139**, 412.

Békésy, G. von. Funneling in the nervous system and its role in loudness and sensation intensity on the skin. *J. Acoust. Soc. Amer.,* 1958, **30**, 399.

Békésy, G. von. Interaction of paired sensory stimuli and conduction in peripheral nerves. *J. Appl. Physiol.,* 1963, **18**, 1276.

Brown, J. E. A parametric study of neuroelectric responses to skin stimuli. Master's thesis, Massachusetts Institute of Technology, 1960.

Casby, J. U., Siminoff, R., & Houseknecht, T. R. An analogue cross-correlator to study naturally induced activity in intact nerve trunks. *J. Neurophysiol.,* 1963, **26**, 432.

Dawson, G. D. The relative excitability and conduction velocity of sensory and motor fibers in man. *J. Physiol. (London)*, 1956, **131**, 436.

Dawson, G. D., & Scott, J. W. The recording of nerve action potentials through skin in man. *J. Neurol. Neurosurg. Psychiat.*, 1949, **12**, 259.

Eccles, J. C., & Krnjevic, K. Presynaptic changes associated with post-tetanic potentiation in the spinal cord. *J. Physiol. (London)*, 1959, **149**, 274.

Efron, R. The effect of handedness on the perception of simultaneity and temporal order. *Brain*, 1963, **86**, 261.

Forsyth, D. B., & Brown, C. R. Flicker contours for intermittent photic stimuli of alternating duration. *J. Opt. Soc. Amer.*, 1959, **49**, 760.

Fraisse, P. *The Psychology of Time*. New York: Harper, 1963.

Gasser, H. S., & Grundfest, H. Action and excitability in mammalian A fibers. *Amer. J. Physiol.*, 1936, **117**, 113.

Gescheider, G. A. The resolving of successive clicks by the ears and the skin. *J. Exp. Psychol.*, in press.

Hensel, H., Strom, L., & Zotterman, Y. Electrophysiological measurements of the depth of thermoreceptors. *J. Neurophysiol.*, 1951, **14**, 423.

Hirsh, I. J., & Sherrick, C. E. Perceived order in different sense modalities. *J. Exp. Psychol.*, 1961, **62**, 423.

Hubel, D. H., & Wiesel, T. N. Receptive fields of single neurons in the cat's striate cortex. *J. Physiol. (London)*, 1959, **148**, 574.

Keidel, W. D., Keidel, U. O., & Wigand, M. E. Adaptation: Loss or gain of sensory information? In W. Roseblith (Ed.), *Sensory Communication*. New York: Wiley, 1961. Pp. 319-338.

Knudson, V. O. "Hearing" with the sense of touch. *J. Gen. Psychol.*, 1928, **1**, 320.

Larrabee, M. G., & Bronk, D. W. Prolonged facilitation of synaptic excitation in sympathetic ganglia. *J. Neurophysiol.*, 1947, **10**, 139.

MacKay, D. M. Interactive processes in visual perception. In W. Rosenblith (Ed.), *Sensory Communication*. New York: Wiley, 1961. Pp. 339-355.

Maturana, H. R., Lettvin, J. Y., McCulloch, W. S., & Pitts, W. H. Anatomy and physiology of vision in the frog. (*Rana pipiens*). *J. Gen. Physiol.*, 1960, **43**, 129.

Melzack, R., & Wall, P. D. On the nature of cutaneous sensory mechanisms. *Brain*, 1962, **85**, 331.

Melzack, R., & Wall, P. D. Pain mechanisms: A new theory. *Science*, 1965, **150**, 971.

Mountcastle, V. B., Poggio, G. F., & Werner, G. The neural transformation of the sensory stimulus at the cortical input level of the somatic afferent system. In R. Gerard (Ed.), *Proceedings of the International Union of Physiological Science. III. Information processing in the nervous system*. Amsterdam: Excerpta Medica Found., 1962.

Mountcastle, V. B., Poggio, G. F., & Werner, G. The relation of thalamic cell response to peripheral stimuli varied over an intensive continuum. *J. Neurophysiol.*, 1963, **26**, 807.

Nafe, J. P., & Wagoner, K. S. The experiences of warmth, cold, and heat. *J. Psychol.*, 1936, **2**, 421.

Perilhou, P. De quelques considerations et experiences sur la sensibilite vibratoire (donnees d'une these manuscrite de 1943). *J. Psychol. Norm. Path.*, 1947, **40**, 293.

Pfaffmann, C. The afferent code for sensory quality. *Amer. Psychol.*, 1959, **14**, 226.

Pieron, H. *The Sensations*. New Haven: Yale Press, 1952.

Pieron, H. *La Sensation Guide de Vie*. Paris: Gallimard, 1955.

Pieron, H., & Segal, J. Recherches sur la sensibilite tactile digitale par stimulation electrique du nerf cutane. *Annee Psychol.*, 1938, **39**, 89.

Rapoport, Amnon. Sequential decision-making in a computer-controlled task. *J. Math. Psychol.*, 1964, **1**, 351.

Rapoport, Anatol. Information processing in the nervous system. In R. Gerard (Ed.), *Proceedings of the International Union of Physiological Science. III. Information processing in the nervous system.* Amsterdam: Excerpta Medica Found., 1962.

Ratliff, F. *Mach Bands: Quantitative Studies of Neural Networks in the Retina.* San Francisco: Holden-Day, 1965.

Rodieck, R. W., Kiang, N.Y.-S., & Gerstein, G. L. Some quantitative methods for the study of spontaneous activity of single neurons. *Biophys. J.*, 1962, **2**, 351.

Rosenblith, W. A., & Vidale, E. B. A quantitative view of neuroelectric events in relation to sensory communication. In S. Koch (Ed.), *Psychology: A Study of a Science. Vol. IV.* New York: McGraw-Hill, 1962. Pp. 334-379.

Rosner, B. S. Effects of repetitive peripheral stimuli on evoked potentials of somatosensory cortex. *Amer. J. Physiol.*, 1956, **187**, 175.

Schmid, E. Temporal aspects of cutaneous interaction with two-point electrical stimulation. *J. Exp. Psychol.*, 1961, **61**, 400.

Segundo, J. P., Moore, G. P., Stensaas, L. J., & Bullock, T. H. Sensitivity of neurones in *aplysia* to temporal pattern of arriving impulses. *J. Exp. Biol.*, 1963, **40**, 643.

Smith, J. E. K. Stimulus programming in psychophysics. *Psychometrika*, 1961, **26**, 27.

Toennies, J. F. Reflex discharge from the spinal cord over the dorsal roots. *J. Neurophysiol.*, 1938, **1**, 378.

Uttal, W. R. A comparison of neural and psychophysical responses in the somesthetic system. *J. Comp. Physiol. Psychol.*, 1959, **52**, 485.

Uttal, W. R. The three-stimulus problem: A further comparison of neural and psychophysical responses in the somesthetic system. *J. Comp. Physiol. Psychol.*, 1960, **53**, 42. (a)

Uttal, W. R. Inhibitory interaction of responses to electrical stimuli in the fingers. *J. Comp. Physiol. Psychol.*, 1960, **53**, 47. (b)

Uttal, W. R. The effect of ischemia on the peripheral nerve action potential in man and its relation to somatosensory magnitude coding. Ann Arbor, *Mental Health Research Institute Preprint 125,* 1964.

Uttal, W. R., & Cook, L. Systematics of the evoked somatosensory cortical potential: A psychophysical-electrophysiological comparison. *Ann. NY Acad. Sci.*, 1964, **112**, 60.

Uttal, W. R., Cook, L., & Kasprzak, H. Computer studies of neurophysiological and psychological events. *Ann. NY Acad. Sci.*, 1964, **115**, 776.

Wall, P. D., & Cronly-Dillon, J. R. Pain, itch, and vibration. *Arch. Neurol. (Chicago),* 1960, **2**, 365.

Weddell, G. Somesthesis and chemical senses. *Ann. Rev. Psychol.*, 1955, **6**, 119.

Zotterman, Y. Thermal sensations. In J. Field (Ed.), *Handbook of Physiology. Section 1: Neurophysiology.* Washington, D. C.: Amer. Physiol. Soc., 1959. Pp. 431-458.

Chapter 13

PATTERN PERCEPTION BY THE SKIN*

Frank A. Geldard

It is peculiarly fitting that the word "pattern" should appear in my title on this occasion. It was fully two-score years ago that the concept of cutaneous pattern first entered my ken, and then from one of the most effective teachers known to man, John Paul Nafe. I am most honored to be permitted to lay this little study at his feet, while asking his forgiveness for the unconscionable delay in doing so.

The long latency, however, is not exclusively traceable to the slow accretion of engrams in my central nervous system; on this point my neural constitution slyly urges the fifth amendment! There are some things that just have to await the technological tides. Multiple stimulation of large areas of the human integument, the stuff of which really extensive cutaneous patterns are made, has not been possible in a nicely controlled way until quite recently. Now we have the inventions of two of my colleagues, Bice and Sherrick. The former described, in 1961, an electromechanical transducer for vibrotactile stimulation (Bice, 1961) based on heavily loading the diaphragm of a miniature earphone to create an inertial vibrator of compact design which, while somewhat fragile and difficult of exact calibration, possessed a number of virtues that made it unique in the world of instrumentation. It was possible for the first time to position a whole constellation of vibrators on the skin, widely dispersed and independent of external supports, and even to maintain the mobility of the observer while thus suited. The Sherrick vibrator, described but a few months ago (Sherrick, 1965), is made of sterner stuff, transduces relatively large powers, and is somewhat more constant in its performance. It is also of the inertial type. Both instruments have been used, in multiple arrays, in the experiments to be reported.

The first of these I shall not dwell on at length here; details of equipment and procedure have been described elsewhere (Geldard and Sherrick, 1965). But it is a fundamental experiment, and we have to know, in general, what was done and what resulted. A multiple vibrator system permitted application of vibratory signals to ten bodily loci simultaneously (see Fig. 13-1). The locations selected involved pretty widespread dispersion and were meant to optimize distance between centers of agitation while

*The work reported here was supported, in part, by a grant from the National Science Foundation, and in part, by a grant from National Institutes of Health, Department of Health, Education, and Welfare.

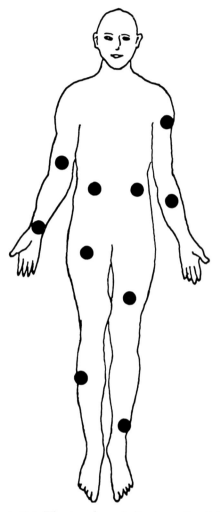

Figure 13-1. The ten sites of vibratory stimulation.

at the same time meeting two other requirements as follows: (a) avoiding positioning of contactors on corresponding points, and (b) avoiding loci which, through bone conduction, might enlist the aid of the cochlea. It is surprising how readily a low-frequency signal comes through to the cochlea from bony areas like the rib cage, shoulders, neck, and head region. Since so much of our earlier communication work had been carried out with the broad expanse of the chest as the stimulation site, it was natural to continue its use in the selection of loci for the 10-vibrator arrangement. But 115 dB SPL (sound pressure level) of steady white noise delivered by phones to the ears would not suppress the hearing — and observers insisted it was hearing — of a 200-msec burst of 60-Hz mechanical vibration at 15 dB SL (sensation level). This does not happen on the fleshy portions of limbs if sufficiently far removed from bony protuberances nor does it happen on the abdomen. Very much lower masking levels are entirely adequate. Hence the locations displayed in Figure 13-1. If we are to conclude about the cutaneous perception of vibration we obviously have to avoid circumvention of the skin's function by the more sensitive cochlea.

In testing pattern perception the general strategy of the Seashore tests proved useful. Patterns created by from one to nine active vibrators were arranged in successive pairs, the observer's task being to form an immediate judgment as to whether the patterns in the pair were "same" or "different." A stratified sample of 500 "different" pairs (of the more than half million conceivable) was selected and intermixed randomly with 500 "same" pairs, any number of loci from one to nine being involved but always the same number in both members of a given pair.

Burst duration was 200 msec, 500 msec separated onsets within pairs, while 2 sec of clearance between pairs allowed time for report. Signal frequency was 60 Hz, so a single burst delivered a dozen impacts. One

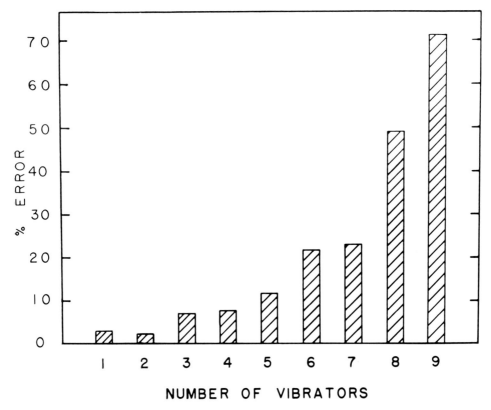

Figure 13-2. Relative amount of error made on patterns of different degrees of complexity.

vibrator (on the upper left arm) was carefully set at 15 dB SL, and all others were matched to it for loudness. A comfortable white noise masker, applied through phones, insured that auditory cues would be preempted.

What happened, in general? Errors in copious quantities occurred, and these become our index of performance. "Sames" called "different" we can forget; such mistakes happened so rarely as almost to appear as inadvertences. "Differents" called "sames" are another matter. These errors proved to be systematically related to stimulus characteristics and hence are of great interest. At first it appeared that the culprit was sheer multiplicity; the more vibrators involved the greater the amount of error. Figure 13-2 strongly suggests this. Indeed, we were tempted to put the project to bed at this juncture with the generality, "Keep things as numerically simple as you can for the skin and a limited amount of signalling will be possible." Then we looked at the matter of communality between successive patterns. Perhaps two patterns fail of discrimination because they are too much alike. Our suspicions were borne out, as Figure 13-3 clearly demonstrates. The greater the overlap between pattern elements the more confusion in discrimination. Now, which is the guilty party, number or similarity? Are the two factors perhaps in cahoots, so to speak?

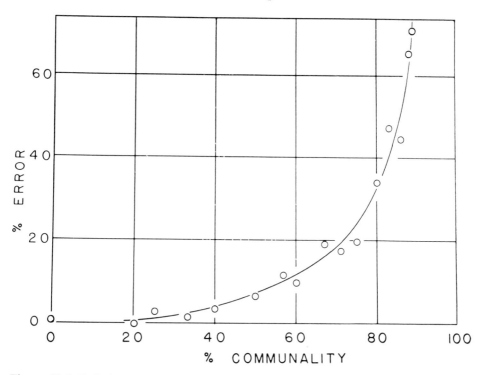

Figure 13-3. Relative amount of error as a function of pattern overlap (per cent communality).

Fortunately, our sample had been carefully designed with such possibilities in view, and it was now only a matter of calculation to separate complexity (number of loci involved) from communality (overlap of stimulation sites). Figure 13-4 tells the story. Number, by itself, is not important.
At least, this is true up to and including nine vibrators; we have not gone
beyond this as yet, though we are now equipped for it. Identity of elements
in immediately successive signals is important. You can readily confuse two
patterns having only four elements, if they possess three in common. You
are extremely unlikely to be fooled by patterns of six vibrators, if they share
only two generating sites.

What is the outcome if, instead of distributing transducers as widely as
possible over the body surface, the constellation of vibrators is restricted to

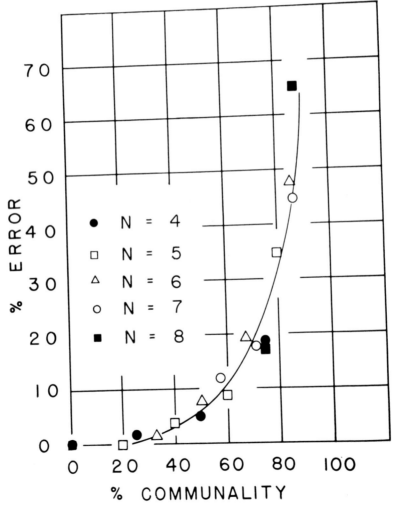

Figure 13-4. Separation of complexity (number of vibrators) and overlap (communality).

the obvious points of contact, the fingertips? Obvious? The fingertips are not really too obviously the favored site if you put first things first, as I believe we did with good reason in dispersing them broadly over the integument. But, whether for convenience (which is strongly suspect) or because the fingertips do, after all, rank high among sensitive skin areas, nearly everyone who has sought to circumvent eyes and ears in communication systems has assumed, almost unreflectively, that the fingers must be served. There is by now a long history of gadgetry connected either with "hearing through the skin" or "reading machines for the blind" which employ tactile outputs. Almost without exception they are designed to accommodate the fingers. So, having laid down some norms, we were in a position to ask about the fingers as mediators of gross cutaneous patterns. The task was taken up in our laboratory by Mr. Richard Gilson.

He began by designing a stimulator based on ten independently suspended Sherrick vibrators. It was arranged for each of the digits to be accommodated in its own vibrating finger stall. The finger pad was contacted securely, but there were imposed no postural strains on hands or arms. Vibratory intercommunication between fingers could occur only by way of the hand itself (see Fig. 13-5). All stimulators were energized with 60 Hz and each was individually adjustable for amplitude. In nearly all other respects the conditions of the "body" experiment, reported above, were reproduced — all but one. It will be recalled that we were careful, in choosing our sites of stimulation, to avoid corresponding bodily points. There are good reasons for doing so, of course. One need only recall the phenomenon of "extinction," made a matter of clinical symptomatology by Morris Bender (1952), to appreciate the fact that skin areas sharing the same spinal segment interact strongly with one another in some contralateral stimulating situations. It is pretty clear that the only circumstance that would avoid the threat of such interaction, in the case of the fingers, would be a sample of monsters endowed with fingers located at noncorresponding bodily sites! The parent population is hard to come by.

Gilson presented the same taped program of patterns, 500 "same," 500 "different," that had yielded the results we have been analyzing. The main outcome was perhaps predictable by a variety of signs, chief of which was the sheer phenomenal appearance of the patterns when imposed upon the fingers. One encounters some difficulty, right at the beginning, in the initial loudness calibration. One finger having been set for a 15-dB burst, each of the others is equated to it in turn. Then, as in the body experiment, all ten are turned on simultaneously, and the observer attempts to "look around the circuit" to make sure that all vibrators are equally noticeable. There is no difficulty about this in the body experiment. Such a procedure often leads to last-minute "trimming" of one or two vibrators. With the fingers, this looking around is a virtual impossibility. To energize all finger stalls simultaneously is to suppress all fingertip localizations and force the pattern into "two handfuls of vibration." Indeed, some observers complain that the resulting diffuse vibratory pattern is not in or on the hands at all but surrounding them, like an aura. The same indistinctness is found, to one degree or another, in all multiple patterns; the fewer the vibrators the less vague the localization.

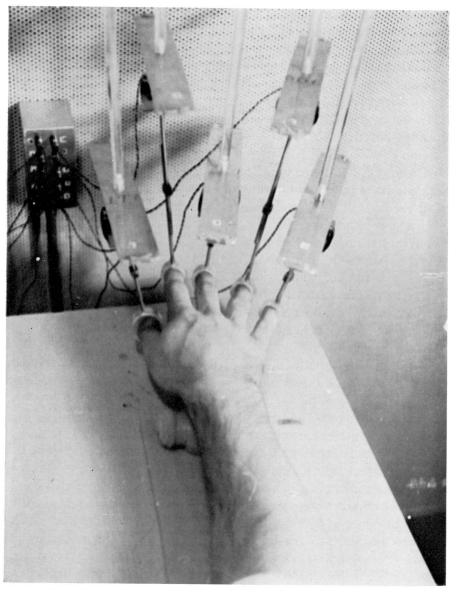

Figure 13-5. Shock-mounting of the vibrators to provide isolated stimulation of each of the fingers.

All this is a harbinger of what is inevitably found on adding up the errors. The fingers make somewhat more than twice as many errors as the body does on "different" pairs, about 45 per cent error as contrasted with 19 per cent on the average. We considered the possibility that we might not be using the fingers optimally, that what might be comfortable for the body in the way of loudness, a 15-dB level, might not be best for the fingers. Accordingly, intensity was systematically varied in one supplementary experiment. Error scores were determined at 7, 15, 21, and 28 dB SL. Loud or soft, errors remained about the same. Then, some of us had the impression that confusion of patterns might stem from what seemed a pretty lively presentation rate, and several subjects did a series with relatively long pauses between pairs to optimize the mobilization of attention. This, too, made no difference. We are trying to give the fingers a chance, and there are still some variables to be fussed with, but the tentative conclusion is that the body does better, much better.

Let us now take a look at the intensive side of the picture. Your curiosity could well have been aroused by the recurrence, in all the work described, of what appears to be an extremely modest level of operation, 15 dB SL. In audition this would be well below a whisper, scarcely more than the sound of a well-dropped pin. But the skin is not the ear, even though in some respects it behaves very much like certain damaged ears. It recruits in a most remarkable fashion. Move vibratory amplitude up from absolute threshold in small steps and loudness bounds rapidly ahead. The skin has a relatively short dynamic range as compared with that of the ear. Just what the detailed metrics of the situation are it would be nice to know. We need, for the skin, systematic families of curves of the Fletcher-Munson (Fletcher and Munson, 1933) variety. We also need measurements based on cutaneous analogs of the numerous indirect methods for ascertaining amounts and rates of auditory loudness recruitment (Békésy, 1965; Hirsh, 1952).

There is another conditioner of stimulus intensity. What makes 15 dB a "comfortable" level in the body experiments is the fact that, while a single vibrator on the upper arm at 15 dB SL creates little commotion by itself, ten vibrators spaced over the body surface and firing in unison at the same intensity sum to a major disturbance. There is a curious overall "squeezing" action at onset and relief from it at offset which, for all the world, reminds one of "gamma" movement in vision, the approach and recession of a flashing light source seen against darkness. Clearly, there is a spatial summation principle at work. Mr. James Craig has made a variety of approaches to it in our laboratory, and some progress is being made. The summation comes out clearly in Craig's experiment, inspired by an earlier one of Stevens' (1959) on cross-modality comparisons, in which he lets the intensity of a matching auditory white noise (delivered by phones) be the measure of vibrotactile loudness. Figure 13-6 shows the intensity increments at the ear needed to match various numbers of simultaneously acting vibrators distributed over the body, the point of departure always being the intensity of white noise providing a match for loudness to a single vibrator. This is one way to make a splash in Békésy's "pool of inhibition"; toss a handful of pebbles into it!

Thus far, everything that has been said has had to do with relatively uncomplicated collocations of stimuli, especially in their spatial relation-

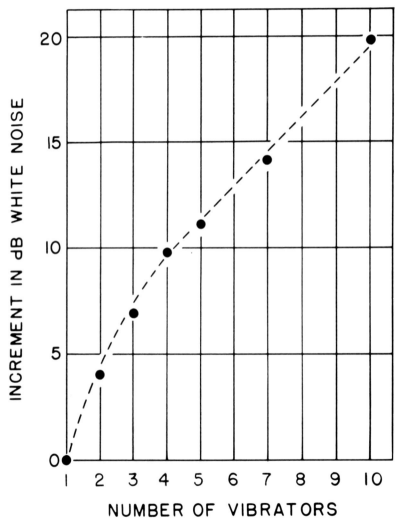

Figure 13-6. Increments of white noise, over and above the intensity needed to match the loudness of a single vibrator, required to match the loudness of various numbers of vibrators in different positions on the body.

ships. Indeed, what has been reported are several salients in a unified attack on the most neglected of all cutaneous dimensions — locus. The most ardent dermophile would have to admit that the cutaneous system plays a poor second to the visual one in handling space. Does it do any better with time? There are some evidences that it does. If the skin cannot make the fine temporal distinctions possible for the ear, a past master in the art, it is at least not the sluggard that the eye is. Some quite rapid events are tactually perceptible, not the least remarkable of which are the interesting localization shifts based on temporal slippage, convincingly demonstrated by Békésy (1963) and confirmed, in general, in Gescheider's (1965) recent experiments.

That there are some temporal phenomena to be observed directly in vibrotactile reception was evident to us some years ago, and Howell (1958), while at Virginia, was able to show that slopes of onset and offset were discriminable with a precision that added a useable second-order dimension to the primary ones already being exploited in cutaneous communication. Now, during the past two years, Mr. Paul Sheldon has taken up the problem anew in the Princeton laboratory. A vastly improved technology has removed many of the limitations of the earlier work.

How is onset slope appreciated by the skin? It is as a single, integrated "attack" pattern, but one in which it is clearly possible to trade off stimulus dimensions against each other. In Sheldon's experiments a standard fixed attack pattern was compared with a variable one which could be altered by the observer (either adjusting time with intensity held constant or — with somewhat greater observational difficulty — adjusting intensity while time was held invariant) until the two patterns felt alike. The systematic manipulation of time (50 to 1,000 msec) and intensity (seven values between 25 and 55 dB SL) yielded a contour (an "isohaptic" one?) reminiscent of the Stevens isophonic contours for the several dimensions (Stevens, 1934). Currently, data which will supply the isohaptic contour for direct electric "attack" are being gathered and, while the observer's task is far from simple, as might be guessed, completion of the work should make possible interesting and valuable comparisons between the growth processes of pressure sensations when adequately and nonadequately aroused.

Stepping up to temporal stimulus variations of a more elaborate kind, let me finally introduce you to some gadgetry designed to challenge the skin, indeed, to challenge its cortical projection areas and connected computer facilities. Figure 13-7 displays the *optohapt*, a device for transmuting the printed word to a spatiotemporal cutaneous pattern. More precisely, it is a signal generator that is activated by light (or, through relays, darkness) and which can be made to convert black marks into tonal configurations, buzzes, or other output. The heart of the machine is an optical system in whose

Figure 13-7. The optohapt. The photoelectric "reader" of the Battelle Optophone is suspended over the motor-driven carriage of an IBM accounting-type (30 in) typewriter. The nine photocells of the optophone unit activate nine Sigma relays, which in turn control nine Sherrick vibrators distributed over the body surface.

conjugate foci are the black marks to be picked up and an array of tiny photocells to react to them. The system was originally conceived a half century or more ago, and has attained recent prominence in such devices as the Battelle Optophone, the "visotoner," and the "visotactor," all designed as central pickup devices in so-called reading machines for the blind. Each is currently rated a howling success or a miserable failure, depending somewhat on how difficult a problem you think circumvention of blindness really is or what confidence you have in alternative proposals for solving the problem.

In the present application a pickup from a Battelle Optophone, kindly loaned by the Veteran's Administration, is rigidly suspended over the 30-in carriage of an IBM electric typewriter of the accounting variety. The type faces have been selected to provide a wide range of characters, 86 of them. All letters are serifless capitals, and there is an unusual collection of little-used signs and symbols. The optophone has nine photocells in a vertical array so that the letter "I," e.g., when passing under the optophone head energizes all of them simultaneously and briefly. The letter "O" would start with the middle cell, spread to the top and bottom ones, then shrink back to the middle again. The letter "V" gives a rapid sweep from top to bottom, then reverses the sequence. A motor drive has been arranged to give any desired speed of travel of the materials past the optophone reading slit.

Each of the nine photocells simply serves as a variable resistor in a single transistor amplifier, the output of which energizes the coil of a sensitive Sigma relay. The relays, in turn, control nine Sherrick vibrators scattered over the body surface in accordance with the plan of Figure 13-1. (One abdominal vibrator is inactivated in the optohapt.) Such an arrangement now provides, of course, something other than the relatively "static" patterns of the earlier experiments. Any curved or slanting line generates a spritely cutaneous movement which is, to say the least, highly attention demanding as it sweeps from ankle to shoulder. The letter "W" or the ampersand (&) makes for pretty lively feeling as it plays back and forth over the body surface.

It was immediately apparent, on trying out some sample patterns, that we had generated a great wealth of symbols for cutaneous communication; a practically infinite variety of spatiotemporal arrangements is possible with the optohapt. The important question was, of course, which patterns are most readily discriminated from others? A direct comparison of each of the 86 with all others seemed formidable — this represents nearly 15,000 pairings. However, there are some shortcuts. One of them is to get a dynamic picture of current changes in the common leg of all nine amplifier circuits as a function of time. This is accomplished simply and satisfactorily by a recording milliameter. Each symbol, as it passes under the photoelectric pickup head, writes its autograph, so to speak. An analysis of these records loses the factor of locus, to be sure, but gives a clear picture of emphases through time, and that is the important feature being added. The analysis yielded some six major categories of patterns and permitted the early elimination of those symbols that would inevitably get confused with each other through close similarity. From such preliminary screening it was possible to reduce the field to 40 promising candidates, and these were entered into a single pair comparison program of 780 items, randomly intermixed.

On each presentation of a pair of patterns the observer was able to report not only whether the two patterns could be distinguished but could give quite reliable estimates of degree of difference on a simple four-point scale (3 = clearly different, would never be confused; 0 = feel exactly alike), thus providing a useful discrimination score. The results of two practiced observers' completion of the full program of comparisons is a table in which all 40 symbols may be ordered with respect to rank.

The maximum possible discrimination score is 234. A symbol receiving such a score would never be confused with any other symbol. The minimum score, is, of course, zero, a condition of total confusion of stimuli and chance performance. It would be difficult to find patterns which, under the conditions of our experiments, could invariably be distinguished from each other visually but not tactually, and it is natural that the discrimination scores fall well up toward the upper end of the scale.

TABLE 13-I

RANK	SYMBOL	DISCR. SCORE	RANK	SYMBOL	DISCR. SCORE	RANK	SYMBOL	DISCR. SCORE	RANK	SYMBOL	DISCR. SCORE
1	≡	213	11	T	191	21	E	171	31.5	Ω	161
2	-	212	12	F	190	23	)	169	31.5	P	161
3	.	211	13	÷	186	23	B	169	33	W	157
4	■	210	14	←	184	23	▫	169	34.5	/	156
5	"	204	15	L	181	26	‡	168	34.5	<	156
6	=	200	16	▫	180	28	◊	167	36	X	155
7	▢	199	17	I	177	28	‡	167	37	&	154
8	→	198	18	Π	176	28	J	167	38.5	V	152
9.5	'	192	19	%	175	29	♦	165	38.5	2	152
9.5	:	192	20	(	172	30	Z	162	40	A	149

OTHER AVAILABLE SYMBOLS :

\ λ 7 > ? + Σ 1 Y ↑ ≠ $ ↓ S U C R K H 5 #

4 N 0 3 M 8 ⓢ Δ ∇ § @ D 6 G 9 ⚹ 8 θ ⊗ ⚹ ⊠

What general trends appear in Table 13-I? In the first place, it seems to be the relatively simple, uncomplicated characters that get the high scores. By and large, the symbols most readily discriminated yield small, unimodal curves when their energy distribution through time is plotted. It is the period, the hyphen, the equality and equivalence signs, the apostrophe, the colon, and one especially distinctive pattern, the solid black square, that lead the pack. It is notable that not a single letter of the alphabet ranks within the first ten symbols. Of the 40 characters to which our population of candidates had been narrowed, alphabetic symbols ranked 25th, on the average, and the letter "A" was 40th. Vowels, which make the most difference in the meaning of English words, averaged 26th in rank. It is clear that a tactual language designed for the optohapt would do well to begin its coding with something other than vowels and consonants.

In assessing receptive areas of the body for relatively static patterns, those having elements with simultaneous onsets and durations, we found the fingers to perform rather badly, it will be recalled. The introduction of the optohapt gave us an opportunity to test the efficacy of manual reception with much more elaborate patterns, those having spatiotemporal rather than simply spatial variations in their composition. We guessed that the fingers might do somewhat better if moment-to-moment shifts in localization were to provide some additional cues. A direct comparison of body and fingers became possible in the course of taking the next step to narrow the field of candidates for language elements.

Fifteen symbols drawn from the population of Table 13-I were selected, not exclusively on the basis of discrimination scores but partially with a view to maximizing reliability in optohapt performance, and were set into a pair comparison design. The 105 pairings were presented both to the body sites and, in a different experimental session, to the fingers. The results of the two experiments are combined in Table 13-II.

It is clear that the best symbols, in this considerably restricted population of them, approach perfection (a discrimination score of 234). These

TABLE 13-II

RANK	SYMBOL	DISCR. SCORE	RANK	SYMBOL	DISCR. SCORE
1	.	233	1	■	231
2	''	231	2	''	230
3.5	■	230	3	-	226
3.5	-	230	4.5	.	222
5	=	229	4.5	ı	222
6	→	223	6	=	220
7	ı	220	7	I	217
8	+	217	8	◊	216
9.5	I	215	9	Π	209
9.5	□	215	10	L	208
11	Π	214	11	→	205
12	>	213	12	/	203
13	/	212	13	>	199
14.5	◊	211	14	+	196
14.5	L	211	15	□	195
		AVE. = 220			AVE. = 213

$r = .66$

are our best orthographic candidates, and the most frequently recurring language elements (Underwood and Schulz, 1960) should be coded to them. It is also clear that our surmise about the conditions under which the fingers might be expected to perform well was essentially correct. With multiple stimuli spread out in time in addition to space, the fingers perform nearly as well as do the body sites. Indeed, the difference in average performance represented on the two sides of Table 13-II is not impressive and does not, in fact, quite pass the test of significance in this small population.

We have now arrived at a point where we can synthesize a straightforward code by assigning symbols to letters of the alphabet. It should be done mainly empirically, and this principle has been followed with some fidelity, but it is also desirable to keep one eye on any advantage to be derived from associative linkage. A possibly useful code is displayed in Table 13-III.

TABLE 13-III

E	.		L	L		P	:
T	-		D	→		B	□
A	‖		U	ı		V	V
O	■		C	/		K	<
I	ı		M	◊		X	>
N	=		F	F		J	J
S	◊		G	\		Z	Z
R	Π		W	▫		Q	‡
H	+		Y	T			

'=ı-.→ ◊-"-.◊ ■F "◊.Πı/"

UNITED STATES OF AMERICA

There are reasons for believing that neither a long nor intricate learning process will be involved in acquiring this cutaneous language. We have had some success with less interesting symbols, indeed some that were quite static and arbitrarily chosen. Whether receiving and interpretation rates can be gotten up to a practically useful level remains to be seen. It is not expected that the finding-out process will be a dull exercise, for at every turn, as perhaps the foregoing account illustrates, we get led into novel and entirely unexplored basic problems.

REFERENCES

Békésy, G. von. Interaction of paired sensory stimuli and conduction in peripheral nerves. *J. Appl. Physiol.,* 1963, **18,** 1276.

Békésy, G. von. Loudness recruitment. *Trans. Amer. Otol. Soc.,* 1965, **53,** 85.

Bender, M. B. *Disorders in Perception.* Springfield, Ill.: Thomas, 1952.

Bice, R. C. Electromechanical transducer for vibrotactile stimulation. *Rev. Sci. Instrum.,* 1961, **32,** 856.

Fletcher, H., & Munson, W. A. Loudness, its definition, measurement, and calculation. *J. Acoust. Soc. Amer.,* 1933, **5,** 82.

Geldard, F. A., & Sherrick, C. E. Multiple cutaneous stimulation: The discrimination of vibratory patterns. *J. Acoust. Soc. Amer.,* 1965, **37,** 797.

Gescheider, G. A. Cutaneous sound localization. *J. Exp. Psychol.,* 1965, **70,** 617.

Hirsh, I. J. *The Measurement of Hearing.* New York: McGraw-Hill, 1952.

Howell, W. C. Discrimination of rate of amplitude change in cutaneous vibration. Doctoral dissertation, Univer. of Virginia, 1958.

Sherrick, C. E. Simple electromechanical vibration transducer. *Rev. Sci. Instrum.,* 1965, **36,** 1893.

Stevens, S. S. The attributes of tones. *Proc. Nat. Acad. Sci. USA,* 1934, **20,** 257.

Stevens, S. S. Cross-modality validation of subjective scales for loudness, vibration, and electric shock. *J. Exp. Psychol.,* 1959, **57,** 201.

Underwood, B. J., & Schulz, R. W. *Meaningfulness and Verbal Behavior.* New York: Lippincott, 1960.

DISCUSSION

DR. R. H. GIBSON: Do you have plans to work with children on the grounds that it takes a little time to acquire a reasonable perceptual learning? Perhaps by using adults who are not actually blind you might be depriving the system of a chance.

DR. GELDARD: I think the latter is a little more demanding than the first. I do not anticipate very much difficulty with learning. We shall probably not investigate the learning process *per se* for this kind of material. What we shall be interested in doing is engineering the learning process to make the most effective one possible for this purpose. I would be more interested in knowing what the blind do with it than I would in knowing what children do with it.

DR. R. T. VERRILLO: In your earlier work, you worked on the back and on the chest. Have you tried this arrangement with this apparatus, shrinking it a bit rather than having it scattered all over the body?

DR. GELDARD: No, we started off on the chest, largely with a view to finding a relatively broad and uniform expanse of skin, one where the traffic was not very heavy, simply because we had in mind various possible military applications. That was about the only place left that would not be disturbed by motility problems. Subsequently we have gotten away from that completely because of the terrific amount of bone conduction to the cochlea, though it might be that, in a practical communication system, this would not be disturbing at all. For the time being, we are trying to find out what the skin can do by itself and not what it can do with the cochlea's help.

Dr. Verrillo: But you never worked with the new Sherrick vibrator (Sherrick, 1965) in a smaller area?

Dr. Geldard: It is not that much smaller. The Sherrick instrument is simply more convenient and more reliable than the older vibrators. The old ones were small enough but they had to be attached by a whole forest of supports and goosenecks in order to get them to the body. That is no longer necessary with the Sherrick vibrator; they attach directly with "Velcro" straps.

Dr. C. Pfaffmann: In that picture showing the finger stalls (Fig. 5), it was not clear to me how that vibration was imparted. It looked to me as if the whole finger was moved. What about the application of the vibration to just the balls of the fingertips?

Dr. Geldard: The problem with attachment is that you do not want interactions between the vibrating elements. These vibrators are suspended independently from the ceiling and suspended by rubber mounts, etc., in order to keep them absolutely independent of each other up to the point of entrance of the vibration to the fingers. This does not preclude the conduction from one finger to another, of course. Nothing can be done about this. It is simply a vibrator, which is moving up and down, and it has a little plastic stall connected underneath it. The fingers are placed in the stalls, which just fit, and the weight of the cushioned forearm keeps them snugly in contact with the fingers. The amount of vibration is a fraction of a millimeter, just enough to give a good secure signal.

Dr. Pfaffmann: I was wondering about the alternative of putting the vibrator in contact with just the soft pad of the finger without the whole member being suspended. This would give you more of the situation which a braille reader would have when he is in excessive stimulation zone.

Dr. Geldard: Yes, we think there are probably better ways of getting localization at the finger. We are currently instrumenting to use high frequencies that do not spread as rapidly. In the experiments I reported, we are using 60 Hz which goes through everything practically unimpeded. But if the vibrator were to be driven at 800 or 1000 Hz it may be that we could keep the patterns fairly well confined to the fingertips and thus improve localization.

Dr. H. Hensel: What is the main advantage of your system as compared with the commonly used braille method?

DR. GELDARD: I do not have any idea that they are even competitors. Braille performance is one which has been developed to a very high degree by those few blinded people who have learned it well. Most people do not do well with braille, even people who have been blinded for many years. It is too difficult. It is strictly a logical language, comprised of a series of combinations which are quite arbitrary. It has not been psychologically designed at all and it is a very difficult language to learn. I would not think of ours as a competitor. We are simply trying to find out what the skin can do about communicating and interpreting, and it may be that the present choice of basic signals is the wrong one. We shall see.

DR. J. A. B. GRAY: I have a small point which is a continuation of what Dr. Pfaffmann was asking about in the discrimination on the fingers. Have you tried using frequencies other than 60 Hz? With a common 60 Hz in all stimulators, you have presumably got synchronous vibrations to all of them and hence you may get mechanical summations of vibration back down the hand, whereas if you used entirely independent frequencies which were not synchronous you might improve discrimination.

DR. GELDARD: Yes, this is one of the possibilities we have in mind in implementing the present modification of the Optohapt. In other words, we are still very much interested in getting the relative convenience of the fingertips; if for nothing else, we would not have to dress and undress a half dozen times a day, the way we have to now.

DR. MELZACK: I was wondering if the subjects read these vibrations as patterns; that is, if they scan a whole word or sentence, as in visual reading.

DR. GELDARD: We have not gone far enough with the learning of this particular system to know whether or not they will do so on this particular array. We do know, from previous learning of such cutaneous systems, that you can do this. You can "follow behind," in very much the same way that the radio code operator follows behind, integrating the signals into an overall pattern and get sufficient cues to give him the whole word. I have no doubt that this will work exactly the same way, since it is a function of the computer (brain), not of the receptor system.

Reference

Sherrick, C. E. Simple electromechanical vibration transducer. *Rev. Sci. Instrum.,* 1965, **36**, 1893.

Chapter 14

TACTILE ADAPTATION*

JOHN F. HAHN

T HE USAGE OF THE WORD *adaptation* is sufficiently confused that anyone who uses the term owes to his readers some guidance as to what he intends to mean by it. Let me say at the outset, therefore, that I do not wish to imply distinctions of the sort that may be involved in such special terms as fatigue, perstimulatory fatigue, accommodation, habituation, temporary threshold shift, and the like. I should like to use adaptation as a general term referring to changes in the properties of a sensory system resulting from a changed stimulus. As examples of the use of this definition, visual light adaptation, dark adaptation, and negative afterimages would be included by it, because the concentrations of visual pigments, and therefore the properties of the visual system, change as a result of change in the visual stimulus. On the other hand, the quickly decreasing generator potential of the intact Pacinian corpuscle in response to a pressure step function would not be included in this usage of adaptation, because this change can be accounted for by the elastic and viscous properties of the capsule rather than by a change in these or other properties (Mendelson and Lowenstein, 1964).

This distinction between change in sensory response and change in sensory properties is essentially the distinction made by Nafe and Wagoner (1941) as a result of studying what was then called pressure adaptation. They showed, you recall, that the tactile sensation produced by a weight resting on the skin disappeared when the rate at which the weight sank into the skin had decreased below a minimum rate required to stimulate. When the weight was no longer felt, its removal produced a clear tactile sensation, showing that the prior disappearance of sensation did not mean that the sensory system had become unresponsive. It thus appeared that what had been called tactile adaptation did not actually reflect a change in receptor sensitivity, but instead resulted from tissue elasticity opposing with steadily increasing force the steady force of the pressure stimulus. This aspect of tactile adaptation was aptly renamed "stimulus failure," the term emphasizing that changed transmission of the stimulus through the tissues was the major factor in the change in sensory response.

It should be noted that implied in the concept of stimulus failure is

*Partial support of these investigations was by U. S. Public Health Service Research Grant NB-04177 from the National Institute of Neurological Diseases and Blindness.

the hypothesis that differences between "fast-adapting" and "slowly-adapting" tactile neural units are the result of differences in the characteristics of the tissues enveloping the receptors.

Does the concept of stimulus failure also imply that the tactile sensory system itself does not adapt, that a change in stimulation is not accompanied by any change in the properties of the sensory system, but that elastic and viscous properties of tissues can account for all of the phenomena which have gone by the name of tactile adaptation? The findings of Lowenstein and Mendelson (1965) suggest not, but in our present state of understanding touch receptors, no direct answer is available.

If tissue elasticity and viscosity were the only factors to be considered, then nothing resembling tactile adaptation should occur when the stimulus is not static pressure but sinusoidal vibrations, since these should be transmitted as some constant proportion of the input. The fact is, of course that both the threshold (Cohen and Lindley, 1938; Weddell and Cummings, 1938) and the magnitude of vibratory sensation (Békésy, 1959) have been found to change as a result of vibratory stimulation.

It is possible that by enlarging the scope of the concept of stimulus failure one could explain the fact that there is a decrease in sensory response to prolonged vibratory stimuli. If the elasticity and viscosity of the tissues changed as a result of such stimulation, with a consequent change in the attenuation of the stimulus between the stimulator and the receptors, we would again be dealing with variation in stimulus transmission rather than with changes in sensory properties, and the concept of stimulus failure would apply.

It would first be desirable, however, to know whether the measures of threshold and of sensation magnitude tell the same story about vibrotactile adaptation. In the case of light adaptation, for example, the two measures indicate very different temporal courses of adaptation (Geldard, 1928). When the direct comparison is made for 60 Hz vibration at 34 dB above threshold (Hahn, in press), it turns out that threshold and sensation magnitude as measured by intensity matching tell roughly the same story, but differ in quantitative details. The temporal course of adaptation appears to be the same with either method, but the decibel change in threshold is almost three times as great as that in subjective magnitude. Moreover, after cessation of the adapting stimulus, subjective magnitude recovers more rapidly than threshold does, except possibly when recovery is nearly complete.

It is difficult to see how any reasonable assumptions about changes in tissue elasticity and viscosity could account for these data in their entirety. Not only would the resulting attenuation have to be greater for the lower intensities of test stimuli involved in the threshold measurements than for the higher intensities required for intensity matching, but during recovery from stimulation the attenuations at these two levels would have to change at different rates. While it is conceivable that not only are the physical properties of the system nonlinear functions of stimulus intensity but in addition the nonlinearities change during recovery, it would seem more plausible at this point to regard the intensity matching data as setting the upper limit of the effect that could be attributed to changes of stimulus transmission through the tissues, and the threshold data as reflecting the operation of additional factors.

In order to approach the problem from another direction, the temporal course of recovery for both threshold and subjective magnitude has been measured as a function of frequency in the range 50-800 Hz. Eight replications of threshold measurement and eight of subjective magnitude measurement were obtained from each of three subjects. The 1.6 mm contactor, in diameter less than a quarter wavelength at the highest frequency employed, rested on the subject's index finger pad with a pressure of 10 gm, which control tests showed not to affect vibrotactile adaptation. The level of the 2.5 min adapting stimulus was set at 20 dB re the just-previously measured absolute threshold for that frequency. During the first 2 min of recovery, either threshold or the subjective magnitude of a brief standard test stimulus was measured at regular intervals. Thresholds were measured by a modified method of limits in which stimulus strength was continuously increased to the threshold level, descending series being omitted because of the adaptation they would have produced. Subjective magnitude was measured by briefly presenting a standard stimulus, of the same frequency and intensity as the adapting stimulus, to the adapted area, followed by a test stimulus of the same frequency on the contralateral unadapted finger. The test stimulus intensity was increased until the subject reported the sensation magnitude to be equal to that produced by the standard stimulus on the adapted area. This procedure was subject to time-order error, of course, and to the error resulting from adaptation produced by the test stimulus during the measurement procedure. Control measurements showed the mean combined effect of these errors to be a 1.1 dB decrease in the intensity match relative to that expected when the intensities were equal. The data plotted in Figure 14-1 have been corrected by this amount.

These data confirm the existence of the difference in the recovery rates of threshold and subjective magnitude, found earlier, and show that the difference occurs over what, for vibrotactile stimuli, is a fairly wide frequency range. The data also show no gross differential effect of stimulus frequency on the degree of adaptation shown by the two measures, there being an increase of roughly 1 dB per octave for each as the frequency is raised.

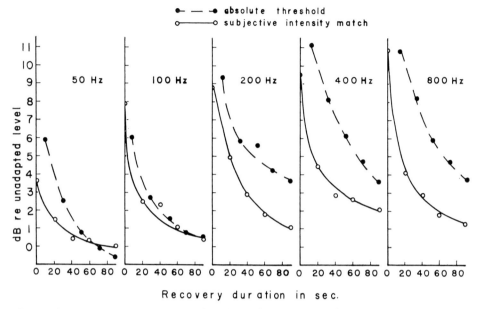

Figure 14-1. Recovery from vibrotactile adaptation at several frequencies. Matching data have been corrected for constant error (see text). Ordinate values are negative for matching data.

Perhaps the most interesting aspect of these data in the present context, however, is that an effect that might have been expected to appear did not. You will recall that the adapting stimulus at each frequency was set at 20 dB re the threshold at that frequency. Because thresholds under the conditions of this experiment were the usual U-shaped function of frequency, so also were the adapting stimulus amplitudes, the values at 50 and 800 Hz being respectively 14.1 and 2.6 times greater than those in the 200-400 Hz region. One would expect higher stimulus energies to produce greater tissue changes of the sort that would be postulated for the enlarged concept of stimulus failure. Yet the degree of adaptation shows no sign of being a U-shaped function of frequency. Therefore these data do not support the hypothesis that some form of stimulus failure is important in adaptation to vibrotactile stimuli.

One can note some similarity between these results and those of tactile adaptation to sinusoidal electric currents. Although there are no such data that can be directly compared with those of Figure 14-1, it is known that adaptation proceeds more rapidly as the frequency of the alternating current is raised. This effect is like that found with mechanical vibration, yet tissue elasticity and viscosity are unlikely to be significant factors in this case.

Considering the evidence as a whole, it appears that both the temporal and intensitive aspects of sensory response to tactile stimuli are affected by the physical properties of the tissues between stimulus and receptor in ways that are already understood. It appears that these aspects of sensory response are additionally affected by factors that are not yet understood. I do not propose to speculate about the roles that spatial summation and inhibition, efferent control, or other factors may play in explaining the similarities and differences in the changes of threshold and sensation magnitude brought about by vibrotactile stimulation or in the other phenomena of adaptation. These quantitative aspects of adaptation require quantitative explanations. Meanwhile, it is clear that, while the threshold of understanding tactile adaptation was crossed when the concept of stimulus failure was introduced, the magnitude of the explanatory task remaining is still considerable.

ACKNOWLEDGMENT

The subjects were Dr. Charles Fry and Mr. Charles Hodge, whose patient and interested cooperation I deeply appreciated. Mr. Hodge also kindly served as experimenter when I was a subject.

REFERENCES

Békésy, G. von. Synchronism of neural discharges and their demultiplication in pitch perception on the skin and in hearing. *J. Acoust. Soc. Amer.,* 1959, **31,** 338.

Cohen, L. H., & Lindley, S. B. Studies in vibratory sensibility. *Amer. J. Psychol.,* 1938, **51,** 44.

Geldard, F. A. The measurement of retinal fatigue to achromatic stimulation. II. *J. Gen. Psychol.,* 1928, **1,** 578.

Hahn, J. F. Vibrotactile adaptation and recovery measured by two methods. *J. Exp. Psychol.,* in press.

Loewenstein, W. R., & Mendelson, M. Components of receptor adaptation in a Pacinian corpuscle. *J. Physiol. (London),* 1965, **177,** 377.

Mendelson, M., & Loewenstein, W. R. Mechanisms of receptor adaptation. *Science,* 1964, **144,** 554.

Nafe, J. P., & Wagoner, K. S. The nature of pressure adaptation. *J. Gen. Psychol.,* 1941, **25,** 323.

Weddell, C. H., & Cummings, S. B. Fatigue of the vibratory sense. *J. Exp. Psychol.,* 1938, **22,** 429.

DISCUSSION

DR. Y. ZOTTERMAN: Where do you believe adaptation occurs? Is it something which has to do with the physical properties of the tissues of the skin? That is all right for mechanical stimulation but you also spoke of adaptation to electrical stimulation. Let us be clear where we locate this process of adaptation; maybe it includes several kinds of tissue.

DR. HAHN: I will say two things. The use of vibrotactile stimuli is a way of bypassing, to a large extent, the action of the intervening tissues which play such a strong part in the adaptation to static pressures, as in the work of Nafe and Kenshalo (1958). I assume that the phase shift and the attenuation which might occur for vibrotactile stimuli would remain constant and would not show up as adaptation. The second thing I will say is, if you will recall Figure 14-1, I said that there was approximately 1 dB per octave increase in the amount of adaptation as a function of frequency. That is essentially no change. Then we ask, "What stimulus characteristic is constant?" As we change the frequency, we change the amplitude of these adapting stimuli very considerably. Implied in what I said, however, what that these adapting stimuli are at approximately equal sensation levels, being 20 dB above threshold. They were not matched for equal sensations but they would be, from other data, at approximately equal sensation levels. This is one feature of the stimulating situation that was constant at all frequencies. If you will then take it a step further, to say that the psychophysical report can reasonably accurately mirror what the nervous system is telling it, then it says that a rather important effect in this kind of adaptation comes not from how hard your system is hit by the stimulus but how hard it responds. It should seem that how hard the system is responding may be an important factor in this kind of adaptation although it was not directly tested.

Dr. R. H. Gibson: Can you separate the effects of frequency, rise time, and these other things you are talking about, by using rectangular pulses?

Dr. Hahn: I would expect to encounter some difficulty in providing truly rectangular pulses at the receptor, where they count, with the mechanical system. It is perfectly possible, for example, as has been done in Dr. Mountcastle's laboratory (Werner and Mountcastle 1963), to construct a beautiful system that follows the commands exactly. But when you hit the receptor with that pulse, I rather expect you would encounter some ringing and other complications.

Dr. A. Iggo: I would like to come back, or at least to continue the discussion of this question of frequency as it affects the behavior of the afferent fibers, which presumably underlie the sensations which you have been talking about. There are in the glabrous skin two quite different classes of afferent unit, those that adapt rapidly and those that adapt slowly, as judged by the persistence of discharge to a maintained mechanical stimulus. These have different dynamic characteristics when the stimulus is being changed. If there is a rapidly changing stimulus, compared with a much more slowly changing stimulus, one would expect that the population of afferent fibers to be excited in these two situations would be rather different. In the situation where there is a high frequency alteration, there will be a discharge in the rapidly adapting units, the frequency of which will follow that of the stimulus and will show both on and off responses. The slowly adapting units will be discharging with a frequency which increases at on and then falls off so that it comes to a much lower value and then increases again with the next onset of the stimulus. At the lower frequency of stimulation, it is possible to set up a situation where the rapidly adapting afferent fibers are silent and the slowly adapting afferent fibers show a discharge in which the frequency increases on the inward thrust of the stimulus probe, which is amplitude dependent, and then falls off on the withdrawal of the probe. I was wondering whether this kind of alteration in the afferent input might underlie, to some extent, the sensory changes that you describe.

DR. HAHN: One point, merely as a matter of avoiding potential confusion. Professor Iggo, in speaking of rapidly adapting and slow adapting units, is using terminology which refers to a shorter time scale than the adaptation I have been talking about. I do not believe this confusion has been made yet so let us try to avoid it. In answer to Professor Iggo, I am not sure which sensory changes you were talking about, because there were, as you recall, some differences which did not change with frequency.

DR. IGGO: What I really wanted to do was to try to emphasize the fact that coming in from the skin, there are at least two different types of afferent input and I think that when you are altering the parameters of your mechanical stimulation, even though the peripheral neural discharge is on a different time scale from your sensory adaptation, you still have the possibility of the input coming in from a periphery, which is very different at different frequency settings. This is a fact that, presumably, needs to be taken into account. I would be very interested to know if you do find changes in sensation that could be related to this alteration in the afferent inflow. Is there a psychological correlate for a switch from stimulating conditions in which both slow- and fast-adapting receptors are active to one in which only the slow-adapting receptors will respond to the stimulus?

DR. H. HENSEL: May I return to this term *adaptation*? In 1932, Lord Adrian said "Adaptation is perhaps a dangerous term to use" (p. 24). I think this still holds today. The general meaning of adaptation is nothing more than the fact that a time factor is involved in the correlation of the external stimulus and the neural output, let us say, of a receptor. The whole system is a sort of black box with a time factor built in. If you have a rectangular stimulus, then the neural discharge frequency is high at first and gradually diminishes. In a general sense, this is adaptation. Now, we go further and ask what are the processes which can account for adaptation and here things become difficult, especially if we try to exclude mechanical events. This means that we are not allowed to use the term *adaptation* until we know what is going on in the system. In most receptors we do not know at all. Let us speak of thermal receptors; nobody knows whether or not

mechanical processes might be involved in the excitation of thermal receptors, so according to your definition, we could not use the word adaptation to describe certain aspects of their responses until we know the nature
of all those processes that are involved in the receptors. The Pacinian corpuscle consists of mechanical and biochemical parts, so is it justified to
exclude the mechanical processes from adaptation and not exclude chemical
processes?

DR. HAHN: I would be the last person to try to legislate the usage of
adaptation. Second, the definition I started with would not rule out
mechanical stimulation. Adaptation in the case of the Pacinian corpuscle
would fit this definition if the elasticity or the viscosity or other mechanical
properties of the corpuscle changed because of the stimulation. Another
analogy might be that if the capacitance of a capacitor changed as a result
of the passage of current, this would be adaptation but variations of the
current passing through an unchanging capacitor, simply because it is a
capacitor, would not fit the definition. Your second point was essentially
that if we are going to follow this kind of definition, most of the time we
could not use the word *adaptation*. This is true. It would not grieve me.

DR. H. DAVIS: I think it is pretty clear that what we need is some all-
inclusive term that will include the various types of stimulus failure, adaptation, accommodation and equilibration. These have all been used in one
context or another. [Ed. note: see the final Note by Geldard].

DR. HAHN: Our problem is, I believe, that many of these terms imply
hypotheses. The differences between fatigue, accommodation, and adaptation are often used in cases where these hypotheses have not been proven.

DR. W. A. ROSENBLITH: I should like to back what Dr. Davis has said but
I would like to raise an issue with Dr. Hahn that is perhaps more philo-
sophical, even temperamental, than scientific. His ethical position is one
in which virtue increases as one resists temptation to speculate. As people
get older, it becomes easier for them to resist certain temptations, and I
think that they ought to compensate by being more courageous in other
dimensions. True teachers need to communicate more than facts; they need
to instill in young people a willingness to take intellectual risks by specu-
lating on the significance and relatedness of facts. If we are not willing to
say, "I am using this term this way, but I must recognize that other people
have used it differently; hence, it behooves me to relate the different usages,"
we are going to build not one Tower of Babel but many.

DR. R. MELZACK: There is a brain in that black box that Dr. Hensel
spoke of; there is a time factor built in, certainly, but there is also a brain.
It is important to realize that, in most of the discussion, we have limited
the portion of the nervous system at which we are looking. What we have

is a system in which we have cut away most of the brain. In these psychophysical kinds of experiments, we have a fixed gate interposed between receptors and the brain, and we are not allowing the brain to act on that gate; to allow in more information or to keep it out.

Dr. HAHN: Your comment is not entirely clear to me. Do you mean conceptually or experimentally in this case?

Dr. MELZACK: Conceptually.

Dr. HAHN: Certainly central factors, efferent control, and many other factors, are ones that one could list, in compiling a list of all possible factors involved. We would all probably come up with the same list of future research topics.

Dr. J. C. STEVENS: I admire, Dr. Hahn, your restraint in not feeling compelled to give an explanation for all these effects, and I would like to add that in the field of vision, adaptation studies have been done over a long time that are exactly analogous to the kind of measurements you made, measurement of the threshold and measurement of brightness changes. Explanations for adaptation in vision come and go, and I am not certain today what the true explanation is. Before we have an explanation, it seems to me we ought to know the facts. This implies measuring the kinds of functions that you have measured, and I am very grateful for your job. I think it will be helpful in the long run.

References

Adrian, E. D. *The Mechanism of Nervous Action*. London: Oxford University, 1932.

Nafe, J. P., & Kenshalo, D. R. Stimulation and neural response. *Amer. J. Psychol.*, 1958, **71**, 199.

Werner, G., & Mountcastle, V. B. The variability of central neural activity in a sensory system, and its implications for the central reflection of sensory events. *J. Neurophysiol.*, 1963, **26**, 958.

Chapter 15

STUDIES OF APPARENT TACTUAL MOVEMENT*

Carl E. Sherrick

JUST A LITTLE MORE THAN HALF a century ago a new school of thought in psychology was founded by a man who, through a series of canny experimental observations and a firmly held belief in the primacy of motion as a perceptual attribute, touched off an intellectual movement that altered forever the mode of thought and experimentation in the psychology of perception. The school of thought was the Gestalt school, and the man was Max Wertheimer (1912). His analysis of the conditions that generated the visual perception of apparent movement led him to the conclusion that movement, however produced, was an attribute of sensation that was not inferred and not synthesized. Wertheimer elaborated on his thesis by suggesting that such a fundamental process must have a physiological basis. The years following Wertheimer's publication were filled with controversy over this and other perceptual phenomena reported by the Gestalt theorists. I do not intend to chronicle that complex series of events, nor to argue the merits of Wertheimer's theory. I would point out that movement, however perceived, may provide useful information to the organism, and that a recent concern of mine has been with the discovery of useful perceptual dimensions in the area of cutaneous communications.

The experiments I wish to discuss were carried out for two purposes: (a) to explore in more detail the variables that affect the perception of apparent movement on the skin, and (b) to set for this phenomenon the boundary conditions within which it may serve as a cue in a cutaneous communications system. If I strike a balance between the pure and the practical aims, I shall be emulating in a small way the illustrious career of the man to whom this symposium is dedicated, Professor Nafe.

EARLY STUDIES OF APPARENT MOVEMENT

Apparent Visual Movement

The well-known reviews by Boring (1942, pp. 558-602) and Neff (1936) obviate an extensive discussion of the older literature, but I shall summarize them briefly in order to contrast the history of visually perceived apparent movement with haptically perceived apparent movement. The physiologist

*This study was supported, in part, by a grant from the National Science Foundation, and, in part, by a grant from the National Institute of Health, U. S. Department of Health, Education, and Welfare.

Exner preceded Wertheimer, by nearly four decades in both research and theory. In the course of an exhaustive survey of the capacities of the senses for detecting the temporal order of events, Exner produced apparent visual movement in the space between two successive electrical sparks and discussed, at length, the physiological mechanisms which he thought underlay the perception. Wertheimer (1912) induced perception of apparent motion in his observers by means of successive tachistoscopic presentation of several simple figures, and went to great pains to demonstrate that this perception was based on a simple, primary neural process, which he called "Φ" and not on suggestion, experience, or the synthesis of simpler perceptual elements. Kenkel (1913), following Wertheimer's methods, described several kinds of apparent movement that appear under various conditions of stimulus presentation. Korte (1915) in a later and related publication described in more detail the degree to which optimal movement is affected by the manipulation of such variables as stimulus duration, interstimulus interval, distance between stimuli, and sensory magnitude of stimuli. Korte summarized his findings by formulating proportional relationships among the above-mentioned variables, and these are often referred to as Korte's laws.

A veritable deluge of papers followed these contributions over the next decade, questioning the introspective reports of the observers, challenging the reported character of the movement, and quarreling with the rigorousness of Korte's laws and with the adequacy of Wertheimer's theory. Despite the activity over the years, it would appear from the review by Neff (1936) that the definitive series of experiments on visual apparent movement have yet to be done, however, and that many questions relating to conditions for visual movement are to this day unanswered. The continuing impression among psychologists that the Gestalt school had the final say about apparent movement recalls the dictum of a Boston psychopathologist of an earlier generation: "When facts and theories do not agree, so much the worse for the facts!"

Apparent Tactual Movement

A similar lineage of research may be traced for the perception of apparent tactual movement. An early study of real tactual movement by Hall and Donaldson (1885) suggested, as did Exner's studies in vision, that movement has primacy in perception because it can be appreciated even when its extent and direction are not. Later, von Frey and Metzner (1902) reported apparent partial movement between two adjacent pressure spots successively stimulated. The earliest complete study of tactual or haptic movement was made by Benussi (1916) who devised a special instrument, the "kinohapt," for investigating the phenomenon. This device consisted of a pair of weighted contactors that could be lowered to the skin and retrieved electrically, affording control over timing, spacing, and duration of stimuli.

Benussi attempted to verify Korte's laws for the skin, and manipulated distance between stimuli, duration of stimuli, and time between stimuli over a wide range of values. He never found conditions for pure movement, but did observe partial movement on occasions. A number of other investigators followed Benussi's lead and obtained results similar to his under a variety of conditions. A striking difference appears between the two lines of investigation of visual and haptic movement at this point. The stability of appearance of visual movement was great, and the cogency of the experience undeniable. Tactual movement, on the other hand, was a labile phenomenon, a psychophysical will-o'-the-wisp. Investigators could report obtaining it sufficiently often to verify its existence, but only rarely so dependably that they could validate Korte's laws for the skin. The character of tactual movement was accordingly described, more ambiguously, in terms of reports of vague shiftings or flutterings, and frequently movements whose trajectories were out of the plane of the skin. As a result, haptic movement was generally considered to be as much the result of the observer's visual imagery as of any primary process. As late as 1961, De Hardt (1961) reported difficulties in producing haptic movement with Bartley's modification of the Benussi kinohapt. She presented four observers with a variety of conditions of timing and spacing of stimuli in an attempt to determine the factors underlying optimal movement, and particularly the conditions generating "off-skin" and "on-skin" movements. Only moderate success marked her efforts, as a result of the unreliability of the appearance of movement.

APPARENT MOVEMENT WITH VIBROTACTILE STIMULI

The earliest study of haptic movement induced by successive bursts of vibration at different skin positions was made by Bice of the Virginia laboratories in the course of development of a compensatory tracking apparatus (Geldard, 1961, p. 82). With an array of six vibrators encircling the chest, Bice could induce a powerful "swirling" illusion, the chief component of which was haptic movement between successively energized vibrators. This "haptokinetic effect" was readily obtained with all subjects in the tracking experiment, and haptic movement was regarded as a stable perceptual event under the conditions described. In the same laboratories a short time later Sumby (1955) examined apparent haptic movement for the purpose of including it as a dimension in a cutaneous communications system. He was able to demonstrate two facts: (a) 200 msec bursts of vibration imposed on two skin positions in the proper time sequence will produce stable reports of good, full haptic movement, and (b) the significant variable for the appearance of good movement is the interval between onsets of stimuli.

The fact that Bice and Sumby had little difficulty in obtaining haptic movement with vibratory bursts suggests that the unreliability reported in earlier studies is owing, in part, to the character of the stimuli employed in them. The most common method of generating a stimulus was to drop a small weighted contactor on the skin, then retrieve it after a short time. It was assumed that the skin followed a simple rectangular displacement pattern in such cases, and that the stimulus had a beginning, a steady state, and an end. The now-classic work of Nafe and Wagoner (1941) tells us that such simple stimuli are rarely found. Depending on the temporal relations, "two" stimuli generated as described above might behave as a quartet or as a double trio of events. In such a situation, it is not surprising to find that the movement effect, which depends on a stable relationship between two successive events, would be an evanescent phenomenon. On the other hand, the vibratory burst has about it the unitary character of the auditory tone burst or of the flash of light, and for this reason may be a superior stimulus for generation of apparent movement.

Following Sumby's work the problem of haptic movement lay untouched, except for the study by De Hardt (1961), already mentioned, until Rogers' (1964) study. This investigator decided that Sumby was correct in modifying the interstimulus onset interval (ISOI) to obtain reports of good movement. To accomplish this same end more conveniently he arranged a system very similar to that shown in Figure 15-1. The Tektronix type 161 Pulse Generators can be triggered at a regular rate and over a certain period by the type 162 Tektronix Wave Form Generators. The pulse generator operates a relay that controls one of the electronic switches shown. In this manner a vibratory burst at the frequency of the oscillator appears at the mechanical vibrator. Varying the duration of the pulse generator output varies the duration of the burst, and varying the pulse delay control varies the point in time at which the burst begins. With a second complete channel, two such bursts are generated, and if one channel has a motor drive attached to the pulse delay control, the observer can modify the interval between burst onsets himself. By means of such an arrangement Rogers had four observers "track" the interval between periodically presented burst pairs from the extreme of perceived successiveness to that of perceived simultaneity of the pair.

Rogers took the midpoint of the extreme values thus found and assumed that this value of the ISOI was the point of optimal movement for the observer. Rogers sought to determine for this optimal ISOI the effect of such variables as sensory magnitude, distance between stimuli, place stimulated, and duration of stimuli. He discovered that the significant variable was stimulus duration, while sensory magnitude and distance had only a minor influence on the ISOI.

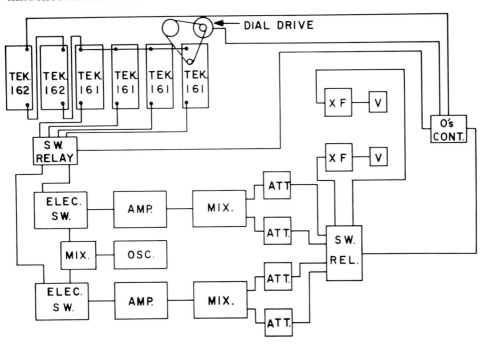

Figure 15-1. Block diagram of the apparatus for determination of conditions for optimal haptic movement (Fig. 1, Sherrick, C. E. & Rogers, R., *Perception Psychophys.*, in press).

PRESENT STUDIES OF HAPTIC MOVEMENT

It has been stated that Rogers did not have his observers judge the point of optimal movement directly. They were permitted to "track" the extremes of successiveness and simultaneity, and, since they regularly reported feeling good movement between the extreme time values, Rogers felt justified in his assumption that the midpoint was at least a good first approximation. He was wary of forcing his observers to examine a narrow range of values for movement presented at isolated points in time, since it appeared that just such a technique had been employed by past investigators with little success in obtaining reports of movement. I have modified Rogers' method to allow the observer to select the time values he judges best for movement. The series of experiments that follows incorporates the modified procedures.

The apparatus is diagramed in Figure 15-1. It is a standard signalling system for vibrotactile or auditory studies, with small modifications. The oscillator signal is gated by the electronic switches, amplified and attenu-

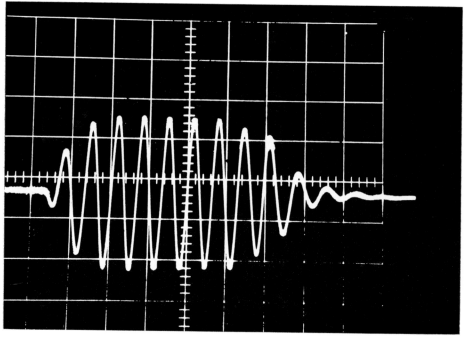

Figure 15-2. Oscillographic tracing of a vibrotactile burst used as one of the stimulus pairs in producing movement. The trace is the output of an MB type M-3 meter and type 127 vibration pickup attached to the piston of the Goodmans V-47 vibrator. Frequency 150 Hz (Fig. 2, Sherrick, C. E. & Rogers, R., *Perception Psychophys.,* in press) .

ated, and impressed on the vibrators. Figure 15-2 is an oscillograph trace of the motion of a V-47 vibrator to a 50 msec burst at 150 Hz. The Tektronix equipment programs the duration, stimulus intervals, and presentation rate of the signal bursts of the electronic switches. The box marked "Observer's Control" contains three switches and performs as many functions. First, by pressing one switch, the observer can trigger a single presentation sequence, in this case two vibrotactile bursts. Second, he can control the direction and extent of movement of the pulse delay dial drive on the third Tektronix 161 pulse generator, thereby changing the interval between burst onsets. (The time interval was read by means of a Hewlett-Packard 522-B counter, not shown.) Third, he can, with the switching relay boxes, switch in either one of the two sets of pulse generators shown, thus instantly permitting comparison of two different burst onset intervals, or two different burst durations. He can also compare two different burst intensities when the alternate attenuators shown are switched in. The vibrators were the Goodmans type V-47, having a contactor of about 6 mm in diameter which was surrounded by a fixed Teflon® ring to stabilize contact with the skin. The observer was seated comfortably in a dental chair, and the vibrators were suspended from counterbalanced beams and allowed to contact the ventral thigh of the observer with a force of about 100 gm. The output of a white noise generator provided a masker in the observer's headphones during the observation periods.

Procedure

The observer's absolute threshold for a 200 msec vibrotactile burst at the distal thigh locus was the standard reference value for all sensory magnitudes described in the experiment. When this value was obtained, the signal was usually raised to a sensation level (SL) of 15 dB. The magnitude of vibration at the other skin locus was then matched to that of the reference locus. When the burst pairs were equated for magnitude, the experimenter would adjust the interval between successive bursts and ask the observer to operate his control box to find the interval that produced the best movement for him. "Best movement" was defined as the longest uninterrupted feeling of movement between the first stimulus site and the second. The observer was permitted to trigger the stimulus sequence as often as he liked, and to change the burst onset interval values in any way he chose. Generally he required 2 to 4 min to complete a single reading, during which time he presented himself with stimuli at the average rate of one every 2 sec. Four such trials made up a single session.

The period over which training and data collection went on was about 14 months. Because Sumby and Rogers had shown that the ISOI or burst onset interval was the most significant variable in the determination of optimal haptic movement, it was made the dependent variable in all the experiments performed.

Results

Under ideal conditions, the haptic movement perceived by the observer was described as a powerful vibratory "gouging" that moved from one stimulus site to the other at a rate depending on the distance between sites and the time between onsets.

In the course of a series of pilot experiments, a number of variables were examined for their effect on the character of movement, or on the value of ISOI for movement. Those that had little or no effect may be listed.

Vibration Frequency

Shifting the frequency of vibration from 60 through 150 to 250 Hz affected neither the quality of good movement nor the ISOI for movement. Apparently any rate of repetitive impact is equally effective. The function performed is that of providing a sustained signal.

Body Locus

Exploration of the dorsal forearm, the back, the stomach, the fingertips and palms of the hands, led to no prominent differences in character of movement, and only small changes (of the order of 10 per cent) in ISOI.

Sensory Magnitude

Variation of stimuli from SLs of 6 dB to 30 dB produced no shift in ISOI or character of movement.

Distance

A variation in distance over the ventral thigh of 12 to 40 cm produced no change in ISOI although, at the longer distances, the movement became weak in the middle of its trajectory. Observers felt good movement, but it lost "clearness" in the center as the distance increased.

Direction of Motion

Proximal-distal and distal-proximal movement are identical qualitatively and quantitatively.

Magnitude Imbalance Between Stimuli

When one stimulus was made double the sensory magnitude of the second, the character of the movement and the ISOI shifted somewhat, but not to a great degree, again of the order of 10 per cent.

The variable having major significance for both the character of optimal haptic movement, and for the value of the burst onset interval, is that of stimulus duration. Four trained observers were presented with burst pairs having stimulus duration ranging from 25 to 400 msec, and manipulated the burst onset interval to obtain optimal movement, as outlined in the procedure. The results are shown in Figure 15-3. The filled and empty squares connected by dashed lines are the limits of good movement similar to those obtained by Rogers. The open circles and the solid line are the presently obtained mean values for optimal movement. The bracketed vertical lines are plus or minus one standard deviation about the mean. It should be noted that the durations of both stimuli were the same in the graph shown. If durations are unequal, the first stimulus determines the onset interval.

Conclusions

From the above results and the work of my predecessors, I have outlined the boundaries for good movement in a communications system. The temporal boundaries are those shown in Figure 15-3. Either the values bracketed by the standard deviation around the mean, or by the limits of

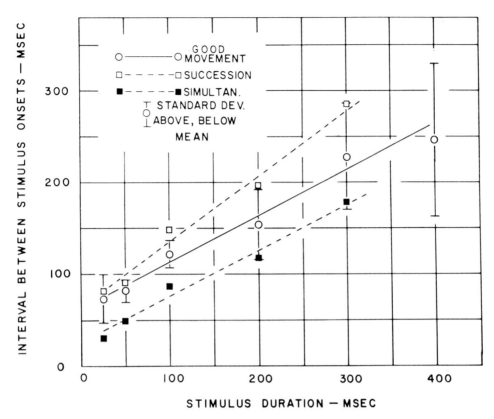

Figure 15-3. Plot of the mean values of burst onset interval for best movement as a function of burst duration (*open circles*). The *open squares* are mean values for successiveness of bursts, and the *filled squares* mean values for simultaneity of bursts. (Fig. 3, Sherrick, C. E. & Rogers, R., *Perception Psychophys.*, in press).

good movement, are acceptable temporal boundaries. Frequency and sensory magnitude of the stimuli do not appear to be critical, nor does body locus. If the space between vibrators gets large, good movement seems to become "smeared" in the center of its path, but near the stimuli it remains good. Finally, it appears that adding stimulus sources at spatial and temporal intervals that prolong the duration and course of movement tends to expand the boundaries given. Thus, a series of three or four stimuli from wrist to shoulder produce an impressive haptic movement that persists even when the intervals between stimuli are doubled or halved.

It would appear to be much simpler to try to validate Korte's laws for the skin then to make the qualitative description just presented, if one were interested in devising recipes for generating haptic illusions. It was for this purpose that I reviewed the literature on visual movement, to be sure that such relationships were valid for vision. In the course of my survey, I discovered the work of Neuhaus (1930) through Neff's review. Neuhaus put Korte's relationships to rigorous test with a very well constructed exposure apparatus, and discovered that only the stimulus duration, distance between stimuli, and interval between stimuli are closely interrelated. The significant relationship was found by Neuhaus to be that of stimulus duration and interval between stimuli, as Rogers had found for the skin.

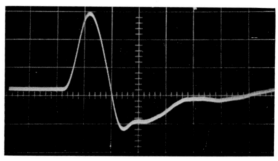

Figure 15-4. Oscillographic tracing of a transient pressure generated by impressing the rectified output of a simple tank circuit on the coil of the vibrator. Record made as in Figure 15-2. Time: each large graticule division is 2 msec (Fig. 4, Sherrick, C. E. & Rogers, R., *Perception Psychophys.,* in press) .

When I compared the values found by Neuhaus with those obtained in the present study, I was struck by their similarity over much of the range of values. Neuhaus found that the relationship between stimulus duration and onset intervals was not linear, as Figure 15-3 shows, but that it deviated at very short durations. Since I had no value comparable to Neuhaus's at these durations, I arranged to generate a unidirectional transient pressure as the lower extreme of the vibrotactile burst. Figure 15-4 illustrates the character of the transient, which feels like a tap. The four observers previously tested were presented with two taps at different loci and allowed to manipulate time between stimuli, as before, to obtain good movement. In Figure 15-5 the open circles and solid line summarize the data from Figure 15-3 plus the new value for the transient tap, which is the first point. The dashed lines and open squares show Neuhaus's data for visual apparent movement, obtained 36 years ago.

It seems safe to say from the data in the figure that the temporal conditions for good apparent movement are not modality-bound, and this suggests that one may find a similar set of values for apparent auditory motion. To my knowledge, no recent studies have been made of such realtionships in audition, but an interesting parallel arises from an earlier study of another perceptual phenomenon. In comparing the eye, ear, and skin for their temporal resolving powers, Ira Hirsh and I found that the modalities did not differ from one another in this capacity (Hirsh and Sherrick, 1961).

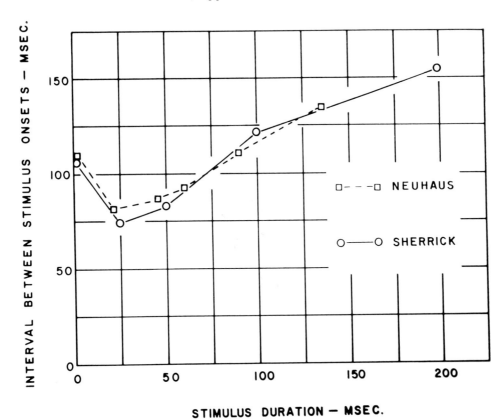

Figure 15-5. Plot of stimulus onset interval against stimulus duration for optimal move ment. *Open squares*, the data of Neuhaus for visual movement. *Open circles*, the present study (Fig. 5, Sherrick, C. E. & Rogers, R., *Perception Psychophys.*, in press).

When the observer was asked to judge the temporal order of two brief stimuli in whatever sense, he required about a 20 msec interval between them to be correct 75 per cent of the time. The following quotation is taken from that publication:

> To be sure, the time intervals used in the visual experiment lay in a range where sometimes apparent movement was seen and there the judgment of "which came first" may have been deduced from "in what direction did the light move" (Hirsh and Sherrick, 1961, p. 432).

This is not to imply that movement is a necessary condition for the perception of temporal order, nor that order must be perceived for movement to occur. These events coexist over a range of stimulus intervals, along with the perception of simultaneity, unordered duality, and clear successiveness. It would seem that for temporal order and movement, at least, the physiological correlates of the perceptual events may be found at some cortical level above the primary sensory area. Whether all these events are mediated at such a level, or whether the same temporal analyzer mechanism comprises the entire set of events, are questions I consign to the physiologist.

ACKNOWLEDGMENT

The author wishes to acknowledge the important pilot work of Ronald Rogers, whose diligence made later research more efficient.

REFERENCES

Benussi, V. Versuche zur Analyse taktil erweckter Scheinbewegungen. *Arch. Ges. Psychol.,* 1916, **36,** 59.

Boring, E. G. *Sensation and Perception in the History of Experimental Psychology.* New York: Century, 1942.

De Hardt, D. C. An investigation of tactual apparent movement. Doctoral dissertation, Michigan State Univer., 1961.

Frey, M. von, & Metzner, R. Die Raumschwelle der Haut bei Successivreizung. *Z. Psychol.,* 1902, **29,** 161.

Geldard, F. A. Cutaneous channels of communication. In W. Rosenblith (Ed.), *Sensory Communication.* New York: Wiley, 1961. Pp. 73-87.

Hall, G. S., & Donaldson, H. H. Motor sensations on the skin. *Mind,* 1885, **10,** 557.

Hirsh, I. J., & Sherrick, C. E. Perceived order in different sense modalities. *J. Exp. Psychol.,* 1961, **62,** 423.

Kenkel, F. Untersuchungen über den Zusammenhang zwischen Erscheinungsgrösse und Erscheinungsbewegung bei einigen sogenannten optischen Täuschungen. *Z. Psychol.,* 1913, **67,** 358.

Korte, A. Kinematoskopische Untersuchungen. *Z. Psychol.,* 1915, **72,** 193.

Nafe, J. P., & Wagoner, K. S. The nature of sensory adaptation. *J. Gen. Psychol.,* 1941, **25,** 295.

Neff, W. S. A critical investigation of the visual apprehension of movement. *Amer. J. Psychol.,* 1936, **48,** 1.

Neuhaus, W. Experimentelle Untersuchung der Scheinbewegung. *Arch. Ges. Psychol.,* 1930, **75,** 315.

Rogers, R. Apparent tactual movement: An experimental study. Senior thesis. Princeton Univer., 1964.

Sumby, W. H. An experimental study of vibrotactile apparent motion. Master's thesis. Univer. of Virginia, 1955.

Wertheimer, M. Experimentelle Studien über das Sehen von Bewegung. *Z. Psychol.,* 1912, **61,** 161.

DISCUSSION

Dr. R. H. Gibson: Did you have your subjects judge the quality of motion, in the last series of studies, or did you arbitrarily select the inter-stimulus interval?

Dr. Sherrick: Well, good movement is rather like being married, you are or you are not.

Dr. Gibson: I cannot agree because other data suggest there is considerable variation in the quality of movement. As a matter of fact, there are gradations of motion with the proper time between stimulus onsets and with the stimulus durations. Across a range of intervals of 25 to 200 msec, just how bad was motion? The fact that the subject sets a different time as optimal for motion for a 200 msec duration does not mean that there is very much of a difference in the character or intensity with these two time differences. These data do not tell you whether there is very much difference between the strengths of the motions.

DR. SHERRICK: Well, these data do not tell you anything about the strength of the motion. These data tell you that the individual was used as a null instrument in such a way that he was deciding that the movement was like that to which he was accustomed in the past, having acquired a standard over a period of 14 months.

DR. H. DAVIS: What is this movement that the subjects feel? Can you tell me a little more about it? Does it seem as though there is an object there that is doing it, or is it pure, disembodied sensation?

DR. SHERRICK: The movement has a vibratory character without the accompanying pressure sensation. It feels as though you took a vibrator with a smooth contact like a ball bearing and ran it down the arm.

DR. A. IGGO: Just a comment. You have been talking about these intervals between the onsets of vibratory stimulation. It was not clear whether the second one always started at some time after the first or whether, on occasion, these overlap.

DR. SHERRICK: They do overlap. If you compare the interval between onset and duration, you will see, for example, that at a 200 msec duration the interval between onsets was only 155 msec, so they overlapped by 45 msec at that point.

DR. IGGO: I was wondering what role this overlap has in determining the movement compared to the interval between onsets. But from what you say, I suppose it is the difference in onsets rather than the overlap interval which is important.

DR. SHERRICK: Interval between onsets, overlap, and duration are all interrelated in these experiments. If you plotted intervals between offset of the first stimulus and onset of the second stimulus against stimulus duration, you would get negative values at some duration, that is to say, overlap, of the offset-onset time difference. Basically, there is no difference in functional relation between this plot and the one I show in Figure 15-3.

DR. GIBSON: That question has been attacked directly. Jim Bliss and Ken Kotovsky (1963) used air jets to answer just this question in a study of apparent motion. They varied independently the duration of the first and the second stimuli as well as the interstimulus interval, finding that the overlap was extremely important. Not simply the time between onsets, and not simply the duration, but also the overlap has a lot to do with the motion; the greater the overlap, the less the motion. [Ed. note: Dr. Sherrick wishes to add the following to his discussion.]

DR. SHERRICK: I take advantage of my proof sheets to insert this reply to Dr. Gibson's comments. I have examined the Kotovsky and Bliss (1963) paper that you describe, and I wish to apologize for neglecting to mention their work. If you recalculate the values they obtained for good apparent movement, you will find no serious disagreement between their results and mine. This is true despite the facts that their stimuli were air pulses of undetermined character, and their procedures were designed primarily to elicit reports of temporal order. Temporal overlap, which Kotovsky and Bliss employed as an independent variable, has something to do with motion, but it fails as a controlling factor if the onsets of the two stimuli are simultaneous. Bliss and Crane (1965) have also pointed out the necessity for onset delays between stimulators (ISOIs, in other words) for good movement to occur.

References

Bliss, J. C., & Crane, H. D. Experiments in tactual perception. Final Report, Contract NAS 2-1679, NASA. Stanford Research Institute, 1965, p. 91.

Bliss, J. C., & Kotovsky, K. Tactual perception of visual information. Interim Report #1, prepared for Electronic Technology Laboratory, Wright Patterson AFB, by Stanford Research Institute, 1962, 1, 1-37.

Kotovsky, K., & Bliss, J. C. Tactual representation of visual information. *IEEE Trans. MIL-7*, **108**, 1963.

Chapter 16

THERMAL SENSITIVITY AND COMFORT*

A. Pharo Gagge and Joseph C. Stevens

T HE PURPOSE OF THE RESEARCH reported here is to learn more about how the experiences of comfort and discomfort depend upon the thermal characteristics of the environment. In these experiments, the subject lies in cool ambient air and is irradiated from above by a strong heat source. It is his task to indicate when he feels comfortable or uncomfortable and to make quantitative estimates of the degree of discomfort he experiences under various conditions. Two goals are implicit in this research: (a) to understand how the two environmental variables, ambient air temperature and the radiant heat absorbed by the subject, combine to exercise their effect on the subject's state of comfort (as we shall see later, a single variable called "operative temperature" can serve as an excellent physical basis describing the conditions that bring about comfort and discomfort), and (b) to obtain a psychophysical function that specifies how the degree of discomfort depends quantitatively on "operative temperature."

Two lines of research preceded the work reported here. The first is the intensive research by the engineering profession over the past fifty years. The earliest study was sponsored by the American Society of Heating and Ventilating Engineers (ASHVE), when the pioneer work, conducted by Houghton and Yaglou (1923a), led to an "effective temperature" scale. This scale is used (ASHRAE Guide, 1965-66) even to this date as an index of the combined thermal effect of dry and wet bulb temperatures. Under the dynamic conditions of their experiments, subjects walked between two rooms controlled at different dry and wet bulb temperatures and compared their sensations of comfort, warmth, and cold. Their studies showed that for a given ambient air temperature those with lower relative humidity appeared to be cooler than those with higher relative humidity. The effective temperature (ET) index developed by these authors combined into a single value the effects of dry bulb, humidity, and air motion on the sensations of warmth and cold and led to the concept of comfort zones and their relation to temperature sensation (Houghton and Yaglou, 1923b).

The original studies of Houghton and Yaglou and those to follow used category scales to estimate subjective reaction. The verbal sequence, most often used even to date, is "Cold," "Cool," "Slightly Cool," "Comfortable,"

*Partial support for the studies reported here was provided by the National Institutes of Health and the American Society of Heating, Refrigerating & Air-Conditioning Engineers.

"Slightly Warm," "Warm," "Hot." Thus comfort seems here to be defined simply as the absence of cold or warm sensation. "Comfortably Cool" or "Comfortably Warm" conditions, common in experience, seem to be ruled out.

In the mid-1930's, Winslow, Herrington, and Gagge (1937b) introduced the additional dimension of "pleasantness" and its various shadings toward "very unpleasant." Their work was primarily with unclothed subjects and was not strictly comparable to the earlier ASHVE studies where the subjects were clothed. However, this was an early attempt to describe thermal com-During the 1930's, Winslow, Herrington, and Gagge (1937a) intro-fort in terms of verbal categories that did not involve temperature sensations. duced the concept of "operative temperature" as a measure of the thermal stress of any radiant environment. When there are no sources of radiation present like the sun, a fireplace, a warm ceiling, or cold window, the ambient air temperature and the operative temperature would be identical. However, when radiation from such sources is present, the operative temperature would then be above or below the ambient temperature, depending on the nature of the radiating source. Operative temperature is defined as the temperature of an imaginary environment with which a subject would exchange the same heat by radiation and convection as he would in the actual environment concerned and represents an average of the wall and air temperature, weighted according to the respective energy transfer coefficients. It has recently been shown (Gagge, Hardy, and Rapp, 1965) that for conditions where humidity and air movement are constant, operative temperature may also be employed as a reliable index of comfort in environments where a source of high temperature radiant heat is present. Of particular interest in the present paper is the fact that radiant heat from a high temperature source is a rapid and experimentally easy method of changing the thermal stress on a subject. If this stress from radiant heat could be measured in terms of operative temperature, one would have a useful independent variable to study comfort and discomfort.

The second line of research relevant to the measurement of thermal comfort is the demonstration by S. S. Stevens (1960) that many sensory continua follow a general psychophysical law which states that the magnitude of sensation ψ grows as a power function of a stimulus magnitude, $\emptyset$; thus

$$\psi = k\emptyset^{\beta}, \tag{1}$$

where k depends on the choice of units and β is a constant whose value is characteristic of the sensory continuum concerned. Values of β vary from one continuum to another; thus β is as high as 3.5 for 60 Hz electric shock through the fingers and is as low as 0.33 for the brightness of a spot of white light viewed by the dark-adapted eye.

Departures from the original psychophysical law (equation 1) have frequently been observed in the close vicinity of the absolute threshold (Stevens and Stevens, 1961), and these have led to a refined version of the power law:

$$\psi = k\,(\emptyset - \emptyset_0)^{\beta}, \tag{2}$$

where $\emptyset_0$ stands for the value of the stimulus at the absolute threshold. The need for the threshold constant is strikingly demonstrated by the thermal continua* because throughout the range of permissible thermal stimulation $\emptyset_0$ is a sizeable portion of $\emptyset$. One of the primary goals of the present research was to learn the extent to which the growth of discomfort obeys the psychophysical power law as expressed in Equation 2.

DESCRIPTION OF TEST CHAMBER

The experiments were performed in a large air-conditioned test chamber 11' x 14' x 25'. The ambient air could be controlled from $-10°$ to $50°C$ dry bulb and from $5°$ to $40°C$ wet bulb. Air movement was turbulent and held to a constant level (25 cm/sec) by the proper adjustment of louvres.

The subject lay supine on a 30" x 84" bed, padded with foam rubber. The bed was mounted on a sensitive platform scale that measured the subject's weight loss, from which can be determined the heat loss caused by the evaporation of sweat.

Above the bed, as illustrated schematically in Figure 16-1, there was mounted a bank of eight T-3 infrared quartz lamps. The lamp filaments were 1.5 meters above the bed surface and so spaced that the irradiance over the surface of the subject was uniform within 10 per cent. The irradiance, I, was measured with a Hardy wide-angle radiometer (Hardy, Wolff, and Goodell, 1952, pp. 73-79) previously calibrated by a Bureau of Standards radiation lamp.

The intensity of the lamp bank could be controlled by a voltage regulator over the range, 0-280 v. As will be described later, the lamp bank was calibrated in terms of the radiant heat actually absorbed by the subject. The regulator itself was located by the bed near an observation window. The experimenter at this station could record directly judgments made by the subject, as well as adjust the lamp intensity.

MEASUREMENT OF THE ENVIRONMENTAL STIMULUS

In any experiment relating comfort to temperature, it is necessary to understand both the general heat balance of the subject and the relation-

---

*see Appendix

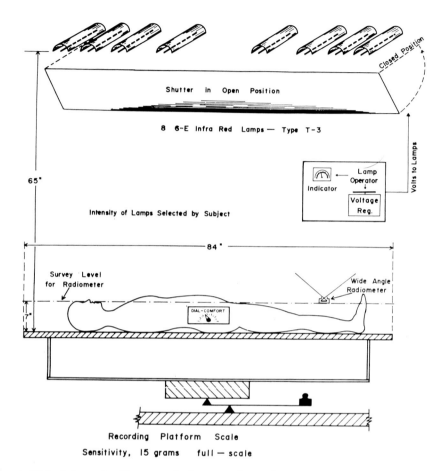

Figure 16-1. Schematic diagram of the experimental arrangement. The subject lies supine under a bank of 8 T-3 IR lamps. The irradiance, I, is measured by a Hardy wide-angle radiometer. The radiant heat absorbed (H_r) under certain conditions (see text) is directly proportional to the heat loss by evaporation of sweat, which is measured by the sensitive platform scale under the bed. In the Dial-Comfort studies, subjects without knowledge of the ambient temperature indicate to an operator the relative voltage level required for comfort.

ship between the combined effect of ambient air temperature, T_a, and of the voltage applied to the lamp bank. The single combined physical effect on the subject in terms of operative temperature must be assessed and related to what he describes as thermally comfortable. For this purpose, two experiments were performed as follows: (a) the evaporation loss caused by sweating was used to validate the direct measurement of the radiant heat absorbed; (b) for a range of ambient air temperatures, the subject was allowed to choose the voltage level to the lamps necessary for comfort.

Direct Measurement of Radiant Heat Absorbed

The radiant heat, H_r, in kcal/hr per sq meter of total body surface absorbed by the subject may be described by the relation

$$H_r = (aA_i I)/A \quad \text{or} \quad a \times A_i/A \times I, \tag{3}$$

where a =   the absorptivity of the skin,

A_i =   the effective area of the body surface irradiated in sq. meters,

I =   the irradiance received directly from the lamps and expressed in kcal/m²/hr,

and A =   the total body area of the subject which is calculated by the Dubois relation for body height and weight.

The term A_i, for a supine subject, may be evaluated by measuring his projected area on a horizontal plane. In the course of this study, the ratio of this irradiated area to the Dubois area A was measured for ten subjects and found to be 0.32 ± 0.02. The technique used was to place the subject on a large sheet of brown wrapping paper. An outline of his body was traced and cut out. The weight of the tracing was compared with that of a sq meter of the wrapping paper.

The term a, the absorptivity of the skin, varies with the voltage applied to the lamps. A typical calculation of a for the rated voltage of the lamps (240 v) is illustrated in Figure 16-2a. Figure 16-2b gives the overall relation of a to the voltage used and has been calculated for the corresponding color temperatures of the lamps, as specified by the manufacturer.

The irradiance, I, as measured by a wide-angle radiometer, varies as the square of the voltage or as the wattage to the lamps. The important quantity to be calculated for this study is the value of H_r in Equation 3, using the value 0.32 for A_i/A, the corresponding value of a for the voltage used (given in Fig. 16-2b), and the radiometric measure of I. These calculated and observed values have been combined in Figure 16-3 to give the value of H_r, the radiant heat absorbed for any applied voltage.

The heat balance equation for a subject supine on the bed is

$$M - E + H_r = h (T_s - T_a) \pm S, \tag{4}$$

where M =   metabolism in kcal/m²/hr,

E =   the evaporative loss in kcal/m²/hr,

H_r =   the radiant heat absorbed in kcal/hr per sq. meter of total area only,

T_s =   average skin temperature in °C,

T_a =   ambient air temperature in °C,

h = the effective heat transfer coefficient which describes
      how heat is lost to a uniform environment, T_a, by
      radiation and convection from the exposed skin surface
      and by conduction through the insulated bed,

and S = the residual body heating (+) or cooling (−) or
      storage when the heat received by the subject (left side
      of Equation 4) does not equal the heat transferred
      directly from the skin surface to the environment.

As one goes from a cool ambient temperature, T_a, to a warm ambient
temperature, there is a range of voltage over which a subject would be
"thermally neutral" (S = 0) ; and where the change in the evaporative
loss, E, would equal the change in H_r, the heat absorbed. In Figure 16-4,
values of E for four subjects have been plotted vs the value of H_r, derived

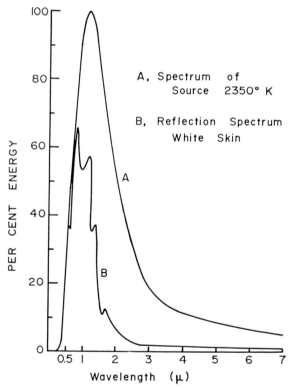

Figure 16-2A. Comparison of the spectrum of a T-3 lamp operating at 240 v (color
temperature 2,350°K) and the rieflection spectrum of white skin. The ratio of the
area under Curve B to the entire area under A represents the fraction, r, of the
energy source reflected from the skin. (1 - r) represents the fraction of the radiant energy
from lamps absorbed by the skin. As the voltage is lowered, the wavelength of maximum
intensity for this source moves to longer wavelengths and less energy is reflected by the
skin.

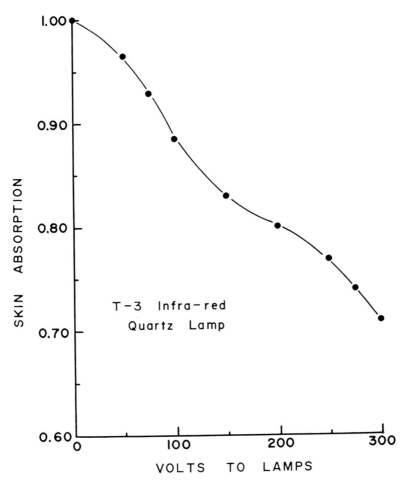

Figure 16-2B. Comparison of white skin absorption and voltage to lamp bank. Each point shown has been calculated by the method outlined in Figure 16-2A for the color temperature corresponding with the voltage indicated.

from the voltage calibration in Figure 16-3. It will be noticed that a linear relationship exists for the various air temperatures concerned, and the unit slope observed thus validates within a reasonable experimental scatter the calibration H_r voltage relationship in Figure 16-3.

A Physical Basis for Comfort

In a second experimental series, the subject was allowed to adjust the voltage across the lamps so that he was always comfortable regardless of the ambient air temperature. Under these circumstances, one would expect the resting subject to select conditions where a constant and desirable level exists for M, E, and T_s, and if body storage is also at a constant or zero level, there would be a linear relationship between the H_r, the radiant heat selected for comfort, and the corresponding ambient air temperature T_a. The slope of this relationship would be, incidentally, a direct measure of h, the heat transfer coefficient.

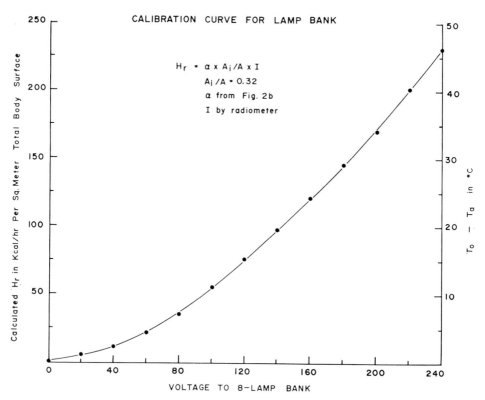

Figure 16-3. Calibration curve for lamp bank. The radiant heat absorbed by the skin is indicated for the voltage level on abscissa and includes the variation of skin absorption and irradiance from lamps with voltages. Because of the uneven contour of the human body, only 0.32 of the irradiance (vertical direction) is absorbed by the body. Since the heat transfer coefficient from the skin surface to the test chamber at uniform ambient temperature, T_a, is 5.0 kcal/m²/hr/°C, a scale, giving the difference between the operative temperature (for definition see text) and the ambient air temperature, has been added on the right ordinate.

For this "Dial-Comfort" test, the subject was placed on the bed in the test room at 28° to 30°C ambient, at which he would presumably be near "thermal neutrality," where there is no regulation by sweating or by vasoconstriction and where the body is in thermal equilibrium. Another starting level was in the range 10° to 12°C, which would be very cold. When this cold condition was used at the start, the subject was asked to seek his comfortable level immediately on entering the test room. It normally took 20 min for a

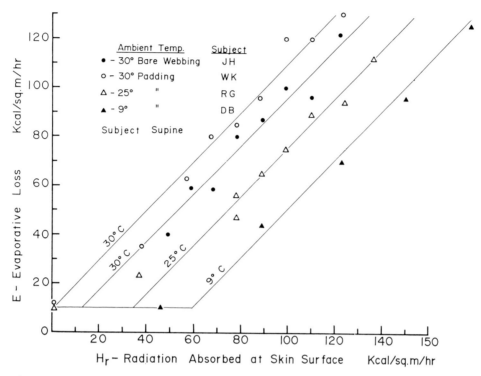

Figure 16-4. Variations of evaporative loss, E, with absorbed radiation, H_r, for various levels of ambient temperature, T_a. In the range where there is a unit slope between the observed evaporative loss, E, and the calculated radiant energy absorbed, the change in evaporative loss is a direct measure of the radiant heat absorbed.

subject to find his final level. After 20 min at the starting levels, whether at 30°C or about 10°C, the ambient temperature of the room was steadily raised or lowered at a rate of 0.4°C/min. During these changes, the subject was asked to maintain a comfortable level.

The observations plotted in Figure 16-5 represent the heat required for the corresponding ambient air temperature when the subject made a change in the voltage regulator. The slopes for each subject have been drawn at a value of 5.0 kcal/m²/hr/°C, a value for h found for supine subjects by direct partitional calorimetrical methods (Winslow, Herrington, and Gagge, 1936). Observations for subjects, DB, WK, and JH agree with this slope value very well. For subject RG, the points for decreasing ambient temperature lie above those for increasing ambient temperature. However, those points for rising T_a follow well a line with slope of 5.0 and lie in the same range as those for WK.

Of particular interest for the latter part of this paper is the relationship of the "dial-comfort" lines to operative temperature. Operative tempera-

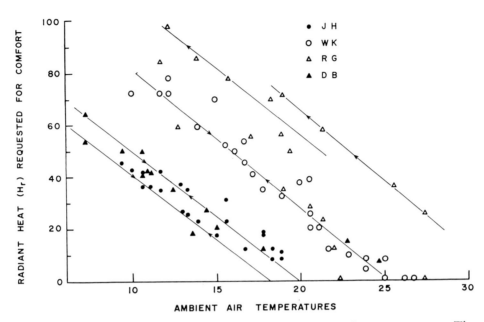

Figure 16-5. Radiant heat requested for comfort at various ambient temperatures. The same four subjects in Figure 16-4 were allowed to choose the voltage level for comfort as the ambient temperature was raised and lowered at a rate of 0.3°C/min. For subjects RG and JH, the ambient air temperature was changed from warm to cold and back to warm. For subjects DB and WK, the ambient air temperature was raised from cold to warm and back to cold.

ture (Winslow *et al.*, 1937) is defined as the temperature of an imaginary environment in which a subject would lose the same net heat from the body at the same transfer rate as he would in the actual environment. Thus for any operative temperature the heat-balance Equation 4 becomes

$$M - E \pm S = h\,(T_s - T_o),\qquad(5)$$

where h is the heat transfer coefficient identical to that used in Equation 4 for a uniform ambient environment at T_a. T_s is the same average skin temperature given in Equation 4. From Equation 4 and Equation 5, it follows

$$T_o = T_a + H_r/h.\qquad(6)$$

When there is no radiant heat, operative temperature, T_o, is equal to the ambient temperature T_a. Using the above value for h, confirmed by the dial-comfort experiments, Equation 6 states that for the supine subject on an insulated bed 5 kcal/m²/hr of absorbed radiant heat are necessary to raise the operative temperature each °C above the ambient temperature. Further, in Figure 16-5, the loci for equal comfort in terms of H_r and T_a

describe, according to Equation 6, lines of constant operative temperature T_o. The intercept of these lines with the abscissa represents the actual level of operative temperature selected by subjects for comfort.

As has been reported elsewhere (Gagge *et al.*, 1965), the dial-comfort lines in Figure 16-5 represent a unique characteristic for each individual concerned. Unclothed subjects differ widely but consistently in their choice of a locus for comfort, described by T_o. From Figure 16-5, it can be seen that the values for comfortable T_o vary from 18° for JH to 30° for RG.

Comfortable T_o's, as high as 40°C with ambient T_a at 15°C, have been observed for a paraplegic (Winslow *et al.*, 1936), who had no temperature sensation in his lower extremities. In general, a subject like RG, who reported he preferred warm conditions in everyday life, consistently selected the relatively warmer T_o conditions as comfortable. Subjects like JH and DB consistently chose the relatively cooler T_o conditions as comfortable.

When the metabolic level is about 40 kcal/m²/hr, the zone of "thermal neutrality" lies between 27° and 28°C, when the heat transfer coefficient is 5.0 kcal/m²/hr/°C. From the intersections of the line with the abscissa in Figure 16-5, it appears that subject WK chose a comfort level in the expected thermally neutral range. Subject RG, at 30°C, preferred slight sweating as the ambient temperature was initially lowered from 25°C; however, when the ambient temperature was raised from 12°C, he selected a thermally neutral level for T_o. Subjects JH and DB consistently chose the cooler levels, where there was probably body cooling at a rate of 25 kcal/m²/hr or 0.3°C/hr. The basal metabolic rate for the four subjects indicated an average level of 41 kcal/m²/hr with an upper value of 42 for WK and lower of 38 for JH.

A second scale has been added on the right side of Figure 16-3 to indicate the difference, T_o–T_a that corresponds to H_r calculated by Equation 1 and a heat transfer coefficient h = 5.0 kcal/m²/hr. The calibration curve in Figure 16-3 may now be used to calculate T_o for any ambient temperature T_a and lamp voltage.

The dial-comfort method thus gives a quantitative physical measure of comfort in terms of an operative temperature. This temperature is applicable principally to the present supine position, where the heat transfer coefficient to the ambient air is 5.0 kcal/m²/hr/°C.

SCALING OF THERMAL DISCOMFORT

In the previous section, it was demonstrated how any comfortable condition may be described physically by an operative temperature T_o, which represents the combined effect of ambient air temperatures and of the radiant heat absorbed by the body from the lamps. It was shown, too, that the T_o level chosen for comfort may not always be one actually associated with "thermal neutrality," where there is neither body cooling nor active sweating, but subjects may even prefer conditions that involve slight sweating or slight body cooling. The level chosen for comfort may also serve as an initial estimate of the value for $\emptyset_o$, the threshold for discomfort, as used in the psychophysical law expressed in Equation 2.

The purpose of the present experiment was to learn whether the experience of discomfort, as related to operative temperature, obeys the same psychophysical power law that describes the growth of sensation on so many perceptual continua. The subjects were asked to assign numbers proportional to the amount of discomfort produced by successive exposures to a wide range of operative temperatures from very cool to very warm. For each level, the subject was first to say whether he felt warm or cold but then to estimate the discomfort without regard to whether it was produced by warm or cold stimulation.

The ambient temperature and relative humidity of the test chamber described above were held constant at approximately 8°C and 40 per cent RH throughout the experiment. By varying the voltage across the radiant lamps, it was possible to raise the operative temperature of the subject's environment from a cold 8°C to a hot 68°C.

Eight young male subjects took part in the present series, including the same four used in the standardization experiments reported above. Each subject undressed in a comfortably warm adjoining room. Upon entering the chamber, the lamps were set at a value that prevented the subject from getting unnecessarily chilled during the preliminary preparations. The subject was blindfolded and lay supine. During the 15-min period prior to the run, the subject was asked periodically whether the voltage should be raised or lowered for comfort. After the experimenter was satisfied that the subject had reached his "comfortable" T_o level, the subject was exposed, one by one, to several operative temperatures above, and below, and equal to the operative temperature just judged to be comfortable. Each level was presented for a 2 min period twice in the course of the test session, except that an operative temperature of 30° above the neutral was given only once at the end of the session in order to avoid overheating the body. The first level was always a cold one, and thereafter warm and cold levels were generally alternated. Otherwise, the levels were presented in irregular order with respect to temperature. This procedure was designed to prevent the occurrence of a net heating or cooling of the body over the course of the test session. Recordings of the tympanic temperature throughout the session for some of the subjects showed that no major systematic effects of this kind took place.

When the operative temperature was changed abruptly from one level

to another, the degree of discomfort changed much more gradually. Preliminary research indicated that a reasonably stable state of discomfort was
reached within a minute or two following any of the changes used in this
experiment. For this reason, a 2 min exposure period was chosen. The
subject was asked to judge the discomfort experienced during the last 15
sec of this 2 min period.

In Figure 16-6, the means of the numerical estimates of discomfort have
been plotted in log-log coordinates as a function of the difference (whether
negative or positive) between the actual exposure T_o and the operative

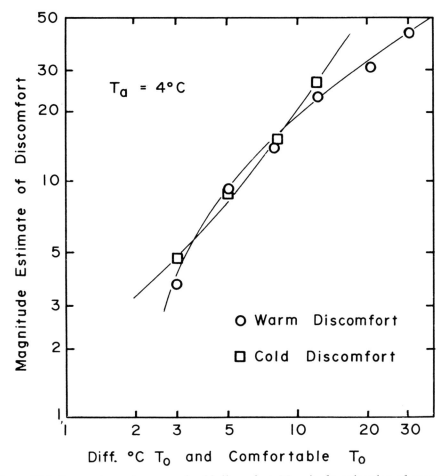

Figure 16-6. Comparison of warm and cold discomfort. Magnitude estimation of apparent
discomfort produced by exposing the body to warmth and cold. The points stand for
the means of the estimates of eight subjects. The abscissa is the difference in °C between
the operative temperature of the exposure and the operative temperature $\emptyset_o$ that was
determined to feel comfortable at the start of the experimental session. The average value
of $\emptyset_o$ was found to be 20°C. The coordinates are logarithmic.

temperature that was determined to feel comfortable for each subject at the start of the test session. (The average of these determinations of $\emptyset_o$ was 20°C, but the range was from 16° to 23°C for these eight subjects.) Two different functions appear to be generated in these coordinates, one for the warm, the other for the cold levels. That both functions depart from linearity in these coordinates would seem, at first glance, to show that discomfort does not obey the psychophysical power law. However, the concave curvature for warmth and the convex curvature for cold strongly suggest that the effective value of the threshold $\emptyset_o$ may have been on the average slightly higher than those indicated by the determinations at the beginning of the session. The probable operative temperature level for "dial-comfort" is certainly higher than 20°C (Gagge and Rawson, unpublished). Moreover, the same levels, thought to be neutral at the start, were frequently judged to be cold later in the session. One explanation for this change is that these sessions were held in warm summer weather. Small upward shifts in the neutral temperature may have occurred so that an environment that felt pleasantly cool during the first part of the session began to feel slightly uncomfortable with extended exposure.

The question arises how the dial-comfort values for T_o for the four subjects WK, DB, JH, and RG compare with the initial "threshold" T_o measured before the magnitude estimations were made. Table 16-I shows the comparison.

TABLE 16-I

Subject	Dial-Comfort Series	Mag. Est. $\emptyset_o$ Series
WK	25°	23°
DB	20°	17°
JH	18°	18°
RG	25°	23°

For the two tests done at least two weeks apart, there was reasonable consistency.

On the assumption that the average effective neutral temperature ($\emptyset_o$) was actually about 22°C, rather than 20°C as initially thought, the average magnitude estimates now generate two good approximations to power functions, as shown in Figure 16-7. A shift of 2°C simultaneously rectifies the concavity of one function and the convexity of the other. The equations of the two functions are

$$D_c = 0.33 \ (22 - T_o)^{1.66}, \tag{7}$$

and

$$D_w = 4.1 \ (T_o - 22)^{0.77}, \tag{8}$$

where T_o is measured in °C and D_c and D_w stand for the discomfort produced by cold and warm respectively in identical but arbitrary units.

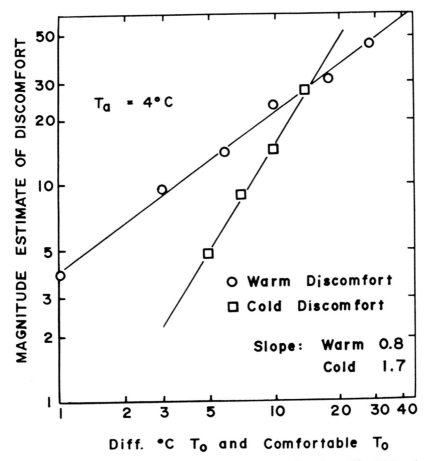

Figure 16-7. The mean estimates of thermal discomfort (taken from Fig. 16-6) plotted
as a function of a revised stimulus scale. Here the abscissa is the difference between the
operative temperature of the exposure and the operative temperature that was believed
to be the effective comfortable level (22°C, rather than 20°C), during the experimental
session. The coordinates are logarithmic.

Figure 16-7 and Equations 7 and 8 suggest that the degree of discomfort
grows faster with respect to temperature deviations below the comfortable
level than to deviations above the comfortable level, as reflected in the
difference between the two exponents (slopes). On the other hand, a small
deviation above the comfortable level may create greater discomfort than
the same deviation below the comfortable level, as reflected in the smaller
intercept value for cold. The same amount of discomfort is produced at

about 14° above or below the comfortable level, where the two functions intersect. Beyond 14°, the cold deviations would appear to be more uncomfortable than the warm.

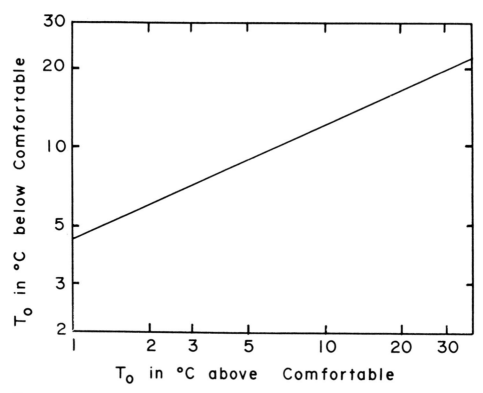

Figure 16.8. The "equal-discomfort" contour. The straight line in the log-log coordinates links the warm and cold exposure levels that produce the same degree of thermal discomfort. The average operative temperature assumed to feel comfortable ($\emptyset_o$) is 22°C.

With the aid of Equations 7 and 8, it is also possible to construct an "equal-discomfort contour," shown in Figure 16-8 that relates operative temperatures that produce the same degree of discomfort above and below the comfortable level. Its equation is the power function

$$22 - T_o = 4.56 \ (T_o - 22)^{0.43}, \tag{9}$$

where $22 - T_o$ is the distance below the comfortable level (assumed to equal 22°C) and $T_o - 22$ is the distance above the comfortable level.

The procedure used in the magnitude estimate experiments for discomfort presented several difficulties. For one thing, a delay of 2 min between judgments places a great burden on the memory. In typical psychophysical scaling experiments, the stimuli may follow one another at intervals of only 5 or 10 sec. For another thing, the long test session, necessitated by the long exposures, places both physical and psychological stress on the subject, compounding the difficulty of making accurate estimations of thermal discomfort. Discomfort, other than the thermal kind, may begin to appear after, say, 30 min of lying still and flat on one's back.

These problems are spelled out in order to underscore the fact that the results of a single attempt to quantify thermal discomfort must be regarded as preliminary and suggestive. Despite several difficulties, the subjects in these experiments were able to make reasonably orderly quantitative judgments of the discomfort experienced, and these results may be meaningfully related to a large body of facts in the area of psychophysical scaling. It is nevertheless encouraging that the results obtained seem, at least to a first approximation, to obey the general psychophysical power law.

The approximately twofold difference between the exponents of the two power functions for discomfort is a prominent and, in one sense, unexpected result of this study. For thermal sensations (see Appendix) aroused by brief stimulation of a small area of the forearm, the exponent for warmth (1.6) turned out under several tests to be larger than that for cold (1.0), which relationship is opposite to the above findings for warm and cold discomfort. Thus it is interesting to note that the psychophysical functions for these localized sensations behave quite differently from the discomfort functions obtained under prolonged exposure of the whole body.

CONCLUSIONS

A subject can make a clear and consistent judgment of his own state of comfort. Moreover, the combinations of ambient temperature and radiant heat that maintain a state of comfort can be stated in terms of a single physical index called the operative temperature.

As a function of operative temperature, the growth of thermally caused discomfort obeys the same psychophysical power law that governs a large number of sensory continua.

The two power functions obtained, one for warm conditions and the other for cold conditions, illustrate that the stimulus level must be measured relative to an operative temperature level judged to feel comfortable.

Differences between the constants of the two power functions indicate that cold and warm environments may operate in different ways to produce discomfort.

APPENDIX

The following is a brief description of an experimental study of the continua of warm and cold sensations described by Stevens and Stevens

(1963). This study illustrates how Equation 2 in the preceding text is used. The method will be useful in understanding the application of the psychophysical law to sensory data.

In two experiments, cylindrical metal stimuli were periodically touched briefly (3 sec) to a small area of the forearm (20 mm in diameter). The subject's instruction was to assign numbers proportional to the degree of subjective warmth (first experiment) or the subjective cold (second experiment) aroused by a set of

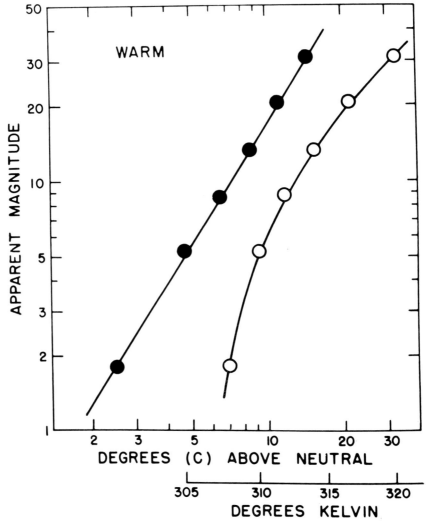

Figure 16-9. Magnitude estimation of apparent warmth. Each point stands for the geometric mean of 36 estimates (12 0_s). The upper abscissa, for the filled points, is a logarithmic scale of the difference in temperature between the stimulus and the assumed physiological zero (32.5°C). The lower abscissa, for the unfilled points, is a logarithmic scale of the absolute temperature (Kelvin).

stimuli. These were spaced at 8 sec intervals and in irregular order with respect to temperature, and they ranged from near thermally indifferent to near thermally painful.

The average results for a dozen observers are plotted in Figure 16-9 (warmth) and Figure 16-10 (cold). The coordinates were both chosen to be logarithmic because in log-log coordinates a power function plots as a straight line, whose slope equals numerically the value of the exponent β. Each graph has two abscissae (both logarithmic), of which the lower is the temperature in degree on the Kelvin scale. As a function of this Kelvin scale, the subjective estimates generate curves having concave-downward shapes. With respect to degrees Kelvin, it is clear that neither warmth nor cold grows as a power function. When, however, the temperature of thermal indifference $\emptyset_0$ (about 32.5°C for the forearm) is subtracted from the temperature of the stimulus, i.e., when the stimulus is reckoned to be a scale of degrees of deviation above or below the temperature that feels neutral (upper abscissae), then the subjective estimates determine a pair of straight lines. Neither the linearity nor the slopes of these functions will depend on the choice of the scale of temperature — provided that the temperature that feels neutral is subtracted from each stimulus temperature.

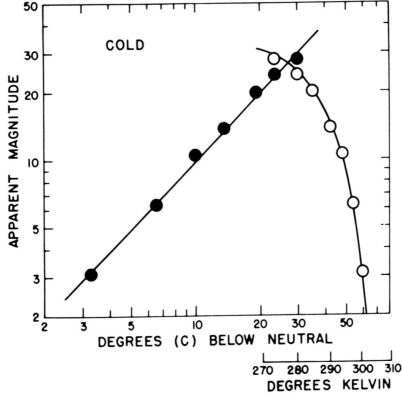

Figure 16-10. Magnitude estimation of apparent cold. Each point stands for the geometric mean of 26 estimates (13 0_s). The upper abscissa is a logarithmic scale of the difference in temperature between the stimulus and the assumed physiological zero (31.0°C). The lower abscissa is a logarithmic scale of the absolute temperature (Kelvin).

This outcome means that warmth and cold both obey the general psycho-physical power law. The striking role of the threshold constant $\emptyset_0$ reflects the fact that in terms of the physical scale of temperature the value of $\emptyset_0$ is a sizeable portion of $\emptyset$ throughout the stimulus range. On no other sensory continuum is the need for the threshold correction so easily demonstrable.

The slopes (exponents) turned out to be about 1.0 for cold and about 1.6 for warmth. Thus, cold sensation appears to grow approximately in proportion to the size of the temperature drop below the neutral; warm sensation, however, grows as an accelerating function of temperature rises above the neutral. It is possible, therefore, to distinguish the two continua not only by quality but also by a difference in their "operating characteristic."

REFERENCES

ASHRAE Guide & Data Book for 1965 - 66. Chap. 7, Fig. 12, P. 113.

Gagge, A. P., Hardy, J. D., & Rapp, G. M. Exploratory studies on comfort for high temperature sources of radiant heat. *ASHRAE Trans.*, 1965.

Hardy, J. D., Wolff, H. G., & Goodell, H. *Pain Sensations and Reactions.* Baltimore: Williams & Wilkins, 1952.

Houghton, F. C., & Yaglou, C. P. Determining lines of equal comfort. *ASHVE Trans.*, 1923, **29**, 163. (a)

Houghton, F. C., & Yaglou, C. P. Determination of the comfort zone. *ASHVE Trans.*, 1923, **29**, 361. (b)

Stevens, J. C., & Stevens, S. S. Physiological zero and the psychophysical law. In *Proc. 16th Inat'l Congress of Psychology.* Amsterdam: North-Holland, 1961. Pp. 192-193.

Stevens, J. C., & Stevens, S. S. Warmth and cold: Dynamics of sensory intensity. *J. Exp. Psychol.*, 1963, **66**, 177.

Stevens, S. S. The psychophysics of sensory function. *Amer. Sci.*, 1960, **48**, 226.

Winslow, C-E. A., Herrington, L. P., & Gagge, A. P. A new method of partitional calorimetry. *Amer. J. Physiol.*, 1936, **116**, 641.

Winslow, C-E. A., Herrington, L. P., & Gagge, A. P. Physiological reactions of the human body to varying environmental temperatures. *Amer. J. Physiol.*, 1937, **120**, 1. (a)

Winslow, C-E. A., Herrington, L. P., & Gagge, A. P. Relations between atmospheric conditions, physiological reactions, and sensations of pleasantness. *Amer. J. Hyg.*, 1937, **26**, 103. (b)

DISCUSSION

Dr. Y. Zotterman: I am not familiar with this approach to the effects of temperature on man, but I have worked on temperature for a while in my laboratory. The question which I have is, what sensory mechanism do you think is operating which results in thermal comfort or discomfort? We have several possibilities; the cutaneous temperature receptors on the body surface, and the centrally situated sense cells in the hypothalamic region which are sensitive to temperature.

Dr. Gagge: Comfort may involve an interplay between many physiological mechanisms. We have no clear answer to give you as yet. We have some unpublished data showing an excellent correlation between comfort and evaporative heat loss. For the short-time stimulations reported here, we find tympanic temperature has little correlation with our measurements of discomfort. Skin temperature has an excellent correlation with discomfort, especially toward the cold, but is not as good towards the warm. We are really in a beginning stage of this study, as this is the first time we have ever been able to measure discomfort quantitatively. Up to the present, judgments of comfort have always been in terms of verbal categories, which defy quantification.

DR. ZOTTERMAN: I am very much interested to know to what extent the central mechanism participates in thermal comfort.

DR. GAGGE: Dr. Benzinger (1963) has made the suggestion that internal body temperature is the best index of comfort towards the warm conditions.

DR. H. HENSEL: If one considers constant temperatures, thermal sensations do not obey the power law at all. If we look at the discharge of thermal receptors, and plot frequency of nerve discharge as a function of the maintained temperature, then we have a curve which starts at a certain temperature, and as we raise the temperature we get more impulses, and then, with further temperature increase, the curve goes down again. This does not look very much like a power function. [Ed. note: See Hensel (1952).] This, I think, corresponds quite well with subjective sensation. At very cold temperatures you have less cold sensation than at higher temperatures and then as the temperature continues to increase, the cold sensation decreases again. I do not understand how this can be described by a power law.

DR. GAGGE: I imagine if all the neurons worked simultaneously you may get a curve as you suggest, but unfortunately, with several million of them working at random times, they may sum up a power function. Dr. Stevens may have a direct answer to your question.

DR. STEVENS: The psychophysical law, Dr. Hensel, that has been proposed by S. S. Stevens is not intended to describe the behavior of individual neurons. It may do so in some sensory systems, and I think that it has been demonstrated to do so, but the psychophysical law is intended to describe the overall input-output characteristic of the sensory system. Incidentally, our measurements of warmth and cold have shown that these do obey a power law, although the exponents of the two modalities are different.

DR. HENSEL: The curve which I described holds also for the total discharge of cold receptors, not only for the individual neurons. It has the same general shape. The total discharge goes up when the temperature falls, and if temperature is lowered further, then it goes down again, and finally it reaches zero. This holds for the total input from cold receptors. This is one question. Sensation behaves in a similar way. The power law may hold in a restricted range of temperatures, but if you decrease the temperature further, then the cold sensation will decrease. I think you did not investigate the low range of temperatures, otherwise you would have found that the power law does not hold.

DR. STEVENS: I would be curious to know how far below the normal skin temperature you expect this reversal in cold sensation magnitude to occur.

DR. HENSEL: I think about 15° to 17°C. You should try this.

DR. STEVENS: We went down about 30°C below the neutral temperature and we did not find any deviation from the power law.

DR. HENSEL: Yes, but I guess you did not make your measurements at constant skin temperature. You used temperature changes. It is a matter of definition of what your stimulus is. I would also say a power function is a matter of definition of what a stimulus should be. If you say absolute temperature is an adequate stimulus, then you do not find a power function at all. If you say temperature change is a stimulus, then it might obey a power law.

DR. STEVENS: That is a good statement, but it is general.

DR. A. J. H. VENDRIK: Would you tell me about the time of exposure? You used 2 min, I think, and after that the subject had to state the number of discomfort he feels.

DR. GAGGE: The last 15 sec of the 2 min exposure.

DR. VENDRIK: Does the duration of the exposure make a difference? You cannot expect to obtain a steady state in 2 min. That means that you can have only a certain skin temperature but nothing which affects the central regulating temperature center. What happens when you increase the time of exposure to a particular radiant heat and ambient temperature?

DR. GAGGE: We did some preliminary experiments on your point. We tried 1 min, 2 min, and 10 min exposures. We found that there was very little difference between the pattern of voting between the 2 min and 10 min exposures. Since we made 36 judgments per session, a use of 10 min for each exposure would have caused the subject to be uncomfortable for a very long period. Also, if you observe the skin temperature with a radiometer during the heating cycle, after a 2 min exposure the skin temperature would have practically leveled off.

DR. P. D. WALL: The experimental situation which you describe is one, I think, which is pretty familiar to residents of Great Britain, who live through the winter in rooms with a single source of radiation and with a low air temperature. I wonder if your comfort index might not be a minimization of two discomforts. I think you said 32 per cent of the body surface is being radiated. What happens if you go to either 100 per cent or very much smaller values?

DR. GAGGE: You could never get a 100 per cent exposure lying on a bed, but we have worked on a man sitting in a chair being radiated from each side, and we have obtained very similar results. I might point out that dial comfort curves for the threshold are characteristic of the particular man. Some men, like subject J. H., always chose cold conditions (e.g., 18°C) as comfortable. He is the type that sleeps in a room with the window open and without a blanket.

References

Benzinger, T. H. Peripheral cold- and central warm-reception, main origins of human thermal discomfort. *Proc. Nat. Acad. Sci.,* 1963, **49**, 832.

Hensel, H. Physiologie der Thermoreception. *Ergebn. Physiol.,* 1952, **47**, 166.

Chapter 17

NEURAL AND PSYCHOPHYSICAL RESPONSES TO GUSTATORY STIMULI*

G. Borg,† H. Diamant, L. Ström and Y. Zotterman

BY A FREAK OF NATURE THE gustatory fibers to the anterior part of the tongue depart from the lingual nerve and run as the chorda tympani via its own bone channel through the middle ear where, in most human subjects, it runs quite free. Thus it is possible during operations on the middle ear, when the drum is laid aside, to place an electrode on this nerve and to record the summated electrical response to the application of various sapid solutions to the tongue of the patient. From 1958 to 1962, successful experiments of this kind were carried out at the Ear Clinic of Karolinska Sjukhuset during operations undertaken in order to mobilize the stapes in cases of otosclerosis. These early investigations gave valuable information about the relation between the strength of the gustatory stimulus and the recorded summated response from the human chorda to various taste solutions (Diamant, Funakoshi, Ström, and Zotterman, 1963).

Working on human subjects offers the possibility of collecting information not only of the relationship between the gustatory stimulus and the peripheral neural response, but also about the relation between the neural and psychophysical responses.

This report presents the results of such combined investigations made at the Department of Otorhinolaryngology at Umeå University since 1963 when one of us (H. D.) was appointed head of that clinic. Most of these results were recently printed in *Acta Physiologica Scandinavica* (Diamant, Oakley, Ström, Wells, and Zotterman, 1965) and in the second volume of *Olfaction and Taste* (Borg, Diamant, Oakley, Ström, and Zotterman, 1966), and will be discussed here together with some more recent data.

METHODS

Subjects

In all, 18 cases of otosclerosis were examined at Umeå in January, April, and October, 1964, in February and October, 1965 and in February, 1966. Chemical solutions used were described recently (Diamant *et al.*, 1965).

*This investigation has been supported by grants from Svenska Maltdrycksforskningsinstitutet and from Statens Medicinska Forskningsråd.

†The authors are from the Department of Otorhinolaryngology, University of Umeå and the Department of Physiology, Veterinärhögskolan, Stockholm 50, Sweden.

Neural Recording

The special precautions to be taken in an unscreened operation room in a big hospital and a description of the summator circuit used have been previously described (Diamant *et al.*, 1965).

Psychophysical Tests

The tests applied for the first six patients (in 1964) were described in a previous report (Diamant *et al.*, 1965). In the more recent experiments ratio scaling methods were used (Ekman, 1961). These methods require that the subjects can understand figures and can make ratio estimations. They also had to make estimations of surfaces of different sizes so that we could screen out those patients who obviously could not make ratio estimations. Five patients of 12 were, thus, left for psychophysical experiments.

Two days before the operation, psychophysical taste experiments with NaCl and citric acid were carried out on the patients. The same stimuli and the same order of presentation were used in the electrophysiological experiments. As a psychophysical method, the "magnitude estimation" method was used. In the first series 0.12 M and in the two following series 0.08 M were used as the standard and called "10." In the last four patients 0.30 M NaCl was used as "10." The stimuli were presented in pairs, the standard with one of the comparative stimuli.

RESULTS

Of 18 patients tested in these experiments fairly satisfactory neural responses from the chorda were obtained in ten cases. In three cases we did not obtain any response at all from the nerve, and in the other five cases the responses were too weak or there were to many disturbances of various kinds, preventing a proper analysis of the records.

The summated chorda tympani nerve response to a 0.2 M NaCl solution will be seen in Figure 17-1. The decline in neural activity in response to a continuous flow of salt solution over the tongue for 3 min may be seen in the records A, B and C from three different subjects. The initial large response to the application of the salt solution is indicated by an arrow, while the application of distilled water is indicated by a dot above the records. The responses to water here were due to cooling and mechanical stimulation. In patient A the response was 95 per cent adapted within 50 sec. In addition to the three records shown here, the adaptation of the salt response in patient 4 and 6 was very similar to that shown in A and C. There is a very distinct contrast between the records of human neural adaptation and that of record D which is taken from the rat's chorda tympani. In the latter record the response declines very slowly over a 3 min

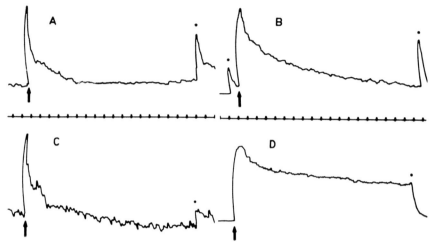

Figure 17-1. The summated chorda tympani response to a continuous 3 min flow of 0.2 M NaCl. A, B and C are human responses for patients 1, 2, 3 respectively and D is a rat response. Arrows indicate the onset of saline solution and dots indicate response during application of distilled water. Tape recorded data were processed under identical conditions with rise and fall time constants of 1.5 sec. The tape recorder was off at beginning of B. Time base is in 10 sec intervals (Fig. 2, Diamant, H., Oakley, B., Ström, L., Wells, C., & Zotterman, Y., *Acta Physiol. Scand.*, 1965, **64**, 67).

period and little or no further decline in amplitude is seen (Beidler, 1953; Zotterman, 1956). Patient 3, whose neural response is seen in record C, indicated in the psychophysical test that the salt taste disappeared after 90 sec. Patient 4 indicated that he could no longer taste salt after 79 sec, which corresponded to a 95 per cent reduction in the magnitude of his neural response.

Cameron (1947) has shown that there are rather substantial individual differences in the gustatory sensitivity to sweet tasting substances. Thus, it is of little value to compare the nerve responses of individual patients with the psychophysical responses obtained from other subjects. In our studies we were able to obtain both psychophysical magnitude estimates of the relative sweetness of different chemicals and summated electrical chorda tympani responses to these same chemicals (Table 17-I). The values in each column were rounded off to the nearest 5 per cent and are relative to the response to 0.5 M sucrose, which has been set at 100. The psychophysical reports are means of two determinations, while the neural values are based upon a single determination. The correspondence between the psychophysical and the neural data seems quite good, especially for the sugars. The artificial sweeteners, saccharin and cyclamate, have qualitatively different tastes from the sugars and this may have affected the judgments of the sweetness. The psychophysical method used with patient 4 produced the better agreement.

TABLE 17-I
COMPARISON OF PSYCHOPHYSICAL AND NEURAL RESPONSE
TO SWEET TASTING SUBSTANCES
The values in each column are relative to 0.5 M sucrose set at 100.
The maximum height of the summator record was measured.

| | | | Patient 3 | | Patient 4 | |
Stimulus			Psy	Neur	Psy	Neur
0.5	M	sucrose	100	100	100	100
0.5	M	fructose	100	100	80	80
0.5	M	maltose	—	40	75	60
0.5	M	galactose	40	45	45	40
0.5	M	lactose	45	45	30	30
0.5	M	glucose	25	45	35	40
0.004	M	Na saccharin	100	65	125	105
0.03	M	Na cyclamate	55	80	115	100

(Table I, Diamant, H., Oakley, B., Ström, L., Wells, C., & Zotterman, Y., *Acta Physiol. Scand.*, 1965, 64, 67)

TABLE 17-II
INDIVIDUAL DIFFERENCES IN THE CHORDA TYMPANI DISCHARGE
The values in each column are relative to 0.5 M Sucrose set at 100.
The maximum height of the summator record was measured.

| Stimulus | | | Patient no. | | | |
			1	2	3	4
0.5	M	sucrose	100	100	100	100
0.2	M	NaCl	105	100	150	50
0.02	M	citric acid	155	195	60	100
0.004	M	Na saccharin	50	70	65	105
0.03	M	Na cyclamate	90	120	80	100

(Table II, Diamant, H., Oakley, B., Ström, L., Wells, C., & Zotterman, Y., *Acta Physiol. Scand.*, 1965, 64, 67)

It was also found that there is a significant individual variation in the response of the chorda tympani to different sapid substances. A comparison of the neural response of patients 3 and 4 in Table 17-I gives an indication of the individual variation for the sugars and artificial sweeteners. Diamant *et al.* (1963) obtained still another order of the neural responses in one patient. In Table 17-II individual differences for other chemicals are presented relative to the response to a 0.5 M sucrose solution which has been given the value 100. It is quite obvious that there is a wide variation in responsiveness to the different chemicals. For example, patient 3 had a poor response to 0.2 M NaCl, and patient 2 had a very good response to 0.02 M citric acid.

The result of a psychophysical group experiment made on 14 young students is seen in Figure 17-2. A straight line may be very nicely adjusted to the psychophysical responses to citric acid when plotted in log-log coordinates. A simple power function, $R = cM^n$, with $n = 0.67$ describes the relation. The adjustment to the salt values is not so good, but the relation may also be described with a power function of the form R $= \alpha + cM^n$, with a rather high α value and n $= 1.0$.

The subjective salt experiments on the five patients have about the same result as the group experiment. The dispersion of the values was, however, rather great and the individual functions rather uncertain.

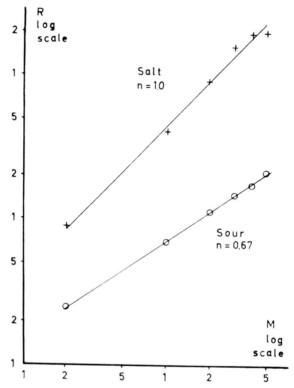

Figure 17-2. Result of a group experiment. Relative subjective intensity plotted against molarity of stimulus in log-log scale (Fig. 2, Borg, G., Diamant, H., Oakley, B., Ström, L., & Zotterman, Y. In T. Hayashi [Ed.], *Olfaction and Taste. Vol. 2.* London: Pergamon Press, 1967).

In Figure 17-3 both the relative psychophysical and neural responses to citric acid are plotted in a log-log diagram (patient C. L.). Straight lines may be adjusted to the values, i.e., a power function may describe the relations. Fechnerian log-function does, however, better describe the variation in neural activity. If, as a first rough approximation, we describe both the neural and the psychophysical responses with power functions of the simple form, R $= cM^n$, we find an astonishingly good agreement. The good correspondence is also seen in Figure 17-4, where the psychophysical estimates are plotted against the neural responses. The exponent of the psychophysical function is $n_R = 0.5$ and of the neurophysical exactly the same, $n_N = 0.5$. This very good correspondence must, of course, be interpreted with great caution, but indicates that further research on this line may be of interest.

In November 1965 only one (V.R.) out of three patients was able to perform the psychophysical tests (Fig. 17-5). Unfortunately her chorda tympani response was very poor. We obtained, however, good responses to citric acid solutions from another patient (H.N.) (Fig. 17-6). When plotted in a log-log diagram, her neural responses fell fairly well along a straight line of very much the same slope as that of the psychophysical data from the patient V.R.

It is obvious that in all these cases the slope of the salt line is definitely steeper than that of the acid line. It is also fairly obvious that the psychophysical as well as the neural data for NaCl seem to be satisfied better by a Fechnerian logarithmic function than Steven's power function.

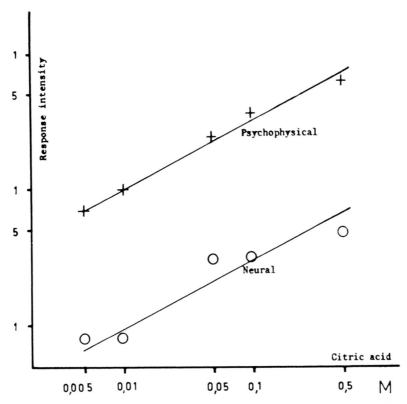

Figure 17-3. Graphs from one patient (C.L.) showing subjective intensity and neural response plotted against molarity of citric acid in log-log scale (Fig. 3, Borg, G., Diamant, H., Oakley, B., Ström, L., & Zotterman, Y. In T. Hayashi [Ed.], *Olfaction and Taste*. Vol. 2. London: Pergamon Press, 1967).

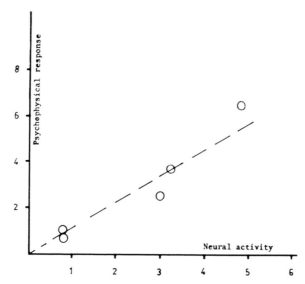

Figure 17-4. Relative subjective intensity in relation to relative neural activity for one patient. Stimulus citric acid (Fig. 4, Borg, G., Diamant, H., Oakley, B., Ström, L., & Zotterman, Y. In T. Hayashi [Ed.], *Olfaction and Taste. Vol. 2.* London: Pergamon Press, 1967).

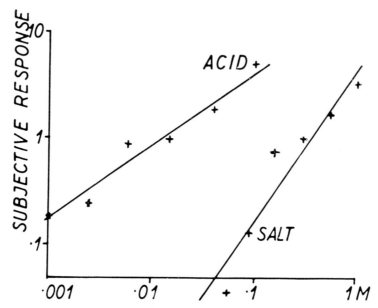

Figure 17-5. Log-log diagram of relation between the subjective response and the molarity of salt and citric acid solutions. Patient (V.R.).

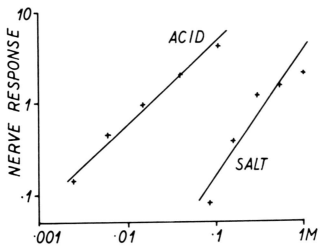

Figure 17-6. Nerve response to salt and acid solutions plotted against molarity. Patient (H.N.).

In textbooks it is maintained that extract of the Indian herb *Gymnema sylvestre* painted on the tongue abolishes the sweet and bitter taste. Figure 17-7 shows the responses from the human chorda tympani to salt, sucrose, critic acid, quinine, and saccharin before and after treatment with Gymnema extracts. We tested five patients in this fashion and found that only the response to sweet tasting substances was affected, *viz*, sucrose, fructose, saccharin and cyclamate. There were no significant effects (i.e., greater than 10 per cent change) upon responses to 0.2 M NaCl, 0.002 M citric acid, or quinine (0.002 M and 0.005 M quinine hydrochloride or 0.008 M quinine sulphate). The main result from the psychophysical experiments was the same, namely, that the sweet taste was eliminated. No subject reported a decrease in bitter taste (quinine).

Ethyl alcohol needs concentrations above 1.0 M to elicit good nerve responses (Fig. 17-8). These neural responses were positively accelerating functions of $\log_{10}$ molar concentration, very similar to the curves of the summated responses from the chorda tympani of the cat and the dog recently presented by Hellekant (1965a). These curves show a course differing completely from the usual linear trend with other taste solutions (Diamant *et al.*, 1963). This is readily explained by the fact that alcohol at higher concentrations, penetrates the mucous membrane of the tongue and stimulates all kinds of sensory nerve endings (Hellekant, 1965b). Use of the strong 5 M and 10 M solutions in five out of six cases resulted in a slowly rising negatively accelerated, summated response which took 10 or

20 sec to reach its maximum height. Concentrations greater than 3 M produce a smarting or burning sensation (Diamant *et al.*, 1963).

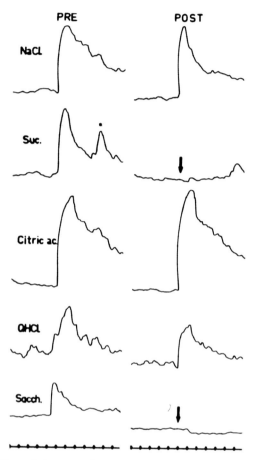

Figure 17-7. Elimination of the neural responses to sweeteners by Gymnema extract. The stimuli were presented in the order shown, before and after treatment of the tongue for 90 sec with 1 per cent Gymnema extract. The arrows show the time at which saccharin and sucrose were applied. The dot in the sucrose record indicates a temperature response to cool distilled water. Time marks are in sec. The responses to quinine are displayed at a somewhat higher amplification. The "pre" response to saccharin was recorded earlier in the experiment. The concentrations were 0.2 M NaCl, 0.5 M sucrose, 0.02 M citric acid, 0.002 M quinine hydrochloride and 0.004 M sodium saccharin. Data from patient No. 1 (Fig. 3, Diamant, H., Oakley, B., Ström, L., Wells, C., & Zotterman, Y., *Acta Physiol. Scand.*, 1965, **64**, 67).

DISCUSSION

Our records, seen in Figure 17-1, suggest that complete adaptation to zero of the neural response to sodium chloride takes place in man in contrast to the rat, where the gustatory receptors are in continuous activity in re-

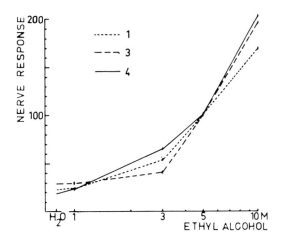

Figure 17-8. The maximum amplitude of the summated chorda tympani response as a function of ethyl alcohol concentration for three patients. The ordinate gives the relative nerve response, where the response of each patient to 5.0 M alcohol has been set at 100 (Fig. 4, Diamant, H., Oakley, B., Ström, L., Wells, C., & Zotterman, Y., *Acta Physiol. Scand.*, 1965, **64**, 67).

sponse to the low salt concentration of the saliva. In this animal you have to wash the tongue with distilled water to abolish the spontaneous activity of the gustatory fibers (Zotterman, 1956).

Bujas (1953) has studied psychophysical salt adaptation in two subjects. Using 0.15 M NaCl to stimulate a tongue area 1 cm in diameter, he found complete adaptation in 50 and 54 sec. These values are of the same order of magnitude as those given by our patients in psychophysical tests when the whole tongue was stimulated with 0.2 M NaCl (79, 90 and 122 sec). The shape of Buja's psychophysical adaptation curves to 0.15 M NaCl are very similar in form to our neural adaptation records in Figure 17-2, but there are too many unknown factors (e.g., the linearity of the ordinates, the appropriate psychophysical base-line level) to permit a precise and quantitative comparison of the two sets of curves.

As we found a reasonable correspondence between the neural and psychophysical records for the time necessary for complete adaptation we may conclude that the rapid and complete salt adaptation reported by our subjects can be accounted for by the declined impulse traffic in the gustatory nerve fibers. There is no need to postulate the existence of central adaptation mechanisms.

The psychophysical data obtained in group experiments, as well as in the patients examined here, gave as a result that the citric acid function fairly well satisfied a simple power function with an exponent about 0.7. The NaCl values are not so easy adapted to a power function. As a first rough approximation it gives, however, an exponent equal to 1.0. The function seems to be positively accelerating at low values, i.e., the exponent being somewhat more than 1 and negatively accelerating at higher levels. "Absolute" comparisons of exponents between the psychophysical and the neural responses may not be allowed, but it is, of course, interesting to find that the same relative differences between the two qualities of taste is reflected in their neural responses.

In spite of the rather scattered data obtained in the individual tests there is no doubt a fair correspondence between the psychophysical and the peripheral neural responses. Thus the impulse frequency code in the peripheral nerves seems to be quite accurately decoded by the central nervous system. We hope to be able to demonstrate this better on patients more suitable for the rather elaborate psychophysical tests and after improvements of the electrical recording in the operation room.

Shore, as early as 1892, reported that extracts of *Gymnema sylvestre* applied to the tongue will temporarily eliminate the ability to taste sweet substances. Andersson, Landgren, Olsson, and Zotterman, (1950), working on dogs and Hagstrom (1957), using hamsters, demonstrated that this drug will suppress the chorda tympani response to sucrose while leaving the response to NaCl unaffected. In our recent research we found that the same Gymnema extract eliminates both the neural and the psychophysical responses to sweet tasting substances in the same human subject. Shore and all textbooks have stated that Gymnema extracts depressed the sensitivity to bitter substances. However, in our experiments this extract had no clear effect on the sensitivity to suprathreshold concentrations of quinine either in psychophysical tests and neural recording sessions with the patients, or in psychophysical tests with three other normal subjects. We are not able to explain this descrepancy.

Convincing evidence for the existence in the monkey of gustatory fibers responding strictly specifically to (a) sweet tasting substances; (b) salt, and (c) acid, was produced by Gordon, Kitchell, Ström, and Zotterman (1959). Gustatory fibers responding to sugars were also found to be excited by saccharin in contrast to the behaviour of the "sweet fibers" of the dog (Andersson *et al.*, 1950) in which animal saccharin elicited a response only from quinine sensitive fibers. In Figure 17-9, from the paper by Gordon *et al.*, (1959) it will be seen that in the monkey in addition to stimulating the "sweet fiber" (large spikes), saccharin, glycerol, and ethylene glycol also stimulate the fibers responding to quinine (small spikes), while sucrose produces a response of the "sweet fiber" with a minimum but still obvious response of "bitter fibers."

In some recent experiments, Békésy (1965, personal communication) found that electrical stimulation of some single papilla in humans produced

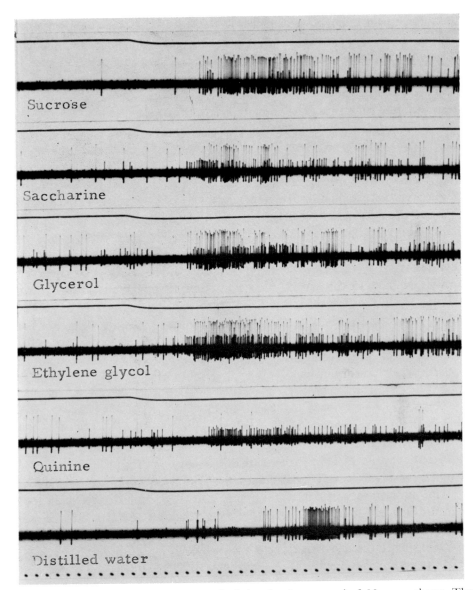

Figure 17-9. Records from a small strand of the chorda tympani of *Macacus rhesus*. The preparation contained few active fibers. Note the large spikes, produced by all sweet tasting substances (and dist. water) and also the smaller spikes appearing in response to quinine and to saccharin, glycerol and ethylene glycol but very sparsely to sucrose. All solutions were made up in Ringer's solution in order to abolish the response to water. Time: 10 per sec (Fig. 4, Gordon, G., Kitchell, R., Ström, L., & Zotterman, Y., *Acta Physiol. Scand.*, 1959, **46,** 119) .

a sweet sensation described by the subjects as "heavenly sweet," a sensation which they never experienced before. It is possible that the electrical stimulation in these cases stimulates selectively the relatively large "sweet fibers," thus giving rise to a very pure sweet sensation. "Bitter fibers" in the dog have been found to be of smaller diameters conducting at very low rates (Andersson *et al.*, 1950; Iriuchijima and Zotterman, 1961).

In our previous report (Diamant *et al.*, 1965) it was emphasized that the correspondence for the sugars between the summated neural response and the psychophysical report suggests that sweetness is determined by the discharge from all of the active gustatory fibers in the nerve, and not only from specific "sweet fibers." The fact that Gymnema extract totally abolishes the effect of sucrose does not solve the problem of specificity. It may as well wipe out the specific sweet sensitivity of the receptive sites of the multiquality fibers as that of the specific "sweet fibers."

It seems reasonable, however, to assume that man, like monkey, possesses a certain number of strictly specific gustatory fibers which could serve as specific switchers in the central nervous system, directing the impulse traffic arriving from the multiquality fibers into specific central channels and closing or depressing the information sent by other pathways. It is, however, futile to enter into more detailed discussions of this problem until we have obtained recordings from individual gustatory nerve fibers in man and from cortical gustatory units.

SUMMARY

The neural response to the application of sapid solutions has been recorded from the middle ear portion of the chorda tympani nerve of otosclerotic patients from whom prior to the operation psychophysical responses to taste stimuli were obtained.

The impulse traffic in the human chorda tympani produced by a constant flow of 0.2 M NaCl over the tongue adapts to zero. The time required agrees with the psychophysical reports. Considerable individual variations were observed in the neural response to different sugars as well as in the patients' estimates of the sweetness of different sugars. The psychophysical measurements corresponded closely with the magnitude of nerve response.

Subjective magnitude estimations of the strength of critic acid and NaCl solutions made in group experiments followed fairly well the same function as that of the neural response. The different function for salt and acid found in the different patients' subjective reports was clearly reflected in the neural responses.

Gymnema extract abolished both the sweet sensation and the nerve response to sweet tasting solutions but did not affect to any marked degree the responses to quinine or other gustatory stimuli. There were large individual differences in the relative size of the neural responses to different taste stimuli.

REFERENCES

Andersson, B., Landgren, S., Olsson, L., & Zotterman, Y. The sweet taste fibers of the dog. *Acta Physiol. Scand.,* 1950, **21**, 105.

Beidler, L. M. Properties of chemoreceptors of tongue of rat. *J. Neurophysiol.,* 1953, **16**, 595.

Borg, G., Diamant, H., Oakley, B., Ström, L., & Zotterman, Y. A comparative study of neural and psychophysical responses to gustatory stimuli. In T. Hayashi (Ed.), *Olfaction and Taste. Vol. 2.* London, Pergamon Press, 1966.

Bujas, Z. L'adaptation gustative et son mécanisme. *Acta Inst. Psychol. Univ. Zagreb.,* 1953, **17**, 1.

Cameron, A. T. The taste sense and the relative sweetness of sugars and other sweet substances. *Sci. Rep. Ser. No. 9.* New York: Sugar Research Found., 1947.

Diamant, H., Funakoshi, M., Ström, L., & Zotterman, Y. Electrophysiological studies on human taste nerves. In Y. Zotterman (Ed.), *Olfaction and Taste Vol. 1.* Oxford: Pergamon, 1963. Pp. 193-203.

Diamant, H., Oakley, B., Ström, L., Wells, C., & Zotterman, Y. A comparison of neural and psychophysical responses to taste stimuli in man. *Acta Physiol. Scand.,* 1965, **64**, 67.

Ekman, G. Methodological note on scales of gustatory intensity. *Scand. J. Physiol.,* 1961, **2**, 185.

Gordon, G., Kitchell, R., Ström, L., & Zotterman, Y. The response pattern of taste fibers in the chorda tympani of the monkey. *Acta Physiol. Scand.,* 1959, **46,**, 119.

Hagstrom, E. C. Doctoral thesis, Brown Univ., 1957. Cited by C. Pfaffmann, The sense of taste. In J. Field (Ed.), *Handbook of Physiology. Section I: Neurophysiology.* Washington, D. C.: Amer. Physiol. Soc., 1959. P. 520.

Hellekant, G. Electrophysiological investigation of the gustatory effect of ethyl alcohol. I. The summated response of the chorda tympani in the cat, dog, and rat. *Acta Physiol. Scand.,* 1965, **64**, 392. (a)

Hellekant, G. The effect of ethyl alcohol on non-gustatory receptors of the tongue of the cat. *Acta Physiol. Scand.,* 1965, **65**, 243. (b)

Iriuchijima, J., & Zotterman, Y. Conduction rates of afferent fibers to the anterior tongue of the dog. *Acta Physiol. Scand.,* 1961, **51**, 283.

Shore, L. E. A contribution to our knowledge of taste sensations. *J. Physiol. (London),* 1892, **13**, 191.

Zotterman, Y. Species differences in the water taste. *Acta Physiol. Scand.,* 1956, **37**, 60.

DISCUSSION

DR. F. B. BENJAMIN: You showed a negative response to water. What happens if you test water as a contrast stimulus — if you first give salt and afterwards water. The subjective sensation obtained under these conditions is one of sweet. Do you get any electrical response under those circumstances?

DR. ZOTTERMAN: That can only be analyzed in preparations in which you have few fibers, where you can see the response of individual fibers.

Dr. C. Pfaffman: In that connection, if there is a temperature effect, would it be possible to use this preparation to systematically investigate the effects of temperature changes?

Dr. Zotterman: Yes, it would be possible to do that very well. Of course, these preparations are very sensitive to temperature. When you are recording the summated responses from the total nerve trunk you have to avoid thermal stimulation. But we have not so far done any systematic studies of temperature on human taste nerves because we have not had time enough. I once poured Coca Cola on the tongue at 7° C, and then I poured it on when it was of the same temperature as the tongue; and I tell you that the total response in the first one was very large, but when I poured it on at the temperature of the tongue, the response was reduced to one third. So the sensation that you usually get from Coca Cola on your tongue is, to a greater extent, derived from stimulation of "cold fibers."

Dr. Rosner: Have you tried fitting a logarithmic or a power function to the psychophysical or to the neural responses for salt stimulation?

Dr. Zotterman: Yes, we have, but so far on the same patient. We have not yet enough data to do a really proper functional analysis of the salt responses, so you must look upon this as not a definite answer to the question; this is just a preliminary approach. We find the subjective and neural data fitting the same function. For salt this is rather a Fechnerian log function.

Dr. H. Davis: You showed us some striking individual differences in the patients and their response to salt. Is it possible to correlate these differences with the diets of the patients? Do you, possibly, have them on a low-salt diet?

Dr. Zotterman: We have not been able to determine the effect of diet upon the salt response. Perhaps Dr. Pfaffmann can help us.

Dr. Pfaffmann: All of the evidence from the animal experiments, in which very severe salt deprivation was induced, show that a change in the magnitude of the response cannot be experimentally produced. That is the present conclusion of a number of different experiments. The trouble is that all of those have been done under pentobarbital anesthesia, and if that reduces the sensory system to zero, it may be that any neural modulation through the deficit is knocked out. A straightforward chemical process, though, mediated by the changes in the body fluids, I think, can be ruled out because in the animal preparations when this occurs no sensory change has been observed. The only qualification would be in the case of a species difference, because the failure of adaptation that you showed in the rat preparation is very different from that in the human. Those are very interesting experiments to clarify that question.

Dr. Zotterman: I hope this is satisfying for the psychologists because, in my opinion, although this is only the first approach, it shows that the psychophysical estimations which the psychologists make are very reliable because there is such a good correlation between them and the electrophysiological responses. The extraordinary thing is that the coding in the peripheral receptors is so well correlated with the decoding which occurs centrally.

I was in Boston talking to an audience a few months ago. Among them was Békésy when I showed Figure 17-9 of my text. Békésy has recently stimulated single papilla of the human tongue with short electrical pulses. He found out that from one papilla he gets a sweet sensation and another papilla gives a bitter sensation, etc. That was really startling and quite unexpected for us who have been studying the electrical response in single fibers, which are, generally, not very specific. He told me before, when I was at his laboratory, that the sweet sensation that this young lady experiences when he stimulates a papilla — for a sweet sensation — was a sweetness which she has never experienced before. She calls it "heavenly" sweet. Figure 17-9 of my text is from a monkey, and you see the response from the sweet tasting substances sucrose, saccharine, glycerol, ethylene glycol, and quinine. What you see here is that the 0.5 M sucrose gives a response of large spikes, while quinine, as you see, produces a response of small spikes. Well, that is what I would expect. We found that fibers in the dog which respond to bitter substances are very slow-conducting fibers. They are conducting at 2 to 3 m/sec while the larger fibers are conducting at about 15 m/sec. And now, you will see here, if you apply ethylene glycol and you compare it with the sucrose response, there are a few small-size fiber spikes. Of course, sucrose is the substance which tastes more pure sweet than anything else. With saccharine stimulation a lot of small spikes are added and still more for glycerol and still more for ethylene glycol. When I was showing that picture in my lecture at Harvard I got the idea that that is the answer to Békésy. When he stimulates electrically he may very well stimulate only the large fibers and does not get an additional excitation of any bitter fibers. But when we pour sucrose on our tongue a few fibers which respond to quinine may also respond to the sucrose. I thought I would tell you about it, for it is not very often that you are in the middle of presenting a paper and you find a new correlation. I do not know whether it is true. It is up to you to judge.

Chapter 18

ELECTROPHYSIOLOGY OF CUTANEOUS THERMORECEPTORS

Herbert Hensel

T HERMOSENSITIVE NERVE ENDINGS can be studied in different ways, namely: (a) by observing the specific temperature sensation in human subjects; (b) by studying thermoregulatory reflexes and behavior of animals at various temperatures, and (c) by recording afferent impulses from units responding to thermal stimulation. This paper will be concerned mainly with the electrophysiological and biophysical aspect of thermosensitive nerve endings in the skin. It should be kept in mind that the definition of a thermoreceptor by temperature sensation and by action potentials is not necessarily identical. For example, a group of cutaneous receptors which respond to cooling with a discharge of afferent impulses may elicit a mechanical sensation.

Concerning the "biophysical" approach to the function of thermosensitive nerve endings, i.e., the recording of afferent impulses on thermal stimulation, it seems clear that qualitative experiments alone are not sufficient and may sometimes be misleading. This is especially true for those types of receptors which respond to more than one quality of stimulus. Therefore, quantitative measurements are necessary to define exactly the properties of a nerve ending excited by thermal stimulation. Cutaneous receptors with specific temperature sensitivity, or, strictly speaking, with selective temperature sensitivity, can be divided into the main groups of cold and warm receptors. For a receptor, the following definition may be proposed: (a) frequency rise on sudden cooling; (b) no response on sudden warming if the fiber is silent, or an inhibition of a resting discharge if one is present; (c) no response to nonpainful mechanical stimulation or, at least, a considerably higher threshold than that of the most sensitive mechanoreceptors, and (d) thermal sensitivity comparable with temperature sense in man. A warm receptor will respond to sudden temperature changes in the opposite way, namely: (a) with a frequency rise on sudden warming, and (b) with an inhibition of the resting discharge on sudden cooling (Hensel, Iggo, and Witt, 1960).

Let us now consider the general reactions of cold and warm sensitive nerve endings to thermal stimulation. These reactions are very similar in various species and preparations, the differences being mainly quantitative in nature. At constant skin temperatures a steady discharge of afferent impulses is seen, the frequency of which is dependent on absolute temperature (Fig. 18-1). The steady discharge of a single thermosensitive fiber has a maximum frequency of 2 to 15 impulses/sec. For the warm fibers in homeotherms, the temperature of the maximum discharge is between 38 and 43°C, whereas the maximum frequency of the steady discharge of cold fibers is between 15 and 34°C (Hensel and Zotterman, 1951a; Dodt and Zotterman, 1952; Hensel *et al.,* 1960). As will be shown later, certain cold receptors in hibernators have much lower maxima at about 4°C. It has been pointed out by several authors that this spontaneous discharge might be due to minute temperature fluctuations rather than to constant temperatures in a strict sense. However, this possibility can be excluded by the following reasons: (a) If the discharge of a cold receptor is elicited only by a change of temperature in time and not by a constant value, phases of excitation should alternate with phases of inhibition as the temperature fluctuations are proceeding in opposite directions (Fig. 18-2). In fact, however, the spontaneous discharge of a single cold fiber exhibits a very regular sequence of impulses, as can be seen in Figure 18-6. (b) In a certain temperature range, the discharge of a cold receptor will continue not only at constant temperatures but even at slow increases (*cf.* Fig. 18-6 *D*). This phenomenon is the physiological basis for the so-called after-sensation, when a cold object is removed from the skin (Weber, 1846).

From the steady discharge alone we cannot conclude, with certainty, whether the nerve ending in question is a cold or a warm receptor since both have a positive temperature coefficient below the maximum and a negative coefficient above the maximum (Fig. 18-1). On sudden temperature changes, however, the discharge frequency will always change in the same direction, independent of the absolute temperature range. A cold receptor will react with a transient increase (overshoot) in frequency during cooling and a transient decrease or inhibition (false start) during warming, whereas a warm receptor will behave in the opposite way. Thus the definition of a cold or warm receptor should be based on its dynamic rather than on its static behavior.

A well known phenomenon in human temperature sense is the "paradoxical" cold sensation at high temperatures. This paradoxical sensation can be correlated with a discharge of cold fibers in the tongue of the cat at constant temperatures above 45°C (Zotterman, 1953). At higher temperatures, the frequency of the paradoxical discharge increases until a maximum level is reached at about 50°C. Above this temperature, damage of the receptor begins and the discharge frequency falls off. Whether a paradoxical warm sensation exists in human subjects is not as well established as in the case of paradoxical cold. In the cat, a phasic discharge of warm fibers is

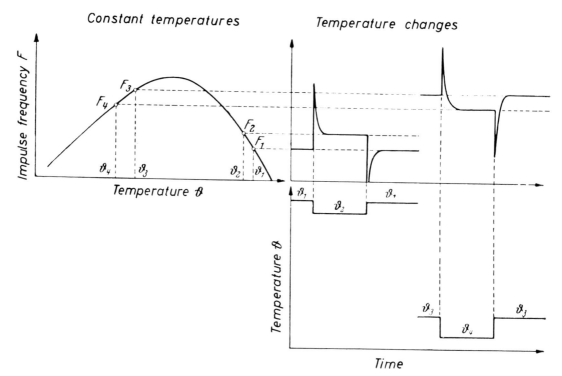

Figure 18-1. Impulse frequency of a single cold fiber with constant temperatures and with rectangular temperature changes (Fig. 36, Hensel, H. In H. Precht, J. Christophersen, & H. Hensel, *Temperatur und Leben*. Berlin: Springer, 1965. Pp. 329-466).

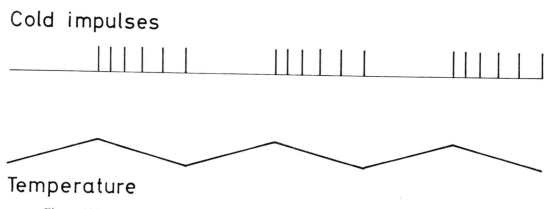

Figure 18-2. Schematic representation of cold fiber discharge at fluctuating temperature.

seen when the tongue is cooled rapidly by more than 8°C (Dodt and Zotterman, 1952; Dodt, 1953).

The afferent discharge of cutaneous thermoreceptors is dependent on two main factors, namely: (a) the absolute temperature, θ, of the skin; and (b) the temporal gradient $d\theta/dt$ of temperature changes (*cf*. Fig. 18-1). This corresponds well with the physiology of human temperature sensation (Hensel, 1952a). The second factor is more important in that the maximum frequency during rapid temperature changes may exceed the frequency of the steady discharge by about ten times.

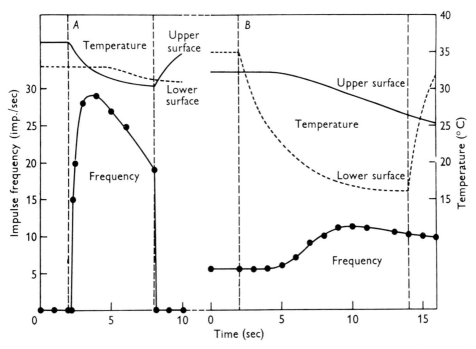

Figure 18-3. Impulse frequency of a single cold fiber in the lingual nerve of cat and temperature on both sides of the tongue when cooling the upper and the lower surface, respectively (Fig. 4, Hensel, H. & Witt, I., *J. Physiol. (London)*, 1959, 148, 180).

The hypothesis of spatial temperature gradients $d\theta/dx$ being the adequate stimulus of thermosensitive nerve endings could not be verified by cooling the tongue with reversed gradients (Hensel and Zotterman, 1951b; Hensel and Witt, 1959). When a cold receptor on the surface of the tongue is cooled from above, its resting discharge will increase by a certain amount (Fig. 18-3). The same increase in frequency, however, is observed when the tongue is cooled from the lower surface, in spite of a reversed spatial gradient. Thus we come to the conclusion that the adequate stimulus of the cold receptor is only the drop in temperature *per se* and not the direction or slope of a spatial gradient.

Cutaneous receptors predominantly responding to thermal stimuli are supplied by small myelinated fibers, belonging to the Aδ group, as well as by unmyelinated C fibers. Thermosensitive A fibers have been found in the tongue of cat and dog (Zotterman, 1936; Hensel and Zotterman, 1951a; Dodt and Zotterman, 1952), in the trigeminal area of cat (Hensel, 1952b) and hamster (Raths, Witt, and Hensel, 1964) as well as in the external skin of the monkey (Iggo, 1963) and in human skin (Hensel and Boman, 1960). Thermoreceptors connected with unmyelinated fibers are found in the external skin of cat, dog and hamster (Hensel *et al.,* 1960; Iriuchijima and Zotterman, 1960; Raths *et al.,* 1964).

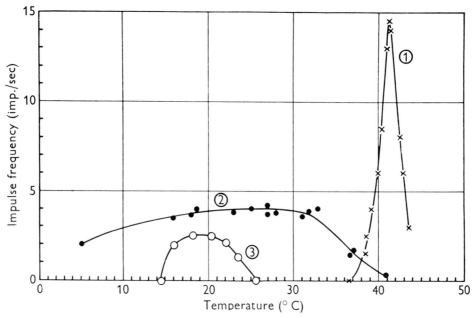

Figure 18-4. Steady discharge frequency of three different single C fibers in the saphenous nerve of the cat as a function of constant skin temperature. (1) Fiber excited by warming; (2) fiber excited by cooling; (3) fiber excited by cooling (Fig. 6, Hensel, H., Iggo, A., & Witt, I., *J. Physiol. (London),* 1960, **153,** 113).

Figure 18-4 shows the frequency of the steady discharge of single thermosensitive C fibers in the saphenous nerve of the cat as a function of constant temperatures. Curve 1 is from a warm receptor, whereas curve 2 and 3 are from cold receptors. In contrast to the findings in the tongue the maximum frequency of some cutaneous C fibers is reached at rather low temperatures, and the range of stationary activity is extended to temperatures below 5°C. Several unmyelinated warm and cold receptors are highly sensitive to temperature changes (Hensel *et al.,* 1960). Starting with neutral skin temperatures of about 33°C, a change of 0.2°C is sufficient to cause a considerable influence on the discharge frequency. As shown in Figure 18-5, the frequency of a C warm receptor in the cat's skin is increased by 10 impulses/sec when the temperature rises by less than 0.2°C. This high sensitivity corresponds well with the threshold of temperature sensation in man.

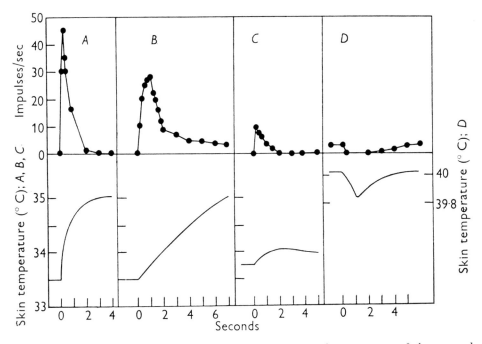

Figure 18-5. Afferent impulses of a single C fiber in the saphenous nerve of the cat and skin temperature during cutaneous thermal stimulation (Fig. 8, Hensel, H., Iggo, A., & Witt, I., *J. Phsiol. (London),* 1960, **153,** 113).

The dynamic response of receptors to temperature changes can be expressed in terms of dynamic sensitivity and of maximum frequency. Dynamic sensitivity (impulses/sec °C) is defined by the change in impulse frequency when a sudden temperature jump of 1°C is applied. For the most sensitive cutaneous thermoreceptors, the dynamic sensitivity is of the order of 30 to 50 impulses/sec °C. The maximum frequency may reach a value of 150 impulses/sec.

Single fiber records have been obtained from the superficial branch of the radial nerve in human subjects (Hensel and Boman, 1960). The receptive field was on the back of the hand or on the dorsal side of the thumb. Besides numerous specific mechanoreceptors and some fibers responding to cooling as well as to pressure, only cold fibers have been found in the A

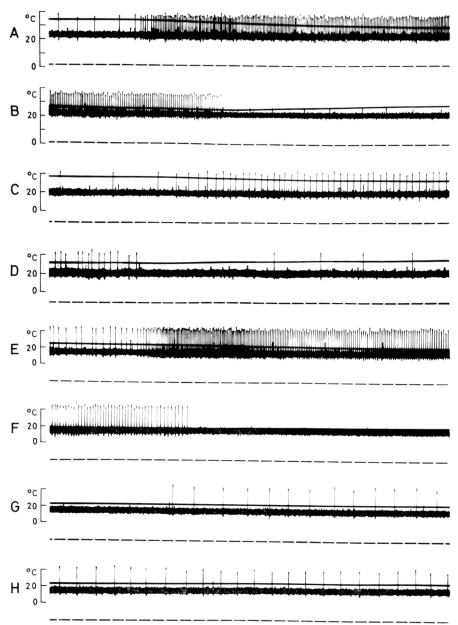

Figure 18-6. Afferent impulses in single cold fiber in the radial nerve in man and temperature during cutaneous thermal stimulation. (A) start of cooling from 34 to 26°C. (B) start of rewarming. (C) start of cooling from 38 to 35°C. (D) start of rewarming. (E) start of cooling from 24 to 16°C. (F) start of rewarming. (G) 13 sec after rewarming has started. (H) continued from record (G). Time: 0.2 sec (Fig. 8, Hensel, H. & Boman, K. K. A., *J. Neurophysiol.*, 1960, **23**, 564.

group but no warm fibers. Presumably the human warm receptors are connected with C fibers but this group has not been studied as yet. In Figure 18-6, the discharge of a single cold fiber from the human hand is shown. This fiber was not excited by normal mechanical stimulation but very sensitive to cooling. At a constant temperature of 34°C, a steady discharge is seen which is accelerated considerably when cooling starts. The response to temperature changes as well as the steady discharge at constant temperatures were that of a typical cold fiber. For the theory of thermoreceptor stimulation, record D seems particularly interesting, where a discharge of the cold fiber is seen in spite of a slowly rising temperature. For this fiber, the temperature of the maximum steady discharge was below 20°C.

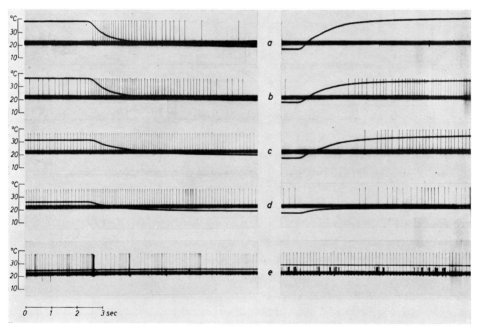

Figure 18-7. Response of a nonspecific A fiber in the saphenous nerve of cat during thermal (a - d) and mechanical (e) stimulation (Fig. 2, Witt, I. & Hensel, H. *Pflügers Arch. Ges. Physiol.,* 1959, **268**, 582) .

In the cat several cutaneous fibers can be found that respond to cooling as well as to light mechanical pressure or touch (Witt and Hensel, 1959). It should be emphasized that both kinds of stimuli are in the normal physiological range. An example of these "cold-pressure" fibers is shown in Figure 18-7. The afferent impulses are recorded from a single A fiber in the cat's saphenous nerve during cooling and warming the skin. The behavior is that of a typical cold fiber, except that the receptor is sensitive to light touch, as can be seen in record *e*, on the left side. Similar results

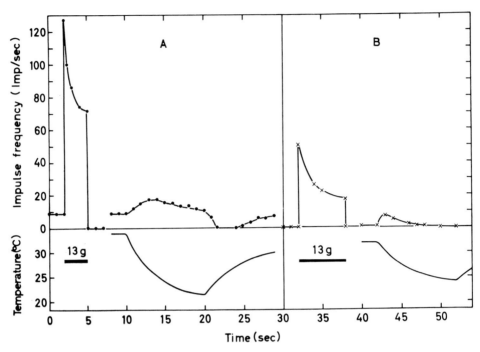

Figure 18-8. Response of two different nonspecific fibers (A) and (B) in the radial nerve in man during cutaneous pressure and cooling (Fig. 7, Hensel, H. & Boman, K. K. A., *J. Neurophysiol.*, 1960, **23**, 564).

are found in human subjects. A number of A fibers in the radial nerve are excited by cooling as well as by pressure (Fig. 18-8). It seems typical that the maximum response of these fibers to rapid cooling will reach only a few impulses/sec, whereas a typical cold fiber can reach 150 impulses/sec under the same conditions. On the other hand, as shown in Table 18-I, the maximum frequency of "pressure-cold" fibers on mechanical stimulation is much higher than their maximum response to cooling. The function of

TABLE 18-I
QUANTITATIVE RESPONSE OF HUMAN CUTANEOUS RECEPTORS
EXCITED BY PRESSURE AND COOLING

No. of Preparation	Spontaneous Discharge at 32°C imp/sec	Mechanical Stimulation Stimulus	Maximum frequency imp/sec	Thermal Stimulation Cooling	Maximum frequency imp/sec	Dynamic sensitivity imp/sec °C
10	1	Pressure 13g/mm²	50	32 − 24	8	−3
21 a	9	Pressure 13g/mm²	127	34 − 21	17	−1.9
18 b	1	Stroking	125	34 − 24	6	−5
29 a	1.5	Light pressure	25	34 − 13	10	−1.7

(Table 1. Hensel, H., & Boman, K. K. A. *J. Neurophysiol.*, 1960, **23**, 564)

fibers excited by light mechanical stimulation and cooling is not clear. From the fact that pressure will not cause any cold sensation in man but that a pressure sensation can be elicited by cooling the skin — a phenomenon called "Weber's deception" (Weber, 1846) — it may be concluded that a mechanical sensation rather than a cold sensation is aroused by stimulation of these nerve endings.

In homeothermic animals, such as cat and dog, the maximum frequency of cutaneous cold receptors at constant temperatures is between 15 and 34°C. The spontaneous A fiber discharge disappears at temperatures below 10°C, whereas the C fibers stop firing at somewhat lower temperatures, in the range of a few degree centigrade above zero. However, there is indirect evidence that in hibernators the cutaneous cold receptors may be active at much lower skin temperatures. It is well known that the thermoregulation of hibernating animals is functioning at body temperatures as low as 5°C. On external cooling, the animal will react with heart acceleration, metabolic increase, and a general arousal reaction. Therefore we can assume that its cold receptors are still firing at temperatures at which the cold receptors of other mammals are completely silent.

In order to answer this question, the impulse discharge from cutaneous cold receptors in hibernators have been investigated (Raths, *et al.*, 1964).

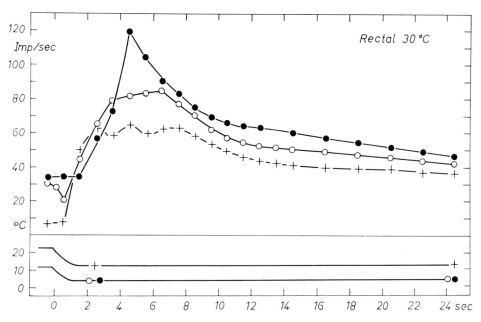

Figure 18-9. Impulse frequency of a thin strand of 3 to 4 Aδ fibers from the infra-orbital nerve in the hamster on cooling the face. *Upper records:* impulse frequency as a function of time; *lower records:* skin temperature (Raths and Hensel, unpublished).

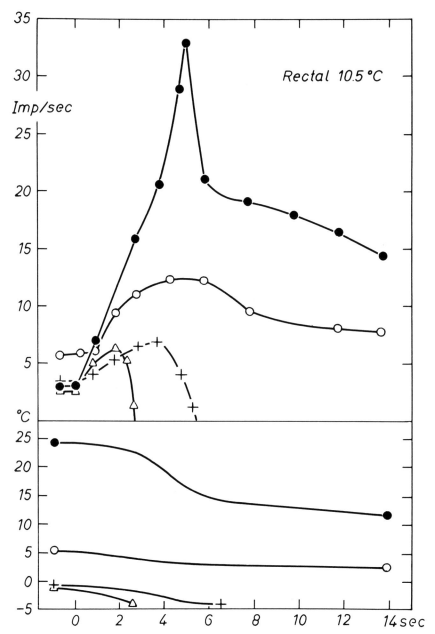

Figure 18-10. Impulse frequency of a single C fiber from the infraorbital nerve in the hibernating hamster on cooling the face. *Upper records:* impulse frequency as a function of time; *lower records:* skin temperature (Raths and Hensel, unpublished).

Our experiments have been performed in hamsters on trigeminal nerve fibers supplying the skin of the face. Figure 18-9 shows the integrated impulse frequency of a small bundle containing Aδ fibers when cooling the skin of the nose. At constant skin temperatures of 11°C a steady discharge can be seen. Cooling the skin to 3°C causes an overshoot in frequency after which the discharge remains at a rather high level even if the temperature is kept constant at 3°C for a long period of time. In the unanesthetized hibernating animal, the same stimulus will cause an arousal reaction. As shown in Figure 18-10, a cutaneous C fiber is firing spontaneously in the hibernating animal with a rectal temperature of 10.5°C and a skin temperature of 3°C. On cooling from 5° to 3°C, a marked increase in frequency occurs. Even a temperature drop from 3° to –5°C will elicit an overshoot in frequency, but the steady discharge is not maintained at a constant temperature of –5°C.

When the stationary frequency of several Aδ and C fibers is plotted against temperature, some of the maxima are found to be at constant temperatures as low as 4°C (Figure 18-11). In this connection it should be mentioned again that the cold receptors with Aδ fibers in other mammals stop firing at temperatures of about 10°C. The average data for various types of single receptors in the hamster are shown in Table 18-II. One group of trigeminal Aβ fibers responds to mechanical stimulation and to cooling as well; it shows a very slow steady discharge with a maximum frequency of 1.5 impulses/sec at a constant temperature of 34°C. The average limits of the range of the steady discharge are 15 and 45°C. In contrast to this group, the cold receptors with trigeminal Aδ fibers fire continuously, with much higher frequencies, within a mean temperature range between 0 and 22°C. About the same values are found for the trigeminal cold receptors connected with C fibers. Both groups show a stationary maximum at about 5°C.

There was no significant difference in the behavior of cold receptors between hibernating animals and animals in the summer. Thus, we can conclude that the peculiar properties of thermoreceptors in the hamster

TABLE 18-II
DISCHARGE OF CUTANEOUS RECEPTORS CONNECTED WITH TRIGEMINAL
FIBERS IN THE HAMSTER (MEAN VALUES)

Type of Receptor	Fiber	Lower limit °C	Static		Upper limit °C	Dynamic	
			Maximum °C	imp/sec		Maximum °C	imp/sec °C
Pressure, Cold	Aβ	+ 15	+ 34	1.5	+ 45	+ 35	− 2.3
Cold	Aδ	0	+ 5	19	+ 22	+ 25	− 4.2
Cold	C	− 2	+ 5		+ 22		

(From Raths, P., Witt, I., & Hensel, H. unpublished)

are due to species differences between hibernators and other mammals and not to seasonal adaptation. One point I would like to mention is the fact that the hibernating hamster is curled up in a spherical form, the nose being in the center of this sphere. Therefore, one can assume that the trigeminal cold receptors are signalling not only the skin temperature but also the internal temperature of hibernating animal.

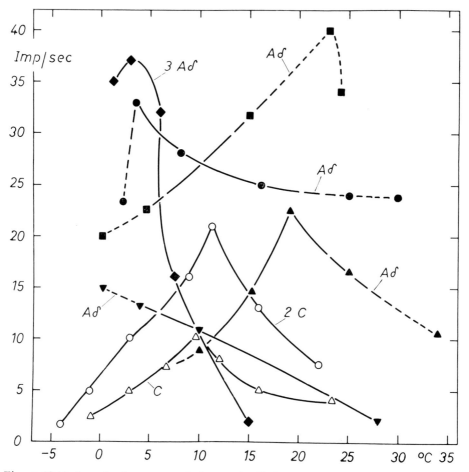

Figure 18-11. Impulse frequency of the steady discharge of Aδ and C fibers from the infraorbital nerve in the hamster as a function of constant skin temperature in the face (Raths and Hensel, unpublished).

SUMMARY

Cold (warm) receptors can be characterized by the following properties: (a) frequency rise (fall) of the afferent discharge on sudden cooling; (b) no response on sudden warming (cooling) if the fiber is silent, or an inhibition of a resting discharge; (c) a steady discharge dependent on temperature, and (d) no response to weak mechanical stimulation. The electrophysiological findings should be in agreement with behavioral responses, thermoregulatory reflexes, and with temperature sensation in man.

Cutaneous thermoreceptors in cat, dog, and monkey are supplied by small myelinated A fibers as well as by unmyelinated C fibers. In human skin, only Aδ cold fibers have been investigated as yet.

The steady discharge of single units has a maximum frequency of 2 to 15 impulses/sec. The temperature of the maximum discharge between 38° and 43°C for the warm fibers and between 15° and 34°C for the cold fibers. In hibernators, the maximum of the steady discharge of cold receptors is at an average temperature of 4° C.

Adequate stimuli of thermoreceptors are as follows: (a) temperature and (b) temperature change in time $d\theta/dt$, i.e., the temporal gradient, whereas the spatial gradient $d\theta/dx$ *per se* has no influence on the receptor discharge.

REFERENCES

Dodt, E. The behavior of thermoreceptors at low and high temperatures with special references to Ebbecke's temperature phenomenon. *Acta Physiol. Scand.,* 1953, **27,** 295.

Dodt, E., & Zotterman, Y. Mode of action of warm receptors. *Acta Physiol. Scand.,* 1952, **26,** 345.

Hensel, H. Physiologie der Thermoreception. *Ergebn. Physiol.,* 1952, **47,** 166. (a)

Hensel, H. Afferente Impulse aus den Kältereceptoren der äusseren Haut. *Pflüger Arch. Ges. Physiol.,* 1952, **256,** 195. (b)

Hensel, H. Mensch und warmblütige Tiere. In H. Precht, J. Christophersen, & H. Hensel, *Temperatur und Leben.* Berlin: Springer, 1955. Pp. 329-466.

Hensel, H., & Boman, K. K. A. Afferent impulses in cutaneous sensory nerves in human subjects. *J. Neurophysiol.,* 1960, **23,** 564.

Hensel, H., Iggo, A., & Witt, I. A quantitative study of sensitive cutaneous thermoreceptors with C afferent fibers. *J. Physiol. (London),* 1960, **153,** 113.

Hensel, H., & Witt, I. Spatial temperature gradient and thermoreceptor stimulation. *J. Physiol. (London),* 1959, **148,** 180.

Hensel, H., & Zotterman, Y. Quantitative Beziehungen zwischen der Entladung einzelner Kältefasern und der Temperatur. *Acta Physiol. Scand.,* 1951, **23,** 291. (a)

Hensel, H., & Zotterman, Y. Action potentials of cold fibers and intracutaneous temperature gradient. *J. Neurophysiol.,* 1951, **14,** 377. (b)

Iggo, A. An electrophysiological analysis of afferent fibers in primate skin. *Acta Neuroveg. (Wien),* 1963, **24,** 225.

Iriuchijima, J., & Zotterman, Y. The specificity of afferent cutaneous C fibers in mammals. *Acta Physiol. Scand.,* 1960, **49,** 267.

Raths, P., Witt, I., & Hensel, H. Thermoreceptoren bei Winterschläfern. *Pflüger. Arch. Ges. Physiol.,* 1964, **281,** 73.

Weber, E. H. Der Tastsinn und das Gemeingefühl. In *Wagner's Handwörterbuch der Physiologie, Vol. III/2.* Braunschweig: Vieweg, 1846. Pp. 481-588.

Witt, I., & Hensel, H. Afferente Impulse aus der Extremitätenhaut der Katze bei thermischer und mechanischer Reizung. *Pflüger Arch. Ges. Physiol.,* 1959, **268,** 582.

Zotterman, Y. Specific action potentials in the lingual nerve of the cat. *Skand. Arch. Physiol.,* 1936, **75**, 105.

Zotterman, Y. Special senses: Thermal receptors. *Ann. Rev. Physiol.,* 1953, **15**, 357.

DISCUSSION

DR. Y. ZOTTERMAN: It was a great pleasure to be reminded about the old days, 15 or 16 years ago, when you were working in my laboratory, and we had some common endeavors. There are several things, quite new and interesting, about the fibers in the hibernating animals. First of all, have you any notion about the speed of conduction or the diameter of these delta fibers in the hamster?

DR. HENSEL: We did some measurements of conduction velocity and they range from 10 to 15 m/sec.

DR. ZOTTERMAN: That is the same as you and I have found in the cat.

DR. HENSEL: I think so, yes. We measured the conduction velocity, not in all but in several of the fibers.

DR. ZOTTERMAN: Have you observed any responses, particularly C fibers, as you do in other nonhibernating mammals, which respond to heavy pressure and which would induce nociceptive reactions?

DR. HENSEL: No, I did not study the response to heavy pressure.

DR. ZOTTERMAN: I mean stimuli which will arouse an animal being of nociceptive character?

DR. HENSEL: I do not think so, because it is possible to get an arousal reaction in the hibernating animal with even a light touch on the skin, which should not be nociceptive. Even if you cool from 5° to 3° or 2°C, if the animal is not anesthetized, you get an arousal reaction. There is quite a good correlation between the fiber discharge and the behavior of the animal. These stimuli are sufficient to cause reactions in the animal.

DR. ZOTTERMAN: May I say one word about the interesting problem of the dual modality fibers. Can you, or have others been able to produce a cool sensation with a thermally neutral mechanical stimulus?

DR. HENSEL: No, you cannot.

DR. R. T. VERRILLO: Can you distinguish between the response characteristics of the "pure" cold and the mixed mechano-cold fibers when they are both stimulated with cold?

DR. HENSEL: Yes, I think it is possible to a certain extent. One difference is that the maximum frequency of these mechano-cold fibers, when excited by mechanical stimulation, might reach more than 100 impulses/sec; but the maximum impulse frequency for cooling will never reach this level. The maximum values are 10 or 15 impulses/sec even when cooling very rapidly to low temperatures. This is a typical feature of this pressure-cold fiber.

DR. VERRILLO: Can you tell the difference between the response characteristics of the two types?

DR. HENSEL: The dynamic sensitivity to cooling is lower for the nonspecific fibers than for the specific ones, but there might be some overlap. At least you can find a certain group of fibers with low dynamic sensitivity and another group which has a high dynamic sensitivity. Another difference is that, on cooling, the specific cold fibers have a much higher maximum of impulse discharge than can be found in the nonspecific fibers.

DR. VERRILLO: Incidentally, I have noticed, when I apply a vibrating stimulus around the lips, feeling a cool sensation. I have never felt it on the hand, though, just on the lips.

DR. E. G. EIJKMAN: At what temperature on the steady state response curve does the peak of maximum frequency occur for the cold receptors? The hump of the curve makes it necessary that you have another receptor to define the temperature precisely. On the other hand, I have the impression that the number of warm fibers is very much smaller than the number of cold fibers.

DR. HENSEL: There are quite a number of warm fibers, but you might be right.

DR. A. IGGO: The point of maximum thermal sensitivity does seem to depend upon the species. For the monkey, as compared with the cat, the maximum for the cold sensitive fiber is somewhere in the region of 25° to 35°C, whereas the units of the cat have maxima at 25° to 20°C.

DR. HENSEL: And in the hamster, it is still lower.

DR. EIJKMAN: When the skin temperature is in the region of 30°C, you certainly are in need of warm receptors, and I am very curious to know some impression of the number of warm fibers and cold fibers.

DR. HENSEL: I cannot tell you exact numbers because this depends very much on preparations. You do not know how many fibers are destroyed by the preparations.

DR. G. WERNER: Some of your records, Dr. Hensel, seem to indicate that the peak discharge rate in the cold fibers was reached prior to the temperature having reached an equilibrium state. I wonder whether this does not imply that the independent variable should be scaled in terms of degrees per sec (rather than degrees), for the purpose of determining a meaningful quantitative relation between temperature stimuli and the corresponding neural responses. Do you consider this a correct interpretation?

DR. HENSEL: Yes, this might be the case. The maximum is reached before the steady state of the temperature is reached. It is much more dependent on the slope than on the final level.

Chapter 19

BEHAVIORAL AND ELECTROPHYSIOLOGICAL RESPONSES OF CATS TO THERMAL STIMULI*

DAN R. KENSHALO

T HERE HAS NOT BEEN A satisfactory answer to the question concerning the nature of the peripheral neural code which is initiated by warming or cooling the skin and which is associated with the sensations of warmth and coolness. Attempts to provide an answer to the question of the form of the neural code for thermal stimuli have been directed toward correlations of physiological specificity with the known facts of psychological specificity. The existence of a psychological specificity is based on the knowledge that (a) the quality of warm sensations is markedly different from that of cool sensations; (b) that warm spots can, and frequently do, exist in separate skin areas from cool spots (Blix, 1884; Donaldson, 1885; Goldscheider, 1884), and (c) that measurements of the threshold of warm sensations differ from those of cool sensations as a function of the temperature to which the skin has been adapted (Ebaugh and Thauer, 1950; Kenshalo, Nafe, and Brooks, 1961; Lele, 1954). These data suggest that warm and cool sensations may be mediated by different sets of receptors and nerve fibers. Attempts to describe the neural code for thermal stimulation have started with the assumption that physiological specificity† will correlate highly with psychological specificity. Accordingly, some nerve fibers should show a response only when the skin is cooled and others should respond only when it is warmed.

Information concerning the physiological specificity of skin afferent nerve fibers, obtained largely by electrophysiological methods, have failed, generally, to confirm the expected correlation of physiological specificity with psychological specificity. These electrophysiological studies of cutaneous afferents agree that there are myelinated nerve fibers of the A delta group which show a high degree of specificity of response to cooling the skin surface and practically no response to mechanical stimulation. These specific "cold fibers" show a tonic level of activity, the frequency of which depends upon the skin temperature and a phasic increase in activity when

*This research was supported by USPHS Grant #NB02992 and NSF Grant GB 2473.

†"Physiological specificity" is used here to indicate the property of a nerve fiber or its terminal to show a low threshold of response to one form of stimulation and very high thresholds for other forms of stimulation. Neural response has usually been used to indicate an initiation of neural activity or an increase in the frequency of an already present level of activity. As will be seen later, it may also mean a decrease in an already present level of activity.

the skin is cooled. Warming the skin results in a phasic reduction in the neural activity. To date, fibers which fit this description have been found to occur in the lingual nerve of cats (Dodt and Zotterman, 1952a; Hensel and Zotterman, 1951; Zotterman, 1936), in the infraorbital nerve of cats (Hensel, 1952), rats, cats, and dogs (Boman, 1958), the median and musculocutaneous nerves of primates (Iggo, 1963) and in one of thirty-four preparations from the radial nerve of man (Hensel and Boman, 1960). In all of these preparations other fibers were frequently encountered which behaved, generally, like specific "cold fibers" but which also showed sensitivity to mechanical stimulation of the skin. In the saphenous and cluneum nerves of cat all single unit preparations which showed a sensitivity to cooling the skin were also sensitive to mechanical stimulation (Witt and Hensel, 1959). In only two of all of these preparations were fibers of the A group found which responded to mild warming of the skin in the sense of a "warm receptor" (Zotterman, 1936; Dodt and Zotterman, 1952b). These were found in the chorda tympani of cats. Their specificity has been questioned recently since fibers which show similar response characteristics to warm stimuli also have been found to respond to sapid solutions (Nagaki, Yamashita, and Sato, 1964).

Fibers of the C group appear to show a greater degree of specificity to thermal stimulation of the skin than the A fibers. Nonmyelinated fibers have been found in the saphenous nerve of cats which respond with an increase in their frequency of activity when the skin is cooled (Douglas, Ritchie, and Straub, 1960). Single unit preparations of C fibers in the saphenous nerve of cats showed that some units responded much like "cold" units of the A group in the tongue of cats but with even greater sensitivity (Hensel, Iggo, and Witt, 1960). In addition, other C fibers were found which could be excited only by warming the skin. These fibers showed a steady state discharge, the rate of which depended on the skin temperature. Upon warming the skin there was a phasic increase in frequency followed by a decrease when cooled. Similar activity in C fibers of the saphenous nerve of rats and the infraorbital nerves of dogs and cats were obtained at the same time in a different laboratory (Iriuchijima and Zotterman, 1960).

The expected correlation between psychological specificity and physiological specificity does not appear to exist in fibers of the A group, but does seem to be present in the C fiber units which have been studied. It is difficult to determine the significance of the apparent lack of specificity of thermally sensitive A fibers compared to the apparent specificity of the C fibers in mediating thermal sensations. Additional information concerning the sensitivity of an organism to thermal stimulation is needed in order to aid in the interpretation of these electrophysiological data.

The work to be reported here consists of psychophysical and electro-

physiological measurements of the temperature sensitivity of cats. Both
methods of measurement employed identical skin sites and temporal configurations of thermal stimulation. In order to change the conditions of
measurement systematically, response measurements were made after the
skin had been adapted to temperatures between 29° and 44°C.

RESULTS

The mean thermal thresholds of an avoidance response were obtained
from two cats using a modified method of limits technique for presentation
of thermal stimuli. The thermal stimulator was strapped to the shaved skin
of the left inner thigh. The cats were trained to use a thermal stimulus as
a cue to lift their right rear leg in order to avoid a mild electric shock. After
the skin had been adapted to one of the several temperatures between 29°
and 44°C for twenty minutes, a graded series of changes in the temperature
of the stimulator was presented at intervals varying from 1 to 3 min duration. The temperature of the stimulator during these stimulations was
either increased or decreased at the rate of 1.5°C/sec until the cat terminated it by lifting its leg, or until it was terminated with an electric shock.
The temperature of the stimulator was then returned to the adapting
temperature. The results of measurements of the warm and cool thresholds,
as a function of the temperature to which the skin was adapted, are shown
in Figure 19-1. In the lower part of the figure, when the skin had been
adapted to 29°C, it was necessary to lower the temperature of the stimulator
by 9°C, or to 20°C before the cats used this cooling as a cue to avoid mild
electric shock. The cool threshold remained approximately constant at
−9°C. up to and including an adapting temperature of 33°C. At higher
adapting temperatures the cool threshold increased by an amount equal to
the increase in adapting temperature above 33°C. The line fitted to these
threshold points has a slope of −1.

The upper part of Figure 19-1 shows the avoidance thresholds to increases in the temperature of the stimulator. When the skin had been
adapted to 29°C, it was necessary to increase the temperature of the stimulator by 22°C before the cats used the warming as a cue to avoid electric
shock. After adaptation to 44°C, it was necessary to increase the temperature
of the stimulator by 6°C in order for the cats to successfully avoid electric
shock. Thresholds at intermediate adapting temperatures are shown as intermediate to these extremes. A straight line, fitted by the least squares method,
best describe these thresholds. The line has a slope of approximately −1,
which indicates that in order for the cats to use warming as a cue to avoid
electric shock, it was necessary to raise the stimulator temperature to
approximately 51°C, regardless of the temperature to which the skin had
been adapted.

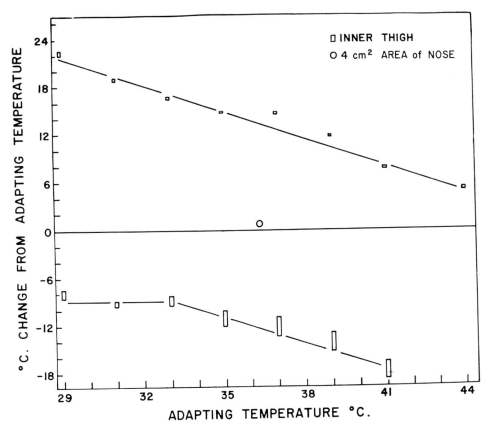

Figure 19-1. Thresholds, measured by the conditioned avoidance response method, to warm and cool stimuli applied over a 6 cm² area of the inner thigh using conducted thermal energy. The bar height represents the standard error of the means of repeated threshold measurements obtained on two cats. Also shown is the avoidance threshold to radiant energy applied to the 4 cm² area of the nose.

These results are consistent with similar measurements made on the shaved skin of the back (Kenshalo, 1964) and on the footpad of the cat (Kenshalo, Duncan, and Weymark, 1967). Furthermore, temperatures this high have been shown to be noxious to the cat (Kenshalo, 1964, Rice and Kenshalo, 1962). The results indicate that cats are not able to sense mild warming of the stimulator applied to the shaved skin of the inner thigh.

Yet, this poses a question, for cats are known to be able to sense areas of greater radiant energy flux density in which to bask, e.g., in sunny window or before a fire. A search for this warmth-sensitive area of skin shows that it is the nose and its surrounding skin areas. Shock avoidance thresholds, using radiant energy as a cue, show that the cat can sense an increase in skin temperature of about 1°C applied to a 4 cm² area around the nose. This is comparable to the sensitivity of the human forehead for a similar area of exposure (Kenshalo, Decker and Hamilton, in press).

Two radically different conditions of sensitivity to warmth exist in the skin of the inner thigh and the skin around the nose. Comparisons of the neural activity resulting from thermal stimulation of these two areas may provide information about the nature of the neural code for thermal stimulation. In making these preliminary comparisons the question of specificity of response of individual nerve fibers has been ignored. The attitude was adopted that any change in neural activity of a fiber constitutes a potential signal to the central nervous system concerning peripheral events. In order to quantify changes in neural activity in few-fiber preparations, the integration technique was used which was first introduced by Beidler (1953).

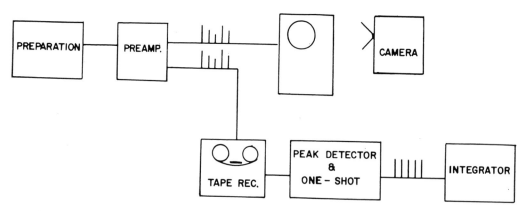

Figure 19-2. Diagram of the recording and neural response analysis equipment. Neural activity was recorded on magnetic tape. The tape playback was fed into a window circuit peak detector, and a one-shot multivibrator which transformed all spikes well above the noise level into spikes of uniform height and width. Thus, the integrated records shown in later figures depend only upon the frequency of the neural activity.

Figure 19-2 shows a diagram of the apparatus which was used to record and analyze the neural activity. Small twigs of either the saphenous or infraorbital nerves, which showed activity changes in response to thermal stimulation of the skin, were placed on electrodes and, after suitable amplification, their activity was displayed on an oscilloscope. Photographic records were obtained to show the actual activity and changes in the temperature of the stimulator. In addition, the neural activity was recorded on magnetic tape, the playback of which was fed into a peak detector, window circuit, and one-shot multivibrator. This device was set to transform action potentials, which appeared above the noise level, into spikes of uniform amplitude and duration. Recordings were made of the inte-

grated activity by means of a Sanborn recorder and logarithmic preamplifier
with a 0.5 sec time constant.

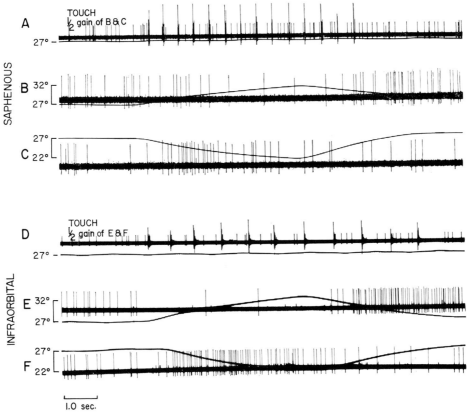

Figure 19-3. Neural activity in "few-fiber" preparations taken from the saphenous and
infraorbital nerves of the cat in response to tactile and thermal stimuli. A and D show
activity, at a maintained skin temperature of 27°C, to tapping the thermal stimulator,
in the saphenous and infraorbital preparations, respectively. In both records, the gain
was one-half that used for the remaining records. B and E show the characteristic decrease in neural activity as a result of warming the skin from 27° to 32°C, while C and
F show the increase in neural activity attendant with cooling the skin from 27° to 22°C.
The rate of temperature change was about 1°C/sec.

Representative samples of the action potentials found in the saphenous
and infraorbital nerves are shown in Figure 19-3. Records A and D show the
activity changes in response to mechanical stimulation produced by tapping
the thermal stimulator when the skin was maintained at 27°C. In both A
and D the gain was one-half of that used on the remaining records. Traces
B and E show the characteristic decrease in neural activity as the result of
warming the skin from 27° to 32°C, while C and F show the increase in
neural activity which results when the skin is cooled from 27° to 22°C.

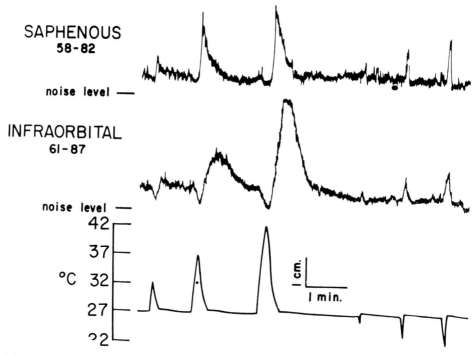

Figure 19-4. Samples of the integrated neural response to warming and cooling the skin taken from "few-fiber" preparations of the saphenous and infraorbital nerves of the cat. The very small spike activity, seen especially in records E and F of Figure 19-3, was excluded from all integrated records by the window circuit.

In Figure 19-4 are shown samples of the integrated responses in twigs of the saphenous and infraorbital nerves to warming by 5°, 10°, and 15° and to cooling of 1°, 3° and 5°C from an adapting temperature of 27°C. The window circuit was set to pass only the larger spike activity to the one-shot multivibrator. The very small spikes, seen especially in records E and F of Figure 19-3, were excluded from all records of integrated activity. In both preparations there was a relatively constant level of activity at the maintained skin temperature. This is shown by the fact that the steady state integrated response is above the noise level. Upon warming the skin of the inner thigh, there was a slight decrease in the neural activity of the saphenous nerve twig. This suppression of activity in this preparation appeared to be independent of the degree of warming applied. It was about as large for 5° warming as it was for 15°C. In the infraorbital nerve, however, the degree of suppression increased with the degree of warming. In both preparations there was a transient increase in activity when the stimulator was cooled to the original adapting temperature of 27°C. Cooling the preparations by 1°, 3°, and 5°C had substantially the same effects on the activity seen in both preparations, although in this preparation the saphenous twig appeared to be a little more sensitive to cooling than the infraorbital twig.

The amount of warm suppression and cool enhancement in the neural activity of the saphenous twigs, which resulted from various degrees of warming or cooling, may be examined as a function of the temperature to which the skin has been adapted. Such a series of integrated responses resulting from initial increases and initial decreases in skin temperature are shown in Figure 19-5. As can be seen, when the initial change in the stimulator temperature was toward warming, there was a suppression of activity, the warming response. This was followed by an enhancement of activity which was the result of the return of the stimulator to the original adapting temperature. The degree of suppression, however, like that shown in Figure 19-4, does not appear to be closely related to the degree of warming. At higher adapting temperatures the amount of warm suppression appears to be slightly greater. When the initial change in the temperature of the stimulator was toward cooling, there was an increase in activity followed by a slight suppression of activity which was the result of the return of the stimulator temperature to the original adapting temperature.

In order to combine the responses of several preparations, the response amplitude obtained from a particular stimulus intensity was computed as a percentage of the maximum response obtained at a particular adapting temperature. Figure 19-6 shows the mean relative response amplitudes of four saphenous nerve preparations which resulted from various intensities of thermal stimulation. A separate curve has been plotted for each adapting temperature. It is apparent from Figure 19-6 that the relative size of the cool enhancement is proportional to the intensity of the cool stimulus. That is, a small temperature decrease produced a small phasic increase in neural activity, and a large temperature decrease produced a large phasic increase in neural activity. On the other hand, the amount of warm suppression does not appear to show such a close relationship with the intensity of stimulation. At the lower adapting temperatures practically all of the suppression of neural activity occurred with intensities of warming of less than $3°C$. For example, when the skin had been adapted to $27°C$, warming the skin by $3°$ produced almost as much suppression in activity of the saphenous twig as warming it by $15°C$.

Figure 19-7 presents curves of constant magnitudes for increases in neural activity, relative to the maxima, as a function of the temperature to which the skin was adapted. These curves were obtained, from the data shown in Figure 19-6, by plotting the intensity of cooling required to produce 70, 80, and 90 per cent of the maximum response obtained at that adapting temperature. The curves show that at adapting temperatures of

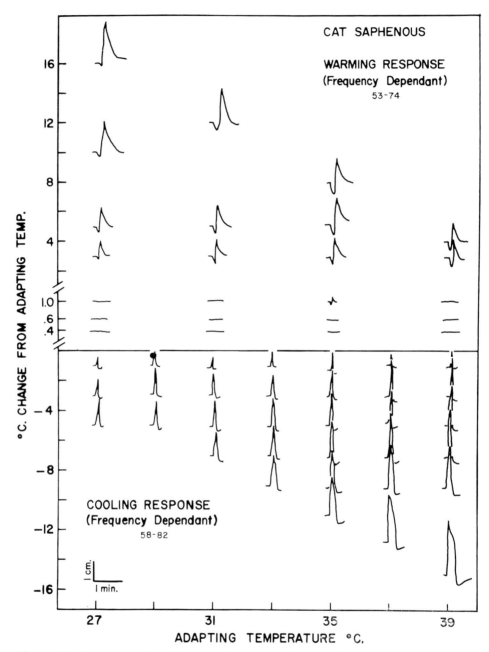

Figure 19-5. A sample series of integrated responses obtained from a "few-fiber" preparation of the saphenous nerve. The skin had first been adapted to each adapting temperature for five minutes before the warm and cool stimuli were presented. The responses
to warm stimuli were obtained from one preparation while those to cool stimuli were
obtained from a different preparation.

less than 31°C, a relative constant degree of cooling was required to produce a constant relative increase in the amplitude of the integrated neural activity record. At higher adapting temperatures greater intensities of cooling are required to produce the same relative increase in response amplitude. The behaviorally measured cool thresholds, shown in Figure 19-1, are re-

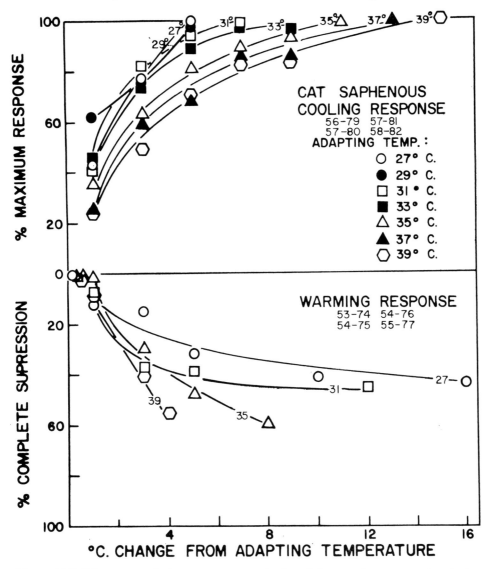

Figure 19-6. The mean relative response magnitudes of four saphenous nerve preparations as a function of the intensity of the stimuli. In the case of responses to cooling, 100 per cent response amplitude was arbitrarily chosen as the maximum response height which was obtained at each of the adapting temperatures. A 100 per cent response to warming was chosen as the integrated level when no neural activity was present.

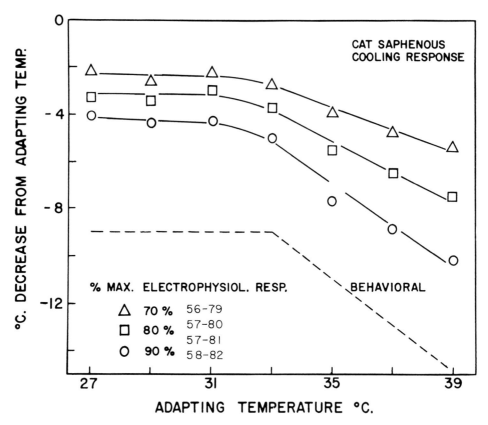

Figure 19-7. Equal response magnitude curves taken from the integrated responses in the "few-fiber" preparations of the saphenous nerve for cool stimuli as a function of the temperature to which the skin of the thigh was adapted. The behaviorally obtained cool threshold curve is also shown for comparison.

produced on Figure 19-7 for comparison purposes. While the behavioral thresholds are considerably larger than even the 90 per cent electrophysiological response curve, they are of similar shape. The large behavioral thresholds probably reflect, at least in part, the insensitivity of the avoidance conditioning method as a means of threshold measurement and the importance of response latency when the rate of the stimulator temperature change is 1.5°C/sec.

Similar curves for equal response magnitudes were not drawn for the warm suppression obtained in the saphenous nerve because behavioral thresholds to warm stimuli were not obtained on the inner thigh. It is believed that the behavioral measurements which were obtained are the result of the operation of a different mechanism (that of pain), a discussion of which is beyond the scope of this paper.

When the same procedures were repeated using twigs of the infraorbital nerve and the site of stimulation was the upper lip adjacent to the nose, a series of integrated responses were obtained on four preparations, one of which is shown in Figure 19-8. As can be seen, the degree of warm suppression is clearly a function of the intensity of warming at all adapting temperatures. One of the interesting features of this series of measurements was that even at very small changes, e.g., 0.4°C, a discernible change in the integrated response was frequently obtained.

The relative response magnitudes to various intensities of stimulation, as a function of the temperature to which the skin was adapted, are shown in Figure 19-9. The relative responses to cooling obtained from the infraorbital nerve are similar to those obtained from the saphenous nerve. However, the relative responses to various intensities of warming are markedly different from those obtained from twigs of the saphenous nerve. Here, the degree of suppression was graded to the intensity of the stimulus throughout the entire range of warm stimulations. Furthermore, warming to a constant temperature of 43°C, regardless of the original adapting temperature, resulted in almost complete suppression in all of the preparations.

Figure 19-10 shows curves of constant magnitudes for changes in the neural activity, relative to the maxima, as a function of the temperature to which the skin was adapted. As in the saphenous preparations, 70, 80, and 90 per cent of the maximum responses were used. The curves in the lower section of Figure 19-10 represent the cooling responses. While they differ in shape from those obtained from the saphenous nerve, they do show that small decreases in the temperature of the stimulator produced relatively larger changes in the response amplitude at low adapting temperatures than at high ones. With respect to the suppression of activity to warming the stimulator, the curve for 90 per cent suppression had a slope of about −1. This shows that this degree of suppression was obtained when the temperature of the stimulator was raised to about 42°C, regardless of the temperature to which the skin had been adapted. This is a similar function for the face region obtained by electrophysiological methods as that obtained by behavioral methods from the inner thigh, except that it is about 8°C lower. Unfortunately, behavioral measurements of the sensitivity of the face at various adapting temperatures have not been obtained. The curves for 70 and 80 per cent relative warm suppression show functions which are generally similar in shape to the human warm threshold of the forearm (Kenshalo, Nafe and Brooks, 1960) and the back (Kenshalo, 1964) .

CONCLUSIONS AND DISCUSSION

There are many issues raised by the data presented which should be discussed but time and space do not permit it. It should also be remembered

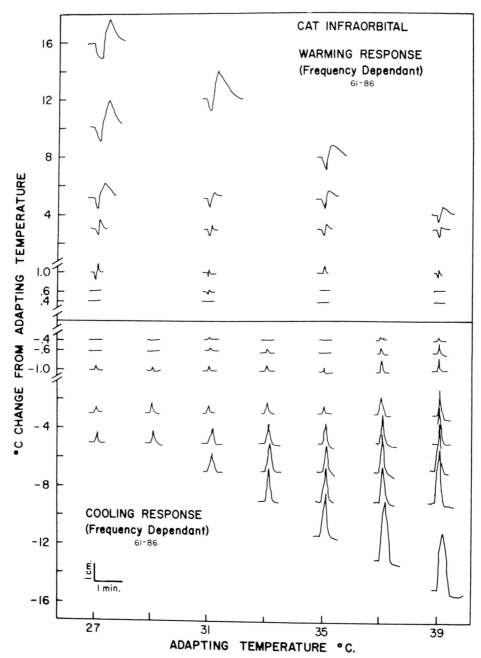

Figure 19-8. A sample series of integrated responses obtained from a "few-fiber" preparation of the infraorbital nerve. As with those shown in Figure 19-5, the skin had first been adapted to each adapting temperature for five minutes before the warm and cool stimuli were presented. Unlike those shown in Figure 19-5, these were all obtained from the same preparation.

that these are preliminary data and that the methods of stimulation and measurement, both behavioral and electrophysiological, are not yet sufficiently refined to allow precise relationships to be determined. Furthermore, there is no reason, which is substantially better than hope, that the index of peripheral neural activity used here should match measurements of temperature sensitivity obtained by behavioral methods.

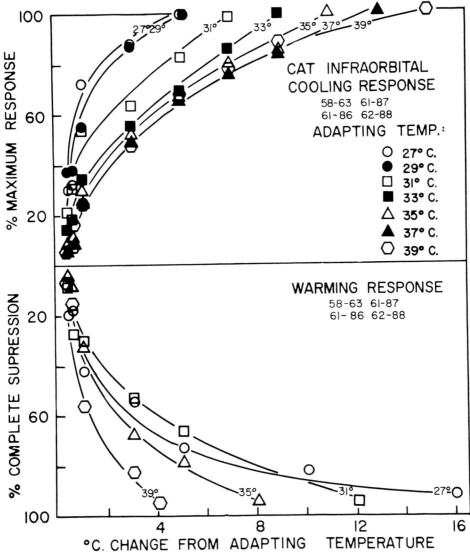

Figure 19-9. The mean relative response magnitude of four infraorbital nerve preparations as a function of the intensity of the stimuli. The criteria of 100 per cent response amplitude were the same as those used in plotting the curves obtained from the saphenous nerve, shown in Figure 19-6.

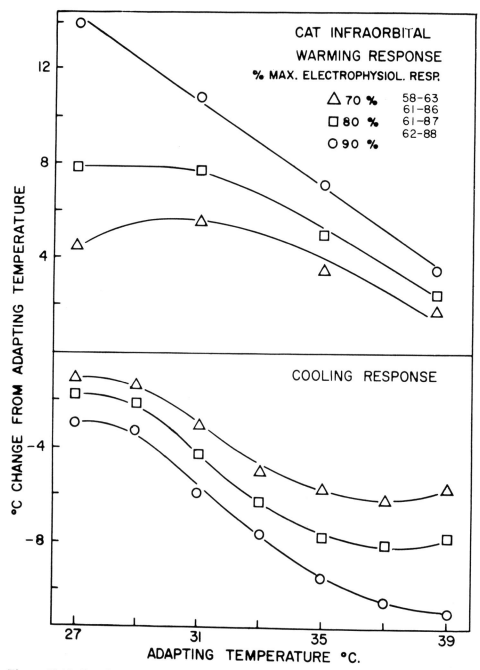

Figure 19-10. Equal response magnitude curves taken from the integrated responses in the "few-fiber" preparations of the infraorbital nerve for warm and cool stimuli as a function of the temperature to which the skin of the face was adapted.

The main aim of this investigation was to obtain information about the nature of the peripheral neural code which is initiated by warming or cooling the skin and which is associated with sensations of warmth and cool. As a result of the work of others and the data presented here, at least two kinds of neural codes appear reasonable. The first adopts the premise that warm and cool sensitivities are separate sensory systems and are the result of the operation of different sets of receptors and peripheral nerve fibers. The selective sensitivity of different C fibers to warming or cooling the skin fulfills this requirement. Different C fibers, some of which increase their frequency of discharge to warming the skin and others which also increase the frequency of their activity when the skin is cooled have been found in both the saphenous and infraorbital nerves of cats (Hensel, Iggo, and Witt, 1960; Iriuchijima and Zotterman, 1960).

Behavioral thermal threshold measurements taken on the inner thigh and the area around the nose showed that only the latter area was sensitive to mild warming. It appears, therefore, that increased C fiber activity in the saphenous nerve does not contribute to a central nervous system process so that an avoidance response can be conditioned to warming the skin of the inner thigh. It is not reasonable, on the basis of present evidence, to deny "warm" sensitive C fibers in the saphenous nerve a role in sensation in order to account for the lack of warmth sensitivity of the inner thigh and to ascribe that role to them in accounting for the warmth sensitivity of the face. Perhaps the C fiber function, rather than being directly concerned with sensory processes, is that of regulating the "synaptic gate bias," as suggested by Melzack and Wall (1965).

An alternative, and one suggested by the data presented here, is that cooling the skin is coded as an increase in neural activity while the neural code for warming the skin is a decrease in the activity of these same fibers. A summary of the behavioral evidence shows that cats are sensitive to cooling the inner thigh but are not sensitive to mild warming. They are sensitive to mild warm stimulation applied to the nose and face region. Electrophysiological measurements of nerve activity show that some nerve fibers in both the infraorbital and the saphenous nerves show graded increases in their integrated response amplitude to graded intensities of cooling the skin. Graded decreases in the integrated response amplitude occurred in fibers of the infraorbital nerve when the skin of the cheek was warmed. Fibers in the saphenous nerve showed some relationship between degree of warming and decreases in the integrated response amplitude but it was slight. The difference between the neural activity in the two nerves is even more striking when the durations of the change in the integrated neural response amplitude in response to warming are compared.

In Figure 19-11, warming the inner thigh and cheek of cats by 10°, 15° and 20°C from an adapting temperature of 25°C produced transient decreases in activity in some fibers of the saphenous nerve. The duration of this transient decrease was only about 15 sec, even though the temperature increase was maintained for another 45 sec. In the fibers of the infraorbital the decrease in activity lasted for the duration of the increase in temperature.

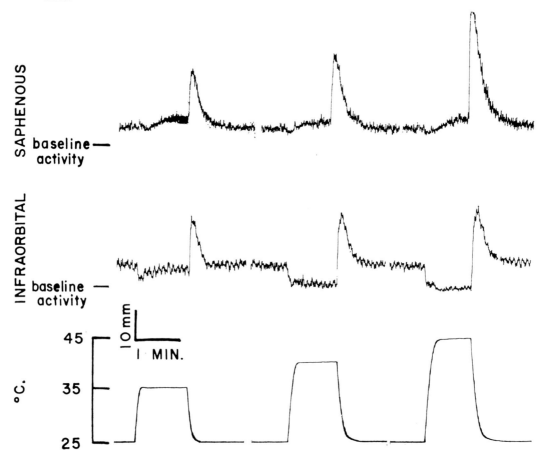

Figure 19-11. Samples of the integrated response to warming the skin of the inner thigh and cheek by 10°, 15°, and 20°C, from an adapting temperature of 25°C for 1 min duration. The transient decrease in the integrated neural activity in twigs of the saphenous nerve lasted for only about 15 sec even though the temperature increase persisted for another 45 sec. The decrease in the integrated activity in twigs of the infraorbital nerve lasted from the duration of the temperature increase and were graded by the intensity of the warming.

REFERENCES

Beidler, L. M. Properties of chemoreceptors of tongue of rat. *J. Neurophysiol.*, 1953, **16**, 595.

Blix, M. Experimentelle Beiträge zur Lösung der Frage über die specifische Energie der Hautnerven. *Ztachr. Biol.,* 1884, **20,** 141.

Boman, K. Elektrophysiologische Untersuchungen über die Thermoreceptoren der Gegichshaut. *Acta Physiol. Scand.,* 1958, **44,** 79. (Suppl. 149)

Dodt, E., & Zotterman, Y. The discharge of specific cold fibers at high temperatures (The paradoxical cold) . *Acta Physiol. Scand.,* 1952, **26,** 358. (a)

Dodt, E., & Zotterman, Y. Mode of action of warm receptors. *Acta Physiol. Scand.,* 1952, **26,** 345. (b)

Donaldson, H. H. Research on the temperature sense. *Mind,* 1885, **10,** 399.

Douglas, W. W., Ritchie, J. M., & Straub, R. W. The role of non-myelinated fibers in signalling cooling of the skin. *J. Physiol. (London),* 1960, **150,** 266.

Ebaugh, F., & Thauer, R. Influence of various environmental temperatures on the cold and warmth thresholds. *J. Appl. Physiol.,* 1950, **3,** 173.

Goldscheider, A. Die spezifische Energie der Temperaturnerven. *Mh. Prak. Derm.,* 1884, **3,** 198.

Hensel, H. Afferente Impulse aus den Kältereceptoren der äusseren Haut. *Pflüger Arch. Ges. Physiol.,* 1952, **256,** 195.

Hensel, H., & Boman, K. K. A. Afferent impulses in cutaneous sensory nerves in human subjects. *J. Neurophysiol.,* 1960, **23,** 564.

Hensel, H., Iggo, A., & Witt, I. A quantitative study of sensitive cutaneous thermoreceptors with C afferent fibers. *J. Physiol. (London),* 1960, **153,** 113.

Hensel, H., & Zotterman, Y. The response of the cold receptors to constant cooling. *Acta Physiol. Scand.,* 1951, **22,** 96.

Iggo, A. An electrophysiological analysis of afferent fibers in primate skin. *Acta Neuroveg. (Wien),* 1963, **24,** 225.

Iriuchijima, J., & Zotterman, Y. The specificity of afferent cutaneous C fibers in mammals. *Acta Physiol. Scand.,* 1960, **49,** 267.

Kenshalo, D. R. The temperature sensitivity of furred skin of cats. *J. Physiol. (London),* 1964, **172,** 439.

Kenshalo, D. R., Decker, T., & Hamilton, A. Comparison of areal summation on the forehead, forearm, and back produced by radiant and conducted heat. *J. Comp. Physiol. Psychol.,* in press.

Kenshalo, D. R., Duncan, D. G., & Weymark, C. Thresholds for thermal stimulation of the inner thigh, footpad, and face of cats. *J. Comp. Physiol. Psychol.,* 1967, **63,** 133.

Kenshalo, D. R., Nafe, J. P., & Brooks, B. Variations in thermal sensitivity. *Science,* 1961, **134,** 104.

Lele, P. P. Relationship between cutaneous thermal thresholds, skin temperature, and cross-sectional area of the stimulus. *J. Physiol. (London),* 1954, **126,** 191.

Melzack, R., & Wall, P. D. Pain mechanisms: A new theory. *Science,* 1965, **150,** 971.

Nagaki, J., Yamashita, S., & Sato, M. Neural response of cat to taste stimuli of varying temperatures. *Jap. J. Physiol.,* 1964, **14,** 67.

Rice, C. E., & Kenshalo, D. R. Nociceptive threshold measurements in the cat. *J. Appl. Physiol.,* 1962, **17,** 1009.

Witt, I., & Hensel, H. Afferente Impulse aus der Extremitätenhaut der Katze bei thermischer und mechanischer Reizung. *Pflüger Arch. Ges. Physiol.,* 1959, **268,** 582.

Zotterman, Y. Specific action potentials in the lingual nerve of the cat. *Skand. Arch. Physiol.,* 1936, **75,** 105.

DISCUSSION

Dr. A. Iggo: I would, first of all, like to say how nice it is to find attempts being made to correlate neural and psychological data, but I would
also like to point out the possibility that this task is not made any easier
by the existence of a variety of different types of afferent units in peripheral
trunks. The first point I would like to make, one that Dr. Kenshalo himself
has made, is that it may be a hopeful assumption that the electrical activity
reported from the nerve corresponds with the afferent input which is
actually used by the animal for any particular purpose. In other words, the
central nervous system may be making a selection from the type of data
which is being fed in. This is particularly important when one makes a
comparison of different parts of the body surface, and here I think you
picked a situation in the saphenous and infraorbital where it is quite important. The reason for this is that in the saphenous nerve there are many
myelinated afferent fibers which can be excited by a fall of temperature, as
Dr. Hensel has been describing. The slowly adapting mechanoreceptive
fibers display much greater sensitivity to a change in temperature than the
rapidly adapting mechanoreceptors. Since these axons are all myelinated,
they have big action potentials and are easy to pick up. The thermal receptors in the saphenous nerve are nonmyelinated and, therefore, they contribute very much less to the electrical records and they are more likely to
be overlooked in preparations where you are dealing with the whole nerve.
The integrated responses that you deal with are largely coming from
mechanoreceptors which display also a thermal response and especially those
that adapt slowly. The situation is, however, very different in the infraorbital nerve where in addition to the mechano-receptors which are excited
by temperature and which are myelinated, there are also many myelinated
thermal receptors, and these myelinated thermal receptors now start to make
a significant contribution to the integrated record. And I think if I could
show your last slide again (Fig. 19-11 of the text) I could perhaps illustrate
what I mean. In the saphenous record there is a very small change when
the temperature is raised and this, I would suggest, is due to the fact that
the activity is very largely in myelinated fibers. They dominate the record.
The nonmyelinated cold fibers do not really show through very well. When
you come down to the infraorbital nerve, where the fibers are much larger,
and greater changes occur with the rise in temperature, you are now dealing
with a situation where it is known that myelinated thermal receptors occur
where the inactivity shows through more on the record not only because
they are firing at higher frequencies than the nonmyelinated fibers, but also
because the action potentials are larger. This is a factor that has to be taken
into account, in making an analysis of this type of preparation or this type

of record. [Ed. note: See Dr. Iggo's paper for a fuller explanation of this statement.]

DR. KENSHALO: You are quite right, Dr. Iggo, these considerations must be taken into account in trying to correlate the behavioral and electro-physiological responses. Nevertheless, the records which I showed give a fair representation of what the CNS sees when a thermal stimulus is applied to the skin, regardless of the receptive elements from which they come.

DR. IGGO: I am not sure that the central nervous system sees only the large action potentials.

DR. KENSHALO: But you call anything which responds exclusively to temperature a thermal receptor, and that is quite right from your point of view. I wish to carry it one step further and limit myself to an investigation of those thermal neural responses which have behavioral consequences. [Ed. note: Dr. Kenshalo wishes to add the following to his remarks at the conference.] The window circuit on the peak detector was set to exclude small fiber activity from the integrated records, not because I feel that they lack a function, but for two other reasons. First, this is an initial attempt at response measurement correlations and one must start somewhere. Second, we did not start with nonmyelinated nerve activity because their role in sensory processes appears less promising. This is suggested by the observations that C fibers, which respond with increased activity to warm or to cool stimuli, have been described in both the saphenous and the infra-orbital nerves. The fact that we were able to condition behavioral responses to warm stimuli applied to the nose but not to the inner thigh suggests that C fiber activity in the saphenous nerve is not involved in mediating a conditioned response. There is no reason, that we can determine, that we should assume that C fiber activity in the infraorbital nerve is involved in mediating that conditioned behavioral response.

DR. Y. ZOTTERMAN: There was a paragraph or two in Dr. Kenshalo's paper — when he talked about the warm fibers, described by Dodt and me, that may to a certain extent respond as well to gustatory stimuli — which reminded me of some old research (Zotterman, 1936). I recorded the electrical activity in fine strands of the lingual nerve of the cat in response to various stimuli. When a drop of water at 14°C was dropped on the tongue, the moment of contact was signalled by large touch spikes followed by much smaller spikes from the cold fibers. When a drop of water at 80°C was applied, again the moment of contact was shown by large touch potentials but smaller spikes followed. These were slightly diphasic and somewhat larger than those produced by the cold. Now if you let a drop of water at 80°C fall on your own tongue, you get a warm and slightly burning sensation. One drop has not the heat capacity to produce more than a smarting or slight pain sensation. In other preparations, drops of water at 50°, 60°,

70°, and 80°C were used. The 50°C drop was at the threshold for the warm fiber response in this preparation. Again, these fibers showed slightly larger spikes than the cold fibers. At 60° and 70°C, there are still more action potentials and even still more at 80°C. This suggests that these fibers have nothing to do with pain but are actually warm fibers. They were not gustatory fibers. If you carefully examine Figure 19-12 you will find that whenever the strength of the thermal or the mechanical stimuli exceeded the pain threshold a certain type of spikes (seen isolated in Figure 19-12E) appeared in the electroneurogram from this branch of the lingual nerve. These fibers were not active except when nociceptive stimuli were applied. When applied to your own tongue such stimuli gave rise to pain. There is no doubt today that these particular spikes are derived from unmyelinated nerve fibers conducting at very low rates.

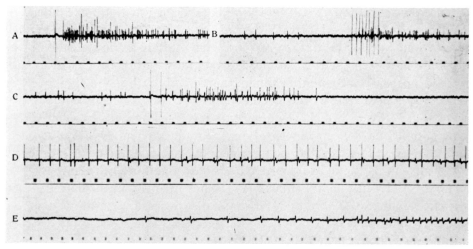

Figure 19-12. Afferent spike potentials from different sensory fibers of a fine strand of the lingual nerve of the cat when applying different stimuli to the tongue: (A) the effect of a drop of water of 14°C falling on the tongue; (B) first the effect of a faint puff of air which does not cause any visible deformation of the surface, followed by the effect of a stronger puff of air which makes a definite deformation; (C) a drop of 80°C falling upon the tongue; (D) the effect of pressing a pointed rod into the tongue; (E) squirting hot water (60°C) over the tongue (Fig. 5, Zotterman, Y. *Skand. Arch. Physiol.*, 1936, **75**, 105).

DR. C. PFAFFMANN: Did you try the gustatory stimuli?

DR. ZOTTERMAN: Yes, they are not sensitive to that. About six years ago we described the activity in fine strands of the infraorbital nerve of cats (Fig. 5, Iriuchijima and Zotterman, 1960). From a steady state temperature of 33°C, we raised the temperature of the skin to 39°C. At 33°C there were several cold fibers which were active, but immediately upon raising the skin temperature the activity in these stopped and activity in another, clearly different, fiber started. When the radiation stopped, activity in this latter fiber also stopped and, after a short pause, activity commenced in the first fibers. I do not know the conduction velocity of these fibers, but I would venture a guess that they were C fibers.

DR. P. D. WALL: When Taub and I studied the response of cells in the trigeminal nucleus to cutaneous stimulation (Wall and Taub, 1962), the only cells we could discover with a high dynamic sensitivity to heating had their receptive field inside the nose or on the edge of the nares. This region is supplied by the ethmoidal nerve. One might suggest that branches of this nerve, rather than the infraorbital, should be examined for fibers responding to warming.

At the end of your paper you were asking the question, "Can one find any property of peripheral nerve firing, preferably the response of one type of fiber, which correlates with the behavior of the animal?" I think one can conclude from Dr. Hensel's paper that one will not find a homomorphic relationship between the firing of any one type of fiber and sensation or behavior. He gave five criteria for temperature-sensitive fibers. He showed that the response of a "warm" fiber depended on the previous adapting temperature and the rate of change of the stimulus. An increased firing could be set off either by a rapid increase of temperature or by a decrease from a high adapting temperature. Given such properties, no one fiber can signal skin temperature. However, the time course of firing in single fibers and the relative firing rates between different fibers does contain the relevant information which would allow the CNS to decide what has actually happened to the skin.

DR. KENSHALO: In the first place, we are working on only one side of the steady state discharge curve, that Dr. Hensel was describing, for both the electrophysiological and behavioral responses. Our steady state temperature, or, as we prefer, adapting temperature, ranged only from 29° to 44 °C. With regard to your question, the data suggest the possibility that warming may be signalled by a decrease in frequency of discharge. Admittedly it is only a hope that there will be isomorphism between neural activity and the behavioral measures, but one is bound to look before discarding it as a possibility. In any event we must have information on the nature of the peripheral neural code before you, recording from the first central cell, can interpret your data in terms of its probable function.

DR. B. S. ROSNER: One difficulty with the behavioral data, of course, is that it is terribly tricky to draw firm conclusions from negative results. A good example of that is the history of work on color vision in the cat. What I might suggest is that perhaps it is a lot easier to condition thermal responses when the stimulus is applied to the nose. Then, once you get that established, suppose you attempt to generalize by moving the position of the stimulator successively further away from the nose. You still may have a problem of technique here.

DR. KENSHALO: That is certainly a possibility. It has occurred to us and we intend to go back and take another closer look at the responses.

DR. PFAFFMANN: Just before concluding this session, since the general tenor of this whole discussion is relevant to things that I have been wondering about and that Dr. Zotterman and I have been debating, with regard to another modality, I think the crucial point here is that the same sensory functions should be investigated by behavioral methods as well as by electrophysiological procedures. This is absolutely essential and I think many of the debates that have been made are based on intuitive comparisons both at the sensory as well as at the behavioral level, and so the open questions here will not be resolved until both the physiological and behavioral dimensions are fed into this kind of analysis.

References

Iriuchijima, J., & Zotterman, Y. The specificity of afferent cutaneous C fibers in mammals. *Acta Physiol. Scand.,* 1960, **49,** 267.

Wall, P. D., & Taub, A. Four aspects of trigeminal nucleus and a paradox. *J. Neurophysiol.,* 1962, **25,** 110.

Zotterman, Y. Specific action potentials in the lingual nerve of cat. *Skan. Arch. Physiol.,* 1936, **75,** 105.

Chapter 20

SENSORY, MOTIVATIONAL, AND CENTRAL CONTROL DETERMINANTS OF PAIN

A New Conceptual Model*

R. Melzack and K. L. Casey†

THE PROBLEM OF PAIN, since the beginning of the century, has been dominated by the concept that pain is a sensory experience. Yet pain has a unique, distinctly unpleasant, affective quality that differentiates it from sensory experiences such as sight, hearing, or touch. It becomes overwhelming, demands immediate attention, and disrupts ongoing behavior and thought. It motivates or drives the organism into activity aimed at stopping the pain as quickly as possible. To consider only the sensory features of pain, and ignore its motivational and affective properties, is to look at only part of the problem, and not even the most important part at that (Cantril and Livingston, 1963; Chapman, Dingman, and Ginzberg, 1965). The theory that pain is a sensory modality is relatively recent. The traditional theory of pain in the 19th century (Marshall, 1894; Dallenbach, 1939) held that it is an affective *quale* — the opposite of pleasure — rather than a sensation, and emphasized the unpleasant affect (or "feeling") that forces the organism into action. That pain is comprised of both sensory and affective dimensions was clear to Sherrington who proposed simply that "mind rarely, probably never, perceives any object with absolute indifference, that is, without 'feeling' . . . affective tone is an attribute of all sensation, and among the attribute tones of skin sensation is skin pain" (Sherrington, 1900, p. 974).

The remarkable development of sensory physiology and psychophysics since Sherrington's time has given momentum to the concept of pain as a sensation and has overshadowed the role of affective and motivational processes. The sensory approach to pain, however, valuable as it has been, fails to provide a complete picture of pain processes. Even the concept of pain as a perception, with full recognition of past experience, attention, and other cognitive determinants of sensory quality and intensity (Barber, 1959; Livingston, 1953; Melzack, 1961), still neglects the crucial motiva-

---

*Supported by contract SD-193 from the Advanced Research Projects Agency of the U. S. Department of Defense.

†Supported by U. S. Public Health Service Special Fellowship from the National Institute of Mental Health, now at the Department of Physiology, University of Michigan.

tional dimension. Our purpose here is to present a model of the sensory, motivational, and cognitive determinants of pain.

THE NEED FOR A NEW APPROACH

The neglect of the motivational features of pain underscores a serious schism in pain research. Characteristically, textbooks in psychology and physiology deal with "pain sensation" in one section and "aversive drives and punishment" in another, with no indication that both are facets of the same phenomenon. This separation reflects the widespread acceptance of von Frey's (1895) specificity theory of pain, with its implicit psychological assumption (see Melzack and Wall, 1962) that "pain impulses" are transmitted from specific pain receptors in the skin directly to a pain center in the brain, so that sensory quality is determined solely by activity of the center. Although there is convincing physiological evidence (Iggo, 1960; Zotterman, 1959) that specialization exists within the somesthetic system, the clinical, physiological, and psychological evidence reviewed by Melzack and Wall ,1962; 1965) is overwhelmingly against the assumption that activity in one type of receptor, fiber, or spinal pathway elicits only one kind of sensation. Moreover, the concept of a pain center implies a "man-in-the-brain" who hears the alarm-bell ring, evaluates the meaning of the input, decides on a response strategy, and pushes the appropriate response button. To avoid this sort of animistic thinking, we must postulate relationships among sensory, motivational, and cognitive systems to account for the facts of behavior.

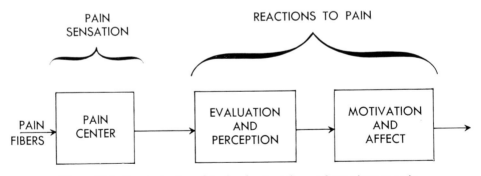

Figure 20-1. Conceptual model of pain sensation and reactions to pain.

The assumption that pain is a primary sensation has relegated motivational and cognitive processes to the role of "reactions to pain" (see Fig. 20-1), and has made them only "secondary considerations" in the whole pain process (Hardy, Wolff, and Goodell, 1952; Sweet, 1959). But the notion that motivational and cognitive processes must follow the primary pain

or medial thalamus (Albe-Fessard and Bowsher, 1965; Albe-Fessard and Kruger, 1962; Casey, 1966; Kruger and Albe-Fessard, 1960), where somato-sensory input, though predominant, is mixed with other sensory inputs (Bell *et al.*, 1964; Scheibel, Scheibel, Mollica, and Moruzzi, 1955; Starzl, Taylor, and Magoun, 1951).

The striking feature of the paramedial ascending system is its strategic relation to the limbic system and associated structures (Fig. 20-4). Its fibers penetrate the medial brainstem reticular formation and the midbrain central gray (Mehler *et al.*, 1960; Bowsher, 1957), which are reciprocally interconnected. The midbrain central gray is part of the "limbic midbrain area" (Nauta, 1958) that (a) projects diffusely to the adjacent reticular formation and mesencephalic tegmentum (Weisschedel, 1937); (b) connects reciprocally with the hypothalamic region via Schutz's fasciculus and thus permits interaction with the limbic forebrain areas by way of the medial forebrain bundle; (c) connects with the medial and intralaminar thalamic nuclei, and (d) receives connections from the granular frontal cortex (Nauta, 1964). Thus the phylogenetically old paramedial ascending system, which is separate from but in parallel with the newer neospino-thalamic projection system, gains access to the complex circuitry of the limbic system.

It is now well established that many limbic system structures play an important role in aversive drives or similar pain related behavior. At the mesencephalic level, stimulation in a region which includes the central gray, the ventral tectum and dorsal tegmentum produces strong aversive drive and behavior typical of responses to naturally occurring painful stimuli (Delgado, 1965; Hunsperger, 1956; Olds and Olds, 1963; Spiegel, Kletzkin and Szekeley, 1954). Lesions of the central gray and adjacent mid-brain tegmentum, in contrast, produce marked decreases in responsiveness to noxious stimuli (Melzack *et al.*, 1958; Skultety, 1958). At the thalamic level, "fear-like" responses, associated with escape behavior, have been elicited by stimulation in the dorsomedial and adjacent medial-intralaminar nuclei of the thalamus (Roberts, 1962). In the human, lesions in the medial thalamus have provided relief from intractable pain (Hecaen, Talairach, David, and Dell, 1949; Mark, Ervin, and Yakovlev, 1963).

Limbic forebrain areas have also been implicated in pain related processes. Electrical stimulation of the hippocampus, fornix, or amygdala may evoke escape or other attempts to stop stimulation (Delgado, 1955; Delgado, Rosvold and Looney, 1956), as well as defensive reactions (Hilton and Zbrozyna, 1963; MacLean and Delgado, 1953). After ablation of the amyg-dala and overlying cortex, cats show marked changes in affective behavior, including decreased responsiveness to noxious stimuli (Schreiner and Kling, 1953). Surgical section of the cingulum bundle, which connects the pos-

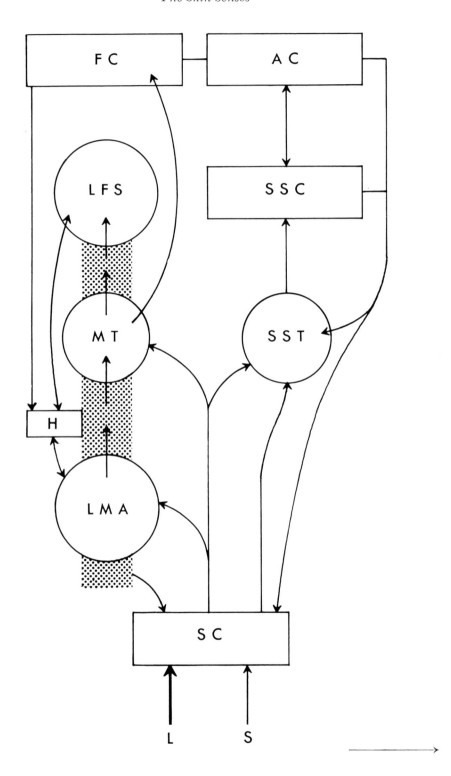

terior frontal cortex to the hippocampus, also produces a loss of "negative affect" associated with intractable pain (Foltz and White, 1962). This evidence indicates that limbic structures, although they play a role in many other functions (Pribram and Kruger, 1954), provide a neural basis for the aversive drive and affect that comprise the motivational dimension of pain.

Intimately related to the brain areas involved in aversive drive and sometimes overlapping with them are regions that are involved in approach responses and other behavior aimed at maintaining and prolonging stimulation. Such regions include the lateral hypothalamus, medial forebrain bundle, and septum (Olds and Milner, 1954; Olds and Olds, 1963). Stimulation of many of these areas, as well as some of the limbic forebrain structures, yields behavior in which the animal presses one bar to receive stimulation and another to stop it. These effects, which may be due to overlap of "aversive" and "approach" structures, are sometimes a function simply of intensity of stimulation, so that low level stimulation elicits approach and intense stimulation evokes avoidance (Grastyan, Czopf, Angyan, and Szabo, 1965). In addition, complex excitatory and inhibitory interactions among these areas (Olds and Olds, 1962; Stuart, Porter, and Adey, 1964; Tsubokawa and Sutin, 1963) may explain why aversive drive to noxious stimuli can be blocked by stimulation of positive reward areas in the lateral hypothalamus (Cox and Valenstein, 1965).

These psychophysiological data leave little doubt that the neural areas comprising the paramedial, reticular, and limbic systems are involved in the motivational and affective features of pain. The manner in which these areas are brought into play deserves consideration. The fact that there are inputs from other sensory systems as well as the cutaneous system (Bell *et al.*, 1964) indicates that these areas are not activated exclusively by noxious stimuli. Moreover, the somatic input has access to areas involved in

---

Figure 20-4. Schematic diagram of the anatomical foundation of the proposed pain model. *On the right:* thalamic and neocortical structures subserving discriminative capacity. *On the left:* reticular and limbic systems subserving motivational-affective functions. Ascending pathways from the spinal cord (SC) are (a) the dorsal column-lemniscal and dorsolateral tracts *(right ascending arrow)* projecting to the somatosensory thalamus (SST) and cortex (SSC), and (b) the anterolateral pathway *(left ascending arrow)* to the somatosensory thalamus via the neospinothalamic tract, and to the reticular formation *(stippled area)*, the limbic midbrain area (LMA) and medial thalamus (MT) via the paramedial ascending system. Descending pathways to spinal cord originates in somatosensory and associated cortical areas (AC) and in the reticular formation. Polysynaptic and reciprocal relationships in limbic and reticular systems are indicated. Other abbreviations: FC — frontal cortex; LFS — limbic forebrain structures (hippocampus, septum, amygdala, and associated cortex); H — hypothalamus. (Adapted from Nauta, W. J. H., *Brain,* 1958, **81,** 319.)

approach or avoidance, and some areas can produce both. On what basis are aversive rather than approach mechanisms triggered by the input?

We propose that these systems function as a *central intensity monitor;* that their activities are determined, in part at least, by the intensity of the T-cell output (the total number of active fibers and their rate of firing) after it has undergone modulation by the gate control system in the dorsal horns. The output of cells in the medial brainstem may be facilitated by the summation of input from spatially separate body sites and by the interaction of temporally dispersed inputs (Amassian and DeVito, 1954; Bell *et al.,* 1964). The poststimulus discharge activity of some of these cells lasts for many seconds (Casey, 1966), so that their activity may provide a measure of the intensity of the total T-cell output over relatively long periods of time. Essentially, both forms of summation transform discrete spatial and temporal information into intensity information. We propose that the output of these cells, up to a critical intensity level, activates those brain areas subserving positive affect and approach tendency. Beyond that level, the output activates areas underlying negative affect and aversive drive. We suggest, therefore, that the drive mechanisms associated with pain are activated when the somatosensory input into the motivational-affective system exceeds the critical level. This notion fits well with Grastyan's (Grastyan *et al.,* 1965) observations that animals seek low-intensity electrical stimulation of some limbic system structures, but avoid or actively try to stop high-intensity stimulation of the same areas. Signals from these limbic structures to motor mechanisms set the stage for response patterns that are aimed at dealing with the input on the basis of both the sensory information and cognitive processes.

The Central Control Determinants

There is convincing evidence that pain is influenced by cognitive or "higher central nervous system" activities. Anticipation of pain (Hill, Kornetsky, Flanary, and Wilker, 1952a), anxiety and attention (Hill *et al.,* 1952b), suggestion and placebos (Beecher, 1959; Melzack, Weisz, and Sprague, 1963), cultural background (Chapman and Jones, 1944), evaluation of the meaning of the pain-producing situation (Beecher, 1959), hypnosis (Barber, 1959), early experience (Melzack and Scott, 1957), and prior conditioning (Pavlov, 1927; 1928) all have a profound effect on pain experience and response. These activities, which are subserved, in part at least, by neocortical processes, may affect both sensory and affective experience or they may modify primarily the affective-motivational dimension. Thus, excitement in games or war appears to block both dimensions of pain (Livingston, 1953; Beecher, 1959), while suggestion (Melzack *et al.,* 1963;

Hernandez-Peon, R., & Hagbarth, K. E. Interaction between afferent and cortically induced reticular responses. *J. Neurophysiol.,* 1955, **18,** 43.

Hill, H. E., Kornetsky, C. H., Flanary, H. G., & Wikler, A. Studies on anxiety associated with anticipation of pain. I. Effects of morphine. *Arch. Neurol. (Chicago),* 1952, **67,** 612. (a)

Hill, H. E., Kornetsky, C. H., Flanary, H. G., & Wikler, A. Effects of anxiety and morphine on discrimination of intensities of painful stimuli. *J. Clin. Invest.,* 1952, **31,** 473. (b)

Hilton, S. M., & Zbrozyna, A. W. Amygdaloid region for defense reactions and its efferent pathway to the brain stem. *J. Physiol. (London),* 1963, **165,** 160.

Hunsperger, R. W. Affektreaktionen auf elekrische Reizung im Hirnstamm der Katze. *Helv. Physiol. Pharmacol. Acta,* 1956, **14,** 70.

Iggo, A., Cutaneous mechanoreceptors with afferent C fibers. *J. Physiol. (London),* 1960, **152,** 337.

Jabbur, S. J., & Towe, A. L. Cortical excitation of neurons in dorsal column nuclei of cat, including an analysis of pathways. *J. Neurophysiol.,* 1961, **24,** 499.

Kennedy, T. T., & Towe, A. L. Identification of a fast leminisco-cortical system in the cat. *J. Physiol. (London),* 1962, **160,** 535.

Kerr, D. I. B., Haugen, F. P., & Melzack, R. Responses evoked in the brainstem by tooth stimulation. *Amer. J. Physiol.,* 1955, **183,** 253.

King, H. E., Clausen, J., & Scarff, J. E. Cutaneous thresholds for pain before and after unilateral prefrontal lobotomy. *J. Nerv. Ment. Dis.,* 1950, **112,** 93.

Kruger, L., & Albe-Fessard, D. Distribution of responses to somatic afferent stimuli in the diencephalon of the cat under chloralose anesthesia. *Exp. Neurol.,* 1960, **2,** 442.

Livingston, W. K. What is pain? *Sci. Amer.,* 1953, **88,** 59.

MacLean, P. D., & Delgado, J. M. R. Electrical and chemical stimulation of fronto-temporal portion of limbic system in the waking animal. *Electroenceph. Clin. Neurophysiol.,* 1953, **5,** 91.

McMurray, G. A. Experimental study of a case of insensitivity to pain. *Arch. Neurol. (Chicago),* 1950, **64,** 650.

Magni, F., Melzack, R., Moruzzi, G., & Smith, C. J. Direct pyramidal influences on the dorsal column nuclei. *Arch. Ital. Biol.,* 1959, **97,** 357.

Mark, V. H., Ervin, F. R., & Yakovlev, P. I. Stereotactic thalamotomy. *Arch. Neurol. (Chicago),* 1963, **8,** 528.

Marshall, H. R. *Pain, Pleasure, and Aesthetics.* London, Macmillan, 1894.

Mehler, W. R. The mammalian "pain tract" in phylogeny. *Anat. Rec.,* 1957, **127,** 332.

Mehler, W. R., Feferman, M. E., & Nauta, W. J. H. Ascending axon degeneration following antero-lateral cordotomy. An experimental study in the monkey. *Brain,* 1960, **83,** 718.

Melzack, R. The perception of pain. *Sci. Amer.,* 1961, **204,** 41.

Melzack, R. Effects of early experience on behavior: Experimental and conceptual considerations. In P. H. Hoch & J. Zubin (Eds.) *Psychopathology of Perception.* New York: Grune & Stratton, 1965.

Melzack, R., & Haugen, F. P. Responses evoked at the cortex by tooth stimulation. *Amer. J. Physiol.,* 1957, **190,** 570.

Melzack, R., & Scott, T. H. The effects of early experience on the response to pain. *J. Comp. Physiol. Psychol.,* 1957, **50,** 155.

Melzack, R., Stotler, W. A., & Livingston, W. K. Effects of discrete brainstem lesions in cats on perception of noxious stimulation. *J. Neurophysiol.,* 1958, **21,** 353.

Melzack, R., & Wall, P. D. On the nature of cutaneous sensory mechanisms. *Brain,* 1962, **85,** 331.

Melzack, R., & Wall, P. D. Pain mechanisms: A new theory. *Science,* 1965, **150,** 971.

Melzack, R. Weisz, A. Z., & Sprague, L. T. Stratagems for controlling pain: Contributions of auditory stimulation and suggestion. *Exp. Neurol.,* 1963, **8,** 239.

Morin, F., Kitai, S. T., Portnoy, H., & Demirjian, C. Afferent projections to the lateral cervical nucleus: A microelectrode study. *Amer. J. Physiol.,* 1963, **204,** 667.

Morse, R. W., & Towe, A. L. The dual nature of the lemnisco-cortical afferent system in the cat. *J. Physiol. (London),* 1964, **171,** 231.

Nafe, J. P. The pressure, pain, and temperature senses. In C. A. Murchison (Ed.), *Handbook of General Experimental Psychology.* Worcester: Clark Univer. Press, 1934. Pp. 1037-1087.

Nauta, W. J. H. Hippocampal projections and related neural pathways to the midbrain in the cat. *Brain,* 1958, **81,** 319.

Nauta, W. J. H. Some efferent connections of the prefrontal cortex in the monkey. In J. M. Warren & K. Akert (Eds.), *The Frontal Granular Cortex and Behavior.* New York: McGraw-Hill, 1964.

Newman, P. P., & Wolstencroft, J. H. Medullary responses to stimulation of orbital cortex. *J. Neurophysiol.,* 1959, **22,** 516.

Olds, J., & Milner, P. Positive reinforcement produced by electrical stimulation of septal area and other regions of rat brain. *J. Comp. Physiol. Psychol.,* 1954, **47,** 419.

Olds, M. E., & Olds, J. Approach-escape interactions in the rat brain. *Amer. J. Physiol.,* 1962, **203,** 803.

Olds, M. E., & Olds, J. Approach-avoidance analysis of rat diencephalon. *J. Comp. Neurol.,* 1963, **120,** 259.

Pavlov, I. P. *Conditioned Reflexes.* Oxford: Milford, 1927.

Pavlov, I. P. *Lectures on Conditioned Reflexes.* New York: International, 1928.

Perl, E. R., & Whitlock, D. G. Somatic stimuli exciting spinothalamic projections to thalamic neurons in cat and monkey. *Exp. Neurol.,* 1961, **3,** 256.

Poggio, G. F., & Mountcastle, V. B. The functional properties of ventrobasal thalamic neurons studied in unanesthetized monkeys. *J. Neurophysiol.,* 1963, **26,** 775.

Pribram, K. H., & Kruger, L. Functions of the "olfactory brain." *Ann. NY Acad. Sci.,* 1954, **58,** 109.

Ramon y Cajal, S. *Histologie du Systeme Nerveux.* Madrid: Instituto Ramon y Cajal, 1952.

Roberts, W. W. Fearlike behavior elicited from dorsomedial thalamus of cat. *J. Comp. Physiol. Psychol.,* 1962, **55,** 191.

Rubins, J. L., & Friedman, E. D. Asymbolia for pain. *Arch. Neurol. (Chicago),* 1948, **60,** 554.

Scheibel, M., Scheibel, A., Mollica, A., & Moruzzi, G. Convergence and interaction of afferent impulses on single units of reticular formation. *J. Neurophysiol.,* 1955, **18,** 309.

Schilder, P., & Stengel, E. Asymbolia for pain. *Arch. Neurol. (Chicago),* 1931, **25,** 598.

Schreiner, L., & Kling, A. Behavioral changes following rhinencephalic injury in cat. *J. Neurophysiol.,* 1953, **16,** 643.

Semmes, J., & Mishkin, M. Somatosensory loss in monkeys after ipsilateral cortical ablation. *J. Neurophysiol.,* 1965, **28,** 473.

Sherrington, C. S. Cutaneous sensations. In E. A. Schäfer (Ed.), *Textbook of Physiology.* Vol. 2. Edinburgh: Pentland, 1900. Pp. 920-1001.

Shimazu, H., Yanagisawa, N., & Garoutte, B. Cortico-pyramidal influences on thalamic somatosensory transmission in the cat. *Jap. J. Physiol.,* 1965, **15,** 101.

Skultety, F. M. The behavioral effects of destructive lesions of the periaqueductal gray matter in adult cat. *J. Comp. Neurol.,* 1958, **110,** 337.

Spiegel, E. A., Kletzkin, M., & Szekeley, E. G. Pain reactions upon stimulation of the tectum mesencephali. *J. Neuropath. Exp. Neurol.,* 1954, **13,** 212.

Starzl, T. E., Taylor, C. A., & Magoun, H. W. Collateral afferent excitation of reticular formation and brain stem. *J. Neurophysiol.,* 1951, **14,** 479.

Sternbach, R. A. Congenital insensitivity to pain. *Psychol. Bull.,* 1963, **60,** 252.

Stuart, D. G., Porter, R. W., & Adey, W. R. Hypothalamic unit activity. II. Central and peripheral influences. *Electroenceph. Clin. Neurophysiol.,* 1964, **16,** 248.

Sweet, W. H. Pain. In J. Field, (Ed.), *Handbook of Physiology. Section I: Neurophysiology.* Washington, D. C.: Amer. Physiol. Soc., 1959. Pp. 459-506.

Tsubokawa, T., & Sutin, J. Mesencephalic influence upon the hypothalamic ventromedial nucleus. *Electroenceph. Clin. Neurophysiol.,* 1963, **15,** 804.

Ward, A. A., Jr., & McCulloch, W. S. The projection of the frontal lobe on the hypothalamus. *J. Neurophysiol.,* 1947, **10,** 309.

Weisschedel, E. Die Zentrale Heubembahn und ihre Bedetung für das extrapyramidalmotorische System. *Arch. Psychiat. Nervenkr.,* 1937, **107,** 443.

Winter, D. L. N. Gracilis of cat. Functional organization and corticofugal effect. *J. Neurophysiol.,* 1965, **28,** 48.

Zotterman, Y. Thermal sensations. In J. Field (Ed.), *Handbook of Physiology. Section I: Neurophysiology.* Washington, D. C.: Amer. Physiol. Soc., 1959. Pp. 431-458.

DISCUSSION

DR. ZOTTERMAN: In the introduction to your very interesting paper you said that a man can be stabbed and he does not feel much pain? Does that mean that you believe that there is a very strong stimulation or excitation of peripheral nerve fibers which in some way generally induce pain in this case?

DR. MELZACK: There is an intense input that, under normal circumstances, will induce pain.

DR. ZOTTERMAN: How do you know that?

DR. MELZACK: There is every reason to believe that it is not otherwise. Do you claim that after lesions of your skin, there is not a massive discharge in the afferent fibers?

DR. ZOTTERMAN: No, that depends upon the kind of stimulus. But this case is when people are in shock or they are dying, or they are run through. I do not think there is much stimulation of afferent fibers in this case. It takes some time to develop this intense stimulation of the fibers which I would call nociceptive fibers. You have no evidence for that. That is the first thing. The next thing, as I understand, you said you have large fibers and small fibers involved when you produce pain. Which of those are the more essential for the production of pain?

DR. MELZACK: Both of them are important. Each makes its particular contribution to afferent processes.

DR. ZOTTERMAN: You say both are important to the production of pain. That means that you think that large fibers that come from Pacinian corpuscles and from other endings in the skin, which you can stimulate by vibratory stimuli up to 1000 impulses/sec, have something to do with the production of pain.

DR. MELZACK: These large fibers will do two things. They will excite the T cell (transmission cell), and they will also, by acting on the substantia gelatinosa, tend to close the gate, preventing summation of the input. [Ed. note: Dr. Melzack's response refers to his and Wall's (1965) theory of pain.]

DR. ZOTTERMAN: Yes, but now comes the other thing. If you cut the dorsal columns where they are going up, what is left?

DR. MELZACK: The anterolateral pathways.

DR. ZOTTERMAN: And then you have, very often, a hyperalgesia.

DR. MELZACK: Right.

DR. ZOTTERMAN: How is that produced when these fibers which you say help to produce pain have been cut? They are interfering with pain. Which is right? What I asked you was, if you thought they would mediate something which would produce pain. Now you say they would interfere with the pain, and I quite agree with you. When the nerve fibers have been cut, you get a much more hyperalgetic skin because of the lack of these large fibers. But then your first answer was not correct.

DR. MELZACK: It was correct because the large fibers do both. Large fibers act on the T cell and contribute to its output. Normally, activation of these fibers below a certain intensity level will contribute to the afferent patterns for warmth, cold, touch, itch, tickle, and other sensations. When the total afferent output from the T cell exceeds a critical level, then you will have pain and these large fibers will contribute to the level of T-cell activity.

DR. CASEY: A number of points that Dr. Zotterman has raised are a source of confusion. The first one he raised was the question about the evidence for the intensity of the input. I think that Dr. Zotterman is probably referring to the intensity of the peripheral nerve input *per se* in terms of the number of impulses firing and the number of fibers active at any given time. We heard, this morning, evidence about experiments which were directed at solving the problem of comparing the input of the peripheral fiber with the behavior of the total organism. One of the features of the gate mechanism that has been proposed by Melzack and Wall (1965) is to circumvent this problem by introducing between the peripheral input and the rest of the sensory system a gate control mechanism. In this mechanism large and small fibers are differentially acting upon the T cell in the dorsal horn and axons from which, we presume, enter the anterolateral spinal tract. When we refer to intensity of input, we are referring to the intensity of the output of the anterolateral spinal tract. A distinction must be made here between peripheral nerve input and the output of the T cell. One of the things that the gate control system assists in explaining is the case of hyperesthesia where, in fact, very light tactile stimuli produce causalgic pains. In those instances, one might expect activity in a very few peripheral nerve fibers to produce a rather intense pain. The gate control is a hypothesis, but it is a testable hypothesis. It is a hypothesis in which one would predict that somewhere within the spinal cord, possibly at the dorsal horn, there would be a population of cells whose output would depend on the ratio of large to small fiber activity. If it is a good hypothesis, it is made to be destroyed, and we would welcome any attack upon it. The other point that Doctors Zotterman and Melzack were talking about was the question of whether or not there is any background activity coming over the peripheral nerve and in particular over the large fiber system. Dr. Iggo has emphasized that in the experimental situation with the animal anesthetized, or otherwise immobilized, there is very little afferent activity in the nerve. But we are talking about a situation in which the animal is up and around, moving joints, the hairs are being stimulated continuously so that it is a different situation that we are talking about. We would submit that there is, in fact, phasic activity going over the peripheral nerve into the gate control system at all times in the awake, moving, and behaving animal.

Dr. S. Weinstein: I would like to contribute two observations, a personal one, if I may, and another one of a patient and then ask a question of Dr. Melzack. Dr. Zotterman suggested that there is no evidence for a great deal of activity in the peripheral nerves resulting from intense stimulation. I think he suggested that we would have to wait a certain period of time. On one of the slides he showed [Ed. note: Figure 19-12 of discussion following Kenshalo's paper], he indicated that a mere drop of warm water on the tongue was followed by a good deal of peripheral afferent activity. The observation that I want to mention is that of the experience of involuntary self-immolation. A couple of wars back I was, unfortunately, doused with gasoline and set on fire. During the entire period of time, which occupied almost half a minute, I was completely aware visually that the flames were engulfing my body, but I had not the slightest painful or tactile sensation. I was able to put out the flames and did not experience any pain at all at the time. I walked a quarter of a mile to the hospital, and during this period I never had any sensation of pain. Subsequently, I had rather severe pain, was given morphine, and was hospitalized for about a month. I do not think you could deny, Dr. Zotterman, that during this rather long period of time that there must have been enormous, massive, peripheral inflow to the system, although I felt no pain. The second observation is quite relevant to the Melzack and Wall theory and I am sure you must have considered this, Dr. Melzack. I have seen several patients who have had therapeutic topectomies, cortical undercutting, for the relief of intractable pain from terminal carcinoma. These patients had been in agony prior to the neurosurgical intervention. I spoke with several of them right after the operation, and they were extremely passive about the pain. They did not deny the pain. They simply reacted toward it as though it were a minor inconvenience. One of them refused to interrupt a poker game while I spoke with him, and used the words pain and agony in less of an affective tone that I am employing now. He claimed that he was aware he had an operation for the relief of pain, which he maintained he still had to the same degree as previously. The cortical undercutting had apparently abolished the affect, but not the intellectual awareness of the pain. I believe that these observations support your theory, and I wonder whether you have incorporated them into your system.

DR. P. D. WALL: Dr. Zotterman, in this discussion you have really said two different things and, in a sense, we are saying what you said in 1939 in your paper on itch and scratch (Zotterman, 1939). What we deny and, in a sense what you denied in the 1939 paper, is this one-for-one relationship between activity in a particular type of fiber and a pain reaction. You have said that there are interactions; that if there were activity in other fibers then the reaction of the animal changed. This is exactly what we are saying here in this interaction between large and small fibers. We do know from the stimulation of human sural nerve, that pain can be produced, provided the stimulation is intense, when any section of the spectrum of fibers is active. It is not a special property of one group of fibers, but as soon as you start sending in different patterns of large versus small fiber activity then, as you yourself said, one gets the effect of scratching, moving, itch, and so on.

DR. ZOTTERMAN: No, it is not right. We had better go to the evidence. If you record from a fine strand of the cat's saphenous nerve and stroke the skin firmly with a blunt probe, what you will see is first, activity in the large myelinated fibers. However, for several seconds there is an after-discharge in delta and C fibers. When you produce the stimulus on your own skin, there is, first, the immediate sensation of the probe, but afterward there is a lingering smarting sensation. When a little glass pearl (see Fig. 20-5) attached to a platinum heating wire, is placed on the skin, and all tactile activity is allowed to adapt out, and then the pearl is heated, there is nothing of the large fibers. You will see only small fiber activity. I have always believed that this activity in the large fibers had a negative effect upon pain sensation. They do that as well on the sensation of tickle. If you press on the tickling spot, it stops. And when you have an itch, you press that, and it stimulates the large fibers and you are relieved. So what I want to know is your evidence for the case you make in your talk, that pain is produced by these large fibers; that it has a positive as well as a negative effect upon the production of pain in the central nervous system.

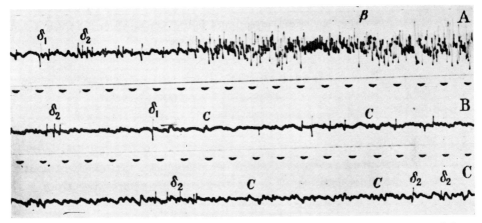

Figure 20-5. Records from a slender branch of cat's saphenous nerve. To be read from right to left. *A* shows the fiber activity at the end of a firm stroke with a wooden pin; *B* shows the activity 3 sec later; *C* gives the spike response to burning the skin lightly with an electrically heated platinum loop covered with glass which rested with very slight pressure on the skin. Time: 50 cycles (Fig. 3. Zotterman, Y., *J. Physiol. (London)*, 1939, **95**, 1).

DR. WALL: The only thing that you have said that I very strongly disagree with is the statement that cutting the dorsal columns results in hypersensitivity. I do not think that is the case. In fact, both in human cases and in animal experiments, if you do the experiments in the ordinary way, you cannot show any shift of threshold whatsoever. The cases that you are speaking of, which show hypersensitivity, always have other things wrong with them. I think this is going to become one of the great paradoxes, that you can apparently cut across the dorsal columns and not have anything happen to epicritic sensation.

References

Melzack, R., & Wall, P. D. Pain mechanisms: A new theory. *Science*, 1965, **150**, 971.

Zotterman, Y. Touch, pain and tickling: An electrophysiological investigation on cutaneous sensory nerves. *J. Physiol., (London)*, 1939, **95**, 1.

Chapter 21

PAIN FOLLOWING STEP INCREASE IN SKIN TEMPERATURE*

J. D. Hardy, J. A. J. Stolwijk and D. Hoffman†

T HERMAL PAIN HAS RECEIVED recent attention from several laboratories (Hardy, Stolwijk, Hammel, and Murgatroyd, 1965; Lele, Weddell, and Williams, 1954; Neisser, 1959) with the result that there has been an increase in our information concerning this phenomenon even though there is a divergence of views as to its cause. One group (Nafe and Wagoner, 1936) has hypothesized that pain arises essentially from stimulation of mechanoreceptors associated with smooth muscles, as these tissue are expanded or contracted by heat whereas a second group (Melzack and Wall, 1965) feels that pain develops essentially at the spinal level due to inhibitory and excitatory activity of interacting neuron pools. A third group favors the concept of stimulation of cutaneous receptors which subserve the sense of pain, these receptors being activated by changes in membrane permeability of peripheral endings by intense electrical, chemical, mechanical, and thermal stimuli (Hardy, 1953).

Among all groups there is general agreement that pain is a sensory experience, i.e., is not identical with emotional responses, and that intense stimuli of a wide variety will evoke the sensation. Several years ago a thermochemical theory of thermal pain was proposed, based on the threshold temperature of 45°C and the rapid increase in pain intensity with tissue temperature above the pain threshold. Both of these data parallel closely those on the rate of production of thermal injury (Henriques, 1947). As noted recently, the discovery by Lele, Weddell, and Williams (1954) of low temperature (36°C) transient pain made it necessary to modify the original hypothesis to account for this phenomenon. As the present report is concerned with experiments designed to test the validity of the modified hypothesis of thermal pain stimulation, a review of the concept and the predictions tested experimentally is appropriate.

As originally conceived the thermochemical hypothesis assumed that the depolarization of the pain receptor by heat was the result of the modification of molecular configurations in the receptor membrane by thermal agitation. The process was assumed to be reversed by a metabolic process.

*The paper was presented by Dr. Stolwijk.

†D. Hoffman is with the Department of Psychology, University of Bridgeport, Bridgeport, Connecticut.

The pain threshold was identified as the temperature at which molecular inactivation was more rapid than the rates of metabolic resynthesis since thermal burns and thermal pain have roughly the same threshold temperature. The reactions were envisioned as

$$P \underset{K_r}{\overset{K_d}{\rightleftarrows}} P^* \tag{1}$$

in which P and P* represent relative concentrations of some natural and inactivated protein complex, respectively, and K_d and K_r refer to the reaction velocities of thermal inactivation and resynthesis. The reaction velocities were assumed to have the form (Sizer, 1943)

$$-K = (e^{\Delta S/R}) \ (e^{-\Delta E/RT}) \tag{2}$$

in which K is the reaction velocity, ΔS = entropy change, ΔE = activation energy, R = gas constant and T = absolute temperature. For protein denaturation by heat, values of ΔE have been found to be of the order 100,000 cal/mol and of ΔS of the order of $200 - 400$ cal/°C/mal. It was assumed that the resynthesis of the natural protein P from P* involved enzymatic processes and thus, that the activation energies $5 - 20,000$ cal/mol and entropy changes of $10 - 20$ cal/°C/mol would be of the right order of magnitude. These values, when put into Equation 2, result in a high degree of temperature sensitivity for K_d (e.g., $Q_{10} \sim 150$) but a relative insensitivity of K_r to temperature (e.q., $Q_{10} \sim 2 - 3$). The consequences of this hypothesis, as stated in Equation 1 are (a) that thermal pain should have a threshold near 45°C; (b) be temperature dependent, and (c) not be time dependent if the temperature is maintained at a constant level.

The discovery of the low temperature transient pain showed the hypothesis of Equation 1 required modification by the inclusion of at least one additional state in the sequence of resynthesis. Thus, the model was changed to include the assumption that P* must be further reduced to a form P_n before the repair process can be completed. This model is shown by Equation 3 and was selected as being

$$P \xrightarrow{K_d} P^* \xrightarrow{K_r} P_n$$
$$\overset{K_n}{\underset{\uparrow \underline{\hspace{6cm}}}{}} \tag{3}$$

the simplest modification of Equation 1 that could account for the available data. To solve the equations relating the active concentrations of P*, the excitor substance, to P and P_n the following additional assumptions were necessary: (a) at normal skin temperature the cell membrane is composed largely of natural protein P with very little P* and P_n and (b) the relative values and temperature dependences of K_d, K_r and K_n were selected as shown in Figure 21-1 (Burger and Furhman, 1964; Sizer, 1943). Equations can thus be written to express the interchanges between the amounts of P, P* and P_n during temperature change or in the steady state as follows:

$$V \frac{dP}{dt} = K_n P_n - K_d P \tag{4}$$

$$V \frac{dP^*}{dt} = K_d P - K_r P^* \tag{5}$$

$$V \frac{dP_n}{dt} = K_r P^* - K_n (P_n - P_{no}) \tag{6}$$

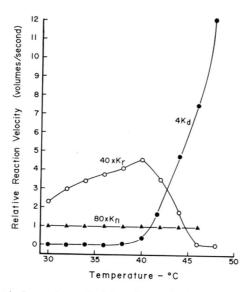

Figure 21-1. Hypothetical reaction velocities of protein inactivation, K_d, and resynthesis, K_r and K_n as affected by temperature.

In these equations V is the volume of tissue, P_{no} is the value of P_n at normal tissue temperature, since at all temperatures there will be some small degradation of P. In an earlier report the three simultaneous first order equations were solved for the situation in which the skin is suddenly immersed in hot water and the temperature changes at a depth of 0.175 mm below the skin surface were used to obtain the values of K_d and K_r (K_n has been assumed to be insensitive to temperature). Within the restrictions of the conditions of reaction velocities as shown in Figure 21-1 and the assumed dependence of the pain upon the concentrations of P* above some critical level, it was found that Equations 4, 5 and 6 would predict the outcome of the several data available. These were (a) heating the skin with radiant heat, as done by Hardy, Wolff and Goodell (1952), would generally overlook the transient pain but would indicate a uniform pain threshold at about 45°C; (b) pain induced by thermal radiation as done by Greene and Hardy (1962) would show no adaptation; (c) pain would increase in intensity with skin temperature as indicated by the experiments of Hardy, Wolff, and Goodell (1952); (d) pain would be evoked transiently by immersion of the skin in water at 38°C and above but the pain could not be restimulated immediately upon reimmersion as observed by Hardy *et al.* (1965), and (e) for the radiant heat stimulus there would be an increase in pain threshold if the skin were cooled and conversely for skin which had been preheated.

Since the data which determined the assumptions included in the model were taken largely from (a), (b), and (c) above, the extension of the theory and its prediction of both (d) and (e) appeared encouraging. However, it would seem unlikely that so simple a model could account completely for the complex of thermochemical reactions involved in the stimulation of cutaneous pain by heat and this report represents a further challenge to the model. Since the original theory involving pain and protein inactivation predicts that temperature alone is the determinant of pain intensity, the equations were solved for the situation in which the skin is immersed in water at different temperatures for 30 sec. In a well-stirred water bath the skin surface is raised to approximately bath temperature and maintained at this level, as shown in Figure 21-2. Experiments, carried out for 3 min or more, showed no appreciable deviation of the skin surface from water temperature, however, vasomotor changes have not been taken into account in the solving of the heat flow equations predicting subcutaneous

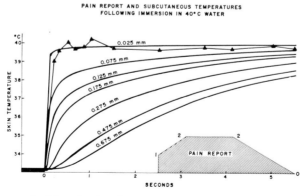

PAIN REPORT AND SUBCUTANEOUS TEMPERATURES
FOLLOWING IMMERSION IN 40°C WATER

Figure 21-2. Measured (*closed triangles*) and calculated (*solid lines*) values of skin temperature and calculated temperatures for various depths below the skin surface during a 5.5 sec immersion in water at 40°C. Occurrence of transient pain is shown.

temperature. Thus, some uncertainties are attached to the predictions of the model in respect to the temperature of the tissue at 0.175 to 0.200 mm depth. However, with these reservations in mind, it is possible to use the temperature-time relationships as shown in Figure 21-2 to predict the values of K_d and K_r at any moment and thus, solve the equations 4, 5 and 6 for the concentration of P* during the 30 sec immersion period. These predictions are shown in Figure 21-3 for water bath temperatures of 40°, 45° and 47°C. Inasmuch as the inferences from these curves include variations in pain intensity at constant skin temperature above the pain threshold, (an extension of deduction (c) above, from the original theory) and as there are no data on the matter, it was deemed worthwhile to explore the problem experimentally.

METHOD

Seven subjects, six male and one female, participated in a total of 90 experimental sessions. Two of the subjects were not considered in the data analysis because of their knowledge of the predicted results and any unconscious bias which could have played some role in their reports. Four of the subjects were first-year medical students, were naive in respect to experiments on pain and were completely passive about the results. The fifth subject, also naive, served as monitor of the protocols but was not informed about the predictions of the theory outlined above. In this sense the experiments were free of bias towards the theory being tested.

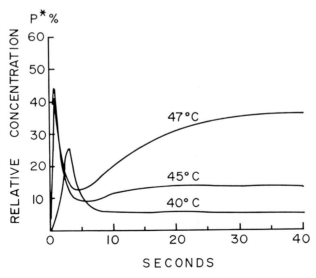

Figure 21-3. Predicted values of hypothetical excitor, P*, following immersion of skin in hot water of 40°, 45° and 47°C.

Two well-stirred water baths equipped with thermostatic controls were placed side by side in a convenient position for the standing subject to immerse his hand and forearm in either bath. One bath contained hot water (40-48°C) the temperature of which could be altered and maintained at a desired level. The second bath contained water which was maintained within the neutral range (32-35°C) and the temperatures of both baths were measured by standardized mercury thermometers located out of view of the subjects. The skin temperature of the hand or forearm was determined by means of a thermocouple looped under tension about the extremity so that the thermojunction pressed slightly into the skin of the dorsal surface of the hand and the volar surface of the forearm. The cold junction of the thermocouple was maintained at 0°C in an ice bath and the output from the system recorded on a high-speed Honeywell pen recorder. The subjects' reports of sensation were marked by the monitor on the temperature chart as they were made. Tests were made of the delays involved in this recording of sensation and the average elapsed time from the subjects' verbalization to the inscription on the record was 0.25 sec. Subjects were instructed to report pain sensations on an eleven-point scale beginning with threshold or minimal pain and increasing to a maximum value of 11 for the "most intense pain imaginable." Although this scale was chosen to parallel the dol scale, devised some years ago, it was clear that the subjects were reporting increases in pain intensity as they perceived them, and thus reports of 12 to 18 were made at the highest bath temperatures. In the absence of pain, verbal descriptions were made using adjectives, "very hot," "hot," "slightly hot," "very warm" and "warm." This nominal scale tends to depress the sensory responses near the neural sensation but the bath temperatures were so high that these sensations were not prominent and the emphasis was on the intense nonpainful sensations.

The experimental procedure involved the subject's holding his hand immediately above the warm bath and, on signal, quickly immersing the hand to the wrist in the warm bath. Reports of sensation were begun as quickly as possible and continued on the subject's initiative for the 30 sec of immersion. The subject then quickly immersed his hand in the neutral bath and continued reporting his sensations for an additional 30 sec. Right and left hands were stimulated in a single experimental session and at least 3 hr separated sessions for any one subject. Protocols were collected and analyzed at the termination of the experiment as a further precaution against bias.

RESULTS

Representative data from experiments on five subjects are plotted in Figure 21-4. Although subjects reported pain of different intensities for a

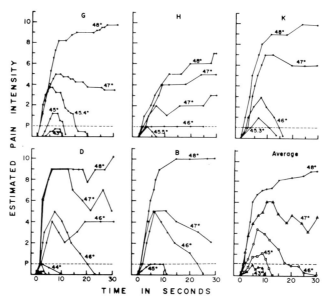

Figure 21-4. Reports of pain by five subjects following immersion of the hand in hot water. Bath temperatures are noted by each experiment. Average of reports are shown in lower right. P = pain threshold, denoted by the dashed lines.

given bath temperature, a definite response pattern is observable. For temperatures lower than 46°C there was an increase in sensation to a maximum 5 to 10 sec after immersion followed by marked adaptation and generally a disappearance of pain in 15 to 20 sec. Temperatures of 46 to 48°C evoked pain with little delay and the pain either reached a peak or a temporary plateau 4 to 12 sec after immersion, generally followed by a further increase during the immersion period. A plot of the most intense sensation reported for a given bath temperature is shown in Figure 21-5 for the five subjects and it is seen that between 40 and 45°C pain was variably reported but only at threshold or slightly above, whereas above 45°C, pain of increasing intensity was always reported. The rapid increase in pain intensity, between 46° and 48°C, is closely parallel to that made some years ago, using thermal radiation (Hardy, 1953), and implies an underlying physiological process highly sensitive to temperature. The reports of sensation at the end of the 30 sec exposure, as shown in Figure 21-6, were markedly reduced from maximal levels at the lower bath temperatures. Complete adaptation to pain occurred for all observations at temperatures of 45.5°C and lower, and was variably reported for temperatures up to 47° C. Sensations of "warmth" were occasionally reported at 46.8°C indicating the functioning of "warmth" receptors throughout the 40 to 46°C range of skin temperature. Above 47°C the pain was nonadapting and the most intense pain, as shown in Figure 21-5, was the pain felt at the end of 30 sec. In one experiment a subject kept his hand immersed for a 3 min period and the results of this single experiment are shown in Figure 21-7 because of its implications for the problem of adaptation. In this experiment the 30 sec experience was similar to that indicated in Figure 21-4 but the pain subsequently increased to a high level after the period of partial adaptation. From

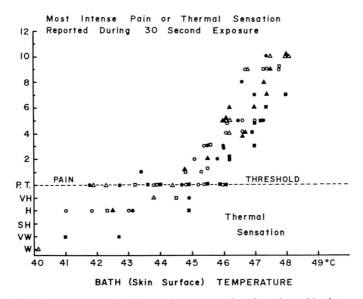

Figure 21-5. Estimates of maximal sensation reported as function of bath temperature.

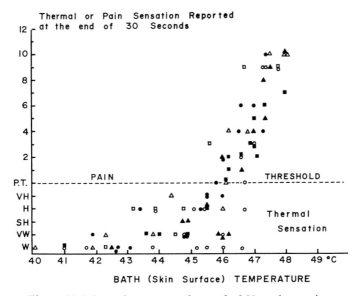

Figure 21-6. Sensations reported at end of 30 sec immersion.

Figure 21-7 it might be inferred that the complete adaptations to pain at 30 sec, as indicated above, for temperatures lower than 45.5°C, would be followed on longer exposure by a reappearance of pain.

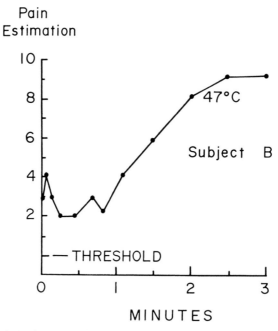

Figure 21-7. Estimated pain intensity during a 3 min immersion at 47°C.

DISCUSSION

The data shown in Figure 21-4 indicate that a constant skin temperature above the pain threshold is not associated with a constant pain intensity but that a peak of sensation may be experienced between 3 to 10 sec. The theory, as stated above, predicts a sharp peak of P* 1 to 5 sec following immersion and a decrease in onset time for the initial pain with an increase in temperature. These predictions are not borne out by the experiments shown in Figure 4 since the delay time is longer than predicted and the peak of pain intensity seems to be delayed rather than shortened by the increase in temperature. However, it is quite possible that the initial sensations may have been overlooked by the subjects and indeed there was an occasional exclamation from a subject as he immersed his hands prior to his beginning of reporting of sensation. The general shape of the P* concentration curves as a function of time seem to very roughly correspond to the shapes of the pain intensity curves for the 30 sec exposure time but a longer time scaling would be needed to be more descriptive of the experiment for a 3 min exposure. The theory correctly predicts no adaptation of pain for temperatures of 47°C and above. The experiments shown in Figure 21-4 show loss of pain perception due to adaptation for bath temperatures in the range 44 to 46°C, a finding which is apparent contradiction to the report of Greene and Hardy (1962) that pain at the threshold level of temperature is not adapting at temperatures of 43 to 45°C. Greene's experimental data are shown in Figure 21-8 for comparison with the data in Figures 21-4 and 21-7. In Greene's experiment the skin was heated with low intensity thermal radiation and during the experiment the subject controlled the radiation so as to maintain a threshold pain for several minutes. It will be noticed that the radiation was initially maintained at a high level and then gradually decreased with time and the skin temperature was raised to 46 to 47°C and then slowly lowered. The adaptation shown in Figure 21-4 in the 44 to 46°C range would thus be expected to be temporary and, as indicated in both Figure 21-7 and Figure 21-8, the pain should return after 1 to 2 min.

Figures 21-5 and 21-6 confirm the previous reports from our laboratory as well as others, as to the importance of temperatures near 45° for pain stimulation, and the sharp increase in pain sensation above 45° is in keeping with present concepts of the relationship of noxious stimulation by heat and tissue damage by burning. It is concluded that the theory in its present form is inadequate to account, in detail, for the experiments described above but it suggests needed experiments in several directions. For example, what are the time-temperature relationships for pain stimulation in primary hyperalgesia and reduced pain threshold a condition in which K_r should be much decreased? Also, how does theory accord with experiment in predicting pain intensity for periods of stimulation as long as 3-5 min? How does pain intensity, measured on the dol scale, relate to the cross-modal power law of Stevens and Stevens (1963) and what are the thermochemical implications of such a relationship? Finally, what are the temperature relationships in membrane permeability *in vivo* and *in vitro* and with the thermochemical or some other theory? In this important sense, the present

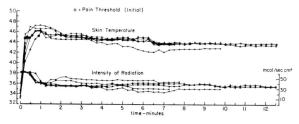

Figure 21-8. Radiation intensity and skin temperature levels for continuous threshold pain maintained by subject for 13 min (Fig. 2, Greene, L. C., & Hardy, J. D., *J. Appl. Physiol.*, 1962, **173**, 693).

theory may be considered to be serving well the proper role of a good hypothesis which is to invite experimental challenge.

REFERENCES

Burger, F. J., & Furhman, F. A. Evidence of injury to tissue after hyperthermia. *Amer. J. Physiol.*, 1964, **206**, 1062.

Greene, L. C., & Hardy, J. D. Adaptation to thermal pain in the skin. *J. Appl. Physiol.*, 1962, **17**, 693.

Hardy, J. D. Thresholds of pain and reflex contractions as related to noxious stimulation. *J. Appl. Physiol.*, 1953, **5**, 725.

Hardy, J. D., Stolwijk, J. A. J., Hammel, H. T., & Murgatroyd, D. Skin temperature and cutaneous pain during warm water immersion. *J. Appl. Physiol.*, 1965, **20**, 1014.

Hardy, J. D., Wolff, H. G., & Goodell, H. *Pain Sensations and Reactions.* Baltimore: Williams & Wilkins, 1952.

Henriques, F. C., Jr. Studies in thermal injury. V. The predictability and the significance of thermally induced rate processes leading to irreversible epidermal injury. *Amer. J. Path.*, 1947, **23**, 489.

Lele, P., Weddell, G., & Williams, C. M. Relationship between heat transfer, skin temperature, and cutaneous sensibility. *J. Physiol. (London)*, 1954, **126**, 204.

Melzack, R., & Wall, P. D. Pain mechanisms: A new theory. *Science,* 1965, **150**, 971.

Nafe, J. P., & Wagoner, K. S. The experiences of warmth, cold, and heat. *J. Psychol.*, 1936, **2**, 421.

Neisser, U. Temperature thresholds for cutaneous pain. *J. Appl. Physiol.*, 1959, **14**, 368.

Sizer, I. W. Effects of temperature on enzyme kinetics. *Advances Enzym.*, 1943, **3**, 35.

Stevens, J. C., & Stevens, S. S. The dynamics of subjective warmth and cold. In C. M. Herzfeld (Ed.), *Temperature; Its Measurement and Control in Science and Industry. Vol. 3. Biology and Medicine.* New York: Reinhold, 1963. Pp. 239-243.

DISCUSSION

Dr. R. K. Winkelmann: There is evidence in the literature that kinins are produced in the subcutaneous tissue, between the temperatures of 44° and 46°C. How do you know that you are not just measuring vasopermeability to a thermal stimulus and its consequent production of kinin as a sensory experience? It seems to me that a study with Evans blue, or something of this nature, to demonstrate local cutaneous leakage would be important.

Dr. Stolwijk: The only thing that we can say about that is that we have used our method of stimulation at various levels of blood filling of the hand and arm, and with and without blood flow. It does not seem to make any difference.

Dr. Winkelmann: You mean you put a cuff around the arm?

Dr. Stolwijk: Yes. We could do this at various levels of filling. And we could also completely occlude blood flow for a long period of time, and then try this experiment. The results were exactly the same as in the unoccluded arm.

DR. WINKELMANN: That is very good proof because kinin production should be inhibited by a tourniquet.

DR. Y. ZOTTERMAN: There's another, quite different tissue, where you can produce pain, and that is in the tooth. Funakoshi and I (Funakoshi and Zotterman, 1963) did some experiments in which we heated a tooth and recorded from fibers which terminated in the pulp. After we drilled away part of the enamel, we put a thermocouple at the pulp- dentine border and heated the tooth in various ways. Starting from a temperature of about 32° C we heated the tooth slowly and when it got to 45°C, the nerve began to fire. There is a remarkable parallel between these and the cutaneous fibers. These were all delta fibers; there were no C fibers in the preparation. So that means that there is some property in these endings, some molecular change, perhaps, in the structure that was started activity at that tempera-ture. Maybe there is a change in the lipid structure which is critical at 45°C.

DR. S. R. ROSENTHAL: We have found in the human and in the dog skin at temperatures of 45° to 47°C, using split thickness skin-glass tube prepara-tions, that histamine is liberated; with more heat applied, larger amounts of histamine are liberated. Dr. Hardy has reported similar findings.

DR. STOLWIJK: I believe the release of histamine would give rise to a more lasting sensation than we find in these experiments. These experi-ments are completely reversible and above 45°C they are restimulatable immediately afterward. If there were histamine released, I would expect that there would be an after effect; that is, there would be a continuing sensation beyond the period of stimulation.

DR. A. IGGO: There is a very interesting parallel between the thresholds that you get in your human subjects and the thresholds for the discharge in nonmyelinated fibers in the cat saphenous nerve. Where they were silent for temperatures below 40° to 43°C, at about 43°C there is a burst of ac-tivity which dies away and then if the temperature is kept up to a high level, 48° to 50°C, there is a persistent discharge. This fits in very nicely with your results, and it would suggest that, in your situation, you are actually bringing in a new set of afferent nerve fibers. This new set of affer-ent nerve fibers may be the prime cause of the sensation that is aroused. At the risk of reopening the previous discussion, I would like to ask Dr. Melzack to comment on this activation of a new set of fibers which causes pain, and how all this fits into the previous discussion we heard.

DR. R. MELZACK: There is clearly great specialization within the nervous system. Here you might have C fibers, in particular, playing the role of opening the gate. It still does not make them pain fibers. These fibers could be doing two things: first, they activate the T cell; and at the same time, via the gate system, they open the gate further to increase the total T-cell output.

Dr. Iggo: Can I suggest, then, that in this system you really have a separate arrangement for nociception or for pain, and what you are now doing is saying, "Let's throw away all that afferent input that does not contribute to pain." And you are really left, it seems to me, with a nociceptive system.

Dr. Melzack: No, that is not true at all. The fibers that respond at lower temperatures do not just fade away when these newer fibers come into play. It seems to me that the low threshold C fibers are being activated as well, are they not? They too are participating in the pain process, yet I doubt that you would call them pain fibers.

Dr. J. A. B. Gray: I wish to ask about one point that Dr. Iggo has raised. Dr. Iggo has raised a point about units which come in with high intensities of a particular type of stimulus. Now we know that all units, it does not matter whether they are phasic or tonic, have working ranges. And one of the main factors of the representation of magnitude is the recruitment of fibers working in new ranges. In other words, you have a continuum from which your new activity is recruited. An unusually intense stimulation is one of the associates of pain, and this means recruiting those units which are least sensitive. What I want to know is why your statement constituted any evidence that this was a specific group of fibers associated with a specific kind of sensation.

Dr. Iggo: The evidence is that this group of units is inactive until the temperature comes up to this high level. This particular group has a threshold, and I think that one must be careful about regarding the afferent fibers as a continuum; they have a continuum of diameters, but do not have a continuum of properties. It is possible to have very sharp distinctions between the cold fibers and the warm fibers, for example. But these units which come in at the high temperature are not being added to the other units which are brought in at a lower temperature. If the arm were put into water and the temperature were raised, what tends to happen is that any activity in the mechanically sensitive fibers is probably cut off by the rise in temperature, rather than increased.

Dr. D. R. Kenshalo: I should like to confirm Dr. Iggo's observations on these fibers in the saphenous nerve. We have made similar preparations. When we have a thermode in place on the skin of the inner thigh, at 40°C, and then the temperature is raised, the fibers which had been responding at the lower temperature in this bundle cease all activity. These are myelinated fibers. After a bit or just about the same time that this activity ceases, there is a distinctly different set of fibers which become active. The ones that we have seen are very tiny; we suspect that they are C fibers although we have not made conduction velocity measures.

DR. ZOTTERMAN: I have seen Dr. Kenshalo's records and they are C-fiber spikes. I showed you this morning [Ed. note: See Fig. 19-12 in discussion following Kenshalo's paper] that as you raise the temperature to about 45°C there are special types of fibers becoming active which are not active at lower temperatures. These fibers are stimulated when you prick the skin, and the same kind of fiber comes up when you pinch the skin. As I showed you this morning, with every stimulation that has an element of a nociceptive stimulus, these fibers are signalling.

Reference

Funakoshi, M., & Zotterman, Y. A study in the excitation of dental pulp nerve fibers. In D. J. Anderson (Ed.), *Sensory Mechanism in Dentine*. New York: Macmillan, 1963. Pp. 60-72.

Chapter 22

CUTANEOUS AND VISCERAL PAIN, AND SOMESTHETIC CHEMORECEPTORS

Robert K. S. Lim

Somesthesis serves to inform the organism of the state of both the external and internal environment. This information is required to regulate a homeostatic function which tends to maintain the body in a condition of "feelinglessness," a nirvanalike state commonly termed comfort. Any disturbance of somesthesis produces uncomfort, and triggers conscious voluntary activity aimed at removing the organism from the disturbing environment, or restoring the environment to limits more compatible with normal function and the feelinglessness of comfort. More severe changes which affect the body, produce discomfort and eventually pain.

Pain, whether cutaneous or visceral, being a body sensation forms part of the somesthetic image created by the contributions of the three basic somesthetic modalities, namely the mechano- (touch and pressure), thermo- (cold and warmth) and chemosensations (usually referred to as ache and pain). When injury strikes, all axons and receptors lying in its path, regardless of their kind, are stimulated by the supermaximal intensity of the injury stimulus, and contribute to the somesthetic image of pain which is evoked. The terms used in describing pain, e.g., pricking, stabbing, cramping, throbbing, burning, etc., testify to the participation of all three basic somesthetic modalities in the characterization of pain. The degree of pain which pervades the image, however, depends upon central factors of facilitation and inhibition, and the subject's personality, experience, circumstances, etc. Peripheral factors may also play a part in influencing pain (Beecher, 1959; Beritoff, 1966; Sherrington, 1906).

Below the skin, tactile and localizing receptors are absent, while mechano- and thermoreceptors are present in less profusion, but chemoreceptors can be found throughout most parts of the body. Evidence in support of the chemosensitive nature of the somesthetic receptor which evokes pain is as follows (Lim, 1966; Lim, Guzman, Rodgers, Gotto, Braun, Dickerson, Engle, Potter, Guy, and Rogers, 1964b).

1. The adequate stimulus for pain is still thought to be nociception or injury, in spite of the fact that hypertonic solutions, potassium salts, acids, alkalis, etc., have long been known to produce pain when injected intra-arterially in amounts which are not necessarily injurious (Keele and Armstrong, 1964; Kimura, 1955; Moore, 1938). The addition of some amines

and peptides, particularly the arginyl-, lysyl, and methionyl-lysyl-bradykinin peptides (Boissonnas, Guttmann, Jaquenoud, Pless, and Sandrin, 1963; Elliott, Horton, and Lewis, 1960; 1961; Pierce and Webster, 1961; Rocha e Silva, Beraldo, and Rosenfeld, 1949; Schröder, 1964), to the list of algesic agents which are active when injected intra-arterially and intraperitoneally, in dog and man in doses of $2\mu g$ or less, indicates that a chemosensitive mechanism is operating at the level of the receptor rather than that of the axon (Braun, Guzman, Horton, Lim, and Potter, 1961; Burch and De-Pasquale, 1962; Coffman, 1966; Dickerson, Engle, Guzman, Rodgers, and Lim, 1965; Guzman, Braun, and Lim, 1962; Lim, Miller, Guzman, Rodgers, Wang, Chao, Shih, and Rogers, in press). Bradykinin-like peptides are postulated to be formed in injured tissues producing inflammation (Cerletti, Stümer, and Konzett, 1961; Cohn and Hirsch, 1960; DeDuve, 1964; Elliott *et al.*, 1960; 1961; Lewis, 1960; 1964; Rocha e Silva, 1964).

2. From the variety of agents (peptides, amines, K^+ and H^+ ions, etc.) which can excite the somesthetic chemoreceptor to evoke pain, it is evident that excitation does not depend upon binding sites which require specific chemical structures. The nonspecific character of the chemoreceptor and the general nature of the algesic agents, suggest that it may be excited by electrophilic attraction, assuming that the nerve endings have free negative charges which attract cationic or positive charges present in some part of the algesic molecules. This concept complements Amoore's (1962) hypothesis of olfaction, which classifies odoriferous substances and olfactory chemoreceptors into seven groups, five of which depend upon specific steric configurations that fit corresponding binding sites on the receptors, and two which depend upon the charge on the receptor membrane, the negatively charged, or electron-rich, receptor sites receiving pungent (or pain producing) substances, and the positively charged, or electron-deficient, receiving putrid substances.

3. The somesthetic chemoreceptors are blocked by all the well-known nonnarcotic antipyretic (or NA) analgesics, such as aspirin, sodium salicylate, N-acetyl-p-aminophenol, aminopyrine, phenylbutazone (Guzman, Braun, Lim, Potter, and Rodgers, 1964). Using intra-arterial injections of bradykinin to evoke pain in dogs, three methods have been used to demonstrate that the NA analgesics block the action of bradykinin at the peripheral receptors and not in the central nervous system (Lim, Guzman, Rodgers, Goto, Braun, Dickerson, and Engle, 1964a; Lim *et al.*, 1964b; Hashimoto, Kumakrua, and Taira, 1964).

Cross perfusion of the vasoisolated but innervated spleen of a recipient dog R by a donor dog D, has shown that pain evoked in dog R (by bradykinin injections into the splenic artery of dog R) is blocked when aspirin or any of the NA analgesics are injected into the blood of dog D perfusing the spleen of dog R, but not when the analgesic is injected intravenously into the circulation of dog R. (The opposite is true with morphine and other narcotic analgesics; these block bradykinin-evoked pain only when given to dog R intravenously.)

Splanchnic nerve potentials, evoked by the intra-arterial injection of bradykinin into the splenic artery of individual dogs, are blocked by giving aspirin (50 mg/kg) intravenously, but not by morphine (1 mg/kg).

When aspirin is given directly into the spleen, intra-arterially, through the same plastic tube as is used to inject bradykinin, less than 10 per cent of the intravenous median analgesic dose of aspirin (3.8 instead of 50 mg/kg) is sufficient to block the pain response to bradykinin, whereas eight times the dose (31 mg/kg) injected into the brain via the brachio-cephalic artery fails to block. Similar, but not so marked, differences are found with other NA analgesics, while less morphine is required to block pain when given into the brain via the brachiocephalic artery than is needed when injected into the spleen via the splenic artery or intravenously.

All three methods show that the NA analgesics are peripheral and not central analgesics in the dog.

4. The application of Na-aspirin to 20 mm of desheathed dog's splanchic nerve in a concentration of 10 mg/ml for 5 min failed to block the conduction of impulses started by electrical stimulation. Substitution of the Na-aspirin with procaine hydrochloride (2.15 mg/ml) results in complete block in less than 5 min, indicating that aspirin does not block nerve fibers at 10 mg/ml, and is not an effective local anesthetic (Lim *et al.*, 1964a).

Bradykinin evokes pain when injected intraperitoneally in dog and man, in the same dose range as is effective intra-arterially and, with the exception of the local signs, produces the same general manifestations. The intraperitoneal method can be used in both species to evaluate analgesic drugs (Dickerson *et al.*, 1965; Lim *et al.*, in press). When 1 ml of a 10 mg/ml solution of Na-aspirin is injected intraperitoneally in the dog, through the same plastic tube as is used to inject bradykinin, the subsequent pain response to intraperitoneal bradykinin is blocked in two of four dogs in 5 to 7.5 min; and when 2.15 ml of the same concentration of Na-aspirin is injected, the response to IP bradykinin is blocked in all the dogs tested (four of four) in 5 min or less (Rodgers, Engle, Guzman, and Lim, unpublished).

When 2 ml of a 10 mg/ml solution of Na-aspirin are injected intraperitoneally in man, three of four subjects showed a 50 per cent or greater reduction in their IP bradykinin-evoked pain response (weighted pain score) during the following hour with a latency of 15 to 30 min. With 2 ml of a 20 mg/ml solution (or a total dose of 40 mg) of Na-aspirin, pain in all (four of four) subjects is blocked, with a latency of 15 min or less. The same dose (40 mg total dose) injected intravenously has no effect on the IP bradykinin-evoked pain response in any subject (none of four). These results show that aspirin acts peripherally in both dog and man, and since it is not an effective local anesthetic, its marked ability to block pain when given intraperitoneally in both species indicates that it is acting on the receptor terminals (Lim, Miller, Guzman, and Rodgers, unpublished).

5. The somesthetic chemoreceptors are identified with the paravascular receptors. Since bradykinin is readily destroyed by kininase in plasma and lymph (Edery and Lewis, 1962; Schachter, 1960), it may be inferred that the receptors on which it acts cannot be far away. Since it evokes pain on intra-arterial injection throughout the body, the chemoreceptors may be assumed to be situated close to the capillaries. The "paravascular" afferent or sensory nerves, which accompany blood vessels nearly everywhere to join the peripheral plexus, and end in free branching unmyelinated terminals, in the connective tissue spaces surrounding capillaries and venules in skin and other organs, are ubiquitous enough to fill the role of the chemoreceptors for pain (Lim, Liu, Guzman, and Braun, 1962).

6. It appears that the somesthetic chemoreceptors are accidentally involved along with the other somesthetic receptors during the act of nociception and play a role only if injury is followed by chemical and tissue changes which lead to inflammation. It is obvious that injury involves the skin before other parts lying more deeply and, being a supermaximal stimulus, will excite all axons and receptors lying in its path. All the somesthetic modalities may be stimulated, but as a signal for defense, it is already too late! Nevertheless, it alerts the organism in case it has failed to note the proximity of harm or the imminence of danger. As Beecher (1959) has pointed out, the intensity of pain experienced at the time of injury depends upon individual circumstances and its influence on the psychic reaction. The major purpose of the somesthetic chemoreceptors is to signal the consequences of injury, the chemical changes which are included in the process of inflammation, regardless of whether infection is present.

Under conditions short of injury, as in ischemia, local acidosis may elicit pain (Edery and Lewis, 1962; Schade, 1924). In both ischemia and inflammation, sensitization of the somesthetic receptors results in pain being elicited by any modality of stimulation. Sensitization may involve a change in the transducer property of the peripheral chemoreceptor, or in the level of chemical mediator acting as the stimulus.

Thus inhibition of kininase, which inactivates bradykinin, by local acidosis (pH 7.5 to 6.0), without a corresponding reduction in the activity of the kinin-forming enzyme (Edery and Lewis, 1962), or activation of the latter from plasma complexes (Frey, Kraut, and Werle, 1950; Werle, 1934), or their release from leucocyte lysosomes (DeDuve, 1964), tends to augment the amount of chemical stimulation. Pain begins to be felt in human skin at pH 6.2 and increases to a peak at pH 3.2 (Lindahl, 1961). None of these possibilities, however, serve to explain the production of pain by slight mechanical or thermal stimulation of a sensitized inflamed part. On the analogy of the motor system (Eccles, 1964), it is possible to consider that pain elicited by liminal nonchemical stimulation of a sensitized inflamed part may result from central disinhibition rather than a change in the properties of the chemoreceptor at the periphery. It would then be necessary to suppose that augmented impulses from sensitized mechano- and thermoreceptors are capable of causing disinhibition in some relay (s), such as those in the substantia gelatinosa, in the pathway serving the chemoreceptors (Frankstein, Bijasheva, and Smelin, 1965).

According to Wall and Melzack (1965), stimulation of the large fibers (from mechanoreceptors) entering the dorsal horn of the spinal cord, results in "closing of the gate control" from inhibition, while stimulation of the small fibers "opens the gate" and facilitates (through disinhibition) the output of impulses which are perceived as pain. The pathway studied (dorsolateral tract), however, has not been shown to be related to the perception of pain in behavioral or clinical studies.

Apart from the proximity of other somesthetic receptors in skin, and the possibility of exciting all when the skin is injured, one other difference between cutaneous and visceral chemoreceptors lies in the distribution of the terminals of the former in the intercellular spaces of the epidermis, while the visceral receptors end in the connective tissue space near the capillaries. Differences in the pain images, especially the ease of localizing the cutaneous stimulus, are to be expected. The difference in location of the terminals may mean that drugs may not reach the intraepithelial fibers as readily as the subcutaneous. This may account for the failure of aspirin to block bradykinin pain evoked from the blister base (Keele and Armstrong, 1965) or by intradermal injections.

It is concluded that pain may be elicited by two kinds of stimuli: (a) by injury causing accidental supermaximal stimulation of the axons and terminals of the somesthetic chemoreceptors which mediate pain, and/or (b) by chemical agents which develop following injury (or disease, or ischemia and local acidosis), and which constitute the "adequate" physiological stimulus.

REFERENCES

Amoore, J. J. The stereochemical theory of olfaction. II. Elucidation of the stereochemical properties of the olfactory receptor sites. *Proc. Sci. Sect., The Toilet Goods Assoc.,* 1962, **1.** (Suppl. 37.)

Beecher, H. K. *Measurement of Subjective Responses.* New York: Oxford, 1959. P. 494.

Beritoff, J. S. The spinal coordination of movements to the psychoneural integration of behavior. *Ann. Rev. Physiol.,* 1966, **28,** 1.

Boissonnas, R. A., Guttmann, S., Jaquenoud, P. A., Pless, J., & Sandrin, E. The synthesis of bradykinin and of related peptides. *Ann. NY Acad. Sci.,* 1963, **104,** 5.

Braun, C., Guzman, F., Horton, E. W., Lim, R. K. S., & Potter, G. D. Visceral receptors, pain, bradykinin and analgesic agents. *J. Physiol. (London),* 1961, **155,** 13P.

Burch, G. E., & DePasquale, N. P. Bradykinin, digital blood flow and the arteriovenous anastomoses. *Circ. Res.,* 1962, **10,** 105.

Cerletti, A., Stürmer, E., & Konzett, H. Bradykinin, Strukturaufklärung, Synthese, physiologisch-pharmakologisch Grundlagen. *Deutsch. Med. Wschr.,* 1961, **86,** 678.

Coffman, J. D. The effect of aspirin and hand blood flow responses to intra-arterial injection of bradykinin in man. *Clin. Pharmacol. Ther.,* 1966, **7,** 26.

Cohn, Z. A., & Hirsch, J. G. The isolation and properties of the specific cytoplasmic granules of rabbit polymorphonuclear leucocytes. *J. Exp. Med.,* 1960, **112,** 983.

DeDuve, C. Lysosomes and cell injury. In L. Thomas, J. W. Uhr, & L. Grant, (Eds.) *Injury, Inflammation and Immunity.* Baltimore: Williams & Wilkins, 1964. Pp. 283-311.

Dickerson, G. D., Engle, R. J., Guzman, F., Rodgers, D. W., & Lim, R. K. S. The intra-peritoneal bradykinin-evoked pain test for analgesia. *Life Sci.,* 1965, **4,** 2063.

Eccles, J. C. *The Physiology of Synapses.* New York: Academic, 1964.

Edery, H., & Lewis, G. P. Plasma kinin-forming-enzyme activity in lymph after injury. *J. Physiol. (London),* 1962, **163,** 48P.

Elliott, D. F., Horton, E. W., & Lewis, G. P. Actions of pure bradykinin. *J. Physiol. (London),* 1960, **153,** 473.

Elliott, D. F., Horton, E. W., & Lewis, G. P. The isolation of bradykinin, a plasma kinin from ox blood. *Biochem. J.,* 1961, **78,** 60.

Frankstein, S. I., Bijasheva, Z. G., & Smolin, L. N. Inhibitory synapses and inflammation. *Nature,* 1965, **205,** 294.

Frey, E. K., Kraut, H., & Werle, E. *Kallikrein (Padutin).* Stuttgart: Enke, 1950.

Guzman, F., Braun, C., & Lim, R. K. S. Visceral pain and the pseudaffective response to intra-arterial injection of bradykinin and other algesic agents. *Arch. Int. Pharmacodyn.,* 1962, **136,** 353.

Guzman, F., Braun, C., Lim, R. K. S., Potter, G. D., & Rodgers, D. W. Narcotic and non-narcotic analgesics which block visceral pain evoked by intra-arterial injection of bradykinin and other algesic agents. *Arch. Int. Pharmacodyn.,* 1964, **149,** 571.

Hashimoto, K., Kumakrua, S., & Taira, N. Vascular reflex responses induced by an intra-arterial injection of azaazepinophenothiazine, andromedotoxin, veratridine, bradykinin, and kallikrein and blocking action of sodium salcylate. *Jap. J. Physiol.,* 1964, **14,** 299.

Keele, C. A., & Armstrong, D. *Substances Producing Pain and Itch.* London: Arnold, 1964.

Kimura, C. Vascular sensitivity. *Acta Neuroveg. (Wein).* 1955, **14,** 170.

Lewis, G. P. Active polypeptides derived from plasma proteins. *Physiol. Rev.,* 1960, **40,** 647.

Lewis, G. P. The role of peptides in the first stages of inflammation. In L. Thomas, J. W. Uhr, & L. Grant (Eds.), *Injury, Inflammation and Immunity.* Baltimore: Williams & Wilkins, 1964. Pp. 242-280.

Lim, R. K. S. A revised concept of the mechanism of analgesia and pain. In R. S.

Knighton & P. R. Dumke (Ed.) *Henry Ford Hospital International Symposium on Pain.* Boston: Little, Brown & Co., 1966. Pp. 117-154.

Lim, R. K. S., Guzman, F., Rodgers, D. W., Goto, K., Braun, C., Dickerson, G. D., & Engle, R. J. The site of action of narcotic and non-narcotic analgesics determined by blocking bradykinin-evoked visceral pain. *Arch. Int. Pharmacodyn.,* 1964, **152**, 25. (a)

Lim, R. K. S., Guzman, F., Rodgers, D. W., Goto, K., Braun, C., Dickerson, G. D., Engle, R. J., Potter, G. D., Guy, J. L., & Rogers, R. W. Mechanism of analgesia and pain. Motion Picture Film: Program 48th Ann. Meet. *Fed. Amer. Soc. Exp. Biol.,* Chicago, 1964. (b)

Lim, R. K. S., Liu, C. N., Guzman, F., & Braun, C. Visceral receptors concerned in visceral pain and the pseudaffective response to intra-arterial injection of bradykinin and other algesic agents. *J. Comp. Neurol.,* 1962, **118**, 269.

Lim, R. K. S., Miller, D. G., Guzman, F., Rodgers, D. W., Rogers, R. W., Wang, S. K., Chao, P. Y., & Shih, T. Y. Pain and analgesia evaluated by the intraperitoneal bradykinin-evoked pain method in man. *Clin. Pharmacol. Ther.,* in press.

Lindahl, O. Experimental skin pain induced by injection of water-soluble substances in humans. *Acta Physiol. Scand.,* 1961, **51**, 1 (Suppl. 179).

Moore, R. M. Some experimental observations relating to visceral pain. *Surgery,* 1938, **3**, 534.

Pierce, J. V., & Webster, M. E. Human plasma kallidins: Isolation and chemical studies. *Biochem. Biophys. Res. Commun.,* 1961, **5**, 353.

Rocha e Silva, M. The participation of substances of low molecular weight in inflammation with special reference to histamine and bradykinin. In L. Thomas, J. W. Uhr, & L. Grant (Eds.), *Injury, Inflammation and Immunity.* Baltimore: Williams & Wilkins, 1964. Pp. 220-241.

Rocha e Silva, M., Beraldo, W. T., & Rosenfeld, G. Bradykinin, hypotensive and smooth muscle stimulating factor released from plasma globulin by snake venom and by trypsin. *Amer. J. Physiol.,* 1949, **156**, 261.

Schachter, M. *Polypeptides which affect Smooth Muscle and Blood Vessels.* Oxford: Pergamon, 1960.

Schade, H. Die Molekularpathologie in ihrem Verhältnis zur Zellularpathologie und zum klinischen Krankheitsbild am Beispiel der Entzündung. *München. Med. Wschr.,* 1924, **71**, 1.

Schröder, E. Über Peptidsynthesen. Synthese von Methionyl-Lysyl-Bradykinin, einem Kinin aus Rinderblut. *Experientia,* 1964, **20**, 39.

Sherrington, C. S. *The Integrative Action of the Central Nervous System.* New Haven: Yale Univ., 1906.

Wall, P. D., & Melzack, R. A duplex theory of the mechanism of cutaneous sensation with special reference to pain. In D. Noble (Ed.), *Proc. XXIII Int. Congr. Physiol. Sci.* Tokyo: Excerpta Medica Found., 1965. Pp. 234-241.

Werle, E. Über die Inaktivierung des Kallikreins. II. Mitteilung. *Biochem. Z.,* 1934, **273**, 291.

DISCUSSION

Dr. R. K. Winkelmann: Since isolated small vessels in dog, of 200-300 microns diameter, which are cut into helical strips, will respond to bradykinin, is it not possible that during intra-arterial injection of bradykinin you are producing vasospasms? This is a species-specific phenomenon, for it will not occur in rabbits; and if that is the case, it would perhaps explain the difference between the various drugs that you use. Since bradykinin is tachyphylactic, I wonder if you did not notice this in these repeated exposures which you use?

Dr. Lim: First, about the vasospasm, I do not believe that this can be the explanation. In any case, you must have sensory nerves to produce the pain response. If you remove the dorsal root ganglia in the appropriate regions, you will not get any response to bradykinin. With respect to your second question, in the dog anyway, we contracted the spleen and we got no vocalization; but the same or less contraction of the spleen with bradykinin, or some of the other algesic agents, was accompanied by the pain response. Furthermore, we found, for example, that rather large doses of arginyl-8 vasopressin will pause pain, but at the same dose the lysyl-8 vasopressin does not. I think this is an effect on pain terminals and not through muscle spasm, although if it is caused through muscle spasm, you still have to excite a sensory nerve ending.

Dr. S. R. Rosenthal: You remember that Elliott, Horton, and Lewis (1961) found that bradykinin intravenously produces pain and it becomes tachyphylactic. Did you encounter the same in your experiments?

Dr. Lim: There is no tachyphylaxis in man or in the dog that we have found. We have done injections in man for six hours, at fifteen-minute intervals. If the interval is shortened, there is some sort of refractory period. You will not get as big a response as initially. There is no apparent tachyphylaxis, There is, however, a reduction in the human pain score. When an individual is first injected with bradykinin, his score tends to be high at the beginning, tapers off and then settles at a lower level, but it is maintained at that level for several hours afterward.

Dr. H. Hensel: Dr. Winkelmann, did I understand that you suggested that bradykinin might cause pain by vasomotor spasm?

Dr. Winkelmann: By an ischemic contraction.

Dr. Hensel: I think that this is not very likely, because bradykinin is a very potent vasodilator, at least in the skin. If you put bradykinin into a skin area you get pain, but at the same time a vasodilation.

Dr. Winkelmann: In isolated smooth muscle strips cut helically from small vessels, it is a vasoconstrictor, however.

Reference

Elliott, D. F., Horton, E. W., & Lewis, G. P. The isolation of bradykinin: A plasma kinin from ox blood. *Biochem. J.*, 1961, **78**, 60.

Chapter 23

RELEASE OF INTRACELLULAR POTASSIUM
AS A FACTOR IN PAIN PRODUCTION

FRED B. BENJAMIN

IT WAS FIRST SUGGESTED IN 1959 that the release of intracellular potassium may be the physiological stimulus for pain sensation (Benjamin, 1959a). Since that time the concept has continued to receive a great deal of support, while no conflicting evidence has emerged. Therefore this appears to be a good time to reevaluate the concept in the light of all information available.

Any proposed explanation of peripheral pain stimulation should fulfill four basic requirements: (a) the explanation should be in agreement with current concepts of nerve excitation; (b) the concept should be applicable to all kinds of pain-producing stimuli; (c) clinical differences in quality, intensity, and duration of pain should be in agreement with corresponding differences in the pain producing process, and (d) inhibition or reversal of the stimulating process should also inhibit pain sensation. Of the existing concepts of pain the closest to fulfilling these requirements is the release of intracellular potassium, as will become apparent from the review of the evidence.

The common denominator for all kinds of pain-producing stimuli is tissue damage. However, the onset, duration, and intensity of pain is not determined by the time and intensity of stimulus application but by the time and intensity of tissue reaction. For instance, in ionizing or ultraviolet radiation or in the case of a sharp cut, the original injury may be painless while the tissue reaction phase may be accompanied by marked pain. The possibility of a noxious stimulus affecting a pain receptor directly cannot be excluded; however, any theory considering all pain being due to the direct effect of the stimulus on the receptor cannot be valid. Some of the differences between clinical and experimental pain (Beecher, 1957) may be due to differences between the direct effect of the stimulus on the receptor and pain due to the tissue reaction. The following discussion will be limited to the pain due to the tissue reaction.

Fenn (1940) and Quinn (Quinn, Bass, and Kleeman, 1953) showed that application of a noxious stimulus to a tissue cell causes a breakdown of the membrane potential and release of intracellular potassium (K). This process is nonspecific, it is reversible, and it is extremely sensitive. Mechanical, electrical, chemical, and thermal stimuli, lack of nutrition, anoxia,

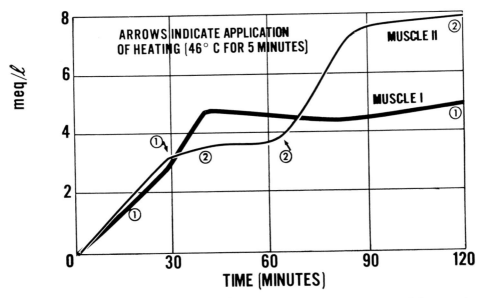

Figure 23-1. The effect of heating two frog muscles on K release (mean of four tests). Leg muscles of a frog, approximately 5.2 gm each, were washed and maintained in glass cylinders filled with 10 ml oxygenated and K-free Ringer's solution. K loss was determined from analysis of bathing fluid using a Perkins-Elmer flame photometer.

hypertonic and hypotonic solutions, any known pain-producing mechanism will release intracellular K. Therefore, it is proposed that K release, as an inherent and universal cellular response to injury, corresponds to pain as the sensory response to injury.

In the first experiment (Fig. 23-1) it was found that heating a skinned frog muscle to 46°C markedly increased release of intracellular K (Benjamin, 1959a).

Danowski (1941) and Smilie (1960) found that glucose inhibits and glycolysis increases loss of cellular K. Therefore a solution of eight units of insulin in 100 ml of isotonic glucose (Index) was prepared, and it was found that this solution inhibits release of potassium of frog muscle (Fig. 23-2). In the next experiment (Fig. 23-3) the protection offered by Index against heat and cold stress was examined. It was found that cold (4°C) is a poor stressor agent for frog muscle. However, with heat as a stressor, the Index-treated muscle maintained intracellular K much better than the control muscle.

Potassium, once released from the tissue cells, will act as a nerve stimulus. This was first demonstrated by Bernstein (1902) and has been confirmed repeatedly since that time. Bommer (1924) showed that K, when introduced into sensitive tissues, produces severe pain. Rosenthal (1964)

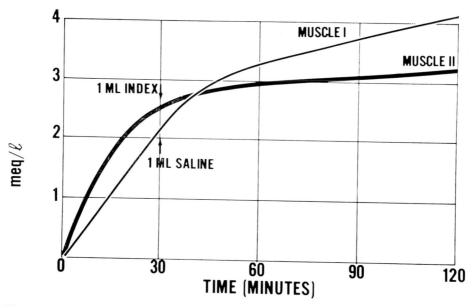

Figure 23-2. The effect of Index (insulin 8u/100ml 5 per cent glucose) on K release of frog muscle (mean of four tests). The experimental design is the same as in Figure 23-1.

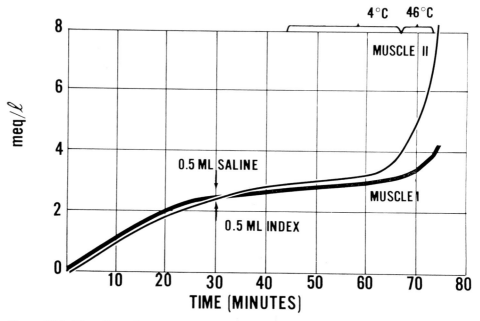

Figure 23-3. The effect of Index on resistance of frog muscle to heat and cold stress. The experimental design is the same as in Figures 23-1 and 23-2.

found that intradermal injection of 0.01 ml of potassium chloride 1:100 produces a sharp, stinging pain, while a concentration of 1:1,000 does not produce any response. Table 23-I shows that the interstitial K concentration expected to occur on release of intracellular K must be close to that producing pain under experimental conditions.

TABLE 23-I
COMPARISON OF PHYSIOLOGICAL K CONCENTRATIONS
AND K CONCENTRATIONS PRODUCING PAIN
UNDER EXPERIMENTAL CONDITIONS

Solution	*meq/1*	*mg/100 ml*
1:100 (pain)	132	515
1:1,000 (no pain)	13	52
Intracellular fluids	112–154	437–600
Extracellular fluids	4.5	17.5
Mean body fluids	83	324

The figures given in Table 23-I for intracellular K may be misleading as part of the K is in bound form. According to Kernan (1965) the bound fraction may vary between 10 to 80 per cent. However, the mean concentration of free K would still be in a range adequate to cause nerve stimulation. The localized effective dose may be considerably higher than the calculated mean concentration. This migration of K is important, from the excitability point of view, as it facilitates repolarization (Connelly, 1959).

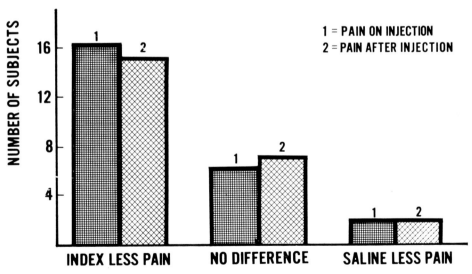

Figure 23-4. The effect of addition of Index and saline to painful injection fluid. The graph represents subjective comparison of intensity of pain caused by two intracutaneous injections of 0.1 ml each in proportion of 1 (active agent): 2 (pain producing substances).

If pain is due to the release of intracellar K, and if Index inhibits K release, then Index should also inhibit pain. The first approach to this concept was an attempt to relieve an existing, steady pain. Therefore, lesions were produced on both forearms by abrading the surface layers of the skin with fine sandpaper. The pain of one lesion was markedly lowered by local application of Index while application of saline to the other lesion increased pain. Subsequently, Index was applied to the control area causing the same pain relief. Next, in two experiments four burns were produced by applying radiated heat 300 mcal/sec/cm² for 12 sec to the volar surface of the forearm. Intradermal injection of 0.2 ml of Index caused a marked pain relief while saline had no effect. Blister formation was not inhibited by the Index injection.

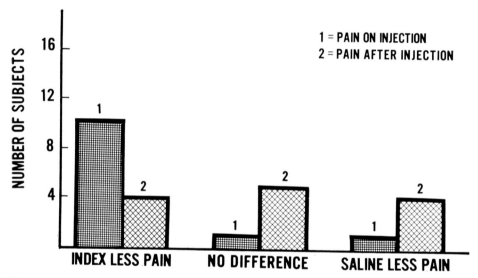

Figure 23-5. The effect of Index on injection pain and itch sensations. The experimental design is the same as in Figure 23-4.

In the next series of experiments a double-blind technique was used to compare the analgesic properties of Index and saline on intradermal injection of various pain-producing materials* according to a technique described earlier (Benjamin, Kempen, Mulder, and Ivy, 1954). As pain is a subjective phenomenon, the response is evaluated by comparison of the two agents. Figure 23-4 shows a marked pain inhibition with Index.

Itch is supposedly closely related to pain (Shelley and Arthur, 1957). However, in these experiments the same technique, that indicated inhibi-

*Thiamine 100 mg/ml, crude liver extract, isotonic KCl, 2.7 per cent saline, histamine 1:100,000, trypsin 1:50,000.

tion of pain sensation with Index, did not show any effects on itch sensation (Fig. 23-5).

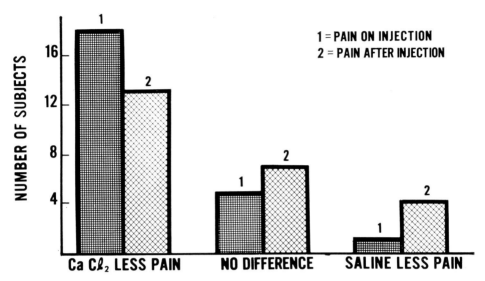

Figure 23-6. The effect of CaCl₂ on injection pain. The experimental design is the same as in Figure 23-4.

Calcium (Ca) decreases cellular permeability (Heilbrunn, 1956), it inhibits nerve excitability (Graham and Blair, 1947) and pain (Flecken-stein, 1950). Using the same technique as before (Fig. 23-6), marked pain inhibition with calcium chloride was found. Ca appears to be more effective than Index in the inhibition of injection pain while for postinjection pain, Index appears to be better. This may be due to Ca decreasing release of intracellular K or neutralizing the stimulating properties of K, and Index producing a slower reversal of the K releasing process. The experimental evidence supporting such a concept is inadequate and a combination of the two agents does not produce greater pain inhibition, as shown by two different experimental procedures (Figs. 23-7 and 23-8).

If pain producing stimuli release intracellular K, and if inhibition of K release decreases pain sensation, then analgesic agents should also inhibit release of intracellular K. To test this hypothesis *in vitro,* distention of the guinea pig intestine was used (Benjamin, 1960). The results (Fig. 23-9) show that the inhibition, though not very marked, is consistent. In a similar test (Fig. 23-10) the effect of the same analgesic agents on K release of human erythrocytes was determined and the differences between experimental and control groups were much greater.

The Skin Senses

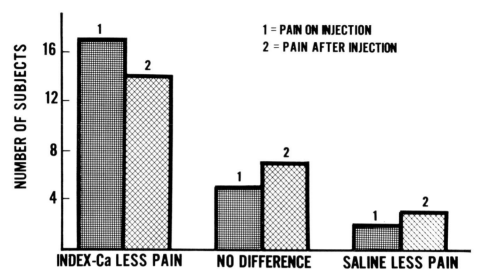

Figure 23-7. The effect of Index-Ca in combination on injection pain. The experimental design is the same as in Figure 23-4.

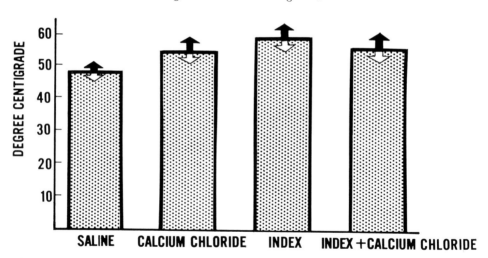

Figure 23-8. The effect of intradermal injections of various substances upon heat-pain tolerance. The experimental design is the same as in Figure 23-4.

TABLE 23-II
IONTOPHORESIS OF K AS A TEST OF PAIN TOLERANCE
(5 subjects, 10 tests within 13 days)

Subjects	Mean (mV)	s.e.
1	23.05	.36
2	19.79	.54
3	11.22	.58
4	20.72	.85
5	19.76	.72

Benjamin, F. B. The analgesic effect of cortisone and hydrocortisone. *Arch. Derm. (Chicago)*, 1954, **69**, 688. (a)

Benjamin, F. B. Effect of histamine releaser 48-80 on inflammatory response in man. *J. Appl. Physiol.*, 1954, **7**, 151. (b)

Benjamin, F. B. Release of intracellular potassium as the physiological stimulus for pain. *J. Appl. Physiol.*, 1959, **14**, 643. (a)

Benjamin, F. B. Spatial summation of pain. *Proc. Soc. Exp. Biol. Med.*, 1959, **101**, 380. (b)

Benjamin, F. B. Inhibition of release of intracellular potassium by non-narcotic analgesic agents. *Proc. Soc. Exp. Biol. Med.*, 1960, **103**, 669.

Benjamin, F. B., Anastasi, J. N., & Helvey, W. M. Effect of stress on potassium content of rat brain. *Proc. Soc. Exp. Biol. Med.*, 1961, **107**, 973. (a)

Benjamin, F. B., Anastasi, J. N., & Helvey, W. M. Effect of stress on potassium release from surviving rat brain. *Proc. Soc. Exp. Biol. Med.*, 1961, **107**, 972. (b)

Benjamin, F. B., & Helvey, W. M. Iontophoresis of potassium for experimental determination of pain endurance in man. *Proc. Soc. Exp. Biol. Med.*, 1963, **113**, 566.

Benjamin, F. B., Kempen, R., Mulder, A. G., & Ivy, A. C. Sodium-potassium ratio of human skin as obtained by reverse iontophoresis. *J. Appl. Physiol.*, 1954, **6**, 401.

Bernstein, J. *Elektrobiologie.* Braunschweig: Vieweg, 1912.

Bommer, S. Die Neutralsalzreaktion an der Hant. *Klin. Wschr.*, 1924, **3**, 1758.

Connelly, C. M. Recovery processes and metabolism of nerve. *Rev. Mod. Phys.*, 1959, **31**, 475.

Danowski, T. S. Transfer of potassium across human blood cell membrane. *J. Biol. Chem.*, 1941, **139**, 693.

Fenn, W. O. The role of potassium in physiological processes. *Physiol. Rev.*, 1940, **20**, 377.

Fleckenstein, A. *Die Periphaere Schmerzausloesung.* Frankfurt: Steinkopf, 1950.

Ghosh, J. J., & Quastel, J. H. Narcosis and brain respiration. *Nature (London)*, 1954, **174**, 28.

Graham, H. T., & Blair, H. A. Effect of environmental K and Ca on action potential and related functions of nerve. *J. Gen. Physiol.*, 1947, **30**, 493.

Greene, L. C., & Hardy, J. D. Spatial summation of pain. *J. Appl. Physiol.*, 1958, **13**, 457.

Halpern, B.-N., & Briot, M. Action des hormes cortico-surrénaliennes sur le métabolisme de l'histamine endogène. *Rev. Franc. Etud. Clin. Biol.*, 1956, **1**, 151.

Hardy, J. D., Wolff, H. G., & Goodell, H. *Pain Sensations and Reactions.* Baltimore: Williams & Wilkins, 1952.

Heilbruun, L. V. *The dynamics of living protoplasm.* New York: Academic, 1956.

Himwich, H. E., Bernstein, A. O., Fazekas, J. F., Herrlich, H. C., & Rich, E. Metabolic effects of potassium, temperature, methylene blue, and paraphenylenediamine on infant and adult brain. *Amer. J. Physiol.*, 1942, **137**, 327.

Kernan, R. P. *Cell K.* Washington: Butterworths, 1965.

Lewis, T. *Pain.* New York: Macmillan, 1942.

Quinn, M., Bass, D. E., & Kleeman, C. R. Effect of acute cold exposure on serum K, Mg, and EEG. *Proc. Soc. Exp. Biol. Med.*, 1953, **83**, 660.

Robbins, B. H., & Pratt, H. A. Changes in serum potassium during and following anesthesia. *J. Pharmacol. Exp. Ther.*, 1955, **56**, 205.

Rosenthal, S. R. Histamine as the chemical mediator for cutaneous pain. *Fed. Proc.*, 1964, **23**, 1109.

Shelley, W. B., & Arthur, R. P. The neurohistology and neurophysiology of the itch sensation. *Arch. Derm. (Chicago)*, 1957, **76**, 296.

Smilie, L. B., & Manery, J. F. Effect of external potassium concentration, insulin, and lactate on frog muscle and respiration rate. *Amer. J. Physiol.*, 1960, **198**, 67.

Tsukada, Y., & Takagaki, G. Effect of potassium on brain slices. *Nature, (London)*, 1955, **175**, 725.

DISCUSSION

DR. R. H. GIBSON: In the graph which you showed on spatial summation (Fig. 23-11), was that a tolerance threshold or an absolute threshold for pain?

DR. BENJAMIN: This was a tolerance threshold.

DR. GIBSON: The differences were small. Is it possible that probability could somehow account for the difference?

DR. BENJAMIN: No, they are statistically significantly different. We had 24 subjects, and the differences look small because we started the graph with 0°C. If we would start with 45°C, the differences would look much bigger.

DR. GIBSON: I do not mean the probability of real differences. I mean the probability of finding more sensitive sites and thus a lower average threshold when you use the larger area of stimulation.

DR. BENJAMIN: We cannot exclude that possibility. The experimental difference of pain threshold observed when changing the area of stimulation is combinable with the concept of pain summation but does not eliminate the possibility of other explanations.

DR. S. R. ROSENTHAL: I think, as Dr. Benjamin mentioned, histamine is released under the same conditions as potassium is released. We have injected, for example, potassium chloride intradermally under a little pressure. In testing for mediators for pain, solutions should be injected under pressure. We found that 1:100 dilution of potassium chloride (wt/vol) caused pain and 1:1000 did not; whereas we were able to go down to almost 10^{-18} dilutions of histamine (wt/vol of base) before we reached a threshold of pain.

DR. BENJAMIN: We find the physiological concentration of the intracellular potassium is somewhere between 112 and 154 milliequivalents/l. The physiological concentration of extracellular potassium is roughly 3 per cent of this, or 4.5 milliequivalents/l. Dr. Rosenthal just described a pain response with something like 130 milliequivalents/l, but no response with about 12 or 13 milliequivalents/l. This fits in very well with the physiological concentration that one might expect to get under potassium release conditions. It was not considered, however, that some of the intracellular potassium is in a bound condition. The bound potassium may be something like 80 per cent. Still, this would not affect the likelihood that we would get, especially near the membrane, some concentration which is very close to that Dr. Rosenthal found to be pain producing.

DR. GIBSON: We reported yesterday that sting thresholds on hairy tissue were accounted for by integrations of rate of current times time; that is, some total amount of current was sufficient to explain, in a very regular way, thresholds for up to two seconds of stimulation. Is there a way you could calculate the amount of potassium we liberate underneath a very small electrode?

DR. BENJAMIN: Yes, we have actually exact calculations. You can determine exactly the number of molecules that should be transferred with a certain current flow.

DR. A. J. H. VENDRIK: I wonder if it is really the potassium release or rather if it has something to do with the depolarization or the change of membrane permeability, and that the potassium release is the usual secondary effect which takes place after you have a change in permeability of the membrane. You are referring to the potassium release, but that is a symptom of a change in permeability. It is much easier to think of stimulation of cells by a change of permeability.

DR. BENJAMIN: I agree that pain might be due to the effect on the membrane, caused by so-called noxious stimuli. However, if you consider something like pressure, to which nerve endings are very resistant, then we would expect that pressure will not have any direct effect on the nerve endings, but it will act on the cellular membrane. It might affect the potential and increase the permeability, but the active process is potassium release and the action of potassium on sensitive nerve endings. This also agrees with the timing of pain response to injury. However, I do agree that the breakdown of membrane potential cannot be separated from the potassium releasing process.

DR. VENDRIK: Yes, but you may ask what is the primary effect. For instance, when you apply Index on your muscle, have you any idea whether there is potassium release and what is the depolarization which takes place? Have you any figures about the membrane potential when you apply Index, for instance.

DR. BENJAMIN: Not with Index. The figures are available from Heilbrunn's work (1956), as far as calcium is concerned. As you know, he determined the effect of calcium, and found a marked stabilization of the potential. This is considered a direct effect on the membrane potential. We assume that the Index works on the chemical processes, but we have no real evidence indicating the nature of the effect.

Reference

Heilbrunn, L. V. *The Dynamics of Living Protoplasm.* New York: Academic, 1956.

Chapter 24

HISTAMINE AS THE CHEMICAL MEDIATOR FOR REFERRED PAIN

SOL ROY ROSENTHAL

Pain caused by visceral disease is often felt on the surface of the body. The surface area to which the pain refers usually lies within the dermatomes associated with the cord segments which receive sensory fibers from the diseased viscus. The outlines of such painful areas resemble the arrangement of the dermatomes and not the distribution of the peripheral nerves. The two mechanisms within the spinal cord for visceral and somatic pain are closely associated. To account for the dermatomal reference of pain, Mac-Kensie (1893) suggested that the sensory impulses from the viscera were unable to pass directly to the brain, having no connection with the spino-thalamic tract, but created an irritable focus in the segment at which they enter the spinal cord. The afferent impulses from the skin were thereby magnified causing pain which was literally cutaneous. MacKensie believed that the irritable focus caused by afferent visceral impulses to the cord facilitate somatic pain impulses normally coming from the skin in insufficient quantities to excite the spinothalamic tract fibers; hyperalgesia and referred pain would be the consequence (Fig. 24-1). In modern physiological terms, Wiggers (1936), Hinsey and Phillips (1940), and others have called this the convergence-facilitation theory to distinguish it from the convergence-projection theory.

Facilitation may well be essential for hyperalgesia of the dermatomal distribution, but it is not essential for the reference of pain. An adequate explanation of referred pain according to the convergence-projection theory is that some visceral afferents converge with cutaneous pain afferents to end upon the same neurons at the same point in the sensory pathway — spinal, thalamic, or cortical — and that the system of fibers is sufficiently organized, topographically, to provide the dermatomal reference. The first opportunity for this is in the spinothalamic tract. The resulting impulses, upon reaching the brain, are interpreted as having come from the skin, an interpretation which has been learned from previous experiences in which the same tract fibers were stimulated by cutaneous afferents. The same explanation serves equally well for referred, parietal or diaphragmatic pain (Ruch, 1960).

According to the doctrine of specific nerve energy, impulses in a spino-thalamic tract fiber are identical whatever their origin. As for impulses of

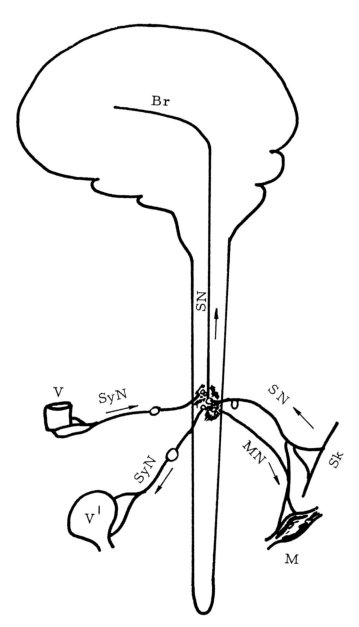

Figure 24-1. MacKensie's concept of the irritable focus in the spinal cord. Sensory impulses from the skin *SK*, afferent impulses from the viscera *V*, motor impulses to the viscera *V¹* and muscles *M* are affected by the "irritable focus." *Br* = brain; *SyN* = sympathetic nerve; *MN* = motor nerve; *NS* = nervous system (Fig. 12, Keele, K. D., *Anatomies of Pain*, Springfield: Charles C Thomas, 1957).

visceral origin, which reach the cerebral cortex, the interpretation is made on built-up experience, that of pain arising from the cutaneous pain neurons. Figure 24-2 illustrates the conversion-projection theory of referred pain applied to visceral sensations. The visceral pain afferents entering the posterior root come in synaptic relation with the cutaneous pain afferent and synapse with an overlapping field in the pool.

Various spinothalamic tract neurons within the field of overlap, when stimulated by visceral afferents, give rise to pain referred to the cutaneous surface. Facilitation of cutaneous nerve impulses within the overlap probably account for hyperalgesia but facilitation is not involved in referred pain. In this way one may avoid the unphysiologic and unnecessary supposition that cutaneous pain afferents are perpetually discharging in amounts in-

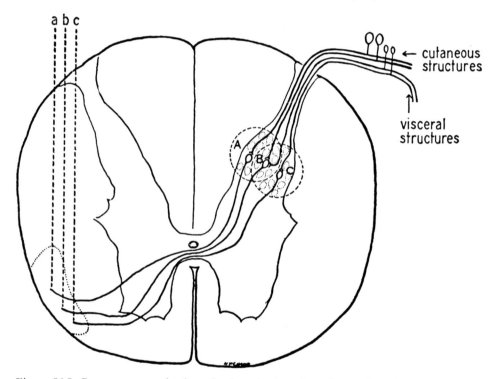

Figure 24-2. Convergence-projection of referred, visceral, and somatic pain. *A-B-C* represents a neuron pool consisting of all spinothalamic tract fibers originating in one segment of the spinal cord. *A* is field of neurons having connections only with afferent fibers from cutaneous sense organs. *B* is field of overlap constituted by neurons which receive impulses from both visceral and cutaneous afferents. Impulses from *B* give rise to pain referred to skin. *C* are neurons of the pool which connect only with afferent fibers from visceral cavities and give rise to unreferred or true splanchic pain. *a, b,* and *c* are fibers in spinothalamic tract having cell bodies in *A, B,* and *C* respectively (Fig. 13, Chapt. 16, Ruch, T. C., & Patton, H. D. [Eds.], *Physiology and Biophysics,* 19th ed. Philadelphia: W. B. Saunders, 1965).

adequate to discharge spinothalamic fibers unless facilitated. The crucial experiment to decide the relative facilitation versus simple convergence-projection would be injection of an anesthetic in an area to which the pain is projected. Such experiments have been carried out on man and animals for a variety of referred and visceral somatic pain but with conflicting results. Weiss and Davis (1928), Travell and Rinzler (1946), and others have injected procaine into the skin over the area of reference and found that referred pain was alleviated or it migrated. Carmichael (1940) on anginal pain and Livingston (1940) on diaphragmatic pain have shown that pro-caine injection in the area of reference had no effect on the reference. In view of the conflicting nature of the evidence, Ruch (1960) suggests that perhaps it is best to accept both mechanisms as operative.

Another explanation of referred pain that has been advanced is that stimulation of the visceral afferent endings in the viscera produces reflexes in the peripheral areas supplied by the corresponding segments in the super-ficial structures, i.e., viscerocutaneous reflexes and in the skeletal muscles, visceromotor reflexes (Wernoe, 1925). In the areas of the hyperalgesia in cases of visceral disease Wernoe saw evidence of the vasoconstriction and ap-pearance of goose flesh. These evidences of visceral activity in areas of hyper-algesia led him to doubt that the hyperalgesia is produced by a hyperirrita-ble focus within the spinal cord but rather to actual changes taking place in the skin itself due to viscerocutaneous reflexes. Verger (1927) stated that algogenetic stimuli from viscera produce a vasomotor reflex with a modification of the vascular bouquet of the skin which excites the sensory corpuscles from which impulses travel over the sensory cerebrospinal nerves through the posterior roots. He traced the impulse from the viscus by way of the sympathetic afferents through the posterior roots to the anterolateral column, then by the sympathetic efferent fibers running antidromically in the posterior roots to the skin. Sensory impulses from the skin are then conducted by way of the sensory cerebrospinal system (Fig. 24-3).

A similar theory was proposed by Spameni and Lunedei (1927) who state that the visceral impulses which reach the lateral column of the cord by afferent pathways stimulate centrifugal nonmyelinated fibers which terminate in the sensory corpuscles. Physiochemical changes are thus pro-duced which stimulate the sensory organs from which impulses travel over the cerebrospinal nerves. Pollach and Davis (1935), in animals, found that by sectioning various nerves, ganglia or the cord that pain produced by faradic stimulation of the peritoneal diaphragm is mediated over the phrenic nerve, enters the cord by way of the posterior roots, descends to the level of the eighth cervical and first, second, and third thoracic segments, where a connection is made with the cells in the intermediolateral column, and sympathetic efferent impulses then travel over the preganglionic fibers

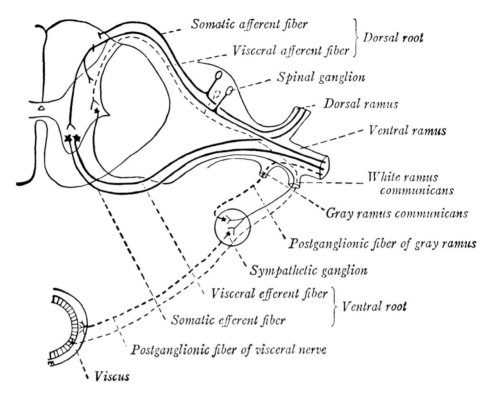

Somatic afferent fiber ⎫
Visceral afferent fiber ⎬ *Dorsal root*

Spinal ganglion

Dorsal ramus

Ventral ramus

White ramus communicans

Gray ramus communicans

Postganglionic fiber of gray ramus

Sympathetic ganglion

Visceral efferent fiber ⎫
                          ⎬ *Ventral root*
Somatic efferent fiber ⎭

Postganglionic fiber of visceral nerve

Viscus

Figure 24-3. One possible course of visceral afferent fibers to cutaneous nerve. The pathway is through splanchnic nerve, sympathetic chain, spinal nerve, dorsal root intermediolateral column, ventral root, sympathetic chain to spinal and cutaneous nerve. Another possible pathway would be from dorsal root antidromically over somatic afferents to peripheral nerve (antidromic vasodilators which are believed to release histamine). A third possibility is given by Verger (1927) (Fig. 116, Ranson, S. W., & Clark, S. L., *Anatomy of the nervous system,* 10th ed. Philadelphia: W. B. Saunders, 1959).

through the anterior roots to the cervical sympathetic ganglia. From here postganglionic fibers travel to the skin, blood vessels and other structures where, by some vasomotor or humoral process, they stimulate sensory endings of the cerebrospinal system. Sensory impulses then travel over the ordinary cerebrospinal system and enter the spinal cord through the posterior roots and ascend to consciousness.

The experiments reported here support the latter theory, that is, that the impulses from the viscera associated with pain are referred directly to the skin. There histamine is liberated which acts on the pain receptors in the skin. These sensory impulses are conducted along the sensory nerves to the posterior roots to the cord and cerebrospinal tracts. The following three experiments were designed to test this hypothesis.

EFFECT OF AN ANTIHISTAMINE ON VARIOUS PAIN
THRESHOLDS WITH SPECIAL REFERENCE TO REFERRED PAIN

The antihistaminic drug thymoxyethyldiethylamine, administered to the unanesthetized dog, produces a generalized elevation of the cutaneous threshold for pain stimuli without evident signs of central narcosis (Rosenthal, 1954; Rosenthal and Minard, 1939). The threshold for pain was determined in an adult untrained dog by electrical stimuli from a Harvard inductorium with 4.5 volts on the primary circuit. Faradic stimuli of graded intensity were applied by means of bipolar electrodes in contact with the shaved abdominal skin, the parietal and visceral peritoneum of the abdomen, mesenteric nerve trunks and the exposed saphenous nerve. The pupillodialator reflex served as a reliable index of pain responses. The electrical threshold for eliciting this reflex is expressed as the distance in centimeters of the secondary from the primary coil. This difference was inversely related to the intensity of the stimulus.

Methods

The drug was administered in 1 or 2 per cent solution of the hydrochloride in doses ranging from 30 to 50 mg/kg, expressed as the base, either parenterally by subcutaneous injection or enterally by rectum or by mouth. In the latter case atropine sulfate (0.05 mg/kg) was injected 15 min before administering the drug to allay drug loss from vomiting. To insure more uniform results all extraneous stimuli tending to disturb the animal, such as loud talking, barking of other dogs, and rough handling was strictly avoided during the initial stages of the drug action. Later such precautions were less essential.

In the first experiment (Dog No. 1, Table 24-I) control values for the various thresholds were obtained before administering the drug, with the abdomen open under local (procaine) anesthesia. In subsequent experiments opening of the abdomen and visceral stimulation was postponed until the drug had taken maximal effect, as indicated by the elevation of skin threshold. In some experiments readings were then taken periodically until the pain threshold of viscera and skin had again approached normal. In five of the 27 experiments the edges of the abdominal wound were infiltrated with solutions of procaine or of the drug, to eliminate a possible decrease in sensory threshold at these sites; a further elevation of the skin and visceral threshold was noted (Rosenthal, Minard, and Lambert, 1943).

Results

The thymoxyethyldiethylamine preparation, used in these experiments, was effective in producing an elevation of cutaneous threshold in approximately 80 per cent of the dogs tested. Its failure to act in some animals cannot be explained.

The experimental result in a series of 27 dogs, in which definite cutaneous analgesia was obtained, are given in the accompanying tables. The values given represent the setting of secondary coil at threshold intensity.

TABLE 24-I
VARIOUS ELECTRICAL THRESHOLDS,
AS DETERMINED BY THE HARVARD INDUCTORIUM, BEFORE
AND AFTER THE ADMINISTRATION OF THYMOXYETHYLDIETHYLAMINE
(Elevation of skin threshold of 3.5 cm or more)

Dog. No.	Skin Threshold, cm		Serosa Intestine, cm		Mesenteric Nerves, cm		Saphenous Nerve Trunk, cm	
	Before	After	Highest Reading	Lowest Reading	Highest Reading	Lowest Reading	Before	After
1	6	2.5	8.5*	2†	10*	4.5	13 –80°	13 –80°
2	6.5	2		2		2	12 –30	12 –30
3	6.75	2.5		2.5	10	4	12.5–70	12.5–60
4	6.25	2	5	2	5.5	2.9	12.5–30	12.5–30
5	6.25	2		2	6	2	12.5–60	12.5–60
6	6.25	2		2	7	5		
7	6.25	2		6.5		8		
8	5	1	8	6			12 –80	12 –80
9	6	2				3		
10	6.75	2		2		5.5		
11	7	2						12 –85‡
12	6.5							3§

*Readings taken before injection of thymoxyethyldiethylamine.
†Abdominal incision injected.
‡Abdomen not opened.
§Pentobarbital sodium and thymoxyethyldiethylamine injected.

The experiments are divided into two groups, the first (Table 24-I) includes dogs in which the skin threshold, following administering of the drug, increased by 3.5 cm or more. The second group (Table 24-II) includes those in which the increase was 3 cm or less. Stimuli with a secondary coil setting of less than 2 cm from the primary were avoided to prevent tissue damage.

In seven of nine dogs of the first group the threshold of pain, for the visceral peritoneum covering the free border of the small intestine, was found to be 2 cm or higher during the maximal drug effect. In the second group this degree of threshold elevation was found in only six of fifteen animals. In all experiments, in which the readings were taken repeatedly, threshold values for both skin and viscera decreased gradually as the drug action diminished. In general, values obtained for parietal and visceral peritoneum varied in the same direction. Similarly the mesenteric nerve threshold was found to be elevated to a greater extent in the first group than in the second. In general, the changes in the threshold of the mesenteric nerves approximately paralleled the threshold changes in the peritoneum. In nine experiments, in which the threshold values for the saphenous nerve were determined both before and after drug administration, little or no change was evident. However, the determination with an instrument giving absolute values of current intensity would be desirable, since intensities in the range used in these experiments were not comparable on an absolute scale.

In one experiment sodium pentobarbital (20 mg/kg) was given with the thymoxethyldiethylamine. The saphenous nerve threshold, taken during light general anesthesia which ensued, was elevated to 3 cm.

TABLE 24-II
VARIOUS ELECTRICAL THRESHOLDS,
AS DETERMINED BY THE HARVARD INDUCTORIUM, BEFORE
AND AFTER THE ADMINISTRATION OF THYMOXYETHYLDIETHYLAMINE
(Elevation of skin shreshold of 3.5 cm or less)

Dog. No.	Skin Threshold, cm		Serosa Intestine, cm		Mesenteric Nerves, cm		Saphenous Nerve Trunk, cm	
	Before	After	Highest Reading	Lowest Reading	Highest Reading	Lowest Reading	Before	After
13	5.75	4.5	8	2	10.5	6	12 −80°	12 −80°
14	6.75	4		2		5		12 −45
15	6.75	5.5		7.5		10		
16	6.5	4.75		1*		5.5	13 −70	
17	6.25	5	10	3*	10	6	13 −60	13 −60
18	6.5	4	8	3*	10	3		12.5−30
19	5.75	3.25		2.5	6	4.25	12 −70	12 −40
20	6.25	3.5	7	3*	8	3		12 −30
21	6.5	4	6	3		6.5		13 −30
22	7	5		2		2		11 −65
23	6.75	3		3		3		12.5−30
24	6	4		6.75		6.75		11 −60
25	6.5	3		1		1		12 −85
26	6.25	3.5	6	2	7	5		
27	6	3.25		2		2		

*Abdominal incision injected.

Summary

Thymoxyethyldiethylamine administered parenterally produced a reversible generalized cutaneous anesthesia in the majority of the dogs tested. The site of the action of the drug is believed to be peripheral, since little or no change in electrical threshold of the saphenous nerve or a somatic sensory trunk could be detected by the method employed. Furthermore, the animals seemed more or less alert and were able to walk and respond to external auditory or visual stimuli in normal fashion during the drug action. This drug produced an elevation of the sensory threshold of viscera and visceral nerves, which was roughly proportional to change in the skin threshold. The above findings support the view that, in the dog, visceral pain is referred wholly or in part to the skin.

SKIN HISTAMINE AFTER SPLANCHNIC NERVE STIMULATION

Work from this laboratory has shown that histamine may be the chemical mediator for cutaneous pain (Rosenthal, 1964; Rosenthal and Minard, 1939). The previous studies showed that visceral pain is referred to the skin. It follows, therefore, that if the first two hypotheses are correct, then visceral pain, elicited by stimulation of the splanchnic nerve, should be associated with an increase in histamine in the skin corresponding to the approximate area of reference.

Methods

A modified direct method of detecting diffusible histamine, as described by Rosenthal and Minard (1939), was used. Uniform pieces of the skin of the dog, about 1 cm in diameter, comparable in thickness to a Thiersch or a split-thickness graft, were placed between anode and cathode chambers for electrodialysis (Fig. 24-4). The raw surface of the skin was placed against a cellophane membrane suspended on the end of a glass tube measuring 8 mm

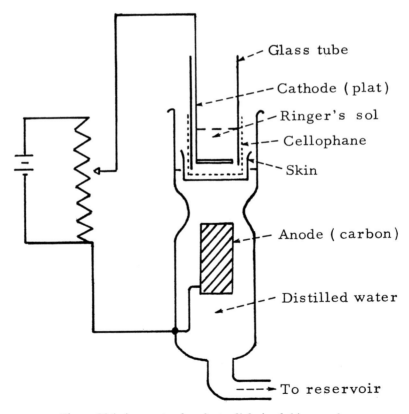

Figure 24-4. Apparatus for electrodialysis of skin samples.

inside diameter. The skin was held securely over the end of the tube by a rubber band. A rubber dam with minute perforation was stretched to reinforce the rubber band and protect the edges of the skin from the anode fluid. Current of 0.3 ma was passed through the skin for a period of 3 min. The cathode fluid, consisting originally of 0.2 ml Ringer-Locke's solution, was removed and heated for 30 min at 100°C with 0.05 ml of normal hydrochloric acid. It was then evaporated dry to remove the excess hydrochloric acid and dissolved in 0.2 ml of distilled water. The pH was adjusted to that of the Ringer-Locke's solution, usually a neutral red indicator. Samples thus obtained were tested on the guinea pig ileum in a 3.5 ml bath of atropinized (0.5 γ/ml) Ringer-Locke's solution using histamine hydrochloride as a standard (Lambert and Rosenthal, 1943).

Results

Normal Dog Skin

Samples of normal skin from the abdomen and chest of dogs, treated as described, yielded an equivalent of 0.00 to 0.005 γ of histamine. The amount in each of several pieces of skin from the same animal was relatively constant (Table 24-III).

Small amounts of histamine (1 to 5 million dilution), injected into the skin of the dog, increased the histamine equivalent of the cathode fluid. Burning of the skin resulted in a large increase of the histamine equivalent. Experiments in which turpentine, xylol or chloroform were applied to 15 samples of skin (intact or removed from the body) for 5 to 10 min periods indicated that these chemical irritants also increase the histamine equivalent of the cathode fluid. That the active substance in the cathode fluid is most probably histamine, is indicated by the following facts: (a) it caused contraction of the atropinized guinea pig ileum; (b) this activity was heat stable in acid; (c) it was heat labile in alkaline solution, and (d) it was inhibited by the antihistamine thymoxyethyldiethylamine.

These observations demonstrate that using the method described, very little histamine can be obtained from untreated dog skin. However, histamine injected or liberated in the skin by burning or chemical irritation can be readily detected.

Stimulation of Splanchnic Nerve

Control samples of skin were taken from the right side of the upper abdomen and lower chest of the dog. Electrodes were then applied to the left splanchnic nerve under procaine or light ether anesthesia. Additional samples of skin were taken from the left side following the operation and after electrical stimulation of the left splanchnic nerve (Harvard inductorium using two batteries; secondary coil at 10 cm or less). Both the control samples and those obtained following electrical stimulation were taken from scattered sites on the skin area mentioned above, since there was no evidence to indicate where maximal viscerocutaneous reflex activity might occur. Immediately after it was obtained, each sample of skin was subjected to the method of extraction, as described above, and later was tested on the guinea pig ileum. The effect of electrical stimulation was tested from four to ten times in each animal. Fifteen experiments were carried out according to this procedure. Table 24-III shows the results of one of these experiments.

TABLE 24-III
HISTAMINE EQUIVALENTS (in γ)
OBTAINED FROM THE SKIN FOLLOWING SPLANCHNIC STIMULATION

Sample No.	Heated in acid	Not heated in acid	Controls
1, 2	.000	.000	
3, 4	.000	.000	
5, 6	.000	.001	
7, 8	.000	.000	
9, 10	.001	.000	Operation
11, 12	.000	.000	
13, 14	.0025	.001	Stimulation
15, 16	.002	.000	Stimulation
17	.0075		
18	.000		Stimulation
19, 20	.0035	.000	Stimulation
21, 22	.0035	.000	
23	.000		
24	.000		
25	.000		

Figure 24-5 is a portion of the assay from another of this series. In each case there was an increase in the histamine equivalent of the skin dialysate following the operation and following stimulation of the splanchnic nerve. Each sample of skin was taken in duplicate and the dialysates of one set were not heated in acid as prescribed above. No change in the histamine equivalent was seen in the latter. This suggests that in unheated dialysates there is either a diffusible substance which is activated by heating in acid or a heat-labile substance which inhibits the action of histamine on the guinea pig ileum. The fact that untreated dialysates of skin, when added to the bath in which the gut is suspended, frequently depress the activity of added standard histamine solution favors the latter explanation.

Six of the remaining experiments were not as clear cut as that described, but showed an increase in histamine equivalent in only occasional samples after splanchnic nerve stimulation. Six experiments showed no appreciable change in histamine equivalent. Three control experiments were carried out in which there was no attempt to apply electrodes to or to stimulate the splanchnic nerve. In these control experiments no change in the histamine equivalent of the skin samples occurred; however a slight increase in histamine equivalent of the skin samples occurs following application of electrodes to the splanchnic nerve without electrical stimulation. This may be due to irritation or mechanical stimulation of the nerve by the application of these electrodes. That the substance in question is closely related to histamine was shown by the several tests mentioned above.

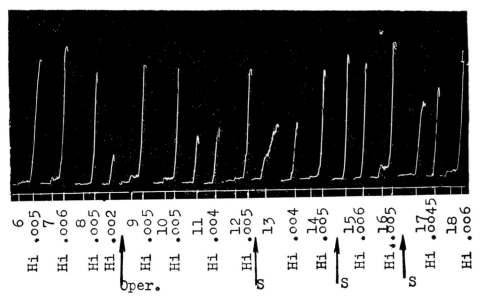

Figure 24-5. Effect on the ileum of standard histamine solution and of skin dialysates. Skin dialysates — samples 6-18. Samples 7 and 8, 9 and 10, and so forth, are duplicates. Odd numbered samples were heated in acid; even numbered samples, untreated. Oper, application of electrodes; S, stimulation. Hi = histamine inγ.

Summary

Histamine may be liberated in the abdominal skin by the application of electrodes to, or stimulation of, the splanchnic nerve. The fact that not all the experiments corroborated these results may be explained by the fact that the exact area of reference in the skin following stimulation of the splanchnic nerve was not known. The depressor effect noted in the dialysates after splanchnic nerve stimulation may also account for some of the negative results obtained. This depressor effect was also noted when the skin was stimulated directly with electrodes from the Harvard inductorium. Thus, the depressor effect is not necessarily due to the stimulation of the splanchnic nerve itself.

LIBERATION OF A HISTAMINELIKE SUBSTANCE ON STIMULATION OF THE SYMPATHETIC NERVES

Pain originating from the viscera of the chest may be referred to the exterior skin by way of the sympathetic trunk and cervical sympathetic ganglia. This study deals with electrical stimulation of sympathetic nerves and cervical sympathetic ganglia and to determine whether histamine is liberated by this type of stimulation.

Methods

The cervical sympathetic trunk of rabbits and its superior ganglion were prepared for stimulation by bipolar electrodes (4-60 sec, primary 3 v, secondary coil at 10 cm). Blood samples, obtained from the great auricular vein by venipuncture before and after nerve stimulations, were compared for their ability to contract an isolated segment of guinea pig ileum. Atropinized Ringer-Locke's solution was used in the muscle bath. Standard histamine solutions were used for comparison of contractions (Lambert and Rosenthal, 1940).

In early experiments blood samples were allowed to clot; the serum obtained was diluted immediately with Ringer-Locke's solution or buffer solution at pH 7.15 and tested on the guinea pig ileum. In these experiments (ten animals) serum obtained 15 to 60 sec following nerve stimulation almost invariably produced a greater contraction of the guinea pig ileum than the control serum (15 to 50 per cent greater). The entire contractor effect of both control and stimulated sera was abolished by previous addition of 0.5 γ of thymoxyethyldiethylamine to the muscle bath.

Rabbit blood already has a high content of histamine which is almost entirely stored in the cellular element (platelets) (Minard, 1937), but is liberated into the serum after clotting (Code, 1937). Since only that histamine found free in the blood plasma is active *in vivo,* an attempt was made to determine whether there was an increase in plasma histamine after nerve stimulation (five animals). Whole blood *in vivo* (0.1 to 0.2 ml) was drawn directly into a syringe containing an equal quantity of heparinized Ringer's solution. These were drawn, mixed and added at once to the muscle bath. It was found that the control samples of unclotted blood contained no demonstrable contractor substance; however, following nerve stimulation, ability to contract the muscle appeared in 0.5-3 min and was usually not detectable after 8-15 min. This property of the whole blood could be abolished by previous addition of thymoxyethyldiethylamine to the muscle bath. This experiment could be repeated more than once using the same rabbit ear (Fig. 24-6). Two experiments with cats, testing blood serum, gave similar results as those in the rabbit. Blood was drawn from the external jugular vein following the stimulation of the superior cervical sympathetic ganglion.

Adrenalin, which inhibits, to some extent, muscle contraction produced by histamine, is liberated on stimulation of sympathetic nerves of the rabbit's ear (Goddum, Jang, and Kiviatkoski, 1939). Frequently in our experiments blood drawn immediately following stimulation inhibited the effect of standard histamine solution added to the bath more than did control samples. Our results may have been made less apparent by this antagonism. The changes in the pH of the blood following nerve stimulation were not sufficient to affect the activity of the muscle strip and most sera were diluted with a buffer solution. On the other hand, the contractor substance obtained in the blood from the rabbit's ear following nerve stimulation was heat stable and active in atropinized bath but inactive after addition of thymoxyethyldiethylamine.

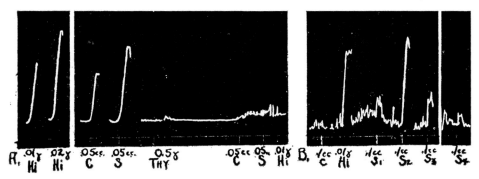

Figure 24-6. A; effect of thymoxyethyldiethylamine on C, control serum, on S, serum obtained after stimulation of the superior ganglion (4 sec), and on Hi, standard histamine. B; effect on the ileum of C, control heparinized, whole blood; S_1 obtained immediately after stimulation of ganglion (10 sec): S_2, 2 min after stimulation; S_3, 4 min after stimulation; S_4, 13 min after stimulation.

Summary

Electrical stimulation of the cervical sympathetic trunk and the superior cervical ganglia in the rabbit and the cat resulted in the liberation of a histaminelike substance in the blood, draining the part innervated by these sympathetics.

DISCUSSION AND SUMMARY

Studies carried on in this laboratory indicate that histamine may be the chemical mediator for cutaneous pain. These studies, published elsewhere, have shown the following: (a) The amount of histamine liberated from the skin is directly related to the intensity of the stimulus, thus, under given conditions the equivalent of 0.004 γ histamine was liberated at the threshold level by the tetanizing current of a Harvard inductorium and as much as 0.03 γ was released following burning with a redhot rod (Fig. 24-7). Similar results were obtained for dog, human, cat (Fig. 24-8), guinea pig, and rabbit skins (Rosenthal, 1964; Rosenthal, 1965; Rosenthal and Minard, 1939). (b) Electrical stimulation of the rabbit's cornea, which supposedly contains only sensory fibers for pain, also demonstrated the liberation of histamine directly related to the intensity of the stimulation (Rosenthal, 1964; Rosenthal, 1965; Rosenthal and Minard, 1939). (c) Various concentrations of histamine introduced into the skin of human subjects elicited pain in direct relationship to the concentration of histamine (Table 24-IV) (Rosenthal, 1950; Rosenthal and Sonnenscheim, 1948). (d) In human subjects the diffusates, following various stimulations of the skin, when reinjected intradermally as superficially as possible in the same subject were associated with the elicitation of pain, the intensity of which was directly related to the intensity of the stimulation (Table 24-V). Threshold stimulation by the Harvard inductorium produced sensations equivalent to 10^{-7}

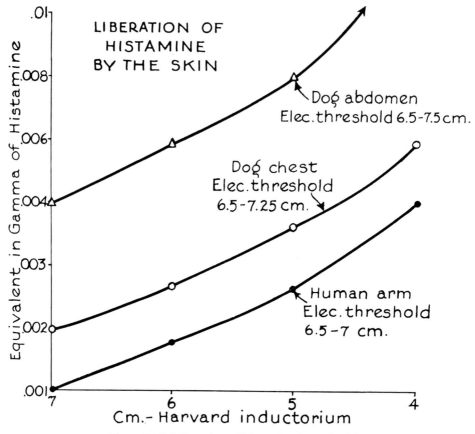

Figure 24-7. Liberation of histamine from the skin.

to 10^{-10} of histamine, whereas following burning the diffusates were equivalent to 10^{-7} to 10^{-5} of histamine. That the substance of the diffusates was histamine was demonstrated by the fact that it was heat-stable, dializable, was neutralized by histaminase, and was counteracted by the antihistamine thymoxyethyldiethylamine (Rosenthal, 1949). (e) Thymoxyethyldiethyla-mine, an antihistaminic, when injected parenterally or orally, produces a

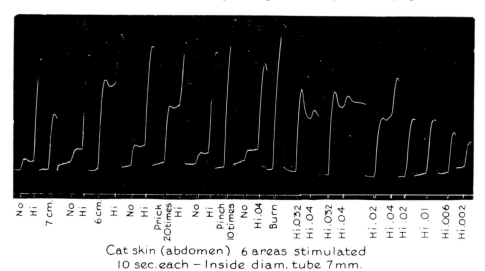

Cat skin (abdomen) 6 areas stimulated
10 sec. each – Inside diam. tube 7mm.

Figure 24-8. Stimulation by Harvard inductorium, pin pricks and burning with redhot rod. Hi = histamine; cm = distance of primary to secondary coil.

TABLE 24-IV
IMMEDIATE PAINFUL RESPONSE ON INTRADERMAL
INJECTION OF HISTAMINE IN HUMAN SUBJECTS

Concentration	No. Subjects	No. Samples	Pain on Injection 0	+	++	+++	% Pos.
Saline	40	48	32	14	2	0	33
10^{-15}	26	37	6	25	6	0	84
10^{-7}	36	28	4	9	11	4	86
10^{-5}	33	30	0	6	9	15	100

TABLE 24-V
PAIN ON INTRADERMAL INJECTION OF HUMAN SKIN
PERFUSATES AFTER STIMULATION

Type Perfusate	No. Subjects	No. Samples	Pain on Injection 0	+	++	+++ ++++	% +
Saline	15	15	9	5	1	0	40
Wash Onset	11	9	4	3	1	1	44
Warm Wire Threshold	7	7	1	4	2	0	86
Inductorium Threshold	14	12	1	6	5	0	91
Wash After	6	7	2	1	3	1	71
Inductorium 2-4 cm	10	5	0	0	2	3	100
Burn	13	11	2	3	1	5	82

generalized cutaneous anesthesia of animal and man without acting centrally. Similar results were obtained in dogs, monkeys, guinea pigs (Rosenthal, 1964; Rosenthal, 1965; Rosenthal and Minard, 1939), and in two human subjects (Rosenthal, unpublished). In the monkeys and human subjects subanesthetic doses of pentobarbital sodium were given parenterally 20 to 25 min before the thymoxyethyldiethylamine was injected. The pentobarbital sodium removed the central inhibition but did not alter, appreciably, the mechanical or electrical threshold for pain of the skin. Thymoxyethyldiethylamine acts as a local anesthetic as do other antihistaminics, albeit they are of different basic chemical compositions (Rosenthal, 1953).

The studies reported here give strong evidence that pain originating in the viscera is referred to the skin. Suggestive evidence is presented that stimulation of the splanchnic nerve is associated with a liberation of histamine in the skin corresponding to the approximate area of reference. Stimulation of the cervical sympathetic nerve and the superior cervical ganglia is associated with an increase in histamine in the blood draining the skin supplied by the sympathetic nerves. It is inferred that the histamine in the blood probably originated from the skin of the stimulated area. These findings support the concept that referred pain is due to a viscerocutaneous reflex as evidenced by the liberation of histamine in superficial layers of the skin. When the visceral afferents are stimulated, the liberated histamine acts on the pain receptors in the epidermis of the skin and initiates afferent impulses that are conducted over the normal pathways by the sensory cerebrospinal system.

Histamine may thus be the chemical mediator for both cutaneous and referred pain.

REFERENCES

Code, C. F. Source in blood of histaminelike constituent. *J. Physiol. (London)*, 1937, **90,** 349.

Goddum, J. H., Jang, C. S., & Kiviatkoski, H. Effect on intestine of a substance liberated by adrenergic nerves in rabbit's ear. *J. Physiol., (London)*, 1939, **96,** 104.

Hinsey, J. C., & Phillips, R. A. Observations upon diaphragmatic sensation. *J. Neurophysiol.*, 1940, **3,** 175.

Keele, K. D. *Anatomies of Pain.* Springfield: Charles C Thomas, 1957.

Lambert, E., & Rosenthal, S. R. Liberation of a histamine-like substance on stimulation of the sympathetic nerves. *Soc. Exp. Biol. Med.*, 1940, **44,** 235.

Lambert, E., & Rosenthal, S. R. Study of skin histamine (with some results of splanchnic nerve stimulation). *Soc. Exp. Biol. Med.*, 1943, **52,** 302.

Livingston, W. K. Personal communication. Cited in J. C. Hinsey & R. A. Phillips. Observations upon diaphragmatic sensation. *J. Neurophysiol.*, 1940, **3,** 175.

MacKensie, J. Some points bearing on the association of sensory disorders and visceral disease. *Brain,* 1893, **16,** 321.

Minard, D. The presence and distribution of histamine-like substances in blood. *Amer. J. Physiol.,* 1937, **119,** 375.

Pollack, L. J., & Davis, L. *Visceral and Referred Pain in Sensations; its Mechanism and Disturbances.* Baltimore: William & Wilkins, 1935.

Ranson, S. W., & Clarck, S. L. *The Anatomy of the Nervous System, its Development and Function.* Philadelphia: Saunders, 1959.

Rosenthal, S. R. Histamine as possible chemical mediator for cutaneous pain; painful responses to intradermal injection of perfusates from stimulated human skin. *J. Appl. Physiol.,* 1949, **2,** 348.

Rosenthal, S. R. Histamine as the possible mediator for cutaneous pain; dual pain response to histamine. *Soc. Exp. Biol. Med.,* 1950, **74,** 167.

Rosenthal, S. R. The effect of histamine analogues on cutaneous pain. *Arch. Inter. Pharmacodyn.,* 1953, **96,** 220.

Rosenthal, S. R. Histamine as the chemical mediator for cutaneous pain. *Fed. Proc.,* 1964, **23,** 1109.

Rosenthal, S. R. Pharmacologically active and lethal substances from skin. *Arch. Environ. Health,* 1965, **11,** 465.

Rosenthal, S. R., & Minard, D. Experiments on histamine as the chemical mediator for cutaneous pain. *J. Exp. Med.,* 1939, **70,** 415.

Rosenthal, S. R., Minard, D., & Lambert, E. Effect of thymoxy-ethyldiethylamine on various pain thresholds with special reference to referred pain. *Soc. Exp. Biol. Med.,* 1943, **52,** 317.

Rosenthal, S. R., & Sonnenscheim, R. R. Histamine as the possible chemical mediator for cutaneous pain. *Amer. J. Physiol.,* 1948, **155,** 186.

Ruch, T. C. Pathophysiology of pain. In T. C. Ruch & J. F. Fulton (Eds.), *Medical Physiology and Biophysics.* Philadelphia: W. B. Saunders, 1960. Pp. 350-368.

Ruch, T. C. Pathophysiology of pain. In T. C. Ruch, & H. D. Patton (Eds.), *Physiology and Biophysics,* 19th ed. Philadelphia: W. B. Saunders, 1965. Pp. 345-363.

Spameni, P., & Lunedei, A. Sui reflessi. *Rev. Clin. Med.,* 1927, **28,** 758.

Travell, J., & Rinzler, S. H. Relief of cardiac pain by local block of somatic trigger areas. *Proc. Soc. Exp. Biol. Med.,* 1946, **63,** 480.

Verger, H. Sur une modification du scheme de Lemaire pour la conception physiologique de réflexe viscuso-sensitil de MacKensie. *Gaz. Sci. Med.,* 1927, **43,** 419.

Weiss, S., & Davis, D. The significance of the afferent impulses from the skin in the mechanism of visceral pain. *Amer. J. Med. Sci.,* 1928, **176,** 517.

Wernoe, T. B. Viscerocutaneous reflexes. *Pflüger Arch. Ges. Physiol.,* 1925, **210,** 1.

Wiggers, C. J. The physiology of cardiac pain. In Levy, R. L. (Ed.), *Diseases of the Coronary Arteries and Cardiac Pain.* New York: MacMillan and Co., 1936. Pp. 163-180.

Wollard, H. H., Roberts, J. E. H., & Carmichael, E. A. An inquiry into referred pain. *Lancet,* 1932, **1,** 337. Cited in J. C. Hinsey & R. A. Phillips. Observations upon diaphragmatic sensation. *J. Neurophysiol.,* 1940, **3,** 175.

DISCUSSION

Dr. L. M. Beidler: In the cornea an epithelial cell envelopes the nerve terminal, and if you bring, for example, tobacco smoke to the cornea, you believe that it is the histamine released by the epithelial cell that stimulates the nerve?

DR. ROSENTHAL: Yes.

DR. R. T. VERRILLO: Do you have any measurements of the time course of some of these events with the skin sample?

DR. ROSENTHAL: This is a very important point. When one injects histamine in the skin there results a dual pain response; one is immediate, and the other is delayed. The higher the concentration, the shorter the time between the primary and secondary pain. For example, with a high concentration of histamine (10^{-5} wt/vol) the pain may be continuous. At 10^{-8}, 10^{-9}, or 10^{-10} concentrations, there is immediate pain, then after a few seconds interval, the secondary pain becomes manifest (Rosenthal, 1950).

DR. F. B. BENJAMIN: We have found in the reactions to very dilute concentrations of histamine that people report itch rather than pain. You reported pain only. Did you also find itch sensations?

DR. ROSENTHAL: With dilutions of histamine as low as 10^{-18} (wt/vol of base), no local reaction occurs but the subjects report a tingling, burning sensation. With dilutions of 10^{-5} to 10^{-8} both pain and itch was experienced. Sometimes the itch was so severe it overshadowed the pain.

DR. A. IGGO: Do you have any indication of which kind of afferent fibers are being excited by the histamine? Do you think that it is having an action principally on "pain fibers"? Because there is evidence from arterial injection work that the histamine, when injected, excites quite a variety of afferent fibers and not just the slowly conducting ones.

DR. ROSENTHAL: That is a study that still needs to be done, Dr. Iggo.

Reference

Rosenthal, S. R. Histamine as a possible chemical mediator for cutaneous pain. Dual pain response to histamine. *Soc. Exp. Biol. Med.*, 1950, **74**, 167.

Chapter 25

KININS FROM HUMAN SKIN

R. K. WINKELMANN

KININS (VASOACTIVE POLYPEPTIDES found in inflammation) have been measured only rarely in the skin. The kinin-forming enzyme, bradykininogen, was detected in sweat by Fox and Hilton (1958) and its capacity to form kinin by action on a globulin substrate was verified. A similar enzyme has been demonstrated in saliva (Hilton and Lewis, 1956) and in plasma (kallikrein) following physical or chemical stimulation (Elliott, 1963). The cutaneous sweat glands were believed by Fox and Hilton to be the source of kinin which they related to heat-induced, reflex vasodilation of the skin. A second cutaneous kinin was studied by Chapman and colleagues (Chapman, Ramos, Goodell, and Wolff, 1961) in a series of experiments leading to their identification of a cutaneous, vasoactive polypeptide which they termed *neurokinin*. This kinin was associated with local axon-reflex vasodilation in the skin.

Dermal perfusion is a technique common to studies of both neurokinin and sweat-gland kinin. It involves perfusion of the dermal-subcutaneous compartment with isotonic or physiologic salt solution (Fig. 25-1) (Winkelmann, in press). If the skin is stimulated by various physical or chemical agents or has been altered by an immunologic, physiologic, or pathologic mechanism, this may be reflected by the materials observed and measured in the dermal perfusate (Winkelmann, Wilhelmj, and Horner, 1965b). Fox and Hilton, in describing such a perfusion, emphasized that the trauma of the needles would produce kinin temporarily in most subjects. In my experience, a continued kinin production rarely occurred. In most cases, no kinin is detectable 15 min after the needles have been inserted and a clear flow of fluid obtained.

Recent studies by the dermal perfusion technique have related the cutaneous kinin production in human skin to vasopermeability. It is my purpose to review these data in dermographism, urticaria pigmentosa (Winkelmann, Vesper, and Horner, 1965a), ultraviolet erythema (Epstein and Winkelmann, in press), cold urticaria, and sensory analgesia to illustrate the role that kinin production may play in a number of physiologic and pathologic cutaneous events.

DERMOGRAPHISM

Dermographism, a pressure-induced edema of the skin, may occur spontaneously, may follow allergic or drug reactions, or may be created at will

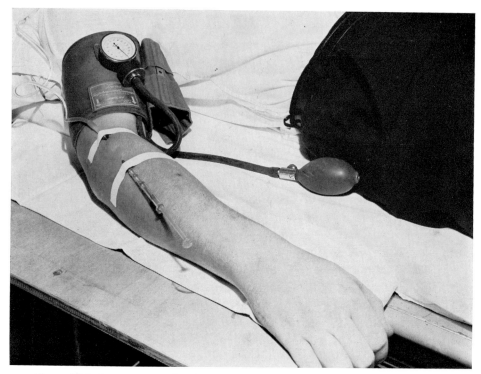

Figure 25-1. Arrangement of delivery and collecting needles for dermal perfusion.

in the skin of normal persons after the application of tetrahydrofurfuryl nicotinate ointment (Trafuril®) (Winkelmann *et al.*, 1965b). This induced predermographic state will last up to 96 hr and is sharply localized to the area of application of the ointment (Fig. 25-2). Other erythema-producing agents, such as ultraviolet irradiation or other rubefacient materials, have not induced a similar predermographic state. Aspirin (10 grains, 0.65 gm) will prevent the appearance of such dermographism by blocking the nicotinate erythema but will not prevent the dermographism if given after the induction of erythema. Injecting the skin with 1 ml of 1 per cent procaine, 0.2 ml of 0.1 per cent atropine, or 30 mg of diphenhydramine (Benadryl®) does not prevent the dermographism. Injection of 2 ml of triamcinolone solution (5 mg/ml) into the skin does not prevent the reaction. Patients taking steroids or antihistaminic agents orally continue to give the dermographic response after application of the nicotinate ointment. Injection of 48/80 (a condensation product of paramethylphenylethylmethylamine with formaldehyde), a histamine-releasing agent, on two consecutive days into the same site produces a markedly diminished wheal on the second day, but when the nicotinate ointment is applied an erythema occurs and dermographism can be elicited. Dermographism is prevented by restricting the circulation (by application of a blood-pressure cuff) and is also prevented by the injection of 0.3 ml of 0.1 per cent epinephrine solution.

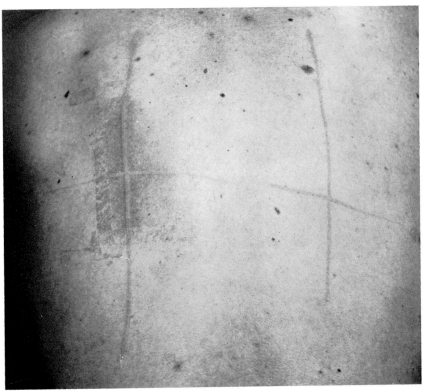

Figure 25-2. Dermographism induced by application of tetrahydrofurfuryl nicotinate. Treated area is on the left; untreated area is on the right (Fig. 1, Winkelmann, R. K., Wilhelmj, C. M., & Horner, F. A., *Arch. Derm.* [*Chicago*], 1965, **92**, 436).

Dermal Perfusion Studies

Dermal perfusion studies of the skin of the forearm were carried out in five normal persons. Two 20-gauge needles one and one-half inches long, each with four 0.013-inch holes along the needle shaft, were placed side by side in the skin and, when a flow of saline was obtained in the collecting needle, the overlying skin was treated with tetrahydrofurfuryl nicotinate ointment and later stimulated by pressure with a tongue blade. In another experiment, the needles were rapidly placed into an area in which dermographism had already been induced. The perfusions were done with and without occlusion of circulation (by blood-pressure cuff, see Fig. 25-1).

Histamine Studies

The bioassay technique with guinea pig ileum determines histamine at a dilution of 1:100,000,000 in physiologic fluids. When histamine was injected into the skin above the needles, as 0.1 ml of a 1:100,000 dilution, it was easily detected in the saline perfusate. All studies of histamine in experimental dermographism were done with occlusion of the circulation to the site, to prevent diffusion (the cuff was well tolerated for 30 min). Release of histamine into the perfusate was induced by application of the nicotinate ointment (Trafuril®) (Winkelmann *et al.*, 1965b). This induced histamine was not detected.

Ten patients with marked dermographism were studied, and no histamine was detected in perfusates of their skin. Since trauma did not produce histamine from the skin of patients with dermographism, the histamine releasing agent, 48/80, was injected, and, in two of the patients demonstrable amounts of histamine were released (Fig. 25-3).

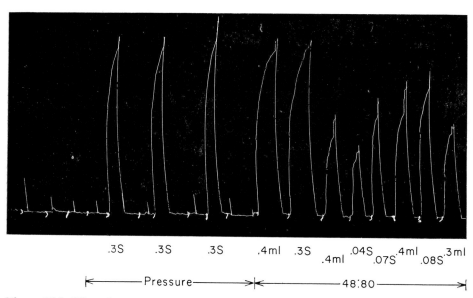

Figure 25-3. Histamine assays of dermal perfusates from a patient with dermographism. Trauma (pressure) did not induce release of histamine. When 48/80 was injected, histamine was found in the perfusate. S = standard (1:100,000,000 dilution of histamine). Perfusate samples are identified by number showing volume applied to guinea pig ileum.

Kinin Studies

Dermal perfusates were assayed for kinins by using the rat uterus standardized against bradykinin. This method will detect nanogram quantities of kinin.

After a control period during which no kinins were produced, nicotinate ointment was applied carefully to the skin over the perfusion site. Within 10 to 20 min after the application, release of kinin activity for 1 to 20 min was noted in six of 11 experiments. When the perfusion site was traumatized with a tongue blade, dermographism occurred and an additional release of kinin activity was detected in three of six tests. (The failure to find kinin activity in all tests may have been due to the limited pressure applied to the tongue blade, because of the presence of the needles in the dermis.) When perfusion was done after the nicotinate dermographism had already been produced, large amounts of kinin were detected for the entire duration of perfusion — up to 40 min. Occlusion of the circulation completely blocked the wheal formation of dermographism, and kinins were not detected until the blood-pressure cuff was released and wheal formation occurred.

Kinin activity was demonstrated in the perfusate in each of the five cases of clinical dermographism in which perfusion was started before dermographism was produced. The circulation was not occluded in these tests.

Comment

Induced or natural clinical dermographism is related to vasopermeability, wheal formation, and kinin production. Histamine is not released into the extracellular space in detectable amounts. Exhaustion of the skin of histamine by histamine-releasing agents or blocking of histamine by antihistaminic agents did not change the dermographism. Kinin production was not affected by atropine, which blocked perspiration, or by procaine, which blocked the axon reflex. Kinin production was only blocked by occlusion of the circulation proximally or by epinephrine-induced vasoconstriction locally. Therefore, trauma-induced vasopermeability can be preconditioned by chemicals such as tetrahydrofurfuryl nicotinate, and the participation of some circulating factors is necessary for cutaneous kinin production.

DERMOGRAPHISM IN URTICARIA PIGMENTOSA

Histamine has long been related to wheal production, and a natural criticism of our work in dermographism might be that the cutaneous histamine depot was too small to release enough histamine for our assay system to detect. Therefore, we studied nine patients who had macular, papular urticaria pigmentosa with masses of histamine-containing mast cells in the skin (Winkelmann *et al.*, 1965a). In two of the cases the disease had involuted so that no obvious clinical lesions were present in the area perfused. Pressure on the skin of patients with obvious lesions induced dermographism. In addition to dermal perfusion, the amount of histamine in punch-biopsy specimens of the skin was determined. The specimens were hydrolyzed and centrifuged; after neutralization, the supernate was assayed for histamine by the guinea pig ileum method. The normal value for histamine in forearm skin by our technique is 8.4μg/gm of tissue (wet weight). Two of the patients were studied for production of kinin activity.

Dermal perfusates from these patients after trauma to the skin did not contain histamine. Therefore, 0.1 ml of 48/80 solution (5 mg/ml) was injected intradermally at the perfusion site, and then large quantities of histamine were released in six of the nine patients. In two of the cases with no histamine release the disease was in the involuting phase. In only one case is there no adequate explanation for the failure to detect histamine. The amounts of histamine found in the forearm skin in the six cases confirmed the increase in cutaneous histamine depots, which is characteristic of urticaria pigmentosa. The values ranged from two to eight times the normal control values (Winkelmann, *et al.*, 1965a).

The release of kinin in the skin was studied in two patients with urticaria pigmentosa. After trauma to or injection of 48/80 into the skin, kinin was released. When the circulation was occluded, no kinin was demonstrable.

Comment

In urticaria pigmentosa, there is a large reservoir of histamine in the mast cells of the skin, yet physical pressure on the skin sufficient to produce whealing did not induce release of this histamine in detectable amounts. Injection of 48/80 did cause the release of the cutaneous histamine into the extracellular fluid, and it was detected by our system. Kinins were released by trauma and by 48/80, but kinin release was blocked by occlusion of the circulation. This study, comparable to our study of patients with simple dermographism, demonstrates that the amount of histamine in the skin is not fundamental to its minor relationship to vasopermeability and dermographism. Kinin production was associated with both forms of dermographism.

COLD URTICARIA

In patients with cold urticaria, wheals develop in the skin in response to the application of a cold stimulus. A standard clinical stimulus is application of an ice cube for 5 min. The response will vary from one area of the skin to another and, as the disease state wanes, the time of exposure to cold must be lengthened to produce a wheal. A preliminary study (Delaus and Winkelmann, unpublished) of seven patients with cold urticaria has indicated that this clinical state is similar to dermographism in that vasopermeability may be induced by a physical agent and that the response is correlated with vasopermeability and with kinin production.

Dermal perfusion studies in cold urticaria show that histamine is not released from the skin into the dermal perfusate but kinins are. When the formation of the wheal is blocked by local injection of epinephrine or by occlusion of the circulation, kinins are not found in the dermal perfusate, but when the occlusion is released, kinins appear.

Comment

The physical agent which produces the vasopermeability and whealing in cold urticaria is a certain degree of exposure to cold, a physical change similar to the pressure effect on vessels in dermographism. Cold urticaria has not been related to histamine release in our patients but is invariably related to the presence of kinin in the dermal perfusate. Since this is blocked by occlusion of the circulation, it is assumed that the circulation participates in the formation of this kinin as it does in the appearance of the wheal.

ULTRAVIOLET ERYTHEMA

Dermal perfusion studies were performed in the forearms of five subjects who were irradiated with a carbon-arc lamp with C carbons (20-min exposure at 2 cm, equivalent to 10 to 15 times minimal erythema dose). The erythema began 2 hr after exposure and reached a maximum in 6 hr. During the irradiation the temperature of the skin did not increase more than $2°$ to $3°C$. No kinin was found in the dermal perfusate during the irradiation, but it was present 6 to 15 min after the irradiation and remained present in some subjects for as long as 40 min (Epstein and Winkelmann, in press). In three subjects who had a history of respiratory allergy, no kinin production was found but ultraviolet erythema occurred as usual after a latent period of 2 hr.

Comment

Ultraviolet erythema may be associated with kinin production if the erythema is intense enough and is accompanied by vasopermeability. However, superficial solar erythema is not necessarily accompanied by vasopermeability and kinin production. Ultraviolet radiation will affect the blood vessels but will not necessarily produce kinin at an erythema-inducing dosage. With severe exposure to ultraviolet radiation, kinin appears long before visible erythema is detectable.

NEUROKININ AND SENSORY ANALGESIA

In 1961, my colleagues and I (Winkelmann, Lambert, and Hayles, 1962) reported, in detail, histologic and neurophysiologic studies of a 9-

year-old, Caucasian boy who had congenital sensory analgesia. Biopsies
revealed a complete absence of organized sensory nerve end organs in the
skin, and neurophysiologic studies failed to reveal sensory nerve conduction
patterns. Interest in the existence of substances, such as neurokinin, specifically related to nerve tissue caused us to study this boy again by the dermal
perfusion technique. Ten perfusions were performed on his forearm, which
represented denervated skin and had no axon flare, and on his torso, which
had a small zone of normal skin and had a positive axon flare. When perfusions were performed on the forearm with the occluding blood-pressure
cuff at 100 mm Hg, kinin was found in two of three instances after injection
of 48/80. When the pressure in the cuff was increased to 150 to 160 mm Hg,
no kinin was found in three perfusions (the systolic blood pressure of this
patient was 130 mm Hg). When the cuff was loosened and the circulation
released, kinin was detected in the perfusate (Fig. 25-4).

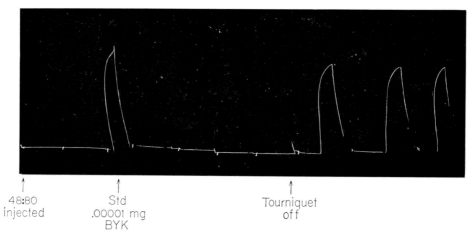

Figure 25-4. Kinin assays of dermal perfusates from a boy with sensory analgesia. 48/80
was injected while circulation was occluded; the tourniquet was subsequently released.
The standard, BYK, was bradykinin.

In dermal perfusates of the torso (normal skin with normal axon flare),
kinin was found in two of three perfusions after injection of 48/80. The
release was not as rapid nor was as large an amount of kinin found as in
the forearm perfusion.

In one study, 20 mg of Evans blue was given intravenously 10 min before
the start of the dermal perfusion. It was possible to demonstrate a blue
wheal on the leg after the intradermal injection of a 1:100,000 dilution of
histamine. No axon flare occurred in this area. The left forearm was then

perfused while the circulation was completely occluded. No kinin was found in the perfusates before or after the intradermal injection of 0.1 ml of 48/80 (0.5 mg/ml). As soon as the occlusion was released, a wheal developed in the area and Evans blue was found within the wheal. At the same time, kinin appeared in the perfusate.

Comment

When vasopermeability was induced by histamine or histamine-releasing agents, kinin was formed in both the denervated and the normal skin. Kinin release was blocked by the interruption of circulation to the denervated forearm (a preparation without circulation and without sensory nerves) but kinin as well as diffusion of Evans blue was readily observed when circulation was restored. It seems that nerves are not necessary for formation of cutaneous kinins but that circulation and vasopermeability are.

DISCUSSION

The dermal perfusion technique has been used for three series of studies. In the first series of studies, Fox and Hilton (1958) concluded that the sweat gland produced a kinin that was responsible for vasodilation. In the second series of studies, Chapman and colleagues (Chapman, Ramos, Goodell, and Wolff, 1963) concluded that the nerves in the skin released a kinin that was responsible for axon-reflex vasodilation. We have demonstrated that, both in skin with eccrine gland function blocked by atropine and in denervated skin, kinin production could be detected by the same techniques that the other investigators used. Since, in our experiments, kinin production does not seem to be directly related to sweat gland activity or to the presence of intact innervation, it is necessary to consider the areas of agreement and of disagreement among these investigations.

Fox and Hilton (1958) heated an arm by reflex vasodilation, by immersing the lower half of the subject's body in warm water. When kinin production occurred under these circumstances, they related it to sweat gland activity and believed that their theory was confirmed by the finding of the kininogen in eccrine gland sweat. Since it has been shown (Hilton and Lewis, 1956) that stimulation of the chorda tympani releases a kinin and causes vasodilation of the salivary glands, a real precedent exists for such an explanation. Chapman and colleagues (Chapman, Ramos, Goodell, and Wolff, 1960) studied a subject with a sympathectomized forearm. Sweating could not be induced, and noxious stimuli did not cause changes in the electrical resistance of the skin. The axon flare was normal in the skin. Injection of histamine into the skin induced the production of a kinin material, indicating that it was possible to have kinin production without the sympathetic nerve-sweat gland mechanism. The experiments with dermographism reported here indicate that local blocking of the sweat gland with atropine does not prevent production of kinin in the skin by circumstances which produce vasopermeability. Thus, neural and local block of eccrine gland function did not interfere with kinin formation. Study of a patient with congenital anhidrosis based on absence of sweat glands would be interesting.

Chapman and colleagues (Chapman *et al.*, 1960) did not induce the histamine wheal directly over the needles in their dermal perfusion experiments but injected the histamine 2 to 4 cm away from the perfusion needles to ensure that the perfused region was in the zone of the axon flare. When they studied a subject who had a brachial plexus injury and no axon flare, it is likely that they were taking samples from outside the zone of immediate cutaneous kinin formation and the diffusion of kinin was decreased by the lack of axon-flare vasodilation.

Chapman and colleagues (Chapman *et al.*, 1961) studied heat-induced erythema and the reflex hyperemia occurring after occlusion of circulation but gave no evidence concerning vasopermeability in these states. Stimulation of the dorsal roots in patients undergoing rhizotomy demonstrated an increase in kinin-like material in the perfused skin. This might or might not be associated with vasopermeability rather than with the release of a kinin from cutaneous nerves. The kinin release might be secondary to an effect of another mediator on blood vessels. Our study of a boy with congenital analgesia demonstrated that kinin can be detected with vasopermeability when no sensory system is present. Thus, if neurokinin does exist in skin nerves, it must share its role with a kinin related to the circulation.

The differences in the reactivities of rat duodenum, rat uterus, and hen cecum and in changes in rat blood pressure cited by Chapman and colleagues (Chapman *et al.*, 1961) to separate bradykinin from neurokinin may be of great significance, but all workers in this field have repeatedly cautioned against making too much of minor differences between the biologic activities of kininlike substances. Responses to these polypeptides can be varied in many ways. For example, the response of a given smooth muscle system to a kinin may vary with the calcium concentration of the bath.

The studies of Rocha e Silva and Antonio (1960) indicated that a separation of chemical mediators does occur because they demonstrated, by dermal perfusion of the heated rat paw, that histamine and kinin were released at definite temperature thresholds. Our studies on dermographism and urticaria pigmentosa extend this concept by showing that vasopermeability conditioned by many factors will produce kinin in large amounts in the absence of detectable amounts of histamine. The entire kininogen-substrate complex could enter the skin from the blood or the skin could participate if an eccrine gland kininogen acted on a plasma globulin. Studies are in progress to attempt to determine if cutaneous kinin is actually plasma kinin.

In all conditions of the skin we have studied, kinin production has been related to vasopermeability. Kinin production can be blocked by occlusion of the circulation, and it has been demonstrated to be related to vaso-permeability by diffusion of Evans blue. Our studies indicate that the dermal perfusion experiments which indicated a sweat gland or neural origin of kinin should be repeated with occlusion of the circulation. It would be simple to prove directly that vasopermeability is not involved and it seems wise not to accept eccrine gland or nerve kinin on the basis of present evidence.

SUMMARY

Kinin release in human skin has been assessed by perfusion of the dermal-subcutaneous compartment of the forearm with isotonic saline. Studies of dermographism, urticaria pigmentosa, cold urticaria, ultraviolet erythema, and sensory analgesia have been carried out. Temporary kinin release occurs in normal human skin after the trauma of needle insertion. Kinin is released from human normal and atopic skin by the histamine re-leasing agent, 48/80. Large amounts of kinin were released by trauma and by 48/80 from the skin of nine patients with dermographism and nine with urticaria pigmentosa and by cold and 48/80 from seven patients with cold urticaria. All kinin release was prevented by occlusion of the circulation with a blood-pressure cuff. Histamine was released by 48/80 but not by cold or by trauma in these patients, but kinin was released by both types of stimulus. Study of a boy with congenital sensory analgesia (no peripheral sensory nerves or nerve endings) demonstrated kinin release with 48/80. The appearance of kinin was correlated with diffusion of intravenously in-jected Evans blue into the cutaneous wheal. Kinin production may occur in the absence of histamine release, and the kinin does not appear to arise from cutaneous nerves or sweat glands. It seems that the appearance of kinin in cutaneous perfusates is the result of vasopermeability and may be used to judge normal and abnormal responses that involve vasoactivity.

REFERENCES

Chapman, L. F., Ramos, A., Goodell, H., & Wolff, H. G. Neurokinin: A polypeptide formed during neuronal activity in man. *Trans. Amer. Neurol. Ass.,* 1960, 42.

Chapman, L. F., Ramos, A., Goodell, H., & Wolff, H. G. Neurohumeral features of afferent fibers in man: Their role in vasodilatation, inflammation, and pain. *Arch. Neurol. (Chicago)*, 1961, **4**, 617.

Chapman, L. F., Ramos, A., Goodell, H., & Wolff, H. G. Evidence for kinin formation resulting from neural activity evoked by noxious stimulation. *Ann. NY Acad. Sci.*, 1963, **104**, 258.

Elliott, D. F. Bradykinin and its mode of release. *Ann. NY Acad. Sci.*, 1963, **104**, 35.

Epstein, J. L., & Winkelmann, R. K. Ultraviolet induced kinin release in human skin. *Clin. Res.*, in press.

Fox, R. H., & Hilton, S. M. Bradykinin formation in human skin as a factor in heat vasodilation. *J. Physiol. (London)*, 1958, **142**, 219.

Hilton, S. M., & Lewis, G. P. The relationship between glandular activity, bradykinin formation and functional vasodilatation in the submandibular salivary gland. *J. Physiol. (London)*, 1956, **134**, 471.

Rocha e Silva, M., & Antonio, A. Release of bradykinin and the mechanism of production of a "thermic edema (45°C)" in the rat's paw. *Med. Exp. (Basel)*, 1960, **3**, 371.

Winkelmann, R. K. The technique of dermal perfusion. *J. Invest. Derm.*, in press.

Winkelmann, R. K., Lambert, E. H., & Hayles, A. B. Congenital absence of pain: Report of a case and experimental studies. *Arch. Derm. (Chicago)*, 1962, **85**: 325.

Winkelmann, R. K., Vesper, L. J., & Horner, F. A. Histamine release from the skin of patients with cutaneous mast cell disease (*Urticaria pigmentosa*). *Clin. Res.*, 1965, **13**, 234. (Abstract) (a)

Winkelmann, R. K., Wilhelmj, C. M., & Horner, F. A. Experimental studies of dermographism. *Arch. Derm. (Chicago)*, 1965, **92**, 436. (b)

DISCUSSION

DR. Y. ZOTTERMAN: Did I understand you correctly that if you arrested the circulation with a cuff you could not find any kinin in the skin? From that it follows that the kinin appearing which you find in the skin is coming in from the circulation.

DR. WINKELMANN: Correct.

DR. ZOTTERMAN: So it diffuses, but because of the first action in the triple response, the permeability of the vessels is changed.

DR. WINKELMANN: That would be correct.

DR. ZOTTERMAN: The next thing is the flare. And the flare, you said, has nothing to do with the kinin. The flare is quite independent because you can produce a flare without having any kinin production.

DR. WINKELMANN: It does happen this way, yes. Just as ultraviolet erythema will occur without kinin production.

DR. ZOTTERMAN: So the flare and the axon reflex and such things could happen without kinin. The kinin is not involved directly in the nervous processes of excitation.

DR. WINKELMANN: Correct. It is my assumption that the effect of the autonomic nervous system, if there is one under these circumstances, would be on vasopermeability and that following vasopermeability the interaction of the kinin system in the blood and possibly with the addition of either kinin materials, enzyme, or substrate in the skin would then cause the additional response.

DR. ZOTTERMAN: So, the soreness, the itch, and such things could very well be produced by the infusions of the kinin from the blood vessels. Do you believe that pruritus is correlated with the appearances of kinin in the skin?

DR. WINKELMANN: Under these circumstances, none of the patients or normal individuals that we have ever studied have reported itching at a time in which we were getting massive amounts of kinin from the skin, so that it is true that if you inject kinin into the skin, as Herxheimer and Schachter (1959) showed, you get itching, but under these circumstances of production, itching is not a sensation which occurs.

Reference

Herxheimer, A., & Schachter, M. Wheal and flare in human skin produced by histamine and other substances. *J. Physiol., (London)*, 1959, 145, 34P.

Chapter 26

ORGANIZATION OF CORD CELLS WHICH TRANSMIT SENSORY CUTANEOUS INFORMATION*

PATRICK D. WALL

T HE SUBJECT OF THIS SYMPOSIUM IS skin sensation and my job is to say something of the role of spinal cord mechanisms in this process. First, one must ask what type of question one should ask of spinal cord cells. Should one expect them to relay without modification the remarkable physiological specificity of peripheral cutaneous fibers or should one expect them to begin the process of abstracting the information contained in combinations of afferent fibers? This is an important question for the physiologist who may design his experiments to "prove" either of these answers.

If behavior shows that the central nervous system can discriminate between particular events on the skin, then discriminably different information must have been transmitted from the skin to the central nervous system over peripheral nerve fibers. This statement is a truism. It should not, however, be taken to mean that every discriminable event is recognized in the CNS by the appearance of activity in a specific set of fibers which remain silent in the presence of all other events. Clinical, psychological, and physiological evidence shows that such a simple-minded specificity theory is quite untenable. The reasons for this rejection have been reviewed elsewhere (Melzack and Wall, 1962; 1965). Clinical evidence, from such diseases as causalgia and the peripheral neuropathies, suggests that destruction of some components of peripheral nerve does not simply eliminate particular qualities of sensation but instead introduces completely new relations between stimulus and response. In these diseases, the threshold for the detection of light pressure stimuli is raised but these stimuli now result in intense pain reactions. Psychological evidence shows that reactions are changed by both spatial and temperal interactions of peripheral stimuli.

As an example of spatial interaction, scratching changes the reaction to small areas of damage (Wall and Cronly-Dillon, 1960; Zotterman, 1939). Temporally separated stimuli result in blocking and metacontrast phenomena (Melzack, Wall, and Weisz, 1963). Physiological investigations have shown a remarkable diversity of different types of receptor-fiber units

*This work was supported in part by The Teagle Foundation, Inc., The National Institutes of Health (Grant 5 RO1 NB-04897-03), and the U. S. Air Force (Aerospace Medical Division) under Contract AF33 (615) -3885.

with exactly specifiable relationships between stimuli and responses, described in a number of papers elsewhere in this symposium. However, in spite of the impressive physiological specificity, investigations have repeatedly failed to discover a particular set of fibers whose impulses will trigger off pain reactions since it would be necessary to find fibers which responded sometimes to very small stimuli and sometimes to very large ones. Physiological studies of peripheral fibers continually demonstrate rigid stimulus response relationships while psychological and clinical studies of pain continually demonstrate enormous threshold variations.

To take another example of the problems of trying to relate the specificity observed physiologically in peripheral fibers to the specificity of behavioral reactions, let us examine those exquisitely sensitive temperature detecting fibers which have been described by Zotterman (1959) and others in this symposium. It will be noticed that these beautiful receptor-fiber units respond also to pressures which are likely to be encountered in the ordinary experience of the animal. This observation tells us that the presence of impulses in that particular group of fibers does not uniquely specify a temperature change at the endings because impulses are also produced by pressure distortion. The animal's behavior shows, however, that he can discriminate between temperature and pressure stimuli. Since no one class of fibers carries out this clear cut separation of events, we must presume that central cells achieve this discrimination by comparing firing patterns in different fibers and/or by examining the temporal course of the firing pattern in individual fibers. This process of abstraction of particular events from the arriving temporal and spatial pattern of nerve impulses could begin at the first central cells on which peripheral cutaneous fibers end. The rest of the paper will review some of what is known of the function and anatomy of these first central cells.

DORSAL COLUMN-MEDIAL LEMNISCUS SYSTEM

The most recently evolved systems on which cutaneous afferent fibers end are the dorsal column nuclei which feed into the medial lemniscus. Classical neurological teaching has been emphatic that all highly discriminative sensory processes depended on the integrity of this transmission system. It is now becoming clear that this view is in error. The reason for this error seems to be twofold. In the first place, tabes dorsalis with its loss of position sense, loss of vibration sense, severe hypersthesia and dysesthesia was thought of as a disease primarily of the dorsal columns. It is in fact a disease primarily of the dorsal roots in which the input to the dorsal horns is severely affected as well as the collaterals of afferent fibers which make up the dorsal columns. In the second place, the relatively rare cases of localized damage to dorsal columns by injury, tumor, infarction, or multiple sclerotic plaque are all found to extend into the dorsolateral columns if accompanied by sensory signs. The dorsal columns are said to be highly organized with respect to the incoming roots so that fibers originating from a particular root run in a very limited region within the dorsal columns. One would therefore expect that small lesions within the dorsal columns would destroy incoming afferents from a neighboring group of segments. Therefore one would expect reports in the clinical literature of cutaneous "scotomata" in which discriminative sensory deficits exist in localized areas. No such reports exist.

The problem of the sensory function of the dorsal columns has now been attacked experimentally with uniformally negative results. De Vito, Ruch, and Patton (1964) showed the dorsal column section in monkeys left intact the ability to discriminate between various weights. Levitt and Schwartzman (1966) showed in eight monkeys that two-point discrimination was unaffected by dorsal column lesions. Vierck (1966) showed in six macaques that limb-position sense was unaffected. Christiansen (1966) showed that tactile placing was only transiently diminished in fifteen monkeys after dorsal column section. Finally, Cook and Browder (1965) report that seven patients, following dorsal column section, showed no permanent deficit on neurological testing for touch, pain, temperature, vibration, and two-point discrimination. These five studies show that a gigantic paradox is now apparent and that, whatever function for the dorsal columns may eventually be discovered, this tract is not essential for discriminative sensation as normally tested by neurological examination. If this pathway is not essential, then one's attention is directed to the systems in dorsal horn which receive cutaneous afferents.

LAMINAR ORGANIZATION OF DORSAL HORN

Evidence is now rapidly accumulating that it is useful to consider the dorsal horn of the spinal cord as a laminated structure. The original evidence was that of Rexed (1952) who demonstrated, by cytoarchitectonic methods, that there existed six laminae within the dorsal horn. We have been able to show by physiological methods that at least five of the six have physiological correlates. It must be stated at once that these laminae are not exact layers containing a single type of specific cell. The physiological studies suggest instead that laminae four, five, and six represent overlapping distributions of three populations of cells. In other words, within each lamina, there is a greatly increased probability of finding a particular type of cell. It is also true that each anatomically defined lamina will be found, physiologically, to contain a minority of cells which have the properties of the majority of cells in the lamina above or below.

The laminar pattern of the dorsal horn, described by Rexed, has been generally neglected by physiologists. This neglect can be partly explained by the low repute to which the whole subject of cytoarchitectonics has been brought by the excessive zeal of cerebral histologists. A more serious reason is that many highly skilled physiologists, recording from single units in the dorsal horns, reported the existence of vague, intermingled clouds of cells rather than laminae of specialized function. It is necessary, therefore, to ask if any aspects of the techniques used by those workers might have obscured an orderly arrangement of cells. The authors who have contributed most to our knowledge of dorsal horn cells include Armett, Gray, Hunsperger, and Lal (1962), Eccles (1964), Frank and Fuortes (1956), Hunt and Kuno (1957), Kolmondin (1957), Kolmondin and Skoglund (1960), Laporte, Lundberg, and Oscarsson (1956), Lundberg (1964), and Oscarsson (1964).

To establish the credibility of this paper, it is obviously important to show why the distinct lamination has not been reported by other physiologists. There are several reasons that may have contributed. The first, and perhaps the most important, is the use of fine-tipped microelectrodes with resistances of 20-100 M by such investigators as Frank and Fuortes (1956), Kolmodin (1957), and Hunt and Kuno (1959). These electrodes used for intracellular recording penetrate axons at least as easily as they penetrate the relatively small cell bodies of dorsal interneurons (Hunt and Kuno 1959, Wall 1959). Obviously, recordings from axons give little or no information about the location of the cell bodies from which they originate. A second disadvantage of intracellular recording in this region is that relatively few successful recordings are made on each particular track. It is therefore difficult to accumulate sufficient cells in any one animal to establish an overall pattern of cell distribution.

The next problem is that of localization of recording sites. If electrode tracks were marked at all, it has been common practice to locate one track and to assume that others run parallel to the one observed. We have repeatedly seen that tracks curve even to the extent that electrodes, apparently parallel on the surface, cross each other within the cord.

In the experiments reported here, we have located several hundred electrode tracks. This would hardly have been practicable if the embedding-sectioning-staining-and-searching method of location had been used. Instead we cut off the electrodes and viewed them directly. This method is simple and fast and does not require a skilled histological technician. Some workers (Armett, Gray, and Palmer, 1961, for example) have avoided locating individual electrodes by using a coordinate system in which the distance of the electrode from the midline and the depth of penetration are used. This method obviously requires that dimensions of cord should repeat exactly from animal to animal. Unfortunately such is not the case, and it is obvious from 60 maps used in this paper. One reason for the variability is that the entering roots themselves vary between prefixation and postfixation of their entry points with respect to the vertebrae (Romanes, 1951; Sprague, 1958). This contributes a considerable variation to the outline of grey matter in any one region of a cord segment. Furthermore, since the cord is attached to the dura by dentate ligaments and to the roots by pia and arachnoid, disturbance of dura and roots during the experiment distorts the shape of the cord. The results of using a coordinate system can be seen in Figure 26-4 (Arnett, *et al.,* 1961) in which units located deep in the dorsal columns are shown where no cells or dendrites exist. Since there is variability in the outline of grey matter and the location of laminae, it is not wise to pool the results of many experiments and project the suspected location of recording points onto a "standard" outline of cord.

The use of electrical stimuli on peripheral nerves may have obscured lamination. It has been shown that the receptive fields of some cells are enormously expanded if electrical stimuli, rather than naturally occurring pressure stimuli (Wall, 1960), are used. The arrival in the cord of highly synchronized volleys may unmask the presence of diffuse connections which are normally insufficient to produce postsynaptic impulses. Anesthesia depresses the response of cells in deeper laminae to natural stimuli and may preclude the observation of sufficient cells. The technique used by Coombs, Curtis and Landgren (1956) for recording the location of massed potentials set up by arriving afferent volleys did not calculate the actual location of sinks (Howland, Lettvin, McCulloch, Pitts, and Wall, 1955) which would have localized the activity much more discretely. Therefore, their results suggest that activity is spread over far wider areas than is the actual case. Orthodromic microelectrode stimulation experiments (Bernhard and Rexed 1945, for example) do not differentiate between stimulation of axons passing through the region and cell bodies. In making extracellular recordings from single units there is a danger, if the electrode position is not adjusted to a position of maximal spike height, that dendritic rather than cell body spikes may be recorded (Wall, 1965).

In the experiments reported here we avoided the ten reasons stated above by which a laminar arrangement of cell bodies might be obscured. This was done by recording maximal spikes extracellularly from single units in unanesthetized preparations with natural stimuli and with histological localization of each recording point. Furthermore, experiments were designed specifically to discover if laminae existed. The method of marking the location of the first unit which showed properties different from more dorsal cells produced three roughly horizontal demarcation lines across the dorsal horn. This line gives an artificial accuracy to the lamination because

rare units were encountered in lamina five which had lamina four properties, and in lamina six which had the properties of lamina five cells. One
must also warn that the method of recording selects the largest cells prefer-
entially, and we have no information on the smaller ones. The laminae
shown here should be regarded as zones of concentration rather than absolutely separate laminae of distinct specialization.

Lamina One

This lamina caps the dorsal horn contain the thinly scattered cells
of Waldeyer. This oppressed minority of cells are squashed flat between
the dorsal columns above, and the substantia gelatinosa below. They are
few in number. In a 20μ-thick cross-section of cat lumbar cord, one usually
sees only one to three of these cells. Their cell bodies are quite large and
their dendrites ramify extensively within the lamina. Anatomical studies
suggest that they receive both large and small diameter peripheral afferent
fibers (Earle, 1952; Ralston, 1965; Szentagothai, 1964). Their axons project
into the lateral columns (Earle, 1952; Ramon y Cajal, 1952). They may
also end in lamina two (Ralston, 1965), but this is more speculative. Our
physiological studies show that extracellular recordings may be made from
these cells although their scattered arrangement means that they are not
encountered at every penetration. In the spinal animal, they are spontaneously active, monosynaptically connected to large peripheral cutaneous receptive fields encompassing as much as one third of the leg skin. There are
some signs that they receive from other types of cutaneous afferents and
from muscles and joints. In the discussion which follows we shall take the
risk of neglecting the role of these cells in the functioning of the deeper
layers for the following reasons: (a) they are few in number; (b) the extreme nonspecificity of their function and their large receptive fields do not
seem to fit with the observed specificities in deeper cells, and (c) their projection to deeper layers seems sparse, if present at all. The functional role
of these cells remains open to investigation and speculation.

Lamina Two; Substantia Gelatinosa

This very obvious lamina contains three neuronal components: (a) entering afferent fibers; (b) small cells, and (c) dendrites rising from cell
bodies in deeper laminae. The area is characterized by the large numbers
of small cells with cell bodies not greater than 10μ in diameter oriented in
a spindle shape in a dorsal ventral direction. The region also contains very
large numbers of fine fibers running in a rostrocaudal direction. These
are believed to be mainly interconnections between the small cells. A group
of these fine fibers collects on the outer edge of the lamina and makes up

the Lissauer tract. A further important characterization of lamina two has recently been proposed by Ralston (1965) who states that Nauta and EM degeneration studies show that no dorsal root fibers terminate within it.

This statement is contradicted by Szentagothai (1964) who states that afferent fibers, especially unmyelinated ones, do end in the region. Golgi studies seem to show clearly that unmyelinated fibers pass from the dorsal root into the medial part of the Lissauer tract and from there stream directly into the substantia gelatinosa (Earle, 1952; Ramon y Cajal, 1952; Szentagothai, 1964). It is possible that these authors have been mistaken either in tracing continuous fibers from the root to lamina two or in identifying endings. On the other hand it is possible that the central ends of peripheral C fibers do not undergo normal Wallerian degeneration either in time course or in nature and that because of this difference, EM or normal Nauta degeneration stains fail to show their terminations.

The physiologist is in a quandary because of this lack of clear evidence for the location of terminals of afferent C fibers. If Ralston is right, then C fibers must end on deeper cells and the lamina two cells can only be influenced indirectly by afferent fibers. If Szentagothai and the older authors are right, then a substantial number of the smaller afferent fibers terminate on lamina two cells. For the purposes of speculation in the rest of this paper, we shall assume that small diameter afferents end directly or indirectly on lamina two cells and excite them. We shall also assume that the axons of lamina two cells end on each other and on the cells of lamina three and possibly on entering afferent axons in lamina three. There is no clear anatomical evidence for the projections of lamina two into lamina three but they are suggested by both Szentagothai (1964) and Ralston (1965). If the anatomy of this lamina is controversial, the physiology is not, because there is none. The small cells have so far resisted attempts to record unit activity and one is therefore free to speculate on their function without any interference from experimental facts.

Lamina Three

This lamina contains the same three types of neuronal components as lamina two: (a) small cells; (b) afferent fibers, and (c) dendrites arising from deeper cells. It is differentiated from lamina two by Rexed (1952) because it contains a wider spectrum of small cell sizes and fewer bundles of longitudinally running fibers. Ralston (1965) makes the further differentiation that it contains osmophilic myelinated fibers and terminations of dorsal root afferents. Since Szentagothai (1964) believes that dorsal root fibers terminate in both laminae two and three, he does not believe that there is a significant difference between the lamina two and three. The region contains synaptic contacts between incoming afferent fibers and presumed dendrites. In addition, there are two types of axo-axonal contact reported by Ralston. One, a glomerular type, has a single large axon surrounded by a number of indented small axons. The other is a triadic complex consisting of an afferent terminal on a dendrite with a third element, apparently an axon terminal, in contact with the afferent terminal.

We propose that the elements observed in laminae two and three make up the anatomical substrate of a physiological control gate. This gate control mechanism determines the post-synaptic effectiveness of entering cutaneous afferent nerve impulses by controlling the membrane potential of the afferent terminals. The external sign of the functioning of this gate is the dorsal root potential originally described by Barron and Matthews (1935). This potential signals a change in the membrane potential of afferent terminals (Wall, 1958) and a change in the transynaptic effectiveness of entering impulses (Howland *et al.,* 1955; Eccles, 1961; Mendell and Wall, 1965).

The three elements in the region have been examined to determine which are responsible for the generation of this presynaptic control mechanism. Direct interaction between neighboring afferent fibers has been ruled out by showing that the phenomenon persists when all direct contacts have been severed by surgical lesions (Wall, 1962). Impulses in the large cells have been eliminated as a cause by showing that dorsal root potentials persist under such deep anesthesia that no impulses are generated in lamina four cells (Wall, 1962). Slow potentials in large cells have been eliminated by showing that they cannot be seen on intracellular recordings (Wall, 1965).

We conclude that it is the small cells which are generating the phenomenon because a source-sink analysis shows that the activity associated with terminal depolarization is located within lamina two and three and because section of the Lissauer tract abolishes the spread of the depolarization from one segment to another, (Wall, 1962). Incoming impulses in large diameter cutaneous afferents set off a prolonged depolarization of all afferent terminals in the region and this depolarization is associated with presynaptic inhibition. By contrast small diameter afferent fibers, including unmyelinated fibers, set off a presynaptic hyperpolarization which antagonizes the effect of the large fibers. It is not known how this antagonistic effect of the two types of afferent fiber fits in with the anatomy but a hypothetical scheme is shown in Figure 26-1. It is also possible that the two types of axo-axonal contact represent the two antagonistic effects.

The presynaptic gate control mechanism is affected by impulses descending from the head as well as by the balanced interaction of large versus

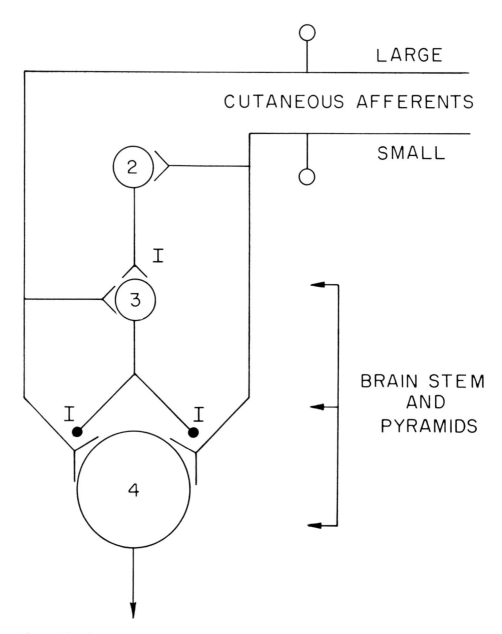

Figure 26-1. Suggested scheme for the relation of afferent fibers to the cells of Rexed laminae two, three, and four. *I* indicates inhibitory connections. As described in the text, this scheme represents one way in which the components of this region may interconnect.

small afferent fibers. Nyberg-Hansen and Brodal (1963) showed some Nauta degeneration in laminae two and three following precruciate lesion in cat cortex. Hagbarth and Kerr (1954) showed that depolarizing dorsal root potentials could be set off by cortical stimulation and Lundberg and Voorhoeve (1962) showed that medullary pyramidal tract stimulation would also produce presynaptic inhibition. It is not known if these descending impulses have a direct or an indirect effect on the small cells which we believe control the membrane potential of the afferent terminal arbors.

Lamina Four

This region is clearly recognizable, histologically, as the most dorsal lamina containing large cell bodies with sufficient cytoplasm to contain obvious Nissl granules. The size of the cells allows physiological observation of single unit activity by both intra- and extracellular electrodes. Some of these cells send large diameter axons into the ipsilateral dorsolateral tract running to the lateral cervical nucleus. It is easy to record from these axons. The inputs to the cells in lamina four are under the control of the gate control mechanism in laminae two and three. Extracellular recording from cells in lamina four or intracellular recordings from their axons shows that these cells have a purely cutaneous input. Passive movement of legs has no effect on their firing. The cutaneous receptive fields of these cells are relatively small. For example, receptive fields on toes cover only a fraction of one toe. More proximal receptive fields are larger but are always a fraction of foot or leg or thigh. The cells within the lamina are arranged in a somatotopic map with medial cells having their receptive fields in the distal part of the dermatome. Fibers of many different types converge onto each cell from within its receptive field. Most cells in the lamina receive impulses from the full range of A fibers and the majority are also stimulated by C fibers (Mendell, 1965; Taub and Bishop, 1965). There is a fundamental difference of the firing pattern to large versus small diameter afferents. Impulses in large diameter afferents produce a burst of high frequency repetitive firing followed by a silent period during which the input to the cell is inhibited presynaptically. In contrast small diameter afferents also excite the cell but the period of firing is followed by a period of facilitation. This trailing facilitation produces a "wind-up" phenomenon in which afferent volleys in small diameter fibers following each other, at one to two second intervals, produce a more and more intense firing of the cells (Mendell and Wall, 1965). Natural stimulation shows that these cells are excited by hair bending, skin pressure, cooling and chemical stimuli. Although the cells respond to many different types of stimuli, the temporal pattern of firing depends both on the nature of the stimulus and on the relative balance of large versus small fibers which are active.

We have examined single cells in this lamina in the decerebrate animal and have then produced a cold block of impulses descending from the head by placing frozen cubes of Ringer saline on a lower thoracic segment. This procedure shows that some steady descending influence from the brain stem is inhibiting the majority of the cells in lamina four. In addition, stimulation of the medullary pyramids produces a transient inhibition of many of the cells in this lamina (Fetz, personal communication).

Lamina Five

As a microelectrode descends through lamina four, cells are suddenly encountered with quite different properties. A line joining the points at which these cells are first observed, roughly coincides with the dorsal border of Rexed's lamina five. This lamina occupies the narrowest portion of cat lumbar dorsal cord, contains a variety of large cell types and bundles of longitudinally running fibers. We have found that the cell bodies in this lamina tend to be spindle shaped with the axis of the spindle lying medio-laterally across the cord. These cells also appear to be dominated by a cutaneous input with no signs of a proprioceptive input by natural stimulation. The receptive fields are considerably larger than those seen in lamina four. For example, if they are receiving from toes, the receptive field will include more than one toe. It is interesting that these larger receptive fields expand along the dermatome which can be observed by plotting the medio-lateral somatotopic map of the cells of lamina four immediately dorsal to the cells observed in lamina five. This fact plus the increased latency of firing after peripheral nerve stimulation suggests that these cells are being fired by a mediolaterally arranged group of lamina four cells. The medio-lateral spindle shape of the cell body might suggest a similar distribution of the dendrites and therefore the anatomical basis for the origin of their axially elongated receptive fields.

A new and curious habituation phenomenon can be observed in these cells in a decerebrate cat. We have called it "novelty detection." If a brush stimulus is applied to one part of the receptive field at one second intervals, the response fades after a few stimuli. If the stimulus is now shifted to another part of the receptive field, the response fades after a few stimuli. If the stimulus is now shifted to another part of the receptive field, the rsponse immediately returns and again fades with repetition. The phenomenon is abolished by blocking the thoracic cord in the cat or by using more intense stimuli. Although we can only see it in decerebrate cats, we have observed it in spinal rats. We have suggested above that these cells are fired by cells in lamina four which do not themselves show this habituation phenomenon. Therefore, it seems likely that some mechanism exists in the linkage between cells of lamina four and five which inhibits any pathway which has been active while leaving the excitability of the lamina five cells untouched, since they are still capable of responding to a new input pattern which could presumably pass over four cells which have not been used in transmitting the previous afferent barrage.

When the receptive fields and responses of lamina five cells are compared in the decerebrate state and the spinal state, using a lower thoracic cold-block, it is apparent that brain stem structures are maintaining a strong inhibition over the cells of lamina five. The size of receptive fields in the decerebrate state is very much smaller than their sizes in the spinal animal. Stimulation of the pyramidal tract in the decerebrate animal excites some cells and inhibits others in this region.

Lamina Six

This lamina occupies the most ventral part of the dorsal horn. Rexed could recognize this lamina only in the cervical and lumbar enlargements. Coombs *et al.* (1956) and Wall *et al.* (1956) had noticed that afferents of muscle origin ended more ventrally in the dorsal horn than did those of cutaneous origin. The presence of a special group of ventral cells associated with the two enlargements and the more ventral region of termination of proprioceptive afferents might suggest that physiological recordings would discover cells in the ventral part of the dorsal horn which respond to movements of the limbs. This turns out to be the case. If electrodes are lowered through lamina five in the decerebrate cat, cells are discovered which respond to passive movement of joints. It is not yet known if these responses are due to joint movement or muscle stretching. If a line is drawn joining the points at which such cells are first recorded, the line roughly coincides with Rexed's dorsal border of lamina six. In the decerebrate animal these cells respond tonically at a particular joint angle and also have a phasic increase of firing rate during movement. In addition to these obvious proprioceptive inputs, most of the cells also have a cutaneous receptive field whose size is of the same order as those observed in the lamina five cells. The lamina six cells show the "novelty detection phenomenon" to both cutaneous and proprioceptive inputs. The latency of response to both skin stimulation and to stimulation of cutaneous nerves is longer than that of lamina five cells and suggests that lamina six cells may be fired by lamina five cells.

It seems likely that proprioceptive afferents converge directly on these cells and cutaneous afferents arrive indirectly. The most interesting and unusual property of the cells is that this convergence and, in fact, the cell's modality is under control. If the lamina is examined in the decerebrate animal, the cells are primarily proprioceptive in nature. Some cells respond only to passive movement and not at all to cutaneous stimuli. Most respond briskly to movement and sluggishly to rather intense pressure stimuli of their cutaneous receptive fields. Individual cells have been observed after either section of the cord at C 1 or more commonly after cold block of the spinal cord at T 12. When the descending impulses from the brain stem are abolished, some cells switch from responding only to muscle and joint inputs to responding only to cutaneous inputs. A more common result is that the relative balance of the effectiveness of the two types of input is shifted toward the cutaneous input which is most effective in the spinal state and away from the proprioceptive input which is most effective in the decerebrate state. This "switching" of modality shows up in the cutaneous modality as a variation of the size of receptive field and a variation of the threshold within the receptive field. In the proprioceptive modality, the variation between the two states shows up as a variation of which joints are effective in exciting the cell and the angle of the joint at which firing commences. In addition to being affected by descending impulses from the brain stem, pyramidal tract stimulation in the decerebrate animal produces excitation of the majority of these cells.

General

It was not possible to follow the differentiation between the various laminae in an animal anesthetized with 25 mg/kilo intravenous Nembutal®. This dose of anesthesia abolishes the effect of unmyelinated afferents which open the gate control mechanism in an unanesthetized preparation. It abolishes most of the spontaneous activity in lamina four cells so that their further inhibition by descending brain stem impulses is difficult to observe. The anesthetic so depresses the responses of cells in laminae five and six, that it is very difficult to evoke responses in these cells by natural peripheral stimuli.

The same general organization of dorsal horn which has been described above for cat has also been observed in spinal rat. The divisions between the laminae tend to slant in a dorsolateral direction in rat lumbar enlargement in contrast to the almost perfectly horizontal placement of the laminae in cat lumbar segments. The major difference of interest between cat and rat is that we have observed the novelty detection phenomenon in lamina five cells of spinal rat. This tends to confirm the hypothesis that this property of cells is due to a spinal mechanism as suggested in Figure 26-2. The fact that the phenomenon disappears from the cat cells if the thoracic cord is blocked might at first suggest that the cord cells must refer to brain stem structures to determine if a particular pattern of afferent impulses had occurred before and if they should be transmitted. However, we have shown that the brain stem exerted a tonic inhibitory effect on the cutaneous input and also that the "novelty detection" phenomenon only occurs with near threshold stimuli. It may be that the brain stem is necessary to activate a cord inhibitory mechanism which is responsible for the turning off of the previously active pathways to the lamina five cells.

The experiments described in this paper are the beginning of a new look at the repertoire of behavior of cord cells. Crude and massive changes in the state of the cord have been induced by cord block or by pyramidal-tract stimulation. Presumably, more specific patterns of descending volleys would induce subtler changes of response in the group of cells which have been examined here. We have not yet observed differences of response in medial versus lateral cells, although these are to be expected. It will be extremely interesting to see if the coupling between these cells and the ventral cells can be unravelled. That coupling will certainly be under control and will be variable. It is unlikely that such a system will be usefully investigated by slamming it repeatedly with synchronized volleys generated electrically

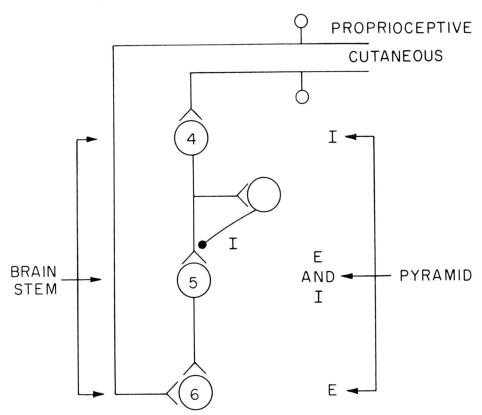

Figure 26-2. Suggested scheme for the organization of laminae four, five and six. *E* and *I* mark excitatory and inhibitory connections. The gate control over incoming afferent cutaneous impulses shown in Figure 26-1 has not been included in this figure.

in peripheral nerves. Similarly, artificially generated descending volleys from the head are likely to prove the existence of anatomical connection rather, than to show the role played by these descending systems in a behaving animal. By studying the transmission systems in as many states as can be induced, it may be possible to extrapolate and predict the range of reper- toire possessed by the cells in the free animal.

SUMMARY

Large cells in cat lumbar dorsal horn were examined. They were found to be organized in three distinct laminae which correspond to Rexed laminae four, five, and six. Cells were affected by both peripheral stimuli and by impulses descending from the head. Two new properties of nerve cells were discovered, "novelty detection" and "switching." The organiza- tion of dorsal horn depended on the nature of descending volleys. The response of single cells was studied during the decerebrate state, pyramidal- tract stimulation, and reversible cold block of segments T 12 and L 1.

Lamina four cells receive only cutaneous afferents, and are organized in a somatotopic map. Their receptive fields are small. In the decerebrate state they are strongly inhibited. In the spinal state they increase their spon- taneous activity and the dynamic pressure range over which they respond to cutaneous stimuli, but do not vary their receptive fields. Stimulation of the pyramidal tract produces a transient inhibition of some of these cells.

Lamina five cells respond only to cutaneous stimuli, have larger recep- tive fields than those in lamina four, and have a longer latency of response to peripheral stimuli. The cell bodies tend to lie transversely across the spinal cord. It is suggested that they receive from lamina four cells. They are very strongly inhibited in the decerebrate state. When segments of thoracic spinal cord are cold blocked, the receptive fields expand markedly, excitability increases, and the slow wave recorded in the region after peripheral stimuli show a very large increase. The great majority of cells are either inhibited or excited by pyramidal-tract stimulation. In the de- cerebrate state, many cells showed a rapid decline of response to a repeated intermittent brushing of their receptive field. If the location of the stimulus was changed, the response returned and faded again on repetition. The ability of these cells to respond only to new patterns of stimulation is named "novelty detection."

Lamina six cells respond both to cutaneous stimuli and to movements of the limb. The cutaneous receptive fields are slightly larger than those seen in lamina five, and there is a further increase of latency between peripheral stimuli and response of these cells. In the decerebrate state, movement is a highly effective stimulus to these cells, and cutaneous stimuli are relatively ineffective. In the spinal state, the effect of cutaneous stimuli is greatly

exaggerated, and the effect of movement is either abolished or greatly diminished. This property of selection between interoceptive and exteroceptive
inputs is named "switching." Pyramidal-tract stimulation had a strong effect
on the excitability of cells in lamina six.

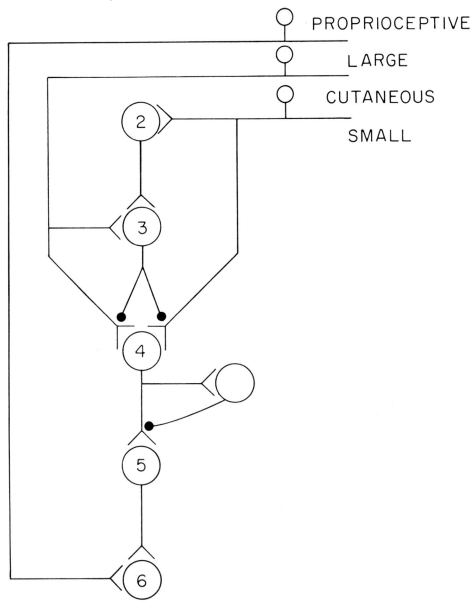

PROPRIOCEPTIVE

LARGE

CUTANEOUS

SMALL

Figure 26-3. Summary diagram of the suggested organization of laminae two, three, four,
five, and six on cat dorsal horn. For simplicity, the diagram fails to show three extremely
important additional features of the organization: 1. convergence; 2. descending controls; 3. lateral interaction.

In the summary diagram (Fig. 26-3) it is suggested that the triple laminar organization allows a segmental collection and filtering of cutaneous afferent information. In the lowest of the laminae, a controlled merging of information about the state of skin, muscles, and joints takes place.

	Lamina		
	4	*5*	*6*
Cutaneous effects	+	+	+
Proprioceptive effects	0	0	+
Small cutaneous receptive fields	+	0	0
Brain stem effects	+	++	++
Pyramidal effects	—	+ —	+
Novelty detection	0	+	+
Switching	0	0	+

REFERENCES

Armett, C. J., Gray, J. A. B., Hunsperger, R. W., & Lal, S. The transmission of information in primary receptor neurones and second order neurones of a phasic system. *J. Physiol. (London)*, 1962, **164**, 395.

Armett, C. J., Gray, J. A. B., & Palmer, J. F. A group of neurones in the dorsal horn associated with cutaneous mechanoreceptors. *J. Physiol. (London)*, 1961, **156**, 611.

Barron, D. H., & Matthews, B. H. C. The interpretation of potential changes in the spinal cord. *J. Physiol. (London)*, 1938, **185**, 73.

Bernard, C. G., & Rexed, B. The localization of premotor interneurons discharging through the peroneal nerve. *J. Neurophysiol.*, 1945, **8**, 387.

Christiansen, J. Neurological observations of macaques with spinal cord lesions. *Proc. Am. Ass. Anat.*, 1966, **00**, 330.

Cook, A. W., & Browder, E. J. Surgical lesion of dorsal columns in man. *Arch. Neurol. (Chicago)*, 1965, **12**, 72.

Coombs, J. S., Curtis, D. R., & Landgren, S. Spinal cord potentials generated by impulses in muscle and cutaneous afferent fibres. *J. Neurophysiol.*, 1956, **19**, 452.

De Vito, J. K., Ruch, T. C., & Patton, H. D. Analysis of residual weight discriminatory ability following section of dorsal columns in monkeys. *Indian J. Physiol. Pharmacol.*, 1964, **8**, 117.

Earle, K. M. The tract of Lissauer and its possible relation to the pain pathway. *J. Comp. Neurol.*, 1952, **96**, 93.

Eccles, J. C. The mechanism of synaptic transmission. *Ergebn. Physiol.*, 1961, **51**, 299.

Eccles, J. C. The excitatory responses of spinal neurones. *Progr. Brain Res.*, 1964, **12**, 1.

Frank, K., & Fuortes, M. G. F. Unitary activity in spinal interneurons of cats. *J. Physiol. (London)*, 1956, **131**, 424.

Hagbarth, K. E., & Kerr, D. I. B. Central influences of spinal afferent conduction. *J. Neurophysiol.*, 1954, **17**, 295.

Howland, B., Lettvin, J. Y., McCulloch, W. S., Pitts, W. H., & Wall, P. D. Reflex inhibition by dorsal root interaction. *J. Neurophysiol.*, 1955, **18**, 1.

Hunt, C. C., & Kuno, M. Properties of spinal interneurones. *J. Physiol. (London)*, 1959, **147**, 346.

Kolmodin, G. M. Integrative processes in single spinal interneurones with proprioceptive connections. *Acta Physiol. Scand.*, 1957, **40**, 1. (Suppl. 139)

Kolmodin, G. M., & Skoglund, C. R. Analysis of spinal interneurons activated by tactile and nociceptive stimulation. *Acta Physiol. Scand.*, 1960, **50**, 337.

Laporte, Y., Lundberg, A., & Oscarsson, W. Functional organization of spino-cerebellar tract in the cat. *Acta. Physiol. Scand.*, 1956, **36**, 188.

Levitt, M., & Schwartzman, R. Spinal sensory tracts and two point tactile sensitivity. *Proc. Am. Ass. Anat.*, 1966, **00**, 377.

Lundberg, A. Ascending spinal hindlimb pathways — the cat. *Progr. Brain Res.*, 1964, **12**, 135.

Lundberg, A., & Voorhoeve, P. Effects from the pyramidal tract on spinal reflex arcs. *Acta Physiol. Scand.*, 1962, **56**, 201.

Melzack, R., & Wall, P. D. On the nature of cutaneous sensory mechanisms. *Brain,* 1962, **85**, 331.

Melzack, R., & Wall, P. D. Pain mechanisms: a new theory. *Science,* 1965, **150**, 971.

Melzack, R., Wall, P. D., & Weisz, A. Z. Masking and metacontrast in the skin sensory system. *Exp. Neurol.*, 1963, **8**, 219.

Mendell, L. M. Responses of single dorsal cord cells to peripheral cutaneous fibres. Ph.D. thesis. Massachusetts Institute of Technology, Cambridge, Mass., 1965.

Mendell, L. M., & Wall, P. D. Responses of single dorsal cord cells to peripheral cutaneous unmyelinated fibers. *Nature (London)*, 1965, **206**, 97.

Nyberg-Hansen, R., & Brodal, A. Sites of termination of corticospinal fibres in the cat. *J. Comp. Neurol.*, 1963, **120**, 369.

Oscarsson, O. Organization of uncrossed and crossed long ascending spinal tracts. *Progr. Brain Res.*, 1964, **12**, 164.

Ralston, H. J. The organization of substantia gelatinosa. *Z. Zellforschung*, 1965, **67**, 1.

Ramon y Cajal, S. *Histologie du Systeme Nerveux.* Madrid: Instituto Ramon y Cajal, 1952.

Rexed, B. The cytoarchitectonic organization of the spinal cord of the cat. *J. Comp. Neurol.*, 1952, **96**, 415.

Romanes, G. J. The motor cell columns of the lumbosacral spinal cord of the cat. *J. Comp. Neurol.*, 1951, **94**, 313.

Sprague, J. M. The distribution of dorsal root fibres in motor cells of the lumbosacral spinal cord of the cat and the site of excitatory and inhibitory terminals in mono-synaptic pathways. *Proc. Roy. Soc. (Biol.),* 1958, **149**, 534.

Szentagothai, J. Neuronal and synaptic arrangement in the substantia gelatinosa Rolandi. *J. Comp. Neurol.*, 1964, **122**, 219.

Taub, A., & Bishop, P. O. The spinocervical tract: dorsal column linkage, conduction velocity, primary afferent spectrum. *Exp. Neurol.*, 1965, **13**, 1.

Vierck, C. J. Spinal pathways mediating limb position sense. *Proc. Am. Ass. Anat.*, 1966, 437.

Wall, P. D. Excitability changes in afferent fibre terminations and their relation to slow potentials. *J. Physiol. (London)*, 1958, **142**, 1.

Wall, P. D. Repetitive discharge of neurons. *J. Neurophysiol.*, 1959, **22**, 305.

Wall, P. D. Cord cells responding to touch, damage, and temperature of the skin. *J. Neurophysiol.*, 1960, **23**, 197.

Wall, P. D. The origin of a spinal-cord slow potential. *J. Physiol. (London)*, 1962, **164**, 508.

Wall, P. D. Impulses recorded in the region of dendrites. *J. Physiol. (London)*, 1965, **180**, 116.

Wall, P. D., & Cronly-Dillon, J. R. Pain, itch, and vibration. *Arch. Neurol. (Chicago)*, 1960, **2**, 365.

Wall, P. D., McCulloch, W. S., Lettvin, J. Y., & Pitts, W. H. The terminal arborisations
    of the cat's pyramidal tract. *Yale J. Biol. Med.,* 1956, **28**, 457.
Zotterman, Y. Touch, pain and tickling. *J. Physiol. (London),* 1939, **95**, 1.
Zotterman, Y. Thermal sensations. In *Handbook of Physiology.* Washington, D. C.: Am.
    Physiol. Soc., 1959. Pp. 431-458.

DISCUSSION

DR. B. S. ROSNER: I notice that you have a descending influence coming from pyramidal tract on both laminae five and six (Fig. 26-2). Is it necessary to postulate the influence coming on to six? It would seem to be that simply by influencing lamina five alone and by having a direct connection from five into six, you could account for all of the phenomena summarized in your table.

DR. WALL: That might be true as far as the cutaneous input is concerned, but it is certainly not true as far as the muscle input. And I must say that those cells are very impressive cells to work with, because if you find the joint angles that start the cell firing, and then move the joint to a silent region and stimulate the pyramidal tract, you see that you have shifted the threshold angle of the joint. This presumably has to be either an effect on the joint afferents or a direct effect on the cell. Furthermore, the anatomy shows a lot of endings in that region so they had better be doing something.

DR. H. DAVIS: This is a fascinating description and a very important analysis of some of the organization of the sensory systems. One of the things that attracts my attention is this novelty affect, something which occurs in the course of time. I do not know whether the word adaptation appeals to you in this respect or does not. However, what I really want to do is to underline the importance that I see in this concept of the switching of an influence from one point to some other part of the nervous system, thereby changing the type of input that is effective for a given cell. This is something that is rather different from a gross change of threshold, a facilitation, a depression, or an inhibition, if you will, of the cell as a whole. There is a selectivity here and we must pay great attention to this feature. I would like to ask if you have any suggestions for us as to the mechanism of this selective control, whether it is changing the excitability of a certain part of the dendritic tree of the cell in question, whether it is presynaptic inhibition, or perhaps the interposition of inhibitory cells with short axons.

DR. WALL: If I can just make a comment on what you said first about adaptation. I can see, as more and more people are now beginning to study these phenomena, that there is going to be an awful semantic mess develop over all these words which have been in some chaos for fifty years or so. I would not call this adaptation, because that is normally reserved for a failing of a response to a steady stimulus. What I am talking about is a failure of a response to an intermittent stimulus, which is usually put in the habituation class. How that novelty phenomenon might work depends on the correctness of this diagram that I showed last (Fig. 26-3), because we certainly have never seen anything like that in the lamina four cell. If the lamina four cells are in fact feeding into the lamina five cells and the lamina five cells show this novelty phenomena, then one has, at least, located where it occurs. It is somewhere between the output of four and the output of five. What it would amount to, then, is simply that a given pathway, which has been active, turns itself off while leaving both the cell and all other pathways receptive. That might be a good place for localized presynaptic inhibition. I should have added that, although we had only seen this phenomena in the decerebrate cat and it disappeared if you made the animal spinal, therefore you might think those cells were asking some structure in the head, "Have I been stimulated before?" I do not think that is the case. "Novelty" appears to be due to a segmental local mechanism. One of the reasons for believing that is that in the rat, which is a more spinal animal than the cat, you can see this phenomenon in the spinal rat. You do not have to use a decerebrate rat.

Turning to your question concerning the mechanism of switching, if a five cell is firing onto a six cell, which is also receiving a muscle input, we know that the five cell is heavily inhibited by the brain-stem descending efferents. So, one could say, it is only necessary to turn off the cutaneous input and the muscle input would then be apparent. However, not only is the cutaneous effect inhibited but the proprioceptive effect is facilitated. This could be achieved by simultaneous inhibition of five cells and facilitation of six cells. It could also depend on a presynaptic control of the proprioceptive afferents which has been shown to exist (Anderson and Eccles, 1962).

Dr. Davis: Thank you very much. I asked the question partly in the hope that you might incidentally develop a model for the kind of gates Dr. Melzack spoke of yesterday.

Dr. Wall: I will add to my manuscript a description of laminae two, three, and four which we believe contain the cells which operate a gate control over the entering cutaneous impulses.

Dr. A. Iggo: You stopped short in your discussion of the gate mechanism. In your previous publications (Melzack and Wall, 1965) you suggested some functional role for it which has relied on the relative balance of inputs in the large and small fibers. It would be useful if you would develop a little further what you think the function of the system is. The other question that I have concerns the spontaneous or the ongoing activity which is so strongly affected in the lamina four cells by cooling the spinal cord. I was wondering if you have any information about the origin of this spontaneous activity.

DR. WALL: The facts are that in the spinal animal most of the lamina 4 cells are spontaneously active and cutting the dorsal roots abolishes that spontaneous activity. I would have said that, directly or indirectly, the incoming afferent barrage is driving those cells. Now, it is quite clear that in the decerebrate animal most of these cells are not spontaneously active. And therefore, there is something coming down, either directly onto those cells or onto the presynaptic structures, which I assume, is either inhibiting the cell or preventing the ordinary incoming afferent barrage from firing the cells. That is a simple-minded answer and I am quite sure that there are also, for example, excitatory lateral connections which allow these cells to bombard each other. That, presumably, has some role in the spontaneous activity. So this is part of the evidence. But, you have very much more information about afferent spontaneous activity than I, and it is something that I am very interested in. There are, presumably, in a zero stimulus situation, some impulses coming in over the dorsal roots. I would like very much to know whether those fibers, which are specially active, just generally pool their impulses on the cell and generally keep up its central excitatory state, or whether they have special contacts which are particularly effective.

DR. IGGO: The amount of incoming activity seems to be extremely small compared with the amount of activity that can be set up by very light stimuli. Very light mechanical stimulation will set up an enormous barrage of activity where previously there is almost none at all. It would seem to me that this amount of input would flood any previous activity and one would expect it to be of very much more significance in the central mechanism.

DR. WALL: I think that Dr. Iggo has raised a very interesting and important question. Let me just add one experimental result. You would think that an obvious experiment to do would be to cut all the dorsal roots except one rootlet, and then examine the response of cord cells to peripheral natural stimuli. The answer, unfortunately, is that I cannot get anything to work centrally. I understand what you are saying here. It looks as though there are very few afferent nerve impulses coming in a zero stimulus situation, but those impulses must be pretty important; they must be maintaining central excitability.

DR. IGGO: But surely if you cut all except one rootlet, then does not this establish how important a large quantity of afferent impulses in the periphery is, rather than establish how important a very small amount of background activity is.

Dr. Wall: I would not have agreed at all. The number of fibers needed to fire off a cell are available in one rootlet. The relevant fibers, or 90 per cent of them from the receptive field of a cell run in a very small micro-bundle. However, the central effect of this microbundle is only apparent if the central excitatory state is maintained by a general afferent bombardment.

References

Anderson, P., & Eccles, J. C. Inhibitory phasing of neuronal discharge. *Nature (London)*, 1962, **162**, 645.

Melzack, R., & Wall, P. D. Pain mechanisms: A new theory. *Science*, 1965, **150**, 971.

Chapter 27

RESPONSES OF CERTAIN DORSAL HORN CELLS TO MECHANICAL STIMULATION OF THE CAT'S PAD*

J. A. B. GRAY

AT A SYMPOSIUM OF THE Society of Experimental Biology (Gray, 1962) two systems of receptor organization were considered. In one, spatial discrimination is obtained at the expense of temporal discrimination and in the other, vice versa. In the former, which was referred to as a "tonic system," the intensity at each point is represented by the frequency of impulses in a single receptor unit. Each receptor unit acts independently so the system simultaneously measures intensity at many points. The impulse intervals must, however, be averaged over a length of time to obtain accuracy and this will prevent precise discrimination of events occurring within short intervals of one another. In the other system the magnitude at an instant is represented by the number of active units. The spread of activity blurs simultaneous spatial distinctions but since the volley is completed very rapidly there is a high degree of discrimination between successive events. This system was called the *phasic system*. The terms *tonic* and *phasic system* should not be held to imply that tonic receptors are always organized in a tonic system and phasic receptors in phasic systems. A variety of organizations is possible.

These two types of representation present different problems in connection with the extraction and analysis of the information contained. The remainder of this paper is built around observations made by D. R. G. Fuller and myself on cells in the dorsal horn of the cat's lumbosacral spinal cord when the foot pad was stimulated with either one or two mechanical stimuli of the type mentioned below. The responses of any cell group, which may have connections both between cells and between outputs and inputs, can be complex and difficult to analyse verbally. An attempt has, however, been made here to divide the functions of this cell group into three basic processes: (a) the extraction of those factors in the primary patterns required by the second order cells as a basis for further action; (b) the change in the distribution and numbers of impulses as between those entering and those leaving the region, i.e., the amplification or attenuation both in the number of units active and in the amount of activity in any one fibre, and

---

*Medical Research Council, London.

different events within a complex stimulus. The division is somewhat arbitrary and the processes may be inextricably mingled.

The word *event* has been used and requires explanation and definition.
In the previous paper it was pointed out that while our aim is to interpret
the representations of complex forms of stimulation, it is essential to break
down the problem into parts which are analysable. It is possible to describe
any complex stimulus in terms of a sufficient number of single events each
arranged in a suitable relationship of space and time to the others. Each
event has a certain magnitude of a particular characteristic at a given time
and at a given point. It is possible, and perhaps likely, that such a theoretical
breakdown is also possible in physical terms. This has, implicitly or explicitly, been the basis of many investigations. It is explicitly the basis of
experiments we have carried out on the cat footpad and dorsal horn system,
which will be the main example quoted in this paper. In these experiments
the stimuli have been displacements of varying amplitude, with velocities
more than twice the critical velocity and with a "rectangular" time course,
applied at points on the pad.

The basis of the discussion in this paper will be that events are represented by various patterns of activity. The word representation will be used
to mean those factors which exist, as a result of a stimulus, in the pattern of
nerve impulses, or other nervous activity, in a population of units, and from
which the characteristics of the applied stimulus may be deduced. This
definition deliberately does not mention the particular factors used by the
animal, since an important step in understanding the transmission of information is to know as much as possible about the factors existing in the
primary, or higher order, representation and the information potentially
available. Furthermore, a single primary population may go to several
junctional regions and at present we have no definite knowledge that the
same factors will be of importance to each one.

INVESTIGATION OF A FIRST JUNCTIONAL REGION

The inputs to such a region are the impulse patterns in the population
of primary receptor units from the pad, the outputs are the patterns of impulse activity in the axons of the second order cells. Such cells in the dorsal
horn are both monosynaptically and polysynaptically connected to the
primary population (Armett, Gray, and Palmer, 1961; Armett, Gray,
Hunsperger, and Lal, 1962). The junctional region consists of the network
of interconnections between the first and second order cells, together with
any connections there are between the primary units and connections between different second order cells and any between output and input. The
network could include cells other than the first and second order receptor

units. One wants to know the relation of the output to the input and the mechanism of the transformation.

The steps taken in this investigation have been the following:

1. The first step is to know as much as possible about the input: (a) by working out the impulse patterns in the whole population of units for a range of stimuli corresponding to a set of single events (Fuller and Gray, 1966) ; and (b) by looking for relations between particular features of both the patterns and the stimuli, and by investigating the errors involved in these relationships; hence obtaining knowledge of the information available (Gray, 1966) .

2. The second step is to perform certain specific experiments to establish certain points of organization and function (Armett *et al.*, 1962; Gray and Lal, 1965) .

3. From these, one makes an hypothesis about the mechanism in the form of a model. The basic outlines of the model which has been developed were indicated by Armett *et al.* (1962) .

4. From the model, predictions are calculated about the behaviour of single second order cells under a variety of conditions including those using more than one stimulus.

5. Then these predictions are compared with observed responses. The responses of single second order cells have been measured and related quantitatively to stimulus amplitude and position. This has been done under different conditions of cell excitability induced by repetitive stimulation or by stimulation of descending inhibitory tracts. Similar observations with two stimuli are being made.

6. Finally, from these observations and from the model, one hopes to work out the output patterns of the population and to relate these to the inputs.

THE INPUT

In the past year certain relevant developments have occurred. Werner and Mountcastle (1965) have published a quantitative analysis of a type of tonic receptor unit. This shows that a tonic unit, which fires regularly, by usual standards, may require to be averaged over several hundred msec for the maximum information (around 3 bits) to be extracted. Estimates of the information potentially available in the phasic system from the pad have also been made (Gray, 1966) . The information transmitted per receptor unit per unit time appears to be similar in the two systems though it would be dangerous to press this point, as there are considerable uncertainties. The discharges recorded by Werner and Mountcastle are longer in duration, more repeatable and more regular than some seen in the mammalian visual system (Barlow, Fitzhugh and Kuffler, 1957; Hubel and is unknown so that any measure of the shape of this distribution, whether obtained directly from experimental results or indirectly from the model, can only be in terms of impulses/unit and not in terms of true density in impulses/mm² of equivalent area of receptor surface. The experimental results obtained so far suggest that the shape of the distribution is indicated approximately by the curves of Figure 27-4. The high values, dotted in the bottom right section, occur only rarely and the model is known to be incomplete in this respect (see below).

The outputs depend on the excitability of the group of junctions concerned, (Armett *et al.*, 1962). This may be altered by stimulating descending fibers in the medulla (Carpenter, Lundberg, and Norrsell, 1963) or by altering the stimulus repeat frequency. Results from both methods are shown in Figure 27-3. Figure 27-4 shows that at high excitabilities the average number of impulses per unit is predicted to increase at all positions in the array of units and at all stimulus strengths and it is predicted that there will be some increase in the proportion of active units in the second order population. The output/input ratio is not constant but increases with the larger inputs. This nonlinear increase is limited by a maximum level of activity for each cell, and usually lies between five and ten impulses/stimulus of the type used. At low excitabilities it is predicted that the number of impulses discharged may be less than the number in the input and that there may be a reduction in the proportion of the population which is active.

The question which then arises, is whether this type of transformation has features which are primarily related to the fact that in this system each event in a complex stimulus is represented, in the primary population, in space and not in time. The same primary representation is also the input to cells in the dorsal column nuclei which lie on a pathway having a different function. Features of the transformations common to both sites are therefore of interest in this context. McComas (1963), using an identical range of stimuli, investigated cells in the dorsal column nuclei of the rat. The caudal cells were certainly connected monosynaptically to primary fibers firing only one impulse per fiber in response to these mechanical stimuli. The cells fired bursts of impulses, the number being related to the stimulus amplitude, and the receptive fields of the cells were large. Certain important features are therefore common to these situations and may, therefore, be related to the nature of the primary representation.

The errors introduced in the transformation in the dorsal horn network are large. With a number of repeated trials for a given set of conditions the coefficient of variation for the number of impulses discharged per trial is often more than 50 per cent and not infrequently more than 100 per cent.

INTERACTIONS BETWEEN REPRESENTATIONS IN SPACE
AND TIME

Hartline and his colleagues (Hartline and Ratliff, 1957; Hartline and Ratliff, 1958; Hartline, Wagner, and Ratliff, 1956) have worked out, for steady states, the system of lateral inhibition in the compound eye of Limulus. They have pointed out that such a network accentuates outlines between areas of different intensity in the stimulus. These arguments have been extended and used by Barlow (1961) and Hubel and Weisel (1959) amongst others. Where the stimulus is a spatial pattern the reduction in redundancy obtained by noting differences in the spatial pattern, i.e., edges or discontinuities, may clearly be an advantage. With the type of representation found in a tonic system, the type of network worked out by Hartline can clearly work in this way. It is the difference between events occurring simultaneously but at different positions which is required; since in an extreme form of tonic system each unit represents events at a single point, differences between the activities of individual units will give a representation of differences between simultaneous events.

The situation in an extreme type of phasic system of the kind discussed here is quite different. In the first place if the arguments put forward above are valid, this type of system is useful and found where there are rapid changes in the stimulus and where contrasts between successive events are important. What is needed to enhance the contrasts and to reduce redundancy is to take the differences between successive events. It must be remembered that what are important are the differences between events and their representations. The differences between the activities of nerve fibers, as such, are not important. If there were lateral inhibition between the units of the primary population of the pad system described here, this would be inhibition between parts of the representation of a single event and would reduce information and not redundancy. Such inhibition would be comparable to a tonic unit inhibiting its own later activity and reducing the time available for averaging to something well below that required to extract all the information. It should also be pointed out that if there were lateral inhibition in the pad primary system, of the type postulated for Limulus eyes, the central units would be inhibited more than the peripheral ones during a single volley; this does not happen.

These arguments are theoretical; how do they fit with present knowledge? The vertebrate cochlear is a system in which representation of the phasic type occurs. Whitfield and Evans (1965) have recently found cortical cells which will respond only to certain time sequences, i.e., rising or falling tones. Barlow and Levick (1965) have also observed sequential contrasts in retinal units in the rabbit. In the dorsal horn the situation is confused.

McComas, A. J. Innervation of cells in rat gracile nucleus. *J. Physiol. (London)*, 1964, **175**, 46P.

Perl, E. R., Whitlock, D. G., & Gentry, J. R. Cutaneous projection to second order neurones of the dorsal column system. *J. Neurophysiol.*, 1962, **25**, 337.

Schmidt, R. F.
    In O. E. Lowenstein (Ed.), *CIBA Foundation Symposium: Touch, Heat and Pain.* London: Churchill, 1966. Pp. 318-321.

Werner, G., & Mountcastle, V. B. Neural activity in mechanoreceptive cutaneous afferents: Stimulus-response relations, Weber functions and information transmission. *J. Neurophysiol.*, 1965, **28**, 359.

Whitfield, I. C. The physiology of hearing. In J. A. V. Butler & B. Katz (Eds.), *Progress in Biophysics and Biophysical Chemistry. Vol. 8.* London: Pergamon, 1957. Pp. 1-47.

Whitfield, I. C., & Evans, E. F. Response of auditory cortical neurones to stimuli of changing frequency. *J. Neurophysiol.*, 1965, **28**, 655.

DISCUSSION

Dr. H. Hensel: Dr. Gray, you really raised a very important question about information theory in saying that if you have a channel transmitting information with a certain information capacity, that any gain in accuracy on one side must combine with a loss somewhere else. Now, may I make this problem concerning cutaneous sensation a bit more general. I think the general problem is that of an isomorphic relationship between a manifold A and a manifold B. Manifold A might be the stimulus which has four independent variables, namely: space, time, quality, and intensity. This manifold is to be related, isomorphically, with another manifold, a nervous pattern which can be varied in space (meaning location and number of the nerve fibers) and time (the temporal pattern of impulses). You spoke mostly about space, time, and intensity. Quality comes in as another dimension, and I think this question is very important, particularly with respect to the problem which has been discussed during the whole symposium, namely, the question of specificity and nonspecificity. If you have specific receptors or fibers, the quality will be related only to space. It means a certain location is connected with a certain quality. If you have the concept of a pattern of nonspecific fibers, then quality is related to time as well as to space. The question is then how will this influence the other dimensions and the accuracy in space and time concerning the detection of the stimulus.

Dr. Gray: This is very true. Again, speaking quite generally, I imagine that this could be done in a number of ways depending on the situation. If you have a situation similar to the one I have been talking about, where there is discrimination of space and magnitude, and you have to bring in some quality as well, the only way that this could be done, without confusion, is the way that we all think it is done; that is, that there are separate classes of fiber units with different excitation characteristics. This, of course, does not necessarily mean that each unit has to be specific in the classical sense. The unit does not have to be exclusively sensitive to, say, temperature. If you are talking about two qualities, temperature and mechanical, it is sufficient to have two distinct classes of units which must have different excitation characteristics. They might both be sensitive to both stimuli but with different ratios. The information would be there and then it would be a problem for the higher centers to extract it.

DR. C. PFAFFMANN: I just wanted to reinforce what Dr. Hensel has been saying on this problem because, as a psychologist, looking at the overall attempt to relate the physiological system to the psychological domain, it has always impressed me that there has been a tendency, at least in the early stages, to make the quality, from the psychological side, isomorphic with a physiological entity. The underlying theme here has been to try to describe what these correspondences will be, without implying a simple isomorphic relationship between quality and space. Dr. Hensel's description of this relationship is an excellent way of emphasizing the fact that if time and space encompass the range of variables with which you are working in the nervous system, and that time, space, intensity, and quality are the variables on the stimulus side, then we have to pay more attention to the interrelation between these in order to resolve this problem of coding.

DR. P. D. WALL: Since "information theory" has raised its ugly head, may I object to that description, now that you have approved of it. The objection is on the grounds that if you talk about information theory, you can talk about it in a number of ways and one is channel capacity, but that description almost assumes that one is transmitting instantaneous events. One of the very important things that Dr. Gray has been saying here is that he gives himself time. He has got another time in there which is the time that the central cells take to examine the incoming signals so that what may be an instantaneous event is examined over a span of time. You mentioned 100 msec as a possible analysis time. It might be seconds if need be. I do not think Dr. Hensel set a real question. It would be a real question if one had to transmit instantaneously and be able to read out all possible qualities of the stimulus at one instant, but if you give yourself 100 msec or a second, you can add the German constitution and still transmit it across the line.

DR. GRAY: Obviously this is true. For example, in an R. F. channel, all the information for a television picture is carried in time, but you end up with a three dimensional picture, an intensity and two positions in space. But I am sure that was not Dr. Hensel's meaning. Perhaps he would rather say it himself.

DR. HENSEL: This dimension of time might be able to signal quality as well as intensity by different temporal patterns. For example, you can use the average frequency of the discharge in order to signal intensity, and you can use a certain grouping for signalling quality. What I mean is only that the possibilities of the nerve fiber are, at one side, a spatial distribution and on the other side a certain temporal pattern.

DR. A. J. H. VENDRIK: Would you draw a relationship between your considerations and the psychophysical experiments that localization is highly dependent on the intensity of the stimulus. When you are doing localization experiments, that is, the discrimination between two patterns, and you raise the intensity of the stimulus, then you can get a much better localization.

DR. GRAY: I can say something about the primary population, but I have not analyzed the second order one. The precision of localization of the pattern becomes greater with stimulus strength up to a certain point. The reason for this is, qualitatively, quite simple. The point is, if you have a widely distributed pattern of activity [Ed. note: reference to Fig. 27-1] and you move the stimulator by a small amount to one side, then that small movement increases the probability of firing of a very large number of units at one side of the field and decreases the probability of firing of an equally large number of units on the opposite side. The bigger the circumference of the active field, the more units are going to be in this state of risk where a shift of probability will affect them. The overall picture is slightly complicated as far as the analysis of this particular calculation is concerned. There is a limit beyond which the precision of localization does not increase and this is related to the confidence limits of predicting the parameters of the stimulus. This involves the function relating input and output as well as the errors. In fact, you reach an optimum intensity of stimulation for discrimination and then it diminishes (Gray, 1966).

Reference

Gray, J. A. B. The representation of information about rapid changes in a population of receptor units signalling mechanical events. In O. E. Lowenstein (Ed.), *CIBA Foundation Symposium: Touch, Heat and Pain.* London: Churchill, 1966. Pp. 299-315.

Chapter 28

NEURONAL POPULATION BEHAVIOR IN THE SOMATOSENSORY SYSTEMS*

Arnold L. Towe

SOMESTHESIS IS UNIQUE among the senses in that its transmission pathways are extended, often exceedingly so. Not that bats and mice present unusual circumstances, but that whales and giraffes do. The journey from fluke to brain in a blue whale is a major undertaking for any nerve impulse, and an impulse on a fine fiber quickly falls behind one on a coarse fiber, to arrive miserably late in the brain stem. Even impulses on fibers of quite similar diameter may, on arrival at their destination after a long journey, fail to act in concert. And if the alpha and delta cutaneous fibers of the whale are like those of the cat, then a brief stimulus to the fluke is seen at the gracile nucleus as a temporal spatter of input that begins 0.25 sec after the stimulus and continues for a full 3 sec! Clearly, there should be a general failure of temporal summation of convergent input over such long pathways, yet these nuclei transmit. Table 28-I shows the conduction times required from hindfoot to gracile nucleus over two afferent fibers of similar diameter in mammals of different sizes. The difference in arrival time to the gracile nucleus increases linearly with conduction distance, and becomes enormous in the large antelopes, pachyderms, giraffes, and cetaceans. Even on the coarsest of cutaneous fibers, say 15μ and 16μ in diameter, the difference in arrival time dwindles only to 17 msec in a 30 m whale (24 m conduction distance). Nonetheless, the large mammals, whales included (Slijper, 1962), show exquisite sensitivity to cutaneous stimulation.

TABLE 28-I
CONDUCTION TIME FROM HINDFOOT TO GRACILE NUCLEUS IN TWO FIBERS

Fiber Diameter	Conduction Velocity	Rat 0.1 m	Cat 0.5 m	Man 1.9 m	Horse 3 m	Giraffe 6 m	Whale 24 m
7μ	42 m/s	2.4 ms	12 ms	45 ms	71 ms	143 ms	571 ms
6μ	36 m/s	2.8 ms	14 ms	53 ms	83 ms	167 ms	667 ms
Difference in conduction time in two fibers		0.4 ms	2 ms	8 ms	12 ms	24 ms	96 ms

To overcome the temporal handicap imposed by sheer size, several tricks could be played. Increasing the number of afferent fibers or restricting the

*The experimental work discussed in this paper was supported by research grants B 396 and NB 5136 from the National Institute for Neurological Diseases and Blindness, U. S. Department of Health, Education, and Welfare.

552

fiber spectrum to the point that temporal convergence of synchronously originating activity becomes a probable event would solve the problem, but neither solution has anatomical support. On the other hand, the time course of each synaptic event could be extended through a prolonged transmitter action or a long membrane time constant, thereby improving summation; or, finally, the animal could evolve obligatory synapses in the dorsal column nuclei. That mammals have sought the last solution seems likely from the presence of "giant" synaptic knobs on the cluster neurons (Rozsos, 1958) and "giant" quantal EPSPs (excitatory postsynaptic potentials) on some neurons of the dorsal column nuclei (J. C. Eccles, personal communication). This solution seems a poor one, however, for each impulse or closely spaced pair of impulses would be read by the system as a signal. An animal with such an obligatory system could scarcely afford to have noisy skin receptors, else more than gadflies would cause it to "gad."

Although no specific data are available for the larger mammals, a look into the cuneate nucleus of the cat may be instructive. In this animal, the conduction distance from forepaw to cuneate nucleus averages 300 mm, so that activity on a 7μ fiber, the modal diameter of cutaneous alpha fibers, reaches the nucleus in a little over 7 msec. The dashed curve in graphs B, C and D of Figure 28-1, a cumulative curve based on the evoked responses of 301 cuneate neurons, shows that the modal spike latency in the cuneate nucleus, following a brief shock to the central footpad of the ipsilateral forepaw of cats, is also about 7 msec. Using the alpha and delta fiber spectra, measured by Gasser and Grundfest (1939) in peripheral nerve (*dashed curve,* Fig. 28-1A), good agreement is obtained between the temporal distribution of afferent impulses arriving in the cuneate nucleus (*solid curve,* Fig. 28-1B) and the distribution of spike activity in that nucleus. However, all is not well, for it seems that relatively few alpha fibers ascend the dorsal columns to this level. Using a modified Alzheimer-Mann method, Häggquist (1936) found an overwhelming abundance of small fibers in the cuneate fasciculus (*solid curve,* Fig. 28-1A). Over three-fourths of the fibers, in contrast to less than one-half in cutaneous nerve, occupy the delta fiber diameter range. In fact, only 6 per cent of the fibers in the cuneate fasciculus are greater than 7μ in diameter. The staining method used by Häggquist could scarcely have failed to reveal the large fibers, for the method only becomes inaccurate with the smallest fibers. Using Häggquist's data, poor agreement is found between the temporal growth and decay of afferent input (*solid curve,* Fig. 28-1C) and the total spike activity in the cuneate nucleus. If the fiber spectrum excited by the electrical shock to the central footpad is uniform in selection, then 85 per cent of the afferent input has yet to reach the nucleus when neuronal discharge begins its decline.

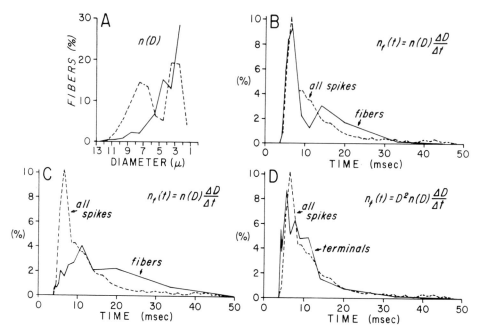

Figure 28-1. Time distributions of fiber, terminal, and spike activity in cuneate nucleus of cat. A; fiber spectra of cutaneous nerve (*dashed curve*) and cuneate fasciculus (*solid curve*). Dashed curve of B, C and D; distribution of spike activity in cuneate nucleus following ipsilateral forepaw shock. Solid curves of B, C and D; fiber (B,C) and terminal (D) activity computed from fiber spectrum of cutaneous nerve (B) and cuneate fasciculus (C,D).

Although the solid curve of Figure 28-1C shows the expected amount of afferent fiber input, it does not necessarily reflect the amount of synaptic bombardment. If each afferent fiber had only one synaptic knob and if all knobs were equipotent, then the solid curve of Figure 28-1C would surely reflect the synaptic bombardment. However, Glees and Soler (1951) showed that large parent fibers proliferate into many more synaptic knobs than do small fibers. In correcting for this observation, it may be supposed that, on the average, the number of synaptic knobs produced by a parent fiber is proportional to the cross-sectional area of the parent fiber. Then the solid curve shown in Figure 28-1D describes the time course and amount of synaptic bombardment. However, because the percentage error in the histological measurements is greatest for the larger fibers, which are relatively few in number, and because the squaring process selectively magnifies these errors, the agreement found between the solid and dashed curves of Figure 28-1D may be spuriously bad; or it may be spuriously good.

The probable existence of obligatory synaptic connections in the cuneate nucleus clouds the entire issue. Rozsos (1958) did not estimate the diameter of the parent fibers that bear "giant" synaptic knobs, but Eccles (personal communication) found the "giant" EPSPs to have a brief latency, implying that the parent fibers are of large calibre. Since these "giant" knobs terminate on cluster neurons, their parent fibers probably originate in hair follicles and, consequently, a large fraction of early-firing cuneate neurons must be hair-sensitive, an expectation in good accord with experimental observations. These cuneothalamic projection neurons show little or no variation in response latency with change in stimulus intensity and therefore comprise a set distinct from other neurons in the same nucleus.

As illustrated by Figure 28-2, a variety of neuronal response types is found in the cuneate nucleus. This is not surprising, for in addition to hair-sensitive relay neurons there are many touch-sensitive, pressure-sensitive and proprioceptive relay neurons, as well as many interneurons, residing in this nucleus. And even though a few neurons show response properties consistent with the idea of obligatory transmission, many others do not. Much of the synaptic transmission is more loosely coupled. The whole time course of discharge and behavior of most neurons is of a different character from the "locked" behavior of the early-firing, obligatory "two-spikers." There are later-firing "two-spikers," double-burst neurons, "sporadic" neurons, and many with a long burst of rather evenly spaced spikes. The interrelations of these various response types remains to be discovered.

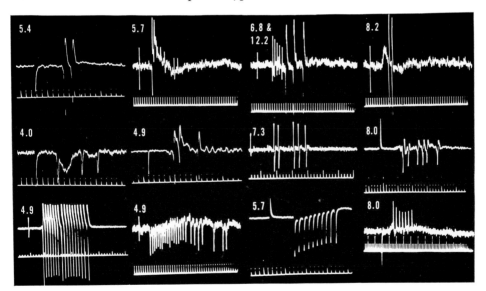

Figure 28-2. Sample records of three basic response types in cuneate nucleus of cat. *Top row;* "two-spikers" (which may be more, or less), often cuneothalamic projection neurons. *Middle row;* "double-burst" neurons, often cuneothalamic projection neurons. *Bottom row;* neurons yielding long duration burst, infrequently being projection neurons. The numbers record mean first spike latency in milliseconds.

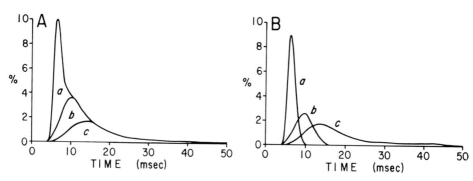

Figure 28-3. Hypothetical fractionation of cuneate response population. A; observed distribution of spike activity, divided into obligatory projection neurons *a*, more loosely coupled projection neurons *b* and interneurons *c*. B; time distribution of activity for the three sets, separately.

It has been asserted that the dorsal column nuclei consist of two basic neuronal types, namely, cuneothalamic relay or projection neurons and inhibitory interneurons (Andersen, Eccles, Schmidt, and Yokota, 1964). If this idea were correct, then the cumulative curve of spike discharge obtained from the cuneate nucleus would consist of only three components, as suggested in Figure 28-3. The discharge of the obligatory projection neurons (component a of Fig. 28-3B) would drive the inhibitory interneurons (component c) to action, thereby blocking their further discharge and depressing the afferent terminals. The more loosely coupled projection neurons, which are clearly present, are suggested by component b of Figure 28-3. In this model, cuneothalamic input should last only 10 to 12 msec rather than about 40 msec. Thus, the numerous small fibers of the dorsal columns are a thorn in the side, unless they can be shown to arise elsewhere than in the periphery or unless they play a role in prolonging the interneuronal discharge. In either case, when thinking about the response of the cerebral cortex to a brief cutaneous shock, the long temporal action in the cuneate nucleus, and the ventroposterior nucleus of the thalamus, could be ignored. This knowledge would come as a great relief to the blue whale, provided it were correct. But careful study of the discharge patterns and latencies, shown in Figure 28-2, leaves the whale some cause for concern.

A definitive answer to the basic questions posed above lies with a combination of "neuronal population analysis" and intracellular study. Although the latter is extremely difficult to accomplish in the dorsal column nuclei because of the pronounced respiratory movements and cardiovascular pulsations, considerable progress is being made in overcoming the handicap (V. E. Amassian, personal communication). Study of the spatial and temporal distribution of spike activity within different cellular groups leads to a description of the general organization or "wiring diagram" of any neuronal aggregation and can reveal which cell types the intracellular technique favors and whether the intracellular electrode alters the cell's response properties. The remainder of this discussion will focus on the technique and results of population analysis in the cerebral cortex, for even though a large amount of data has been accumulated from dorsal column and thalamic nuclei the analysis is too preliminary and the story too complex to recount in this limited space. However, the foregoing issues have been raised to set the stage for thinking about the cerebral cortex and to emphasize that in spite of a wealth of information our present understanding of nuclear organization and transmission in the somatosensory system is primordial, at best.

FUNCTIONAL SETS

The primary somatosensory receiving areas of the cat's brain, as defined by the evoked potential method, lie crowded anteriorly, the more rostral parts merging into the histologically apparent "motor" cortex to form the "sensorimotor" cortex. Neurons isolated in these areas display great versatility, their specific response properties varying with the nature of the afferent input and the type of anesthetic agent used in the experiment. The excitatory receptive fields of these neurons increase dramatically in size and change in character as one samples at progressively more rostromedial sites, starting from the "classical" sensory cortex (Buser and Imbert, 1961). Significantly, this feature, more than any other, explains the striking differences found among the various somatosensory cortical sites (Morse, Adkins, and Towe, 1965; Towe, Patton, and Kennedy, 1963; 1964). Figure 28-4 shows the four recording sites of concern for this discussion. They span the primary sensory and "sensorimotor" cortex that is intimately related to the contralateral forepaw. Between the caudolateral coronal site (Cor) and the two rostral juxtacruciate sites (PreC and PostC) lies a transitional midsylvian site (MidS), unique only in that it lies halfway between two quite different and interesting sites. Microelectrode penetrations were made in a 3 mm² circular area centered on each grid point, the grid size being adjusted according to the size of the particular cat's brain.

In accord with earlier work (Buser and Imbert, 1961), the average size of the neuronal receptive field was found in increase progressively from the coronal to the postcruciate sites. However, neurons with small receptive fields can be found throughout the somatosensory cortex, but with decreasing frequency as one samples rostrally. A crude estimate of receptive field size may be obtained by electrical stimulation of the central footpad of each of the cat's appendages. Those neurons that respond only to stimulation of the "on focus" paw, the contralateral forepaw in this study, may be classed

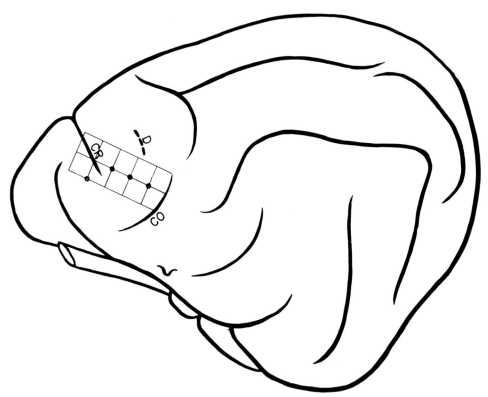

Figure 28-4. Lateral view of cat cerebrum. Grid used to define four recording sites (*small circles* at grid intersections). CR; cruciate sulcus. CO; coronal sulcus. D; "dimple" on posterior sigmoid gyrus.

as *s* neurons and distinguished from those neurons responsive to stimulation of at least one additional paw. The latter may be classed as *m* neurons. Such a classification, while not taking into account the variations in field size among *s* neurons, nonetheless reveals quite systematic changes with recording site. As shown in Figure 28-5, the coronal cortex consists almost exclusively of *s* neurons, but *s* and *m* neurons occur in equal proportions in post-cruciate tissue. The dashed line serves as a reminder that the deep cruciate sulcus separates the two pericruciate recording sites, so that more tissue lies between them than is indicated by the figure.

The double-hatched area in Figure 28-5 marks the fraction of neurons whose axons leave the cerebral cortex to course through the medullary pyramids; they may be classed as PT neurons (Towe *et al.*, 1963). They are most numerous in the region of the cruciate sulcus and gradually diminish to a negligible fraction in coronal tissue, in good agreement with the histologic findings of van Creval and Verhaart (1963). Few PT cells have limited receptive fields. Most are *m* cells which respond to electrical stimulation of any appendage and often have "natural" fields that include the entire skin surface. Why these corticofugal elements receive such extensive afferent convergence is not clear.

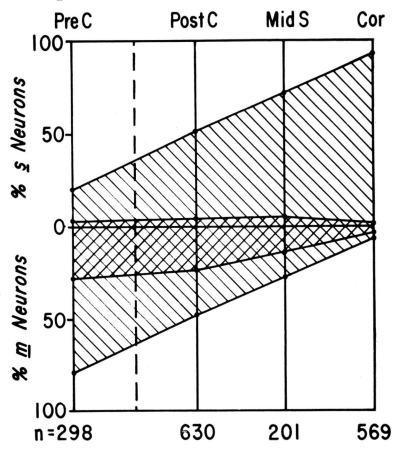

Figure 28-5. Percentages of *s* and *m* neurons at the four cortical recording sites. Double hatching shows percentages of PT neurons. *n;* Number of neurons in sample at each site.

When response to "natural" stimulation is tested, an unexpected feature emerges. Submodality sensitivity is not uniformly distributed among the *s* and *m* neurons. The expected ratios of *s/m* and non-PT/PT neurons, shown by the dashed lines of Figure 28-6, are formed from the ratios actually observed at each recording site. When parcelled among touch-sensitive, hair-sensitive and other neurons, the nonuniformity becomes quite apparent. Touch-sensitive neurons are more often classed as non-PT,*s* neurons than expected and hair-sensitive neurons are more often classed in the PT,*m* set. This finding is true at each of the cortical sites where sufficient data have been gathered and analyzed to test the idea. Evidently, there is, on the average, less convergence in the afferent pathways from touch receptors than from hair follicles although the touch and hair routes themselves converge to a limited extent onto common neurons.

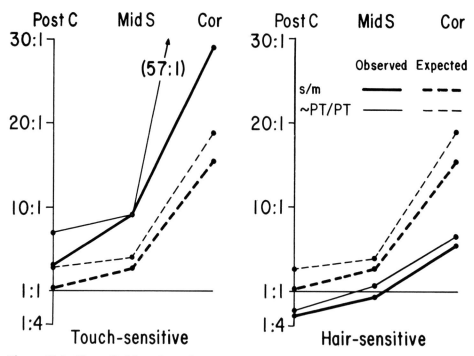

Figure 28-6. Class affinities of touch and hair sensitive neurons at three cortical sites. *Solid lines;* Observed ratios of *s/m* and non-PT/PT (light). *Dashed lines;* Expected ratios, based on observed ratios of *s/m* and non-PT/PT without regard to "natural stimulus"; includes hair, touch, touch and hair, pressure, "mute" and proprioceptive neurons.

At the three recording sites shown in Figure 28-6, about 50 per cent of the neurons were touch-sensitive, 30 per cent were hair-sensitive, and 10 per cent responded to either touch or hair stimulation. The remaining 10 per cent were either not evokable or were responsive to pinching and pressure. Since some *s* neurons respond to hair-bending and many *m* neurons respond to light taps, four general sets may be formed and studied, as illustrated in Figure 28-7. The average latency for each response type is coded by position, the average number of spikes per discharge is coded by spike number, including fractions, and the average interspike intervals are shown by the spacing between spikes. From study of a large sample, several generalities can be made as follows: (a) *s* neurons discharge earlier than *m* neurons, but they have a higher threshold to electrical stimulation of the skin

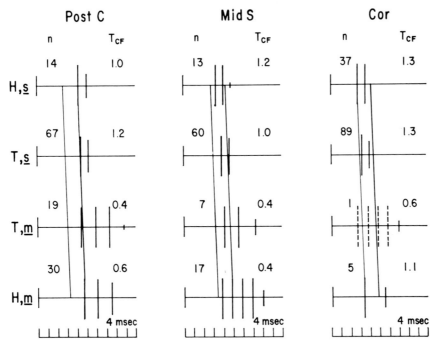

Figure 28-7. Average response characteristics of four subsets of neurons at three cortical sites following contralateral forepaw shock. (Note that a different set of afferents drives each subset.) H,s; hair-sensitive s neurons. n; number in sample. T_{CF}; mean threshold to forepaw shock. Position of spikes show mean latency, number of spikes show average spike/discharge (size of last spike codes fractional value).

and a somewhat poorer frequency-following capability; (b) *m* neurons produce more spikes per discharge than *s* neurons, but at a lower frequency within each burst, and (c) coronal neurons respond first, midsylvian neurons next, then postcruciate and finally the precruciate neurons. Each of these statements, true only in a statistical sense, finds support from the small sample analyzed for Figure 28-7. Perhaps the most significant feature shown in Figure 28-7 is the consistent sequencing of activity, H,s - T,s - T,m - H,m, at all three cortical sites. The process develops in about 2.4 msec, and could roughly have been predicted from the work of Hunt and McIntyre (1960) on peripheral nerve. Using dorsal root filaments (sural nerve), they found hair fibers to be among the largest of cutaneous alpha fibers, but to occur throughout the alpha and delta fiber spectrum. Touch fibers, on the other hand, were confined to the cutaneous alpha group, but did not have a representation among the largest fibers. Thus, the small latency difference for H,s versus T,s neurons may result from the small differences among the peripheral alpha fibers leading from different afferent structures. Such an explanation, however, says nothing about the systematic differences in latency from one cortical site to the next, yet the same sequence of discharge is found at all cortical sites.

The clear lesson conveyed by these data is that classification by receptive field size, even though crudely estimated here, leads to more meaningful physiological or functional sets than does use of the natural stimulus. Stating that a neuron is a member of the *s* or the *m* set tells much more about its specific discharge properties than does categorizing it as non-PT or PT, H or T (or other "natural" stimulus categories). However, PT neuron discharge properties are very *m*-like, for nearly all PT neurons belong to the *m* set. Likewise, hair-sensitive neurons, on the average, are rather *m*-like and touch-sensitive neurons are quite *s*-like, for the same reason. The marked differences in discharge properties between *s* and *m* neurons suggests that they may be activated via distinct afferent routes and may function in separate neuronal networks. To discover this, considerably more information about the response of the cerebral cortex to an afferent volley and about the afferent routes themselves must be gained. In the cerebral cortex, much additional information about *s* and *m* neurons may be obtained from another form of analysis.

POPULATION RESPONSE PATTERNS

The method of single neuron analysis suffers from a defect quite analogous to the situation with an isolated vacuum tube, that is, characteristic curves may be measured and an amplification factor, plate resistance and transconductance determined, but the circuit from which this tube was taken, or to which it will contribute, can hardly be guessed without additional information. In the case of neuronal aggregations, the overall response pattern can be reconstructed from individual measurements to yield the requisite information. Along a single electrode track through the cerebral cortex, several neurons may be isolated and quite thoroughly studied and a few others may be fleetingly glimpsed. Such a single track yields a poor estimate of the distribution of cellular activity within the tissue in response to a particular input, but summing the activity recorded along many closely-spaced electrode tracks and from the same site in many animals allows a reasonably accurate reconstruction of the overall response pattern in the tissue. However, the resulting picture reflects properties of both the experimenter and the microelectrode, the latter does not record subthreshold activity and favors isolation of certain neuronal types. It is known that PT neurons with large axons are isolated more frequently than those with smaller axons (Towe *et al.*, 1963). There is little doubt, however, that the microelectrode is selective about the region it tends to "see" along an active neuron. If this were not so, then the systematic nature of previous results (Morse *et al.*, 1965; Towe *et al.*, 1963; 1964) and their perfect repeatability would be difficult to understand.

To picture the overall neuronal response pattern in any tissue, the mean position of each spike of a neuron's response following some particular input could be represented as a dot on a graph of depth of isolation and time after the evoking stimulus. The assembly of such dots, representing the spike activity of several hundred neurons, thus would display the effects of a shotgun blast at five paces. Dot density — spike density — can be well represented by a contour map, such as that shown in Figure 28-8B, for the

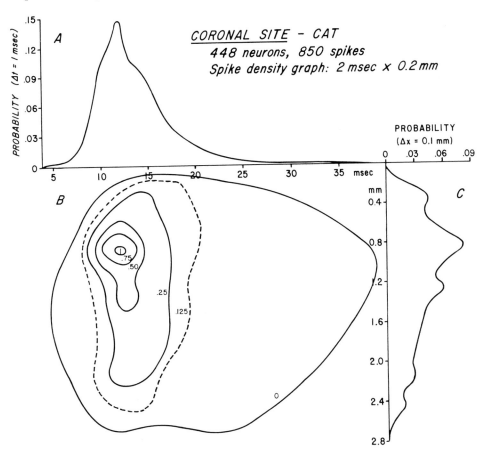

Figure 28-8. Population response pattern at coronal site following supramaximal shock to contralateral forepaw at once/second. Contour lines in B code spike density, from maximum (1) through half of maximum (0.5) to zero. *Abscissa* of A,B; time after forepaw shock. *Ordinate* of B, C; depth in cerebral cortex (Fig. 1, Towe, A. L. In P. W. Nye [Ed.], *Proceedings of the Symposium on Information Processing in Sight Sensory Systems*. Pasadena: California Institute of Technology, 1966).

response of neurons in the coronal cortex to a strong contralateral fore-paw shock. The spacing of the contour lines may be chosen to portray the major pattern and at the same time to suppress the small variations that may be sensitive to sample size. In the population response pattern of Figure 28-8B, the greatest spike density occurs 840μ below the pial surface, 12 msec after a brief shock to the contralateral forepaw. If the map were interpreted as a surface showing the probability of finding a particular spike somewhere within the time-depth domain of the surface, without re-strictions, then the 100 per cent spike density contour line corresponds to $p = 0.012$ per 1 msec by 0.1 mm time-depth block. The curve of Figure 28-8A shows the time distribution of spike activity. It could be obtained by integrating over the surface of Figure 28-8B with respect to depth. Like-wise, the curve of Figure 28-8C shows the depth distribution of spike activity. Since, at this coronal site, the mean number of spikes per discharge is nearly constant with depth, the curve of Figure 28-8C also reflects the distribution of active neurons as sampled in depth.

Because the x and y coordinates differ in character, it is rather difficult, in spite of its origin, to interpret the population response surface as a con-tour map. It is more easily understood as a probability surface. While the abscissa codes time after the evoking stimulus, the ordinate codes more than simply depth in the cortex, it codes depth in a vertical cylinder of cor-tical tissue — depth through a stack of wafers. Imagine a wafer 0.1 mm thick and of 1 mm radius, lying in the 800μ to 900μ depth interval of the coronal recording site. Following a brief shock to the contralateral forepaw, neu-ronal activity in the wafer begins at 6.5 msec, rises to half its maximum at 9.5 msec and attains its maximum at 12 msec. Thereafter, neuronal activity drops to half by 14.5 msec, to a fourth at 17 msec, an eighth at 20.5 msec and ceases altogether 38 msec after the stimulus. A similar wafer located 400μ to 500μ below the pial surface behaves differently. Neuronal activity does not begin until 8 msec after the stimulus and attains its maximum, a local maximum that is about 40 per cent of the absolute maximum of the surface, at 13.9 msec. The apparent velocity of upward movement of neu-ronal activity, measured from the curve of maximum spike density with depth, is about 0.2 m/sec. The relation is nonlinear, starting at 0.3 m/sec around 800μ and decreasing to 0.05 m/sec at the 200μ level. This feature is true of the s neurons at each recording site. The coronal sample, consist-ing almost wholly of s neurons, displays a smooth rise and fall of spike activity, with most of the cellular discharge occurring below the level of "reversal" of the associated primary evoked response.

Both somatosensory area II and coronal cortex are "early birds." Neu-ronal response begins later and rises to its maximum more slowly at the

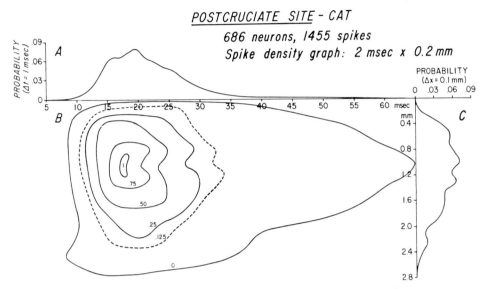

Figure 28-9. Population response pattern at postcruciate site following supramaximal shock to contralateral forepaw at once/second (Fig. 2, Towe, A. L. In P. W. Nye [Ed.], *Proceedings of the Symposium on Information Processing in Sight Sensory Systems.* Pasadena: California Institute of Technology, 1966).

more rostromedial recording sites. Figure 28-9 shows the response in post-cruciate cortex following a brief, strong shock to the contralateral forepaw. As with Figure 28-8, the stimulus was repeated at 1/sec or less through the observations, and the resulting surface thus displays a steady-state response. Neuronal activity again rises smoothly to a single peak, although deeper and later than in the coronal cortex, and declines without incident. When the postcruciate and coronal population response patterns are superimposed, as in Figure 28-10, their differences become apparent. Figure 28-10C shows that the depth distributions of activity are similar, but the time distributions of Figure 28-10A are quite dissimilar. It appears that the coronal tissue is not essential for the response to develop in postcruciate tissue, but rather that both these cortical regions are driven directly by thalamocortical afferent input. The coronal site could be driven almost exclusively by the cutaneous alpha input, for the 5 msec discrepancy between peak cuneate response and peak coronal response is forecast from earlier data (Morse, *et al.,* 1965). But the later, more prolonged postcruciate activity poses a problem.

Since about half of the postcruciate sample consists of *s* neurons, which usually respond before the *m* neurons, it may be informative to construct separate population response patterns for these two sets of elements. This

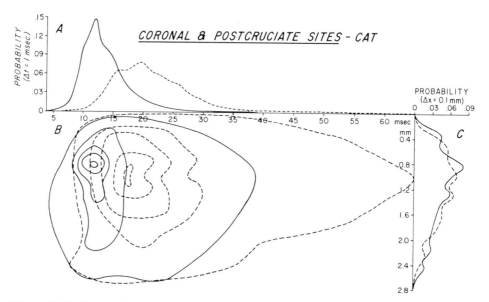

Figure 28-10. Comparison of coronal (*solid lines*) with postcruciate (*dashed lines*) population response patterns (Fig. 3, Towe, A. L. In P. W. Nye [Ed.], *Proceedings of the Symposium on Information Processing in Sight Sensory System.* Pasadena: California Institute of Technology, 1966).

has been done in Figure 28-11, with shading used where spike density is within 50 per cent of its maximum, in order to emphasize the main loci of activity. The smooth, single-peaked pattern for the whole population (Fig. 28-9) here breaks into two peaks, displaced from each other both in time and in depth. The *s* neurons indeed respond earlier (*heavy contour lines* of Fig. 28-11B and *solid curves* of Fig. 28-11A and 28C). But until now it had not been apparent that the *s* set is concentrated in the upper half of the cortex while the *m* set spreads more widely over the lower two-thirds of the cortex. The time-depth "area" of activity is broader for the *m* than for the *s* set, just as it is broader for the postcruciate than for the coronal population (Fig. 28-10B). But nearly 9 msec intervenes between the peak cuneate activity and the peak Post C,*s* activity. No "delay" network is known to exist at any level of the somatosensory system. Activation via a more slowly conducting pathway is clearly implied.

On examination of the two curves of Figure 28-11A, an intriguing possibility arises. About half of the *m* neurons are known to be PT — corticofugal. There is reason to believe that nearly all *m* neurons are corticofugal (corticospinal, corticobulbar, corticopontine, corticostriatal, etc.). If there are any cortical interneurons, then they are either *s* neurons or are not recordable with an extracellular microelectrode. Figure 28-11A shows the

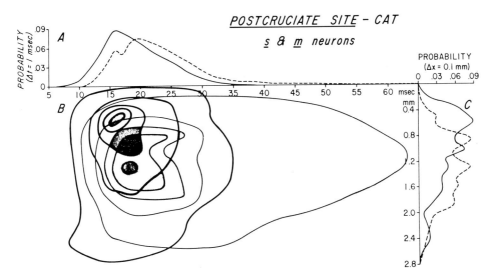

Figure 28-11. Comparison of *s* (*solid lines*) and *m* (*dashed curves and light contours*) fractions of the postcruciate sample (shown in Fig. 28-9 above) (Fig. 7, Towe, A. L. In P. W. Nye [Ed.], *Proceedings of the Symposium on Information Processing in Sight Sensory Systems*. Pasadena: California Institute of Technology, 1966).

time distributions of neuronal activity in the two sets to be similar but displaced by about 2 msec. Thus, the contralateral forepaw input (CF in Fig. 28-12A) may excite *s* neurons, which in turn may drive the *m* neurons to action; the ipsilateral forepaw input (IF), an "off focus" input, must obviously excite the *m* neurons directly. This model requires only one general surge of afferent input from the "on focus" stimulus, but the model can be shown to be inadequate. The electrical threshold of *s* neurons is higher than *m* neurons, rather than equal or lower (Fig. 28-7). The *s* neurons fail to follow such high rates of iterative stimulation as do the *m* neurons. Most significantly, the population response pattern of *m* neurons is almost the same to stimulation of any paw, merely shifted in time (Fig. 28-13). Cortical interneurons cannot be identified for the "off focus" responses, yet these responses occur. It is therefore necessary to conclude that the model in Figure 28-12A is needlessly complicated. The more adequate model, shown in Figure 28-12B, however, gives rise to several questions that prior thinking has not prepared us to contemplate.

Examine the four curves and the two surfaces of Figure 28-13. The population response patterns to contralateral (*solid contour lines*) and ipsilateral (*dashed contour lines*) forepaw stimulation are quite similar, but not identical. Slightly more neuronal discharge occurs in the upper half of the cortex in response to contralateral forepaw shock. The effect may be

due to a facilitatory action of *s* neurons, as suggested in Figure 28-12B. However, the similarities in response patterns outweigh the differences. It is
difficult to understand how two quite different anatomical pathways (actually four, because the two hindpaws yield the same pattern as that shown
for the ipsilateral forepaw in Fig. 28-13) can produce the same response
pattern in a particular population of cortical neurons. One might think
that these cortical neurons are so thoroughly interconnected that they are
predisposed to discharge in a particular sequence. These neurons tend to
occupy the same relative position with respect to their fellows in each of the
four response patterns studied (in response to stimulation of each of the
four appendages), suggesting that *m* neurons simultaneously play the role
of excitatory interneurons and corticofugal efferents. Kubota and Takahashi (1965) have shown that slow PT cells play such a role with respect to
fast PT cells.

The two afferent pathways implied in Figure 28-12B that are excited by
stimulation of the contralateral forepaw may appear anatomically as one
but behave physiologically as two, or even more. At least two temporally

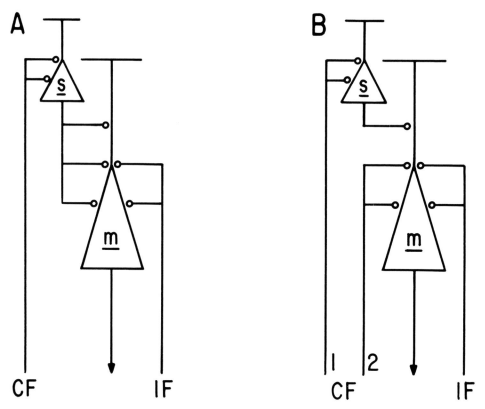

Figure 28-12. Hypothetical innervation patterns for *s* and *m* neurons. A; conceivable
network, not compatible with data. B; network consistent with experimental observations.

distinct surges of input bombard the cerebral cortex, each activating a functionally distinct set of neurons. The data imply the presence of *m* neurons in the thalamus. They are readily found and have been under intensive study for some time (Harris, 1965). These neurons reside more caudolaterally and slightly more ventrally in nucleus ventralis posterolateralis than estimated by other investigators (Landgren, Nordwall, and Wengström, 1965). Whatever may be the resolution of that issue, the thalamic *m* neurons are largely hair-sensitive and, in the chloralose preparation, possess the temporal properties expected of neurons in the CF2 pathway shown in Figure 28-12B. However, further analysis reveals that the CF2 pathway itself consists of two distinct components. Each component drives a different group of neurons, although there is also convergence onto the same neurons. If, instead of plotting total neuronal discharge, only the mean first spike latencies are plotted, then the resultant map shows the time-depth "regions" where profuse neuronal activity begins and should thus reflect the locus of intense afferent bombardment. Two such first spike response patterns are shown in Figure 28-14 for PT neurons isolated in the postcruciate (*solid contour lines*) and the precruciate (*dashed contour lines*) recording sites. The most intense discharge begins in layer V around 15 msec after the stimulus, with a secondary surge in layer III around 21 msec. This second-

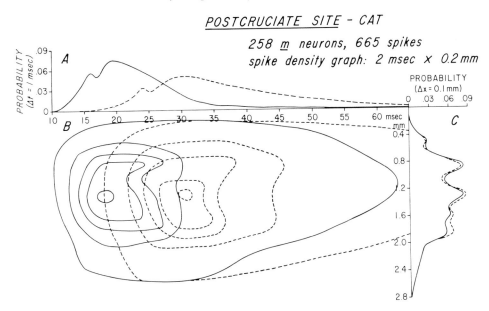

Figure 28-13. Comparison of population response patterns of same set of postcruciate *m* neurons following supramaximal stimulation of contralateral (*solid lines*) and ipsilateral (*dashed lines*) forepaws at once/second (Fig. 5, Towe, A. L. In P. W. Nye [Ed.], *Proceedings of the Symposium on Information Processing in Sight Sensory Systems.* Pasadena: California Institute of Technology, 1966).

ary surge of afferent input prolongs the discharge of layer V PT neurons, probably via layer III PT cells (Kubota and Takahashi, 1965). It seems to be the major, if not the only, afferent input to the precruciate PT neurons. Thus, the CF2 input, postulated in Figure 28-12B, consists of two components, CF2a, driving chiefly the postcruciate layer V corticofugal neurons and CF2b, exciting layer III neurons directly and layer V neurons indirectly in both pericruciate recording sites. If the widely distributed secondary surge depends upon a cutaneous alpha input for its existence, then the central fibers on this pathway average about 1μ in diameter, an unlikely situation. If conduction velocity were uniform from forepaw to cerebral cortex, then the average fiber diameter would be about 3μ. Pending confirmation, it must be tentatively concluded that cutaneous delta fibers are involved in an essential way in the activation of at least some m neurons.

INVARIANCES

The population response patterns shown in this discussion are representative of a steady state condition. Mean spike latencies entered into the depth-latency graphs were calculated from responses to 1/sec stimulation of the central footpad, a rate so low that no transient is detectable at the start

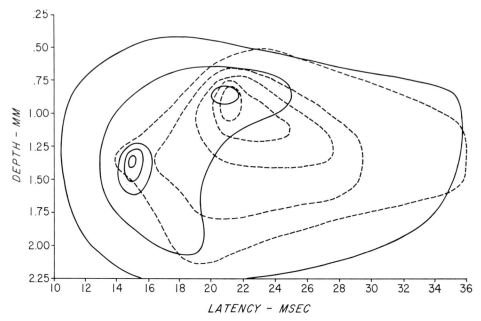

Figure 28-14. Comparison of "first spike" response patterns of PT neurons at postcruciate (*solid lines*) and precruciate (*dashed lines*) sites following supramaximal stimulation of contralateral forepaw at once/second (Fig. 9, Towe, A. L. In P. W. Nye [Ed.], *Proceedings of the Symposium on Information Processing in Sight Sensory Systems*. Pasadena: California Institute of Technology, 1966).

of the repetitive train. At higher rates of stimulation, response latency, spikes per discharge and interspike intervals vary systematically according to which shock of the iterative train is examined. Furthermore, the evoking stimuli were all supramaximal, in the sense that there were no measurable changes in response parameters with moderate decrease or increase in cutaneous shock strength. However, in order to discern any possible intracortical networks, the evoking stimulus must be varied both in intensity and in frequency of application while attention is given to any invariances among the neurons under the different input conditions. Although such studies have been in progress at Seattle for some time, the sample is still much too small at each recording site to allow any firm statements. Preliminary analyses of these data show that neurons drop out progressively above and below the level of afferent termination as the stimulus is reduced to near-threshold intensity (a large range for the whole sample). The pattern of the population response is desynchronized, becomes rather distorted and slides later in time. With increasing rates of iterative stimulation, negligible changes develop in the response pattern, until the rate approaches 10/sec, when only a small fraction of the neurons is still active. The *m* neurons undergo greater changes and behave in a more labile fashion than the *s* neurons. Because of the small sample sizes, the behavior of "submodality" groupings cannot yet be assessed.

A CORRECT POPULATION RESPONSE PATTERN

The neuronal population response analyses have yielded much that is new concerning the somatosensory cortex and the behavior of its afferent pathways. A well-ordered mental image of the events that occur in the cerebral cortex following a cutaneous shock can now be conjured up, at least for the chloralose-anesthetized cat. However, there is cause to suspect the extracellular recording method of stacking the deck in favor of the larger neurons. Among PT neurons, where the sampling bias can be tested, the distribution of antidromic response latencies (Towe *et al.,* 1963) does not correspond with that expected on the basis of the pyramidal fiber spectrum (Brookhart and Morris, 1948). Many more PT neurons with short antidromic latencies are sampled than should be, relative to those with longer antidromic response latencies. The ratio between the observed and expected proportions at each small interval of fiber size forms a smoothly declining relation from large to small diameters and provides a basis for "correcting" the sampling bias. If big cells have big axons and little cells have little axons, as seems to be true in spinal cord (Henneman, Somjen, and Carpenter, 1965), and if the average size of cells changes with depth in the cerebral cortex, then a "correction" can be approached.

The average linear dimensions of neurons in the postcruciate cortex can be derived from Ramon-Moliner's (1961) data on neuronal packing density and the fraction of cortical tissue occupied by neurons. These measurements were made in approximately 90μ depth intervals. By fixing a zero point on the "observed/expected" ratio for PT neurons, a number could be assigned to each successive interval of depth below the pial surface to correct for the estimated sampling bias. Figure 28-15 shows the response pattern that results from applying this series of correction factors to the postcruciate sample. Dashed lines mark the experimentally-obtained population response pattern while the solid lines reveal the "correct" response pattern. How well this adjustment succeeds, or how badly it misses, remains to be discovered. Several important assumptions have been taken to arrive at this result, each plausible but poorly documented. Yet, the curve showing density of spike activity in depth (*solid line* in Fig. 28-15C) agrees almost exactly with the histologically-measured density of neurons in depth (Ramon-Moliner, 1961), a feature which lends considerable credance to the entire "sleight of hand" procedure.

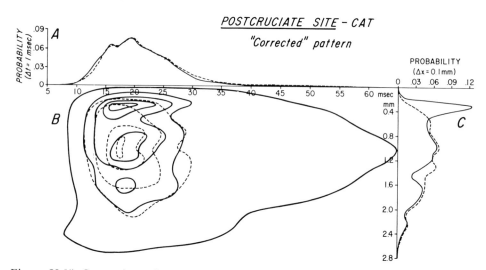

Figure 28-15. Comparison of experimentally obtained and "corrected" values for a postcruciate sample. *Dashed lines* mark the experimentally obtained population response pattern; *solid lines* show the "corrected" response pattern.

EPILOGUE

The foregoing remarks have raised many problems but offered few solutions. Their burden has been that little is known of the detailed operation of the mammalian somatosensory system, in spite of a wealth of experimental data. Knowledge of the principles of nervous conduction and synaptic transmission is not enough to explain how sensory input is transferred and treated in the central nervous system. It is necessary to know what primary afferent fibers end on what neurons, how much they diverge within a neuronal cluster and how much convergence there is onto secondary neurons. It is necessary to determine the efficacy of each primary fiber type in changing postsynaptic membrane conductance. It is essential to know what subsets exist in any neuronal cluster, how they interconnect and which are projection neurons. This knowledge must be obtained at each relevant "relay" station in the somatosensory system. The method of neuronal population analysis discussed in this paper is capable of yielding this information.

ACKNOWLEDGMENT

Various phases of the work were done in collaboration with Harry D. Patton, Thelma T. Kennedy, Russell W. Morse, Ronald J. Adkins, David Whitehorn, Judith Nyquist, and Lawrence Berger. The computer programs used to analyze the original data were written by Gary W. Harding.

REFERENCES

Anderson, P., Eccles, J. C., Schmidt, R. F., & Yokota, T. Identification of relay cells and interneurons in the cuneate nucleus. *J. Neurophysiol.*, 1964, **27**, 1080.

Brookhart, J. M., & Morris, R. E. Antidromic potential recordings from bulbar pyramid of cat. *J. Neurophysiol.*, 1948, **11**, 387.

Buser, P., & Imbert, M. Sensory projections to the motor cortex in cats: A microelectrode study. In W. Rosenblith (Ed.), *Sensory Communication*. New York: Wiley, 1961. Pp. 607-626.

Creval, H. van, & Verhaart, W. J. C. The "exact" origin of the pyramidal tract. *J. Anat.*, 1963, **97**, 495.

Gasser, H. S., & Grundfest, H. Axon diameters in relation to the spike dimensions and the conduction velocity in mammalian A fibers. *Amer. J. Physiol.*, 1939, **127**, 393.

Glees, P., & Soler, J. Fiber content of the posterior columns and synaptic connections of nucleus gracilis. *Z. Zellforsch.*, 1951, **36**, 381.

Häggquist, G. Analyse der Faserverteilung in einem Rückenmarkquerschritt (Th 3). *Z. Mikr. Anat. Forsch.*, 1936, **39**, 1.

Harris, F. A population study of neurons in nucleus ventralis posterior of the cat thalamus. *Physiologist*, 1965, **8**, 186.

Henneman, E., Somjen, G., & Carpenter, D. O. Functional significance of cell size in spinal motoneurons. *J. Neurophysiol.*, 1965, **28**, 560.

Hunt, C. C., & McIntyre, A. K. An analysis of fiber diameter and receptor characteristics of myelinated cutaneous afferent fibers in cat. *J. Physiol. (London)*, 1960, **153**, 99.

Kubota, K., & Takahashi, K. Recurrent facilitatory pathway of the pyramidal tract cell. *Proc. Japan Acad.*, 1965, **41**, 191.

Landgren, S., Nordwall, A., & Wengström, C. The location of the thalamic relay in the spino-cervical-lemniscal path. *Acta Physiol. Scand.*, 1965, **65**, 164.

Morse, R. W., Adkins, R. J., & Towe, A. L. Population and modality characteristics of neurons in the coronal region of somatosensory area I of the cat. *Exp. Neurol.*, 1965, **11**, 419.

Ramon-Moliner, E. The histology of the postcruciate gyrus in the cat. I. Quantitative studies. *J. Comp. Neurol.*, 1961, **117**, 43.

Rozsos, I. The synapses of Burdach's nucleus. *Acta Morph. Acad. Sci. Hung.*, 1958, **8**, 105.

Slijper, E. J. *Whales.* New York: Basic Books, 1962.

Towe, A. L., Patton, H. D., & Kennedy, T. T. Properties of the pyramidal system in the cat. *Exp. Neurol.*, 1963, **8**, 220.

Towe, A. L., Patton, H. D., & Kennedy, T. T. Response properties of neurons in the pericruciate cortex of the cat following electrical stimulation of the appendages. *Exp. Neurol.*, 1964, **10**, 325.

Chapter 29

SOMATOSENSORY ACTIVITY IN THE HUMAN CAUDATE NUCLEUS*

Burton S. Rosner and Richard A. Davis†

T HE CAUDATE NUCLEUS IS PART of the basal ganglia and traditionally has been treated as an "extrapyramidal" motor structure. Laursen (1963) and Krauthamer and Albe-Fessard (1964) have reviewed the experimental evidence on motor functions of the caudate. Laursen's own studies indicate that many effects on behavior previously ascribed to electrical stimulation of the caudate actually reflect the results of spread of current to the adjacent internal capsule. Stimulation of this nucleus in man requires relatively high currents to disrupt speaking (Van Buren, 1963) and repetitive manual tasks (Rosner, Blankfein, and Davis, 1966). Low intensities of stimulation over a wide range of frequencies produce no visible motor effects. These observations reinforce the doubts raised by Laursen about participation by the caudate in control of motor systems.

Recent studies on the caudate nucleus have shifted the emphasis away from its putative motor functions to its possible sensory and integrative activities. Denny-Brown (1962) suggests in his Croonian lectures on the basal ganglia that the caudate integrates visually and tactilely controlled "automatisms." Albe-Fessard, Oswald-Cruz, and Rocha-Miranda (1960a) discovered that visual, auditory, and somatic stimuli evoked nonspecific electrical responses in this nucleus in chloralosed cats. Galambos and Sheatz (1962) obtained sensory responses from caudate in unanesthetized animals. Microelectrode explorations (Albe-Fessard, Rocha-Miranda, and Oswald-Cruz, (1960b) showed that afferent inputs from different modalities converged at the level of single caudate cells. The somatosensory input lacked topical organization. Stimulation of any limb could activate a given cell. The multisensory properties and relatively long latencies of these responses suggested that they are related to similar potentials observed in the intra-laminar nuclei of the thalamus and at "association areas" of cerebral cortex (Albe-Fessard and Rougeul, 1958; Amassian, 1954; Buser and Borenstein, 1959).

*This work was supported, in part, by a Clinical Research Center Grant 3MO-FR-40, Division of Research Facilities and Resources, National Institute of Health, by grant K3-MH-23691 and MH-10848 from the National Institute of Mental Health, and by the Charles H. and Bertha L. Boothroyd Foundation.
†Richard A. Davis is associated with the Philadelphia General Hospital, Philadelphia, Pennsylvania and The University of Pennsylvania.

Recently, Krauthamer (1963) and Krauthamer and Albe-Fessard (1964; 1965) found that a burst of high frequency electrical stimuli to either caudate inhibited peripherally evoked nonspecific responses at cerebral cortex bilaterally, at centrum medianum of thalamus, and in brain stem reticular formation. Figure 29-1 reproduces some of their records of blockade of non-specific cortical responses. The figure shows that specific responses were unaffected by stimulation of caudate. Injection of moderate amounts of strychnine into the preparation abolished the blockade. Krauthamer and Albe-Fessard concluded that the mechanism of the blockade involved hyperpolarizing inhibitory postsynaptic potentials. They felt that the reduction of cortical responses passively mirrored inhibition of nonspecific evoked activity at subcortical levels.

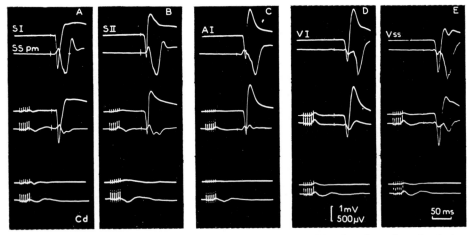

Figure 29-1. Inhibition of nonspecific sensory responses in chloralosed cat by stimulation of caudate. Top trace of each column shows specific responses to somatic (SI, SII), auditory (AI), and visual (VI, VII) stimulation. Second trace shows nonspecific response of suprasylvian gyrus. Middle two traces show effects of prior stimulation of caudate with high frequency burst of pulses, on specific and nonspecific responses respectively. Bottom traces show absence of responses at specific and at suprasylvian loci to stimulation of caudate alone (Fig. 2, Krauthamer, G., & Albe-Fessard, D. *J. Neurophysiol.*, 1965, **28**, 100).

The studies reported here represent an attempted extension of these recent experiments on sensory responses in animals to the human caudate nucleus. The subjects were selected patients undergoing neurosurgical treatment of various motor disorders. In the hope of securing further information on the pathophysiology of these conditions, chronically implanted electrodes were placed in the caudate nucleus. As part of a broader program of stimulation of, and recording from, this structure we investigated some possible somatosensory functions of this center.

PATIENT MATERIAL AND METHODS
Patients

Six patients served as subjects in this study. Two were classified as parkinsonians, two had cerebellar intention ataxia, and two presented with choreo-athetosis. Recording and stimulation began four to seven days after implantation of electrodes. Sessions limited to 90 min were conducted every one to three days over a period of three weeks. Upon completion of these studies, a stereotaxic lesion was placed in an effort to alleviate the patient's motor disorder.

Electrodes and Stereotaxic Methods

Details on the electrodes and stereotaxic methods appear elsewhere (Rosner *et al.*, 1966). Each electrode assembly was a miniature, six-contact unit (Manning, 1964) made of stainless steel wires 0.09 mm in diameter insulated with Teflon®. Contacts were 1 mm of bared wire; adjacent contacts were separated by 5 mm, so that 25 mm of tissue were spanned. The electrodes were soldered to a miniature Cannon connector. The unit had a total diameter of 0.4 mm.

Bilateral trephine openings were made at appropriate places on the skull and a Leksell stereotaxic frame was secured to the calvarium. A rubber cannula was inserted into the lateral ventricle and 5 cc of Pantopaque® were injected to outline the anterior and posterior commisures and the third ventricle. The stereotaxic coordinates of the center of the head of the caudate nucleus were determined from the Schaltenbrand-Bailey atlas (1959) with reference to the middle of the intercommisural line. The deepest contact of the electrode assembly was aimed 1 mm below this line. Anteroposterior and lateral roentgenograms were obtained with the frame in place to confirm the anatomical position of the electrode units. Figure 29-2 summarizes the roentgenographic determinations of electrode positions in all patients. Electrode "A" was deepest and "F" most superficial in each placement.

Stimulation and Recording

Electrical stimuli were provided by a constant current stimulator. Single rectangular pulses 0.5 msec in duration were applied percutaneously to the median, ulnar, and common peroneal nerves by overlying Grass disc electrodes filled with conducting paste. A metal strap covered with paste was placed around the limb proximal to the stimulating electrodes and was grounded to minimize artifact. A Grass photic stimulator was used to provide binocular flashes of light. A second constant current stimulator afforded trains of pulses for stimulation of the caudate.

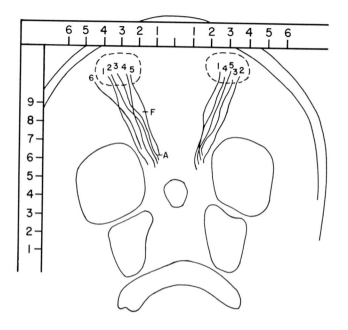

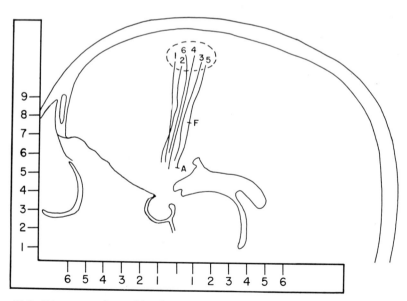

Figure 29-2. Diagrams of combined anteroposterior and right lateral roentgenograms showing electrode placements. Numbers indicate electrodes in different patients. (Patient 6 had only one caudate implanted.) *A* through *F* show respectively the deepest through the most superficial electrode contacts on one unit.

Recordings of spontaneous rhythms from caudate and scalp were made with an Offner eight-channel Type R Dynograph. Responses evoked by peripheral stimuli were amplified by Biocom 120 preamplifiers. For exploratory work, the responses were displayed in overlapping fashion on a Tektronix 564 storage oscilloscope and then were photographed. For detailed study of evoked activity, the analog data and a trigger pulse were recorded on a Precision Instrument 6100 magnetic tape recorder. The responses were analyzed "off line" by a LINC computer. A general purpose averaging program yielded average responses and estimates of the standard deviations around the averages. The program also allowed measurement of the latency, amplitude, and standard deviation of the amplitude of any selected deflection on an average response.

Psychophysical Methods

The method of limits was used to obtain absolute thresholds to electrical stimulation of the median nerve at the wrist. Measurements were also made, with this method, of the minimal interval which could separate two successive suprathreshold shocks to the nerve and still yield a sensation of two temporally distinct events. Reaction times to a single suprathreshold shock at the nonpreferred wrist were obtained by requiring the patient to remove his preferred hand as quickly as possible from a telegraph key. These three tests were each done with and without concurrent stimulation of the caudate in a counterbalanced design. Finally, two successive suprathreshold shocks separated by 3 sec were used to evaluate the effects of stimulation of caudate on apparent intensity of electrical pulses to the median nerve. One shock was accompanied by stimulation of the caudate while the other was not. The order in which caudate stimulation occurred varied from trial to trial. The patient had to select one of the two peripheral stimuli as more intense. In all psychophysical studies, the patient never was informed whether a given trial included caudate stimulation.

RESULTS

When a patient was relaxed and his eyes were closed, the spontaneous activity of the caudate was a mixture of slow and sharp waves with interspersed spindles of an 8 to 12 Hz rhythm. This pattern appears in the left half of Figure 29-3. When the patient opened his eyes, the spindles disappeared, leaving the slow and sharp waves. In Figure 29-3 the top six channels are "monopolar" derivations from caudate against the bridge of the nose. The seventh channel shows a bipolar derivation from caudate and the eighth shows activity from a scalp lead against the bridge of the nose. Thus caudate activity, like the electroencephalogram, gave an arousal response to sensory inflow. Other standard maneuvers for inducing arousal, such as presenting a problem in mental arithmetic to the patient, produced the same effects.

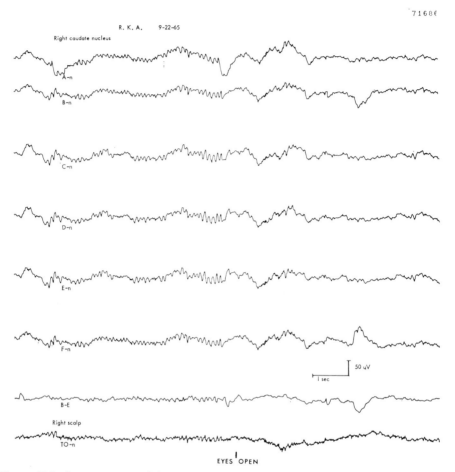

Figure 29-3. Spontaneous activity of human caudate nucleus, showing blocking of spindles by arousal. *Top six channels:* monopolar leads in right caudate referred to nose; *seventh channel:* bipolar caudate leads; *eighth channel:* temporo-occipital scalp lead referred to nose.

Transient visual and electrocutaneous stimuli evoked complex electrical responses in the human caudate nucleus. The responses were often large enough to be detected on single oscilloscopic traces. All four limbs projected to the caudate nucleus of each hemisphere. Figure 29-4 shows average responses from two electrodes in the left caudate to stimulation of left and right median nerves. The time base is bilinear and the sweep speed to the left of the dotted vertical line is faster than to the right. Ten msec elapsed between the stimulus and the first sample in the average response. The earliest visible deflection is a small negativity which starts about 18 msec after the stimulus. Cerebral responses from scalp leads in this patient to the same stimuli began about 16 msec after a shock to the wrist. Thus, the caudate response starts later than evoked activity seen at scalp leads. The rest of the response from the caudate is a sequence of two or three waves which seem predominately negative or else diphasically negative-positive. The peak of the final prominent negativity has a latency of 120 to 140 msec. The large succeeding positivity ends about 600 msec after stimulation, apparently outlasting evoked activity at scalp leads by some 300 msec. Some of this difference between the durations of evoked activity at the scalp and in caudate may reflect attenuation by the skull of evoked responses generated by the brain and picked up at scalp. None of our records show a prominent positivity with a peak latency around 60 to 100 msec, such as one would expect from the findings of Albe-Fessard *et al.* (1960a).

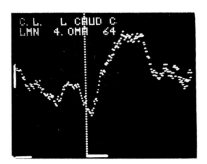
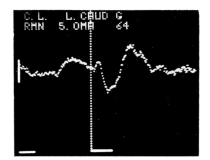
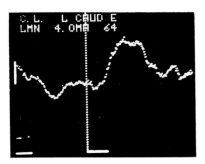
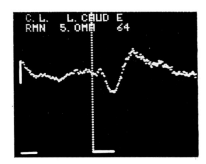

Figure 29-4. Average evoked response (n=64) from two different leads (C and E against nose, *top* and *bottom* rows respectively) in left caudate. Stimuli to left median nerve (LMN, *left column*) and right median nerve (RMN, *right column*). Ten msec elapsed between stimulus at start of trace and first sample in records. Time bases: 20 msec to left and 100 msec to right of vertical dotted line. Voltage calibration on left: 10μV.

Somatic evoked activity in the human caudate did not show any obvious topical organization. Since we have relatively few electrode placements, however, we cannot eliminate the possibility that a loose somatotopic arrangement exists. Other findings, however, demonstrate that the caudate receives information about intensity of stimulation. The left hand column of Figure 29-5 shows average somatic evoked potentials in caudate to three different intensities of stimulation of the contralateral median nerve. Homolateral stimulation gave similar results. The right hand column of the figure shows the same responses plus and minus one quarter of a standard deviation. Around the peak of the large, late positivity, the standard deviations are very small. Other regions of the response show similar declines in variability. The variability in these regions becomes even smaller than that in the earliest part of the record where there is no evoked potential but merely spontaneous activity.

We have made several unsatisfactory attempts to reproduce the finding by Krauthamer and Albe-Fessard of blockade of cortical potentials by a prior burst of high frequency stimulation to the caudate. Evoked responses from scalp leads in our patients have been quite small and variable. Consequently, it is impossible to say whether or not stimulation of caudate influences sensory evoked activity recorded from scalp leads in man. We are still working on this problem.

Tests of the effects of stimulation of the caudate nucleus on psychophysical tasks yielded unequivocal results. For these studies, a burst of five pulses at 200 p/sec was applied to the caudate prior to peripheral stimulation. Pulse durations for the caudate stimuli ranged from 0.5 to 3.0 msec and intensities from 1.5 to 4.0 ma. The interval between the end of the caudate stimuli and the peripheral electrocutaneous shock varied from 20 to 75 msec. These times yielded the maximal effects in the physiological experiments by Krauthamer and Albe-Fessard. The patients never could detect when stimuli were applied to the caudate.

Prior unilateral stimulation of caudate nucleus produced absolutely no effect on performance of any psychophysical task which we used. Absolute thresholds and apparent intensity of a fixed suprathreshold stimulus remained constant, whether or not the peripheral stimuli followed a burst of electrical pulses to the caudate. There also was no effect on temporal resolution of two successive, equally intense stimuli to the median nerve. The separation between peripheral shocks needed for discrimination of "twoness" remained around 20 msec, a normal value. Finally, reaction times to electrocutaneous stimuli were not affected by shocks to the caudate. Our patients had reaction times between 180 and 220 msec, which are larger than those in normal adults. Their reaction times stayed constant in the presence of concurrent stimulation of caudate.

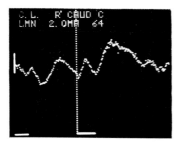 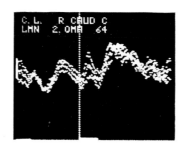

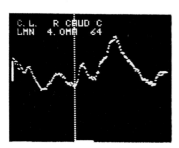 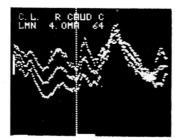

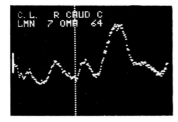 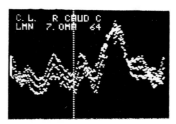

Figure 29-5. *Left column:* average evoked response (n=64) from electrode in right caudate to stimulation of left median nerve at each of three intensities, 2.0, 4.0, and 7.0 m *(top to bottom). Right column:* same responses plus and minus 0.25 standard deviation. See Figure 29-4 for explanation of time and voltage calibrations.

DISCUSSION

The results of our studies on the human caudate nucleus confirm findings in animals of polysensory evoked activity from this structure. The responses carry information about intensity of stimulation. Our limited evidence, however, indicates that locus of stimulation is poorly represented at best. We must withhold judgment on whether all of the activity recorded by electrodes in the caudate actually is generated there. In a few cases where the most dorsal electrodes apparently lay in white matter, judging from the low voltage and rapid spontaneous activity from these sites, evoked responses were relatively small. This suggests that the generators producing the evoked activity are in the caudate or in structures ventral to it. The first 100 msec of the responses which we obtained in the caudate did not contain a large positivity. Such an event would be expected from the work of Albe-Fessard *et al.* (1960a). The small early negativity seen in our records, how-ever, sometimes appears in their data. A partial explanation of the differ-ences between their findings and ours may lie in their use of chloralosed preparations.

Besides evoking activity which is time-locked to the stimulus, peripheral sensory inputs affect the spontaneous activity of caudate in two ways. First, they can produce an "arousal" reaction, consisting of suppression of the 8 to 12 Hz rhythm. Second, they modulate the amplitude or frequency charac-teristics of ongoing activity during the evoked response itself. This effect is manifested by the smaller standard deviations in various regions of the evoked potential compared to the levels of variability seen during spon-taneous activity alone. Such modulation of ongoing activity by sensory stimuli is not unique to the caudate. We have seen a similar phenomenon in records from scalp leads. The properties of this modulation and its rela-tionship to firing of single units merit serious investigation.

Anatomical studies on primates show that the intralaminar nuclei of the thalamus (Powell and Cowan, 1956) or frontal cortex (Mettler, 1943; 1947), or both, are regions which could pass along sensory inputs to the caudate. Numerous clinicopathological findings support the presence of such pro-jections in man (*cf.* Denny-Brown, 1962; Laursen, 1963). The polysensory nature of evoked potentials in the caudate make the intralaminar nuclei the stronger candidate. Connections from these nuclei to the caudate also may mediate "arousal" effects on spontaneous activity of that structure.

The current anatomical and physiological data suggest that the caudate may play a role in organizing sensory information from the environment. Bilateral lesions in the caudate, however, do not disrupt visual discrimina-tions between two simultaneously presented stimuli (Battig, Rosvold, and Mishkin, 1960; Rosvold, Mishkin, and Szwarcbart, 1958). Such lesions will produce defects in "go, no-go" discriminations (Battig, Rosvold, and Mishkin, 1962) and in delayed response or delayed alternation tasks (Battig *et al.,* 1960; Chorover and Gross, 1963; Dean and Davis, 1959; Rosvold and Delgado, 1956; Rosvold *et al.,* 1958). These findings all suggest that the caudate is involved in matters beyond the level of straightforward detection of, or immediate comparisons between, discrete stimuli. Our psychophysical studies tentatively support this suggestion since we did not obtain any evi-

EPILOGUE

A Chairman's Comments on the Neural Organization of Sensory Systems

Hallowell Davis

THESE COMMENTS, written immediately after the close of the Symposium on the Skin Senses, constitute a combined discussion of several of the presentations. They are inspired, in part, by the writer's interest in a closely related sensory system, the auditory, and in the electrical activity of the cortex.

Dr. Melzack stated explicitly the proposition that sensory information is handled by two neural systems of different phylogenetic origin and with different functions and characteristics. The old limbic-reticular system operates slowly, integrates widely across anatomical inputs and different modalities, and is responsible for motivation in response and other interesting aspects of life. The new neocortical system is more rapid in action and provides the fine discriminations that have been the chief interest of psychophysics. It is theoretically possible that the primary sensory neurons of these two systems are anatomically independent, but whether the systems share a common input or not they are interconnected at many levels and they cooperate in parallel.

Even within a neocortical "discriminative" system we should recognize the principle of parallel processing of sensory information. Dr. Gray emphasized the spatiotemporal *pattern* of the nerve impulses that carry tactile information and made it clear that a system could be optimized either for spatial or for temporal resolution, but for each only at the expense of the other. Actually there is at work here a physico-mathematical principle of uncertainty exactly analogous to the Heisenberg uncertainty principle of quantum physics. It has been elaborated in specific detail for the auditory system (Gabor, 1947; Licklider, 1951; 1959), and the actual best resolutions of frequency (pitch) and of temporal information are better than can be accounted for by any single resonant system with fixed characteristics.

A system designed to differentiate small differences in *space* must almost certainly employ inhibitory processes to enhance contrast at the boundaries; but such "lateral inhibition" will discard information which should be retained and integrated if the objective is instead to assess the overall *intensity* of the input. Good discrimination in respect to either space or intensity requires integration over time and the rejection of temporal information such as phase relations or the exact moment of onset of the stimulus. Differ-

ent processes and different neural circuits are required to extract these
various types of information (spatial, intensive, and temporal) from the
total input to the central nervous system that is coded as patterns of nerve
impulses by the peripheral array of sense organs. My emphasis here is not
on the optimal performance of the separate subsystems when "attention" is
given to one or the other but on the necessary differences in properties and
connections of the components of the subsystems. It is these different components (or perhaps the various subsystems) that are represented by the
neuronal populations studied by Dr. Towe and by Dr. Wall.

The first step in central organization is the branching of the primary
sensory neurons so that all of the incoming information is delivered to each
of the several subsystems for simultaneous parallel processing. The first
synaptic connections are not merely the proverbial drab "relay stations" but
the beginnings of several *different* parallel systems that extract different
types of information from the original input.

We have been preoccupied with the qualities and the spatial distributions and discriminations of the cutaneous (and other) senses. These we
have related to the anatomical characteristics of nerve fibers and their
receptor organs and their peripheral distribution and to the mechanics or
the chemistry of the accessory structures that determine their stimulation,
but we have tended to overlook or to minimize the dynamic temporal aspects of such stimulation. Static two-point discrimination hardly gives a
proper picture of the senses of touch and pressure. "Adaptation" (change of
amplitude of output with time) discussed by Dr. Hahn (and others) is
only part of the temporal story. The use of vibration instead of steady pressure helps to circumvent adaptation, but the skin is a better channel for
communication (Geldard, Sherrick) if a temporal pattern is involved.

An important aspect of the sense of touch that was not discussed in our
sessions is the active exploration of objects by our motile sensory surfaces,
notably the fingers, the tongue, and the lips. "Feeling" should be recognized
as an active, not as a passive verb. We heard a reference to the active components of the system when Dr. Wall mentioned the strong central control
exerted on some of his neuronal populations and the interplay of proprioceptive with cutaneous inputs in layers 5 and 6 of his dorsal horn cells.
At quite another level of the nervous system Dr. Weinstein discussed the
large apportionment of area in the somatosensory cortex to the glabrous
skin of the motile areas. Two-point discrimination is excellent in these
areas, to be sure, but that is by no means the whole story. The motor cortex
for these parts is apportioned in the same way and is so closely associated
with the sensory cortex that, in some species such as cat, it is hard to draw
a dividing line. And remember that the pyramidal tracts terminate in sen-

sory input layers in the dorsal horns (Wall). Sensory and motor cortex together constitute part of a single *exploring* mechanism.

The Greeks had a word for it. Their verb *haptein* has given us the adjec-
tive "haptic," meaning, according to Webster, "pertaining to the sense of
touch." Dr. Geldard used "haptic" in this way, but the original Greek
verb means "to fasten." I believe that the common ground here is the idea
of "taking hold of and feeling." Such touch is active, not passive. "Haptic
communication" is thus correct from the point of view of the sender but it
corresponds better to speaking than to listening.

An active exploring mechanism needs a short-term *memory* (for auto-
correlation) to keep track of what it has encountered and thus build up a
neural description of an object, "perceived" in a *spatial* frame of reference.
Illusions of haptic (or visual) movement (Sherrick) are the interpolations
of the short-term memory mechanism. I personally believe that a major
function, if not the major function, of the cerebral cortex is to provide this
active short-term memory, and perhaps also the long-term memories implied
by a spatial frame of reference and by the recognition patterns for speech
and hearing. (The faculty of foresight and long-term planning is said to be
dependent on the frontal lobes of the cortex.) And incidentally the learned
motor skills of our hands and of our lips, tongue and larynx probably arose
as developments from the original basic function of exploring the environment. I believe we explored before we manipulated. Here is true glory for
the tactile cutaneous sense!

But to return to the principle of parallel processing, this principle has
an obvious and important corollary, namely integration. We perceive a
single unified object or event with all of its attributes of quality, its intensity, its position in space and its duration in time. Integration of the output
of parallel channels of intermediate sensory processing must occur, often
combined with information from distant anatomical inputs. An example
of a neuronal mechanism that has properties appropriate for such terminal
integration is the *m* class of neurons of Towe in the cerebral cortex. Early
integration of anatomically disparate elements is seen in the variable receptive fields of some of Wall's dorsal horn neurons.

Even broader integrations may occur across sensory modalities. This is
perfectly obvious from the subjective point of view, a view which I hope
retains some aura of respectability in modern psychology. (The power-law
functions which we have discussed during the conference seem to give subjective sensations the kind of scientific status that can be achieved only by
the use of numbers and mathematical formulae.) It is not yet clear whether
the slow electric evoked responses of the caudate nucleus (and frontal lobe),
describes by Dr. Rosner, represent the activity of such a cross-modality inte-

grating mechanism. At least they have some of the necessary properties, and thus may be associated with the action of an integrative mechanism. Incidentally the effective inputs to this nonspecific response system have curious dimensional properties. Certain sensory modalities interact strongly with one another while others interact much less. The electric response to any event in any modality is the same, provided only the beginning of the stimulus is sharply enough defined in *time*. It is strictly an on-effect and an off-effect. (The chairman is now drawing on his own experience with the slow cortical evoked response of the frontal lobe.) Quality, spatial location and anatomical pathway of input are of secondary importance. Intensity is reflected in the response. The relation is described by the power law, but with a small exponent and often obscured by a high degree of variability, both across subjects and across trials. Thus the late component of the evoked response, apparently related to an "indirect" pathway, probably the reticular-limbic system, seems to signal disembodied sensory events or changes, with emphasis in the temporal domain. An aftereffect, in the form of reduced response to a second stimulus, persists for ten seconds or more. This is at least one form of short-term memory. On the other hand the earlier specific evoked responses in the appropriate cortical projection areas represent activity in the familiar fast "direct" discriminative system. However, the chairman cautions against any premature thought that the slow electrical phenomena reflect in any intimate way the physiological processes that must underlie the psychological phenomenon of perception. They more likely represent mere incidental housekeeping procedures, like the background EEG activity in general, but they do suggest integration, even across modalities, and a primitive kind of short-term memory.

REFERENCES

Gabor, D. Acoustical quanta and the theory of hearing. *Nature (London)*, 1947, **159**, 591.

Licklider, J. C. R. Basic correlates of the auditory stimulus. Chapt. 25. In S. S. Stevens (Ed.), *Handbook of Experimental Psychology*. New York: John Wiley and Sons, Inc., 1951.

Licklider, J. C. R. Three auditory theories. In S. Koch (Ed.), *Psychology: A Study of a Science*. New York: McGraw-Hill, 1959.

A NOTE ON "ADAPTATION" AND ALLIED TERMS

Frank A. Geldard

Sufficient frustration over conflicting meanings of the ofttimes competing terms, *adaptation, fatigue, habituation,* and *equilibration,* has been expressed during the past days to prompt the question whether it is not time to organize some resistance to the tyranny of these words. Our annoyance with this quartet of terms springs from the devious historical roots of several allied sciences. Each word could be traced to many sources; each could be shown to have become immersed in ambiguity.

Of the four, a psychologist finds *habituation* the least denotative in the sensory context (since it clearly derives from "habit" and hence belongs to learning theory!) and *equalibration* the least informative (since it may refer indiscriminately to labyrinthine phenomena or to the esthetic balance in a picture or musical passage as well as to spike spacing in a neural record). The terms *adaptation* and *fatigue,* even in their restricted sensory connotations, have had a long, strong exposure for at least a century and have gotten themselves thoroughly encrusted with kindred, if not entirely identical, meanings.

To be sure, this confusion between *adaptation* and *fatigue* has not been a matter of universal unconcern. One notable effort to unscramble the two words was made by C. S. Myers (1925), but he tried to retain both words in sensory and motor contexts, letting *fatigue* carry the connotation of *exhaustion* (sensory or motor) and *adaptation* mean a move toward a new state of balance between opposed mechanisms (whether sensory or motor). Indeed, near the end of his paper, just before going under, he called loudly to Hering (for whom there was no real difference in meaning between the terms) to throw a life preserver.

The general predicament is familiar to everyone in this symposium, as doubtless is also the history of these frustrating words. What may not be so familiar is the fact that an attempt to circumvent the conflict they create was made a half century ago by Leonard T. Troland. Caught in the snare that still traps us all, he suggested a new word, made up of whole cloth, "to designate, in place of the inappropriate word 'fatigue,' any decrease in the sensitivity of a sense organ, due to stimulation." The term was *minuthesis* (literally, a setting down, a reduction), a word that falls a little strangely on the ear, to be sure, but one which possesses the undeniable virtue that it had hitherto carried no meaning whatever. Moreover, the adjectival form, *minuthetic,* is at least as acceptable as *adaptational* and its cognates or *fatiguesone* or *equilibrational.*

Troland's term had a short life. Its coiner used it once in the title of a minor paper, referred to it once in an almost incidental manner in his well-known (Troland, 1922) monograph on "The present status of visual science," and apparently then accepted the judgment that words do not acquire usage by sheer force of having been suggested. I have never seen the word in print nor heard of its being used by anyone else, then or since. Does this mean that it was a bad or a useless word? I suppose it depends on how hard up you are for words. To be sure, there have been no outright cries of anguish surrounding this problem in the past few days, but that there is some concern with it is more than evident. Troland was well ahead of his time in certain other respects, notably in the development of the technicolor process and its application to motion pictures. Perhaps he was also prescient with his coined word, *minuthesis;* perhaps, after a full half century, it is time to take it from the shelf and dust it off. It may be a bit more awkward to *minuthesize* than to adapt, fatigue, habituate, or even equilibrate, but if Troland's original definition were to be preserved — any decrease in the sensitivity of a sense organ due to stimulation — we would at least know what in the general way we are talking about, and that is not always true of our current crop of troublemakers.

REFERENCES

Myers, C. S. Conceptions of fatigue and adaptation. *Psychol. Rev.,* 1925, **32**, 1.

Troland, L. T. The laws of visual minuthesis: The threshold preexposure time and equilibrium time for a projected after-image. *J. Franklin Inst.,* 1916, **181**, 579.

Troland, L. T. Present status of visual science. *National Research Council Bulletin,* 1922, #27 (Vol. 5).

NAME INDEX